D. E. BESSETTE

MATHEMATICS DICTIONARY

MATHEMATICS DICTIONARY

Giving the meaning of the basic mathematical words and phrases, including an exhaustive covering of the terms from Arithmetic through the Calculus and the technical terms commonly used in the applications of these subjects.

COMPILED FROM THE LITERATURE
AND EDITED
BY

GLENN JAMES

ASSOCIATE PROFESSOR OF MATHEMATICS, UNIVERSITY
OF CALIFORNIA AT LOS ANGELES

and

ROBERT C. JAMES

BENJAMIN PEIRCE INSTRUCTOR,
HARVARD UNIVERSITY

Revised Edition

THE DIGEST PRESS
VAN NUYS, CALIFORNIA
1946

THIRD PRINTING OF SECOND EDITION,

WITH CORRECTIONS

PRINTED IN THE UNITED STATES OF AMERICA

COMPOSED, PRINTED AND BOUND BY GEORGE BANTA
PUBLISHING COMPANY, MENASHA, WIS.

CONTENTS

I. Definitions of the basic words and topic phrases used in mathematics, including a complete coverage of those ordinarily used in arithmetic, elementary algebra, plane and solid high school geometry, college algebra, mathematics of finance, trigonometry, analytic geometry, and differential and integral calculus. The dictionary is essentially a condensation of these subjects.

II. Formulas for solving triangles, trigonometric reduction formulas, compound interest and annuity formulas, formulas for computing lengths, areas, volumes, centroids, etc., all appearing in definitions or as definitions.

III. (In the appendix.) Tables of denominate numbers, compound interest tables, American experience mortality table, a table of logarithms of numbers, a table of the trigonometric functions and their logarithms, differentiation formulas, a very extensive table of integrals, the Greek alphabet, and a very complete list of mathematical symbols.

PLAN

Leading words are printed in bold capitals beginning in the left margin. Subheadings are printed in bold at the beginning of paragraphs and in alphabetic order on the basis of their leading words.

Different statements of essentially the same meaning of a term or phrase are separated by semicolons, while definitions of different meanings for the same term are numbered: (1), (2), (3), etc.

Citations give the leading word in capitals (unless the citation is under the leading word), followed by a dash and then by the sub-heading if necessary, as: ANGLE—adjacent angle. Cross-references are cited in numerous instances where they especially aid the reader in understanding the current definition, or are needed to complete this definition or to avoid duplication.

Illustrative examples and figures have been used freely. These have been selected upon the basis of the importance of the concepts to the general reader and the difficulty of understanding and remembering them from verbal statements only.

Both working, or semi-popular, and technical (*Tech.*) definitions have been given where there is too wide a difference between the two to amalgamate them. Definitions of concepts too technical for all readers to comprehend, without a great deal of study, have been attuned to the mathematical maturity of those who are likely to be looking them up. For instance, Taylor's theorem is attuned to the college sophomore, while the east-west definition of the addition of positive and negative numbers is adapted to high school freshmen.

PREFACE

The wide use of mathematics, extending as it does into almost all fields of industry and science, and the increasing volume of mathematics itself have created a great need for reference books, such as other subjects have long enjoyed. The mass of facts that one has learned in arithmetic, algebra, trigonometry, geometry and calculus can not be retained in the conscious mind for long, and when the occasion arises where such knowledge is needed neither the time nor the facilities are usually available to "look them up."

It is now necessary for students of mathematics to devote their study time to understanding the subject and its applications and to depend upon the literature for the facts when they need them. Indeed, as one goes into practical applications of mathematics or continues his study of the subject he is very likely to become inefficient unless he has acquired the habit of looking up the concepts he once knew and has forgotten or never understood. A stack of books designed for sequential study rather than reference work does not serve his purpose.

This dictionary is designed primarily to meet this need and to provide a condensed source of facts and principles for men in the practical field. However, the fact that the book is built from the writings of many authorities on the various subjects makes it of additional value as a supplement to text books.

One phase recognized in the first edition and emphasized in this revision has been the simplification of elementary concepts in the interest of students in secondary schools and the laymen. For the more advanced students we have included many of the basic terms beyond calculus, so that this dictionary contains most of the terms which form the foundation of any advanced course in mathematics Terms from the more advanced courses will be included in a second volume, which is now being planned.

In revising the first edition the chief changes that have been made are the addition of many new terms, introduction of more "working examples," simplification of definitions, addition of irregular plurals, correction of typographical errors, substitution of five place logarithm tables for four place, and addition of extensive integral tables.

A great deal has been added to the value of this dictionary by the suggestions of the following mathematicians and friends of mathematics who have as a "work of love" read critically the following parts of the manuscript of the first edition: Dr. Paul H. Daus, the entire manuscript; Dr. Clifford E. Bell, the mathematics of finance; Dr. Paul C. Hoel, the statistics; Dr. E. Lee Kinsey, the physics; Dr. Frederick C. Leonard, the astronomy; Mr. Jules Charney, a large part of the manuscript; and Mr. Clarence Ablow, the computations and cross-references. The work of Arthur James and Glenn Davis James, at typing and checking syllabication, etc., has helped over one big hurdle. And without the aid and encouragement of "Mother," Inez James, the construction and publication of this dictionary would probably not have been possible. Most of all, the compilers and users of this dictionary are indebted to the great retinue of mathematicians whose thinking has developed the concepts that we have tried to portray in the following pages.

It is hoped that this dictionary will aid in an evolutionary standardization of mathematical terms that will be a great help to those who study and use mathematics. To this end, users of this dictionary are urged to send us their criticisms and suggestions. We wish to thank the several teachers, engineers, and others, especially Dr. G. A. Miller, Prof. Emeritus of the University of Illinois, for their constructive criticism of the first edition and encouragement in its distribution.

GLENN JAMES
R. C. JAMES

A

A-FORM OF THE GENERAL ALGE-BRAIC EQUATION. An algebraic equation of the form

$$a_0 x^n + a_1 x^{n-1} + \cdots + a_n = 0.$$

AB'A-CUS, *n.* ⌊*pl.* **abaci.**⌋ A counting frame to aid in arithmetic computation; an instructive plaything for children; used as an aid in teaching place value; a primitive predecessor of the modern computing machine. One form consists of a rectangular frame carrying as many parallel wires as there are digits in the largest number to be dealt with. Each wire contains nine beads free to slide on it. A bead on the lowest wire counts unity, on the next higher wire 10, on the next higher 100, etc. Two beads slid to the right on the lowest wire, three on the next higher, five on the next and four on the next denote 4532.

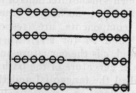

ABEL'S THEOREM on power series: (1) If a power series, $a_0 + a_1 x + a_1 x^2 + \cdots + a_n x^n + \cdots$, converges for $x = c$, it converges absolutely for $|x| < |c|$. (2) If a power series converges to $f(x)$ for $|x| < 1$ and to s for $x = 1$, then $\lim_{x \to 1} f(x) = s$, $(0 \leqq x \leqq 1)$. The latter theorem is variously designated, most explicitly by "Abel's Theorem on Continuity up to the Circle of Convergence."

A-BRIDGED', *adj.* **abridged multiplication.** See MULTIPLICATION.

Plücker's abridged notation. A notation used for studying curves. Consists of the use of a single symbol to designate the expression (function) which, equated to zero, has a given curve for its locus; hence reduces the composition of curves to the study of polynomials of the first degree. E.g. if $L_1 = 0$ denotes $2x + 3y - 5 = 0$ and $L_2 = 0$ denotes $x + y - 2 = 0$, then $k_1 L_1 + k_2 L_2 = 0$ denotes the family of lines passing through their common point $(1, 1)$. See PENCIL—pencil of lines through a point.

AB-SCIS'SA, *n.* ⌊*pl.* **abscissae** or **abscissas.**⌋ The horizontal coordinate (the coordinate running from left to right) in a two dimensional system of rectangular coordinates; usually denoted by x. Also used in a similar sense in systems of oblique coordinates. See CARTESIAN—Cartesian coordinates in the plane

AB'SO-LUTE, *adj.* **absolute constant.** See CONSTANT—absolute constant.

absolute convergence. See CONVERGENCE—absolute convergence.

absolute inequality. See INEQUALITY—absolute inequality.

absolute maximum (minimum). See MAXIMUM (MINIMUM).

absolute number. A number represented by figures such as 2, 3, or $\sqrt{2}$, rather than by letters as in algebra.

absolute symmetry of a function. See SYMMETRIC—symmetric function. Absolute symmetry requires that a function remain unchanged under all interchanges of variables, while cyclosymmetry requires only that a function remain unchanged under cyclic changes of the variables. The word absolute is usually omitted, symmetry and cyclosymmetry being sufficient. The function

$$abc + a^2 + b^2 + c^2$$

has absolute symmetry, while

$$(a-b)(b-c)(c-a)$$

has only cyclo-symmetry.

absolute term in an expression. A term which does not contain a variable. *Syn.* Constant term. In the equation $ax^2 + bx + c = 0$, c is the only absolute term.

absolute value of a complex number, a + bi. The value $\sqrt{a^2 + b^2}$. See MODULUS—modulus of a complex number.

absolute value of a real number. Its value without regard for sign; its numerical value. The cardinal number 2 is the absolute value of both $+2$ and -2.

absolute value of a vector. See VALUE—absolute value of a vector.

AB'STRACT, *adj.* **abstract word or symbol.** (1) A word or symbol which is not concrete; a word or symbol denoting a concept built up from consideration of many special cases; a word or symbol denoting a property common to many individuals or individual sets, as yellow, hard, two, three, etc. (2) A word or symbol which has no specific reference, in the sense that the concept it represents exists quite independently of any specific cases whatever and may or may not have specific reference.

    abstract mathematics. See MATHEMATICS—pure mathematics.

    abstract number. Any number as such, simply as a number, without reference to any particular objects whatever except in so far as these objects possess the number property. Used to emphasize the distinction between a number, as such, and concrete numbers. See NUMBER, and CONCRETE.

AC-CEL'ER-A'TION, *n.* **acceleration for motion in a straight line.** The rate of change of speed, with respect to time, taken *positive* or *negative* according as the speed is increasing or decreasing. (In the latter case it is sometimes called **deceleration.**) If an aeroplane flying 2 miles per minute *in a straight line* picks up speed constantly until it is flying 5 miles per minute at the end of the next minute, its increase in speed, which is its acceleration, has been 3 miles *per minute per minute.* If the change in speed were not constant, 3 miles *per min. per min.* would be the average acceleration during the one minute interval of time. Suppose t_1 is the time when its speed is 2 miles per min., and t_2 is a little later time. Then the limit of the **average speed** during the time interval $t_2 - t_1$, as t_2 is made nearer and nearer to t_1, is called the acceleration at t_1 (the INSTANTANEOUS ACCELERATION). E.g. if the speed at time t is t^2, then the average acceleration during the time $t_2 - t_1$ is $(t_2^2 - t_1^2) \div (t_2 - t_1) = t_2 + t_1$, which approaches $2t_1$ as t_2 approaches t_1. Hence the acceleration at time t_1 is $2t_1$. *Tech.* If the speed at time t is t^2, then the derivative of s, the distance, with respect to time, equals t^2. That is, $ds/dt = t^2$ (see SPEED—speed of a particle). And the acceleration is $d^2s/dt^2 = 2t$, which is $2t_1$ at time t_1. In general, *acceleration in a straight line* is equal to the second derivative of the distance with respect to time.

    angular acceleration. The signed (algebraic) rate of change of angular velocity relative to time; the second derivative of the angle of rotation with respect to time. See VELOCITY—angular velocity.

    normal acceleration. See below, total acceleration for motion in a plane.

    tangential acceleration. See below, total acceleration for motion in a plane.

    total acceleration for motion in a plane. A vector quantity equal to the rate of change of vector velocity with respect to time. See below, total acceleration in space. When resolved into components in the directions of the tangent and the normal to the path, these components are respectively d^2s/dt^2 and v^2c (or v^2/r) where v is the speed, c is the curvature and r the radius of curvature of the path. These are called the **tangential** and the **normal acceleration,** respectively. The former determines the speed along the path; the latter keeps the particle in the path. (When the normal component is zero the particle moves in a straight line.)

    total acceleration in space. A vector quantity equal to the rate of change of velocity with respect to time, that is

$$\lim_{\Delta t \to 0} \frac{\Delta V}{\Delta t}, \text{ where } \Delta V$$

is the vector difference between the vectors $V + \Delta V$ and V, that is between $V(t + \Delta t)$ and $V(t)$ (see ADDITION—addition of vectors); the directed resultant of the accelerations along the axes, in absolute value the square root of the sum of the squares of the second derivatives of x, y, and z with respect to time. See VECTOR.

    uniform acceleration. Acceleration in which there are equal changes in the velocity in equal intervals of time. *Syn.* Constant acceleration.

AC'CENT, *n*. A mark above and to the right of a quantity (or letter), as in *a'* or *x'*; the mark used in denoting that a letter is primed. See PRIME—prime as a symbol.

AC-CEPT'ANCE, *n*. acceptance of a draft, by the drawee (or payer). The writing of the word *accepted*, with the date and the signature of the drawee (or just the signature) across the front end or at the end of a commercial draft. This is *unqualified* acceptance or simply acceptance. If the payer stipulates that payment is to be made at a particular bank, the acceptance is said to be *special* acceptance; if he changes the amount or mode of payment it is said to be *qualified* acceptance. An *accepted* draft is negotiable.

trade acceptance. A bill of exchange drawn by the seller on the purchaser and accepted by the latter.

AC-CRUE', *v*. To accumulate as the necessary result of some law or process. One speaks of accrued interest, profits, or dividends on stocks or bonds.

AC-CU'MU-LAT'ED, *adj*. accumulated value. Same as AMOUNT at simple or compound interest.

accumulated value of an annuity at a given date. The sum of the compound amounts of the annuity payments to that date. *Syn*. Accumulation of an annuity, amount of an annuity.

AC-CU'MU-LA'TION, *n*. Same as AC-CUMULATED VALUE.

accumulation of discount on a bond. Writing up the book value of a bond on each dividend date by an amount equal to the interest on the investment (interest on book value at yield rate) minus the dividend. See VALUE—book value of a bond.

accumulation factor. The name sometimes given to the binomial $(1+r)$, or $(1+i)$, where r, or i, is the rate of interest. The formula for compound interest is $A = P(1+r)^n$, where A is the amount accumulated at the end of n years from an original principal P at a rate r. See COMPOUND—compound amount, and TABLE III in the appendix.

accumulation problem. The determination of the amount when the prin-

cipal, or principals, interest rate and time for which each principal is invested are given. See TABLES III and IV in the appendix.

accumulation schedule of bond discount. A table showing the accumulation of bond discounts on successive dates. Interest and book values are usually listed also.

AC'CU-RA-CY, *n*. Correctness, usually referring to numerical computations.

accuracy of a table. (1) The number of decimal places appearing in the irrational numbers in the table (mantissas of a logarithm table). (2) The number of correct places in computations made with the table. (This number of places varies with the form of computation, since errors may repeatedly combine so as to become of any size whatever.)

AC'CU-RATE, *adj*. Exact, precise, without error. One speaks of an accurate statement in the sense that it is correct or true and of an accurate computation in the sense that it contains no numerical error.

accurate to a certain decimal place. All digits preceding and including the given place being correct and the next place having been called zero if less than 5, 10 if greater than 5, and if 5, zero or 10 as is necessary to leave the last digit even. E.g. 1.26 is accurate to two places if obtained from either 1.264 or 1.256 or 1.255. See ROUNDING OFF NUMBERS.

AC'NODE, *n*. See POINT—isolated point.

A'CRE, *n*. The unit commonly used in the United States in measuring land; contains 43,560 square feet, 4840 square yards, or 160 square rods.

A-CUTE', *adj*. acute angle. An angle numerically smaller than a right angle; usually refers to positive angles less than a right angle.

acute triangle. See TRIANGLE.

AD'DEND, *n*. One of a set of numbers to be added, as 2 or 3 in the sum $2+3$.

AD-DI'TION, *n*. addition of algebraic quantities (algebraic addition). Two positive numbers are added as in arithmetic; two negative numbers are added by adding their numerical values and making the result negative; a positive and a negative number are added by subtracting the lesser numerical value from the greater and giving the difference the sign of the number which has the greater numerical value. E.g. a). $(-2)+(-3)=-5$; b). $(-2)+3=1$; c). $(-3)+2=-1$ The significance of this definition becomes apparent when we let positive numbers denote distances eastward and negative numbers distances westward and think of their sum as the place reached by travelling in succession the paths measured by the addends. E.g. in illustration c one would travel three miles west, then two miles east, and finish one mile west of the starting point.

addition of angles. *Geometrically*, a rotation from the initial side through one angle, followed by a rotation, beginning with the terminal side of this angle, through the other angle, having regard for the signs of the angles; *algebraically*, the ordinary algebraic addition of the same kind of measures of the angles, degrees plus degrees or radians plus radians.

addition in arithmetic. See below, addition of integers.

addition of complex numbers. *Algebraically*, the addition of the real parts, and the imaginary parts, e.g. $(2-3i)+(1+5i)=(3+2i)$; *geometrically*, same as the addition of the corresponding vectors in the plane. In the figure $OP_1+OP_2=OP_3$, $(OP_2=P_1P_3)$.

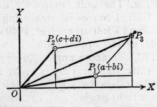

addition of decimals. Placing digits with like place value under one another, i.e. placing decimal points under decimal points, and adding as with integers, putting the decimal point of the sum directly below those of the addends.

addition of directed segments of a line. Adding one to the other, keeping them both in the same straight line and giving consideration to their directions; connecting the segments in such a way that the initial point of one is on the terminal point of the other and they both have the same or exactly opposite directions. E.g. five miles east plus two miles west is 3 miles east. See above, addition of algebraic quantities.

addition formulas of trigonometry. Formulas expressing the trigonometric functions of the algebraic sum of two angles in terms of the functions of the angles. The most important are

$$\sin (A \pm B) = \sin A \cos B \pm \cos A \sin B,$$
$$\cos (A \pm B) = \cos A \cos B \mp \sin A \sin B$$

and

$$\tan (A \pm B) = \frac{(\tan A \pm \tan B)}{(1 \mp \tan A \tan B)}$$

where the upper signs and the lower signs are taken together.

addition of fractions. The same process as the addition of integers, after a common denominator (common unit) has been established. E.g. 1/2 and 2/3 are the same respectively as 3/6 and 4/6, and 3 sixths plus 4 sixths is 7 sixths.

addition of integers. Counting all the units of two sets into one; e.g. the sum of 2 and 3 is obtained by counting 1, 2—3, 4, 5; the process of finding the number which represents all the units in the numbers to be added, taken collectively. *Tech.* The process of finding the number-class which is composed of (is the class of) the number-classes denoted by the addends.

addition of irrational numbers. Addition of the corresponding integral digits and decimals. E.g.

$$2.3333 \cdots + 5.1212 \cdots = 7.4545 \cdots .$$

The addition of irrationals is usually left in indicated form, after similar terms have been combined, until some specific application indicates the degree of accuracy desired. Such a sum as $(\sqrt{2}+\sqrt{3})-(2\sqrt{2}-5\sqrt{3})$ would thus be left in the form $6\sqrt{3}-\sqrt{2}$.

addition of mixed numbers. Adding the integral parts and fractions separately, then adding these results. E.g. $2\frac{1}{2}+3\frac{1}{4}=2+3+\frac{1}{2}+\frac{1}{4}=5\frac{3}{4}$.

addition of series. See SERIES.

addition of similar terms in algebra. The process of adding the coefficients of terms which are alike as regards their other factors: $2x+3x=5x$, $3x^2y-2x^2y=x^2y$ and $ax+bx=(a+b)x$. See DISSIMILAR TERMS.

addition of two vectors in the plane. *Algebraically*, the addition of the corresponding components, for instance $2i+3j$ plus $i-2j$ equals $3i+j$; *geometrically*, finding the third side of the triangle of which the addends form the other two sides, the initial point of one addend being on the terminal point of the other, the initial point of the latter coinciding with the initial point of the sum. In the figure $OA+AB=OB$. See PARALLELOGRAM—parallelogram of forces, and VECTOR—vector components.

addition of two vectors in space. *Algebraically*, the addition of corresponding components, for instance $(2i+3j+5k)+(i-2j+3k)=3i+j+8k$; *geometrically*, the addition of the two space vectors in the plane which they determine when drawn so that they intersect, just as two vectors in the plane are added. See above, addition of two vectors in the plane.

proportion by addition. See PROPORTION.

proportion by addition and subtraction. See PROPORTION.

AD′I-A-BAT′IC, *adj.* **adiabatic expansion (or contraction)** (*Thermodynamics*). A change in volume without loss of gain of heat.

adiabatic curves. Curves showing the relation between pressure and volume of substances which are assumed to have adiabatic expansion and contraction.

AD IN′FI-NI′TUM. Continuing without end (according to some law); denoted by three dots, as $\cdots$; used, principally, in writing infinite series, infinite sequences and infinite products.

AD-JA′CENT, *adj.* **adjacent angles.** See ANGLE—adjacent angles.

AD-JOINED′, *adj.* **adjoined number.** See DOMAIN.

AD VALOREM DUTY. A duty which is a certain fixed percent of the value of the goods.

AF-FINE′ TRANSFORMATION. (1) A transformation of the form

$$x'=a_1x+b_1y+c_1, \; y'=a_2x+b_2y+c_2,$$

where $\begin{vmatrix} a_1 & b_1 \\ a_2 & b_2 \end{vmatrix}=a_1b_2-a_2b_1\neq0$.

(2) A transformation of the form given in (1) except that the determinant of the coefficients may or may not be zero. The determinant of the coefficients is denoted by Δ. The following are important special cases of the affine transformation, $\Delta\neq0$; (a) **a translation** ($x'=x+a$, $y'=y+b$); (b) **a rotation** ($x'=x\cos\theta+y\sin\theta$, $y'=-x\sin\theta+y\cos\theta$); (c) **a stretching and shrinking** ($x'=kx$, $y'=ky$), called *transformations of similitude* or *homothetic transformations*; (d) **reflections** in the x-axis and y-axis, respectively, ($x'=x, y'=-y$ or $x'=-x$, $y'=y$); (e) **simple elongations and compressions** ($x'=x$, $y'=ky$ or $x'=kx$, $y'=y$), sometimes called *one-dimensional strains* and *one-dimensional elongations and compressions*. The affine transformation carries parallel lines into parallel lines, finite points into finite points and leaves the line at infinity fixed. An affine transformation can always be factored into the product of transformations belonging to the above special cases.

homogeneous affine transformation. An affine transformation in which the constant terms are zero; an affine transformation which does not contain a translation as a factor. (See FACTORIZATION—factorization of a transformation.) Its form is

$$x'=a_1x+b_1y, \; y'=a_2x+b_2y,$$
$$\Delta=a_1b_2-a_2b_1\neq0.$$

isogonal affine transformation. An affine transformation which does not change the size of angles. It has the form

$$x' = a_1x + b_1y + c_1,$$
$$y' = a_2x + b_2y + c_2,$$

where either $a_1 = b_2$ and $a_2 = -b_1$ or $-a_1 = b_2$ and $a_2 = b_1$.

non-singular affine transformation. Same as the transformation given in (1) under AFFINE TRANSFORMATION. Usually called simply an affine transformation.

singular affine transformation. See above, AFFINE TRANSFORMATION, (1). The form is that given except that $a_1b_2 - a_2b_1 = 0$.

AFTER DATE DRAFT. See DRAFT.

AFTER SIGHT DRAFT. See DRAFT.

AGE AT ISSUE. (*Life insurance.*) The age of the insured at his birthday nearest the policy date.

age-year. (*Life Insurance.*) A year in the lives of a group of people of a certain age. The age year A_x refers to the year from x to $x+1$, the year during which the group is x years old.

AG'GRE-GA'TION, *n.* Signs of aggregation: Parenthesis, ( ); bracket, [ ]; brace, { } and vinculum or bar, ———. Each means that the terms enclosed are to be treated as a single term. E.g. $3(2-1+4)$ means 3 times 5, or 15. See DISTRIBUTIVE.

AGNESI, witch of Agnesi. Same as WITCH.

AHMES (RHYND or RHIND) PAPYRUS. Probably the oldest mathematical book known, written about 1550 B.C.

AL'GE-BRA, *n.* (1) A generalization of arithmetic. E.g. the arithmetic facts that $2+2+2 = 3 \times 2$, $4+4+4 = 3 \times 4$, etc. are all special cases of the (general) algebraic statement that $x+x+x = 3x$, where x is any number. Letters denoting any number, or any one of a certain set of numbers, such as all real numbers, are related by laws that hold for any numbers in the set; e.g. $x+x = 2x$ for all x (all numbers). On the other hand conditions may be imposed upon a letter, representing any one of a set, so that it can take on but one value, as in the study of equations; e.g. if $2x+1 = 9$, then x is restricted

to 4. Equations are met in arithmetic, although not so named. For instance in percentage one has to find one of the unknowns in the equation, interest = principal × rate, or $I = p \times r$, when the other two are given. (2) A system of logic expressed in algebraic symbols.

fundamental theorem of algebra. See FUNDAMENTAL—fundamental theorem of algebra.

AL'GE-BRA'IC, *adj.* algebraic expression, equation, operation, etc. An expression, etc., containing or using only algebraic symbols and operations, such as $2x+3$, x^2+2x+4, or $\sqrt{2} - x + y = 3$.

algebraic addition. See ADDITION—addition of algebraic quantities.

algebraic deviation. See DEVIATION.

algebraic multiplication. See MULTIPLICATION.

algebraic operations. Addition, subtraction, multiplication, division, evolution and involution (extracting roots and raising to a power), no infinite processes being used.

algebraic proofs. Proofs which use algebraic symbols and no operations other than those which are algebraic. See above, algebraic operations.

algebraic subtraction. See SUBTRACTION—algebraic subtraction.

algebraic symbols. Letters representing numbers, and various operational symbols including those of arithmetic. See MATHEMATICAL SYMBOLS in the appendix.

irrational algebraic surface. See IRRATIONAL.

real algebraic number. See REAL.

AL'GO-RITHM, *n.* Some special process of solving a certain type of problem.

Euclid's Algorithm. A method of finding the greatest common divisor (G. C. D.) of two numbers—one number is divided by the other, then the second by the remainder, the first remainder by the second remainder, the second by the third, etc. When exact division is finally reached, the last divisor is the greatest common divisor of the given numbers (integers). In algebra the same process can be applied to polynomials. E.g. to find the highest common factor of 12 and 20, we have $20 \div 12$ is 1 with remainder 8; $12 \div 8$ is 1 with remainder 4; and $8 \div 4 = 2$, hence 4 is the G. C. D.

AL'I-QUOT PARTS. Any exact divisor of a quantity; any factor of a quantity; used almost entirely when dealing with integers. E.g. 2 and 3 are *aliquot parts* of 6.

AL'PHA, *n.* The first letter in the Greek alphabet, written α.

ALPHABET, GREEK. See the APPENDIX.

AL'TER-NATE, *adj.* **alternate angles.** Angles on opposite sides of a transversal cutting two lines, each having one of the lines for one of its sides. See ANGLE—angles made by a transversal.

alternate exterior angles. *Alternate angles* neither of which lies between the two lines cut by a transversal. See ANGLE—angles made by a transversal.

alternate interior angles. The *alternate angles* lying between the two lines cut by a transversal. See ANGLE—angles made by a transversal.

AL'TER-NAT'ING SERIES. A series whose terms are alternately positive and negative, as

$$1 - 1/2 + 1/3 - 1/4 + \cdots + (-1)^{n-1}/n \cdots .$$

alternating series test for convergence. An alternating series converges if each term is numerically equal to or less than the preceding and if the nth term approaches zero as n increases without limit. This is a sufficient but not a necessary set of conditions—the term by term sum of any two convergent series converges and if one series has all negative terms and the other all positive terms their indicated sum may be a convergent alternating series and not have its terms monotonically decreasing. The series

$$1 - 1/2 + 1/3 - 1/4 + 1/9 - 1/8$$
$$+ 1/27 - 1/16 + \cdots$$

is such a series. See NECESSARY—necessary condition for convergence.

ALTERNATION, PROPORTION BY. See PROPORTION—proportion by alternation.

AL'TI-TUDE, *n.* **altitude of a celestial point.** Its angular distance above, or below, the observer's horizon, measured along a great celestial circle (vertical circle) passing through the point, the zenith, and the nadir. The altitude is taken positive when the object is above the horizon and negative when below. See figure under HOUR—hour-angle and hour-circle.

altitude of a cone. See CONE.

altitude of a cylinder. The perpendicular distance between its bases.

altitude of a frustum of a cone. The perpendicular distance between its bases.

altitude of a parabolic segment. See PARABOLIC—parabolic segment.

altitude of a parallelogram. The perpendicular distance between two of its parallel sides. The side to which the altitude is drawn is called the base.

altitude of a prism. The perpendicular distance between its parallel bases.

altitude of a pyramid. See PYRAMID.

altitude of a rectangle. See above, altitude of a parallelogram.

altitude of a spherical segment. The perpendicular distance between the bases if the segment has two bases, otherwise the perpendicular distance between the base and the tangent plane, to the segment which is parallel to the base. See figures under SEGMENT—spherical segment.

altitude of a trapezoid. The perpendicular distance between the parallel bases.

altitude of a triangle. The perpendicular distance, or the perpendicular, from a vertex to the opposite side. This side is then regarded as the **base.**

altitude of a zone. The perpendicular distance between the planes of the the bases of the zone.

AM-BIG'U-OUS, *adj.* Not uniquely determinable.

ambiguous case in the solution of plane triangles. The case in which two sides and the angle opposite one of them is given. One of the other angles is then found by use of the law of sines; but there are always two angles less than 180° corresponding to any given value of the sine (unless the sine be unity, in which case the angle is 90° and the triangle is a right triangle). When the sine gives two distinct values of the angle, two triangles result if the side opposite is less than the side adjacent to the given angle (assuming the data is not such that there is no triangle possible, a situation that may arise in any case, ambiguous or non-ambiguous). In the figure, angle A and sides a and b are given $(a < b)$; triangles AB_1C and AB_2C are both solutions. If $a = b \sin A$, the right triangle ABC is the unique solution.

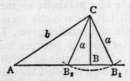

ambiguous case in spherical triangles. See SPHERICAL.

AMERICAN EXPERIENCE TABLE OF MORTALITY. (1) A table of mortality (mortality table) based upon the lives of Americans, constructed from insurance records about 1860. (2) A mortality table constructed from data obtained from American insurance companies and census records.

American men mortality table. A mortality table constructed from the records of the larger insurance companies in the United States covering the period from 1900 to 1915 inclusive.

AMICABLE NUMBERS. Two numbers, each of which is equal to the sum of all the exact divisors of the other except the number itself. E.g. 220 and 284 are amicable numbers, for 220 has the exact divisors 1, 2, 4, 5, 10, 11, 20, 22, 44, 55 and 110, whose sum is 284; and 284 has the exact divisors 1, 2, 4, 71, and 142, whose sum is 220.

A-MOR'TI-ZA'TION, *n.* The process of amortizing.

amortization of a debt. See AMORTIZE.

amortization equation. An equation relating the amount of an obligation to

be amortized, the interest rate, and the amount of the periodic payments. See AMORTIZE, and TABLE IV in the appendix.

amortization plan. See AMORTIZE.

amortization of a premium on a bond. Writing down (decreasing) the book-value of the bond on each dividend date by an amount equal to the difference between the dividend and the interest on the investment (interest on the book-value at the yield rate). See VALUE—book value of a bond.

amortization schedule. A table giving the annual payment, the amount applied to principal, amount applied to interest, and the balance of principal due. See AMORTIZE.

A-MOR'TIZE, *v.* To discharge a debt, including interest, by periodic payments, usually equal, which continue until the debt is paid without any renewal of the contract. The mathematical principles are the same as those used for annuities.

A-MOUNT', *n.* amount of a sum of money at a given date. The sum of the principal and interest (simple or compound) to the date; designated as *amount at simple interest* or *amount at compound interest* (or *compound amount*), according as interest is simple or compound. In practice the word *amount* without any qualification usually refers to amount at compound interest. See TABLE III in the appendix.

amount of an annuity. See ACCUMULATED—accumulated value of an annuity at a given date.

compound amount. See COMPOUND.

AM-PERE', *n.* A unit of measure of electric current; the current which flows through a conductor whose resistance is one *ohm* and for which the difference of potential between its two terminals is constantly one *volt*.

absolute ampere. One tenth of an electromagnetic unit (e.m.u.) of current, one e.m.u. of current being that current which will produce a force of 2π dynes on a unit magnetic pole placed at the center of a circular coil of wire of 1 turn and of 1 centimeter radius.

international ampere. The current which when passed through a standard solution of silver nitrate deposits silver at the rate of .001118 grams per sec.

AM′PLI-TUDE, *n.* **amplitude of a complex number.** The angle that the vector representing the complex number makes with the positive horizontal axis. E.g. the *amplitude* of $2+2i$ is $\tan^{-1}2/2 = \tan^{-1}1 = 45°$. See COMPLEX—polar form of a complex number.

amplitude of a curve. The greatest numerical value of the ordinates of a periodic curve. The *amplitude* of $y = \sin x$ is 1; of $y = 2 \sin x$ is 2.

amplitude of a point. See POLAR—polar coordinates in the plane.

amplitude of simple harmonic motion. See HARMONIC—simple harmonic motion.

A-NAL′Y-SIS, *n.* [*pl.* **analyses**]. That part of mathematics which uses, for the most part, algebraic and calculus methods—as distinguished from such subjects as synthetic geometry, number theory and group theory.

analysis of a problem. The exposition of the principles involved; a listing, in mathematical language, of the data given in the statement of the problem, other related data, the end sought, and the steps to be taken.

diophantine analysis. See DIOPHANTINE ANALYSIS.

proof by analysis. Proceeding from the thing to be proved to some known truth, as opposed to synthesis which proceeds from the true to that which is to be proved. The most common method of *proof by analysis* is in fact by *analysis* and *synthesis*, in that the steps in the analysis are required to be reversible.

trigonometric analysis. The study of the algebraic relations between the trigonometric functions, such, for instance, as the values of the functions of the sum (or difference) of two angles in terms of the functions of the angles.

unitary analysis. A system of analysis that proceeds from a given number of units to a unit, then to the required number of units. Consider the problem of finding the cost of 7 tons of hay if $2\frac{1}{2}$ tons cost $25.00. Analysis: If $2\frac{1}{2}$ tons cost $25.00, *1 ton costs* $10.00. Hence 7 tons cost $70.00.

ANALYTIC, *adj.* **analytic function of a variable.** A function which can be expressed as a polynomial, or as an infinite series in ascending powers of a binomial of the form $(x-a)$, which is identical with the function in some region (a, b)—that is, the limit, as n increases, of the sum to n terms of the series, for any value of x in this region, is equal to the value of the function for that value of x. See TAYLOR'S THEOREM.

analytic geometry. See GEOMETRY—analytic geometry.

analytic proof. A proof which depends upon that sort of procedure in mathematics called analysis; a proof which consists, essentially, of algebraic rather than geometric methods.

analytic solutions. Solutions which use, for the most part, algebraic methods. See above, analytic proof.

solid analytic geometry. See GEOMETRY—solid analytic geometry.

AN′A-LYT′I-CAL-LY, *adj.* Performed by analysis, by analytic methods, as opposed to geometrically.

ANCHOR RING or TORUS. A surface the shape of a doughnut with a hole in it; a surface generated by the rotation, in space, of a circle about an axis in its plane but not cutting the circle. If r is the radius of the circle, k the distance from the center to the axis of revolution, in this case the z-axis, and the equation of the generating circle is $(y-k)^2+z^2=r^2$, then the equation of the anchor ring is

$$(\sqrt{x^2+y^2}-k)^2+z^2=r^2.$$

Its volume is $2\pi^2 kr^2$ and the area of its surface is $4\pi^2 kr$.

AND INTEREST PRICE OF A BOND. See PRICE.

AN′GLE, *n.* In *geometry*, the inclination to each other (the divergence) of two straight lines; the figure formed by two straight lines drawn from the same point. In *trigonometry*, a figure which has been formed by one straight line (called the **terminal** line, or side) having been revolved about a fixed point on a stationary straight line (called the **initial line,** or side). If the motion is counter-clockwise, the angle is said to be **positive;** if clockwise, it is said to be **negative.** "Angle" is used for "plane angle."

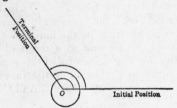

acute angle. See ACUTE.

addition of angles. See ADDITION—addition of angles.

adjacent angles. Two angles having a common side and common vertex and lying on opposite sides of their common side. In the figure AOB and BOC are adjacent angles.

angle between a line and a plane. The smaller (acute) angle which the line makes with its projection in the plane.

angle between two intersecting curves. The angle between the tangents to the curves at their point of intersection. See below, angle between two lines in a plane.

angle between two lines in a plane. (1) The angle from line L_1, say, to line L_2 is the smallest positive angle through which L_1 can be revolved counter-clockwise about the point of intersection of the lines to coincide with the line L_2, angle ϕ in the cut. (2)

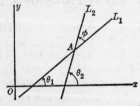

Otherwise defined as the least positive angle between the two lines and as the numerically least angle between them. The tangent of the angle from L_1 to L_2 is given by

$$\tan \phi = \tan (\theta_2 - \theta_1) = \frac{m_2 - m_1}{1 + m_1 m_2},$$

where $m_1 = \tan \theta_1$ and $m_2 = \tan \theta$.

angle between two lines in space. The angle between two intersecting lines which are parallel respectively to the two given lines. The cosine of this angle is equal to the sum of the products in pairs of the corresponding direction cosines of the lines. See DIRECTION—direction cosines.

angle between two planes. The dihedral angle which they form (see DIHEDRAL); the angle between the normals to the planes (see above, angle between two lines in space). When the equations of the planes are in normal form the cosine of the angle between the planes is equal to the sum of the products of the corresponding coefficients (coefficients of the same variables) in their equations.

angle of depression. The angle be-

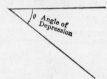

tween the horizontal plane and the oblique line joining the observer's eye to some object lower than (beneath) the line of his eye.

angle of elevation. The angle between the horizontal plane and the

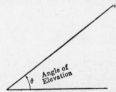

oblique line from the observer's eye to a given point above the line of his eye.

angle of a lune. See LUNE.

angle of reflection. See REFLECTION.

angle of refraction. See REFRACTION.

angles of a polygon. The angles made by adjacent sides of the polygon and lying on the interior of the polygon. This definition suffices for any polygon, even if concave, provided no side (not extended) cuts more than two sides. If this condition does not hold, the sides must be directed in some order when defining the polygon in order to uniquely define the angles between them. See DIRECTED—directed line.

angles made by a transversal. The angles made by a line (the transversal) which cuts two or more other lines. In the figure, the transversal t cuts the lines m and n. The angles a, b, c', d' are **interior angles**; a', b', c, d are **exterior angles**; a and c', and b and d' are the

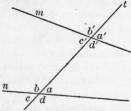

pairs of **alternate-interior angles**; b' and d, a' and c are the pairs of **alternate-exterior angles**; a' and a, b' and b, c' and c, d' and d are the **exterior-interior** or **corresponding angles.**

base angles of a triangle. The angles having the base of the triangle for their common side.

central angle. See CENTRAL.

complementary angles. See COMPLEMENTARY.

conjugate angles. Two angles whose sum is a perigon; two angles whose sum is 360°. Such angles are also said to be *explements* of each other.

co-terminal angles. See CO-TERMINAL.

dihedral angle. See DIHEDRAL.

direction angles. See DIRECTION —direction angles.

eccentric angle. See ELLIPSE— parametric equations of an ellipse.

equal angles. Angles which can be made to coincide, vertex upon vertex and sides upon corresponding sides.

Euler's angles. See EULER'S ANGLES.

explementary angles. See above, conjugate angles.

exterior angles. See EXTERIOR.

face angles. See below, polyhedral angle.

flat angle. A straight angle.

general formula for all angles having the same sine, cosine, or tangent. See GENERAL—general formula.

hour angle of a celestial point. The angle between the plane of the meridian of the observer and the plane of the hour circle of the star—measured westward from the plane of the meridian. See HOUR—hour angle and hour circle.

interior angle. See INTERIOR.

measure of an angle. See DEGREE and RADIAN.

negative angle. An angle generated by revolving a line in the clockwise direction from the initial line. See ANGLE.

obtuse angle. An angle numerically greater than a right angle and less than a straight angle; sometimes used for all angles numerically greater than a right angle.

opposite angle. See OPPOSITE— opposite vertices (angles) of a polygon.

perigon (angle). An angle containing 360°.

plane angle. See above, ANGLE.

polar angle. See POLAR—polar coordinates in the plane.

polyhedral angle. The configuration formed by the lateral faces of a polyhedron which have a common vertex (A-$BCDEF$ in the figure); the positional relation of a set of planes determined by a point and the sides of some polygon whose plane does not contain the point. The planes (ABC etc.) are called **faces** of the angle; the

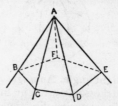

lines of intersection of the planes are called **edges** of the *polyhedral angle*. Their point of intersection (A) is called the **vertex.** The angles (*BAC*, *CAD*, etc.) between two successive edges are called **face angles.**

positive angle. An angle generated by revolving a line in the counter-clockwise direction from the initial line. See ANGLE.

quadrant angles. See QUADRANT.

quadrantal angles. See QUAD-RANTAL.

reentrant angle. An angle which is an interior angle of a polygon and greater than 180° (angle *HFM* in figure).

reference angle. Same as RELATED ANGLE. See RELATED.

reflex angle. An angle greater than a straight angle and less than two straight angles; an angle between 180° and 360°.

related angle. See RELATED.

right angle. Half of a straight angle; an angle containing 90° or $\frac{1}{2}\pi$ radians.

sides of an angle. The straight lines forming the angle.

solid angle. See SOLID.

spherical angle. The figure formed at the intersection of two great circles on a sphere; the difference in direction of the arcs of two great circles at their point of intersection. In the figure the spherical angle is *APB*. It is equal to the plane angles *A′PB′* and *AOB*. See DIRECTION—direction of a curve.

straight angle. An angle whose sides lie on the same straight line, but extend in opposite directions from the vertex; an angle of 180° or π radians. *Syn.* Flat angle.

supplementary angles. See SUPPLEMENTARY.

tetrahedral angle. A polyhedral angle having four faces.

trihedral angle. A polyhedral angle having three faces.

trisection of an angle. See TRISECTION.

vertex angle. The angle opposite the base of a triangle.

vertex of an angle. The point of intersection of the sides.

vertical angle. The angle at the vertex of a triangle. Usually called vertex angle.

vertical angles. Two angles such that each side of one is a prolongation, through the vertex, of a side of the other.

zero angle. The angle between two coincident or two parallel lines.

AN′GU-LAR, *adj.* Pertaining to an angle; circular; around a circle.

angular acceleration. See ACCELERATION—angular acceleration.

angular distance. See DISTANCE—angular distance between two points.

angular speed. See SPEED.

angular velocity. See VELOCITY.

AN′NU-AL, *adj.* Yearly.

annual premium (net annual premium). See PREMIUM—net annual premiums.

annual rent. Rent, when the payment period is a year. See RENT.

AN-NU′I-TANT, *n.* The life (person) upon whose existence each payment of a life annuity is contingent, i.e. will be paid as long as this life continues.

AN-NU′I-TY, *n.* A series of payments at regular intervals over a specified term of years, or over a lifetime.

accumulated value of an annuity. See ACCUMULATED.

accumulation of an annuity. See ACCUMULATED—accumulated value of an annuity at a given date.

amount of an annuity. See ACCUMULATED—accumulated value of an annuity.

annuity bond. See BOND.

annuity certain. An annuity that provides for a definite number of payments, as contrasted to a life annuity.

annuity contract. The written agreement setting forth the amount of the annuity, its cost, and the conditions under which it is to be paid.

annuity due. An annuity in which the payments are made at the beginning of each period.

annuity policy. A contract to pay a certain annuity for life beginning at a certain age. Sometimes used instead of *contract* in the case of *temporary* annuity contracts.

apportionate annuity. Same as COMPLETE ANNUITY. See COMPLETE.

cash equivalent of an annuity. Same as PRESENT VALUE.

complete annuity. See COMPLETE —complete annuity.

complete joint annuity. See COMPLETE—complete joint annuity.

consolidated annuities (consols). See CONSOLIDATED ANNUITIES.

contingent reversionary annuity. See CONTINGENT.

continuous annuity. See CONTINUOUS.

curtate annuity. See CURTATE.

deferred annuity. See DEFERRED.

deferred annuity certain. See DEFERRED—deferred annuity certain.

deferred annuity due. See DEFERRED.

deferred reversionary annuity. See DEFERRED.

deferred temporary annuity. See DEFERRED.

discounted value of an annuity. Same as PRESENT VALUE. See VALUE—present value.

foreborne annuity. A life annuity whose term began sometime in the past, that is the payments have been allowed to accumulate with the insurance company for a stated period. In case a group contributes to a fund over a stated period and at the end of the period the accumulated fund is converted into annuities for each of the survivors, the annuity is also called a *foreborne annuity.*

immediate annuity. See IMMEDIATE ANNUITY.

intercepted annuity. Same as DE-

FERRED ANNUITY. See DEFERRED.

joint life annuity. See JOINT.

last survivor annuity. See LAST—last survivor annuity.

life annuity. See LIFE.

ordinary annuity. An annuity whose payments are made at the end of the periods.

reversionary annuity. See REVERSIONARY.

single life annuity. See LIFE—life annuity.

temporary annuity. See TEMPORARY.

temporary annuity due. See TEMPORARY.

temporary reversionary annuity. See TEMPORARY.

term of an annuity. See TERM.

tontine annuity. See TONTINE.

ANN′U-LUS, *n.* [*pl.* annuli.]. The portion of a plane bounded by two concentric circles in the plane. The area of an annulus is the difference between the areas of the two circles, namely $\pi(R^2 - r^2)$, where R is the radius of the larger circle and r is the radius of the smaller.

A-NOM′A-LY, *n.* anomaly of a point. See POLAR—polar coordinates in the plane.

AN′TE-CED′ENT, *n.* The first term (or numerator) of a ratio; that term of a ratio which is compared with the other term. In the ratio 2/3, 2 is the *antecedent* and 3 is the *consequent.*

AN′TI-DE-RIV′A-TIVE of a function. Same as the PRIMITIVE or INDEFINITE INTEGRAL of the function; e.g. the anti-derivative of $3x^2$ (with reference to x) is $x^3 + c$, i.e. if $dy/dx = 3x^2$, $y = x^3 + c$, where c is a constant independent of x. See INTEGRAL—indefinite integral.

ANTI-HYPERBOLIC functions. Same as INVERSE-HYPERBOLIC functions. See HYPERBOLIC—inverse-hyperbolic functions.

AN-TI-LOG′A-RITHM, *n.* antilogarithm of a given number. The number whose logarithm is the given number; e.g. antilog₁₀2 = 100. *Syn.* Inverse logarithm. To find an anti-logarithm corresponding to a given logarithm that is not in the tables, subtract the next smaller mantissa from the given one and from the next larger one, divide the former difference by the latter and annex the quotient to the number corresponding to the smaller mantissa. See CHARACTERISTIC.

AN-TI-PAR'AL-LEL LINES with respect to two given lines. Two lines which make, with the two given lines, angles that are equal in opposite order. In the figure the lines AC and AD are antiparallel with respect to the lines EB and EC since $\angle EFD = \angle BCD$ and $\angle ADE = \angle EBC$. Two parallel lines have a similar property. The parallel lines AD and GH also make equal angles with the lines EB and EC, but in the same order; i e. $\angle EFD = \angle BGH$ and $\angle ADE = \angle GHD$

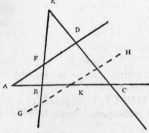

ANTI-TRIGONOMETRIC FUNCTIONS. Same as INVERSE TRIGONOMETRIC FUNCTIONS. See INVERSE.

A'PEX, *n.* [*pl.* apexes.] A highest point relative to some line or plane. The apex of a triangle is the vertex opposite the side which is considered as the base; the apex of a cone is its vertex.

APOLLONIUS, problem of Apollonius. To construct a circle tangent to three given circles.

A POS-TE'RI-O'RI, a posteriori knowledge. Knowledge from experience. *Syn.* Empirical knowledge.

  a posteriori probability. See PROBABILITY—empirical or a posteriori probability.

A-POTH'E-CAR'IES' WEIGHT. The system of weights used by druggists. The pound and the ounce are the same as in troy weight, but the subdivisions are different. See DENOMINATE

NUMBERS in the appendix.

AP'O-THEM, *n.* apothem of a regular polygon. The perpendicular distance from the center to a side. *Syn.* Short radius.

AP-PAR'ENT, *adj.* apparent distance. See DISTANCE—angular distance between two points.

  apparent time. Same as APPARENT SOLAR TIME. See TIME.

APPLIED MATHEMATICS. The study and use of mathematical principles as tools in other fields (subjects)—especially in physics, chemistry and engineering; refers to the application of the principles of mathematics to any other subject or to practical life. E.g. proving that a triangular system of braces is rigid by means of the fact that two triangles are equal if the corresponding sides are equal is *applied mathematics,* while proving the triangles equal is pure or abstract mathematics.

AP-POR'TION-A-BLE ANNUITY. See COMPLETE—complete annuity.

AP-PRAIS'AL METHOD in depreciation. A method of determining depreciation charges based on estimates of periodic future values.

AP-PROACH', *v.* approach a limit. See LIMIT—limit of a variable.

AP-PROX'I-MATE, *adj.* approximate result, value, answer, etc. One that is nearly but not exactly correct. Sometimes used of results either nearly or exactly correct.

  approximate root. See ROOT.

  approximate yield of a bond. The average annual interest divided by the average capital invested.

AP-PROX'I-MATE, *v.* To calculate nearer and nearer to a correct value; used mostly for numerical calculations. E.g. one *approximates* the square root of 2 when he finds, in succession, the numbers 1.4, 1.41, 1.414, whose successive squares are nearer and nearer to 2. Finding any one of these decimals is also called approximating the root, that is, to *approximate* may mean either to secure one result near a desired result, or a succession of results approaching a desired result.

  approximate a root. See HORNER'S

METHOD, and NEWTON—Newton's method of approximation.

AP-PROX′I-MA′TION, *n.* One of a set of repeated calculations (successive approximations) which lead nearer and nearer to an exact result. E.g. successive approximations to a root of the equation $x^2 = 3$ are 2, 1.7, 1.73, 1.732.

approximation by differentials. See DIFFERENTIAL—differential of a function of one variable. E.g. to find the approximate change in the area of a circle of radius $2'$ when the radius increases $.01'$, we have $A = \pi r^2$, from which $dA = 2\pi r dr = 2\pi \times 2 \times (1/100) = 1/25\pi$ sq. ft., which is the approximate increase in area.

approximation by Newton's method. See NEWTON.

successive approximations. The successive steps taken in working toward a desired result or calculation. See APPROXIMATE.

A PRI-O′RI, *adj.* Proceeding from first principles.

a priori fact. Used in about the same sense as axiomatic or self-evident fact.

a priori knowledge. Knowledge gotten from pure reasoning from cause to effect, as contrasted to empirical knowledge (knowledge gotten from experience); knowledge which has its origin in the mind and is (supposed to be) quite independent of experience.

AR′A-BIC, *adj.* Arabic numerals: 1, 2, 3, 4, 5, 6, 7, 8, 9, 0; introduced into Europe from Arabia, probably originating in India, although the source is not definitely known.

AR′BI-TRAR′Y, *adj.* arbitrary assumption. An assumption constructed at the pleasure of the writer without regard to its being consistent either with the laws of nature or (sometimes) with accepted mathematical principles.

arbitrary constant. See CONSTANT.

arbitrary ϵ. An idiom meaning a number as small as you desire to choose it; an arbitrarily small number not equal to zero.

arbitrary function in the solution of partial differential equations. A function which may take many forms and still satisfy the differential equation under consideration. E.g. $z/x = f(y)$ or $F[(z/x), y] = 0$ (where the last equation can be solved for z/x) are solutions of $x(\partial z/\partial x) - z = 0$, in which f and F are arbitrary functions.

arbitrary parameter. Same as *parameter* in its most commonly used sense. The addition of the attribute *arbitrary* places emphasis upon the fact that this particular parameter is entirely subject to the values directly assigned by the thinker, rather than by the conditions of the discussion or problem at hand.

ARC, *n.* A segment, or piece, of a curve.

arc length. The length in linear units of an arc of a curve. In a circle, the arc is equal to the radius times the angle (measured in radians), since the radian measure of an angle is defined to be the arc divided by the radius.

differential of an arc. See ELEMENT—element of arc of a curve.

element of arc. See ELEMENT.

length of arc of a curve. The length of a curve between two given points; the limit of the sum of the differential arcs between these two points, which is the same as the limit of the sum of the cords subtended by these arcs. I.e. the *arc length* is the definite integral of the differential arc, ds, between the two points as limits, the algebraic sign depending upon the order in which the points are taken. *Tech.*

$$s = \int_{s_1}^{s_2} ds,\ \text{which is usually written}$$

or
$$\int_{x_1}^{x_2} \sqrt{1 + (dy/dx)^2}\, dx$$
$$\int_{y_1}^{y_2} \sqrt{(dx/dy)^2 + 1}\, dy$$

or in the corresponding polar form,

$$\int_{\theta_1}^{\theta_2} \sqrt{\rho^2 + \left(\frac{d\rho}{d\theta}\right)^2}\, d\theta.$$

See ELEMENT—element of arc of a curve.

limit of the ratio of an arc to its chord. See LIMIT—limit of the ratio of an arc to its chord.

minor arc of a circle. See SECTOR —sector of a circle. *Syn.* Short arc.

short arc. See SHORT.

ARC-COSECANT, *n*. arc-cosecant of a number x. Written $\csc^{-1} x$ or arc csc x; an angle whose cosecant is x. E.g. $\csc^{-1} 2$ is equal to 30°, 150°, or in gen-

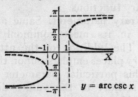

$y = \text{arc csc } x$

eral, $n180° + (-1)^n 30°$. See VALUE—general value of an inverse trigonometric function. *Syn*. Inverse cosecant, anticosecant. (In the figure, y is in radians.)

ARC-COSINE, *n*. arc-cosine of a number x. Written $\cos^{-1} x$ or arc-cos x; an angle whose cosine is x. E.g. arc cos $\frac{1}{2}$ is equal to 60°, 300°, or in general $n360° \pm 60°$. See VALUE—general value of an inverse trigonometric function. *Syn*. Inverse cosine, anti-cosine. The graph shows $y = \cos^{-1} x$ (y in radians).

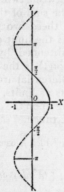

ARC-COTANGENT, *n*. arc-cotangent of a number x. Written $\cot^{-1} x$, $\operatorname{ctn}^{-1} x$ or arc cot x; an angle whose cotangent is x. E.g. arc cot 1 is equal to 45°, 225°, or in general $n180° + 45°$. See VALUE—general value of an inverse trigonometric function. *Syn*. Inverse cotangent,

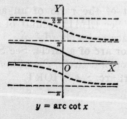

$y = \text{arc cot } x$

anti-cotangent. (In the figure, y is in radians.)

ARCHIMEDES, spiral of. See SPIRAL.

ARC-HYPERBOLIC SINE, COSINE, ETC. See HYPERBOLIC—inverse hyperbolic functions.

ARC-SECANT, *n*. arc-secant of a number x. Written $\sec^{-1} x$ or arc sec x. An angle whose secant is x. E.g. arc sec 2 is equal to 60°, 300°, or in general, $n360° \pm 60°$. See VALUE—general value of an inverse trigonometric function. *Syn*. Inverse secant, anti-secant. (In the figure, y is in radians.)

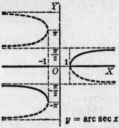

$y = \text{arc sec } x$

ARC-SINE, *n*. arc-sine of a number x. Written $\sin^{-1} x$ or arc sin x. An angle whose sine is x. E.g. arc sin $\frac{1}{2}$ is equal to 30°, 150°, or in general $n180° + (-1)^n 30°$. See VALUE—general value of an inverse trigonometric function. *Syn*. Inverse sine, anti-sine. The figure is the graph of $y = \sin^{-1} x$ (y in radians).

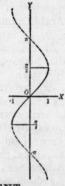

ARC-TANGENT, *n*. arc-tangent of a number x. Written $\tan^{-1} x$ or arc tan x.

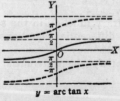

$y = \text{arc tan } x$

An angle whose tangent is x; e.g. arc tan 1 is equal to 45°, 225°, or in general, $n180°+45°$. See VALUE— general value of an inverse trigonometric function. *Syn.* Inverse tangent, anti-tangent. (In the figure, y is in radians.)

A′RE-A, *n.* **area of a curved surface (a sphere, ellipsoid, etc.).** The limit approached by the sum of the areas of the faces of a circumscribed (or inscribed) polyhedron as the lengths of the edges of the polyhedron approach zero. In case the surface is not of such a nature as to permit speaking of a circumscribed or inscribed polyhedron (e.g. if it is not closed) it can, in general, still be covered by a set of polygons, each tangent to the surface, in such a way that each edge can be made to approach zero. The resulting limit of the sum of the areas of the polygons is the area of the surface (if the limit exists). See SURFACE—surface area.

area of a lune. See LUNE.

area of a plane surface (a triangle, square, circle, etc.). The number of times the area of a unit square (a square with unit sides) is contained in the given surface. See the special configuration, and ELEMENT—element of plane area.

area of a zone. See ZONE.

center of an area. Same as the CENTROID of the area.

differential of area. Same as ELEMENT OF AREA.

element of area. See ELEMENT— element of plane area, and SURFACE —surface area, and surface of revolution.

lateral area of a cone, cylinder, parallelepiped, etc. See the specific configuration.

AREAS OF SIMILAR SURFACES, relations between. Areas of similar surfaces have the same ratio (vary as) the squares of corresponding lines. E.g. (1) The areas of two circles are in the same ratio as the squares of their radii; (2) the areas of two similar triangles are in the same ratio as the squares of corresponding sides, or altitudes.

ARGAND DIAGRAM. Two perpendicular axes on one of which real numbers

are represented and on the other pure imaginaries, thus providing a frame of

reference for graphing complex numbers. These axes are called the **real** and the **imaginary** axis or the **axis of reals** and the **axis of imaginaries.**

AR′GU-MENT, *n.* **argument of a complex number.** Same as AMPLITUDE. See AMPLITUDE—amplitude of a complex number.

argument of a function. Same as the INDEPENDENT VARIABLE. See FUNCTION.

argument in the theory of interpolation. The independent variable of a function which is being evaluated for a value of the argument between certain known values of the function. See INTERPOLATION.

arguments in a table of values of a function. The values of the independent variable for which the values of the function are tabulated. The arguments in a trigonometric table are the angles for which the functions are tabulated; in a log-table, the numbers for which the logarithms are tabulated.

AR-ITH-MET′IC or AR-ITH-MET′I-CAL, *adj.* Employing the principles and symbols of arithmetic.

arithmetic mean, or means, between two given numbers. The other terms of an arithmetical progression of which the given numbers are the first and last terms; a single *mean* between two numbers is their average, that is, one half of their sum. When the number of terms, n, and the first and last are given, the other terms can be written out after finding the difference, d, from the formula, $l=a+(n-1)d$, where a and l are the first and last terms respectively. See below, arithmetic progression.

arithmetic number. See NUMBER —arithmetic numbers.

arithmetic progression. Denoted by **A.P.** A sequence, each term of which is equal to the sum of the preceding term and a constant; written: $a, a+d, a+2d, \cdots, a+(n-1)d$, where a is called the **first term**, d the **common difference** or simply the **difference**, and $a+(n-1)d$ the **last** or **nth term.** The positive integers, 1, 2, 3, $\cdots$ form an arithmetic progression. The sum of the terms of an A.P. is sometimes called an A.P. See below, arithmetic series.

arithmetic series. The sum of the terms of an *arithmetic progression*. This sum, to n terms, is denoted by S_n and is equal to

$$\tfrac{1}{2}n(a+l) \quad \text{or} \quad \tfrac{1}{2}n[2a+(n-1)d].$$

A-RITH'ME-TIC, *n.* The study of the integers 1, 2, 3, 4, 5, $\cdots$ under the operations of addition, subtraction, multiplication, division, raising to powers, and extracting roots, and the use of the results of these studies in everyday life.

four fundamental operations of arithmetic. Addition, subtraction, multiplication and division.

AR-ITH-MOM'E-TER, *n.* A computing machine.

ARM, *n.* **arm of an angle.** A side of the angle.

AR-RANGE'MENT. Same as PERMUTATION.

AS-CEND'ING, *adj.* **ascending power series.** Same as POWER SERIES. See SERIES.

ascending powers of a variable in a polynomial. Powers of the variable that increase as the terms are counted from left to right, as in the polynomial

$$a+bx+cx^2+dx^3+\cdots.$$

AS-SEM'BLAGE, *n.* **infinite assemblage** of points or numbers. Same as INFINITE SET. See INFINITE.

AS-SESSED', *adj.* **assessed value.** A value set upon property for the purpose of taxation.

AS-SES'SOR, *n.* One who estimates the value of (evaluates) property as a basis for taxation.

AS'SETS, *n.* **assets of an individual or firm.** All of his (or its) goods, money, collectable accounts, etc., which have value; the opposite of **liabilities.**

fixed assets. Assets represented by equipment for use but not for sale—such as factories, buildings, machinery and tools.

wasting assets. See DEPRECIATION.

AS-SO'CI-A'TIVE, *adj.* **associative law for addition:** When a series of additions are to be made, any set of the terms may be added first; usually stated: $a+(b+c)=(a+b)+c$, from which the law can be extended to any number of terms by letting one of these letters represent a sum of terms.

associative law for multiplication: In any product of several factors any set of successive factors may be multiplied together first; usually stated $(ab)c=a(bc)=abc$. It suffices to state the law for three numbers. It can then be proved for any number of factors. E.g. $(ab)(cd)=a(bcd)$, since by taking (cd) as one term one can write $(ab)(cd)=a[b(cd)]=a(bcd)$.

AS-SUMP'TION, *n.* See AXIOM, and below, fundamental assumptions of a subject.

empirical assumption. See EMPIRICAL—empirical formula, assumption, or rule.

fundamental assumptions of a subject. A set of assumptions upon which the subject is built. For instance, in algebra the commutative and associative laws are *fundamental assumptions.* Sets of fundamental assumptions for the same subject vary more or less with different writers.

AS-SUR'ANCE, *n.* Same as insurance.

AS'TROID, *n.* The hypocycloid of four cusps.

ASYMMETRIC RELATION. A relation which is not symmetric. The property of *being older than* is *asymmetric*, since if a is older than b, then b is not older than a.

AS'YMP-TOTE, *n.* A line such that a point, tracing a given curve and simultaneously receding to an infinite distance from the origin, approaches indefinitely near to the line; a line such that the perpendicular distance from a moving point on a curve to the line approaches zero as the point moves off an infinite distance from the origin. *Tech.* an asymptote is a tangent at infinity; i.e., a line tangent to (touching) the curve at an ideal point. See figure under HYPERBOLA.

asymptote to the hyperbola: When the equation of the hyperbola is in the standard form $x^2/a^2 - y^2/b^2 = 1$, the lines $y = bx/a$ and $y = -bx/a$ are its asymptotes. This can be sensed by writing the above equation in the form $y = \pm(bx/a)\sqrt{1-a^2/x^2}$ and noting that a^2/x^2 approaches zero as x increases without limit; *Tech.* the numerical difference between the corresponding ordinates of the lines and the hyperbola is

$$(bx/a)(1-\sqrt{1-a^2/x^2})$$
$$= (ab/x)/(1+\sqrt{1-a^2/x^2})$$

which approaches zero as x increases, and the distances from the hyperbola to the lines are the product of this infinitesimal by the cosines of the angles the lines make with the x-axis, hence the distances between the lines and the hyperbola each approach zero as x increases. See above, ASYMPTOTE.

AT-TRAC'TION, *n.* **attraction of gravitation.** The force with which one particle attracts another. It is proportional to the product of their masses divided by the square of the distance between them. Usually called simply gravitation.

center of attraction or center of gravity. The point at which a mass (body) can be concentrated without altering the effect of the attraction that the earth has upon it; the point in a body through which the resultant of the gravitational forces, acting on all its particles, passes regardless of the orientation of the body; the point about which the body is in equilibrium; the point such that the moment of weight about any line is the same as it would be if the body were concentrated at that point. See MOMENT—moment of a force about a line. The coordinates $\bar{x}$, $\bar{y}$ and $\bar{z}$ of the center of gravity are given by

$$\bar{x}=(1/m)\int_s xdm; \quad \bar{y}=(1/m)\int_s ydm;$$
$$\bar{z}=(1/m)\int_s zdm,$$

where m is the total mass of the body, x, y, z are the coordinates of some point in the element of mass, dm, and $\int_s$ indicates that the integration is to be taken over the entire body, the integration being single, double or triple depending upon the form of dm; dm may, for instance, be one of the forms: ρds, ρxdy, $\rho dydx$, $\rho dzdydx$, where ρ is density. If elements such as ydx or xdy are used, one must take for the point in the element of mass the approximate center of gravity of these strips (elements), in the first case $(x, \frac{1}{2}y)$ and in the second $(\frac{1}{2}x, y)$.

differential of attraction. See ELEMENT—element of attraction.

AUG-MEN'TED MATRIX. See MATRIX.

AUXILIARY EQUATION. See DIFFERENTIAL—linear differential equations.

AV'ER-AGE, *n.* **arithmetic average of a set of numbers.** Their sum divided by the number in the set. The average of 1, 2 and 3 is 6/3 or 2. *Syn.* Mean.

average curvature. See CURVATURE—average curvature of a curve in a plane.

average date or average due date. Same as EQUATED DATE.

average deviation. Same as MEAN DEVIATION. See DEVIATION—mean or average deviation.

average or mean ordinate of a curve, $y = f(x)$, over an interval (a, b). The quotient of the area under the curve and the length of the interval, $(b-a)$, where the area under the curve is bounded by the curve, the x-axis, and the lines $x = a$ and $x = b$; the other side of a rectangle, whose area is equal to the given area and one of whose sides is equal to $(b-a)$.

average speed, over an interval of time. The quotient of the distance traveled and the length of the interval of time. See SPEED—speed of a particle.

average velocity. See VELOCITY.

geometric average of n **positive**

numbers. The positive nth root of their product. The geometric average of 4 and 9 is $\sqrt{36}$ or 6. *Syn.* Geometric mean.

AVERAGING AN ACCOUNT. Finding the *average date.* See EQUATED DATE.

AV′OIR-DU-POIS′ WEIGHT. A system of weights using the pound as its basic unit, the pound being equal to 16 ounces. See DENOMINATE NUMBERS in the appendix.

AX′I-AL SYMMETRY. Symmetry with respect to a line. The line is called the axis of symmetry.

AX′I-OM, *n.* (1) A self-evident and generally accepted principle. (2) An assumption or postulate. The distinction between postulate and axiom is not very sharp. *Axiom* refers more to the *a priori* truth of a theorem than *postulate.* One may postulate something that could be proved but would hardly call it an axiom.

axiom of continuity: To every point on the real axis there corresponds a real number (rational or irrational); the assumption that there exist numbers such as those indicated by the Caúchy Necessary and Sufficient Conditions for Convergence, and the Dedekind Cut Postulate. *Syn.* Principle of continuity.

axiom of superposition: Any figure may be moved about in space without changing either its shape or size.

axioms of equality: (1) If equals are added to equals, the sums are equal; (2) if equals are subtracted from equals, the remainders are equal; (3) if equals are multiplied by equals, the products are equal; (4) if equals are divided by equals (other than zero) the quotients are equal.

Euclid's axioms or "common notions." (1) Things equal to the same thing are equal to each other; (2) if equals are added to equals, the results are equal; (3) if equals are subtracted from equals the remainders are equal; (4) things which coincide with one another are equal; (5) the whole is greater than any of its parts. Axioms (4) and (5) are not universally attributed to Euclid.

AX′IS, *n.* [*pl.* **axes.**] **axis of a right circular cone.** The line joining the vertex to the center of the base. The term axis is also used with reference to a line in any conical surface about which the surface is symmetrical.

axis of coordinates. Lines (usually perpendicular) along which (or parallel to which) coordinates are measured. See CARTESIAN.

axis of a curve. Same as an AXIS OF SYMMETRY. See SYMMETRY.

axis of a cylinder. See CYLINDER —axis of a cylinder.

axis of an ellipsoid. See ELLIPSOID.

axis of the parabola, hyperbola, and ellipse. See PARABOLA, HYPERBOLA, and ELLIPSE.

axis of a pencil. See PENCIL— pencil of planes.

axis of reals. See below, real axis, and REALS.

axis of reference. See REFERENCE—axis of reference.

axis of revolution. See SOLID— solid of revolution.

axis of symmetry. See SYMMETRY.

imaginary axis. A straight line upon which the scale of imaginaries has been laid off; the vertical coordinate axis when plotting complex numbers in rectangular coordinates. See ARGAND DIAGRAM.

major and minor axis of an ellipse. See ELLIPSE.

polar axis. See POLAR—polar coordinates in the plane.

radical axis of circles, of spheres. See RADICAL, *adj.*

real axis. A straight line upon which the real number scale has been laid off; the axis of abscissas (x-axis) when plotting complex numbers in rectangular coordinates.

reflection in an axis. See REFLECTION.

semi-conjugate axis. See HYPERBOLA.

semi-transverse axis. See HYPERBOLA.

transverse and conjugate axis of the hyperbola. See HYPERBOLA.

AZ′I-MUTH, *n.* **azimuth of a point in a plane.** See POLAR—polar coordinates in the plane.

azimuth of a celestial point. See HOUR—hour angle and hour circle.

B

BACTERIAL GROWTH, law of: The increase per second of bacteria growing freely in the presence of unlimited food is proportional to the number present. It is defined by the equation $dN/dt = kN$, where k is a constant, t the time, N the number of bacteria present, and Nk the rate of increase. The solution of this equation is $N = ce^{kt}$. This is also called the **law of organic growth.** See DERIVATIVE.

BANK, *n.* **bank discount.** See DISCOUNT.

bank note. A note given by a bank and used for currency. It usually has the shape and general appearance of government paper money.

mutual saving bank. See MUTUAL.

BAR, *n.* Same as VINCULUM. See AGGREGATION.

bar graphs. See GRAPH.

BASE, *n.* **base angles of a triangle.** The two angles which have the base of the triangle for a common side.

base of a cone. See CONE.

base of a cycloid. See CYCLOID.

base of an isosceles triangle. The side between the two equal sides.

base of a logarithmic system. The number (base) which affected by the logarithm (of a given number) as an exponent, results in the given number. The base of common logarithms is 10, of natural or Naperian logarithms is e. See LOGARITHM, and e.

base in mathematics of finance. A number, usually a sum of money, of which some percent is to be taken; a sum of money upon which interest is to be calculated.

base of a parabolic segment. See PARABOLIC—parabolic segment.

base of a spherical sector. The spherical portion of the surface of the sector. The base is a zone. See SECTOR—spherical sector.

base of a spherical segment. The plane circular area of its plane surface if it is formed by cutting the sphere with only one plane. If it is formed by cutting the sphere with two planes it has **two bases.** See SEGMENT—spherical segment.

base of a system of numbers. The number of units, in a given digit's place or decimal place, which must be taken to denote 1 in the next higher place. E.g. if the base is ten, ten units in units place are denoted by 1 in the next higher place, which is ten's place; if the base is twelve, twelve units in units place are denoted by 1 in the next higher place, which is twelve's place— that is, when the base is twelve, 23 means $2 \times$ twelve $+3$. *Tech.* a number to any base is of the form $d_0 + d_1(\text{base}) + d_2(\text{base})^2 + d_3(\text{base})^3 + \cdots$, where d_0, d_1, d_2, d_3, etc. are each equal to or less than the base.

base of a triangle or pyramid or any geometric figure. A side upon which (perpendicular to which) an altitude is constructed, or is thought of as being constructed.

base of a zone. See ZONE.

change of base in logarithms. Finding the logarithm referred to one base from that referred to another. The relation by which this is accomplished is $\log_a n = (\log_b n)/\log_b a$. This is obtained from the relation $a^u = n$ by taking the logarithms to base b of both members; that is $u \log_b a = \log_b n$. But $u = \log_a n$, whence $\log_a n = \log_b n/\log_b a$. E.g. setting $n = 10,000$, $b = 10$ and $a = 100$, we have

$$\log_{100} 10,000 = (\log_{10} 10,000)/\log_{10} 100,$$
or $2 = 4/2$.

BASES, *n.* **bases of a cylinder.** Its two plane surfaces.

bases of a frustum of a pyramid. Its parallel faces; the base of the pyramid and the plane section parallel to the base. See PYRAMID—frustum of a pyramid.

bases of a prism. See PRISM.

bases of a trapezoid. Its two parallel sides.

bases of a truncated cone. See CONE—truncated cone.

bases of a truncated pyramid. See PYRAMID—truncated pyramid.

bases of a zone. See ZONE—bases of a zone.

BEAR'ING, n. bearing of a line. (*Surveying*.) The angle which the line makes with the north and south line; its direction relative to the north-south line.

bearing of a point, with reference to another point. The angle that the line through the two points makes with the north and south line.

BEND POINT. A point on a plane curve where the ordinate is a maximum or minimum.

BENDING MOMENT. See MOMENT.

BEN'E-FI'CI-AR'Y, n. (*Insurance*.) The one to whom the amount guaranteed by the policy is to be paid.

BENEFITS OF AN INSURANCE POLICY. The sum or sums which the company promises to pay provided a specified event occurs, such as the death of the insured or his attainment of a certain age.

BERNOULLI; Lemniscate of Bernoulli. See LEMNISCATE.

Bernoulli's equation. A linear differential equation of the form

$$\frac{dy}{dx}+yf(x)=y^n g(x).$$

Bernoulli's numbers. The numerical values of the coefficients of $x^2/2!$, $x^4/4!$, $\cdots$, $x^{2n}/(2n)!$, $\cdots$ in the expansion of $x/(1-e^{-x})$, or $xe^x/(e^x-1)$. Substituting the exponential series for e^x and starting the division by the expansion of (e^x-1) one obtains for the first four terms of this quotient,

$$1+(1/2)x+(1/6)x^2/2!-(1/30)x^4/4!.$$

The odd terms all drop out after the term $(1/2)x$. Some authors denote the Bernoulli numbers by B_1, B_2, etc. Others use B_2, B_4, etc. With the first notation: $B_1=1/6$, $B_2=1/30$, $B_3=1/42$, $B_4=1/30$, $B_5=5/66$, $B_6=691/2730$, $B_7=7/6$, $B_8=3617/510$. In general,

$$B_n=\frac{(2n)!}{2^{2n-1}\pi^{2n}}\sum_{i=1}^{\infty}(1/i)^{2n}.$$

There are many other forms for B_n.

BERTRAND'S POSTULATE: There is always at least one prime number between n and $(2n-2)$, provided n is greater than 3. E.g. if n is 4, $2n-2=6$ and the prime 5 is between 4 and 6.

BESSEL FUNCTIONS. Certain solutions of Bessel's equations. The nth Bessel function is denoted by $J_n(x)$ and is the coefficient of t^n in the expansion of $e^{x(t-1/t)/2}$ in powers of t.

BESSEL'S EQUATION. The differential equation

$$x^2\frac{d^2y}{dx^2}+x\frac{dy}{dx}+(x^2-n^2)y=0.$$

BE'TA, n. The second letter in the Greek alphabet, written β.

BI-AN'NU-AL, adj. Twice a year. *Syn.* Semi-annual.

BI-EN'NI-AL, adj. Once in two years; every two years.

BILL, n. A statement of money due, usually containing an itemized statement of the goods or services for which payment is asked.

BIL'LION, n. (1) In the U. S. and France, a thousand millions (1,000,000,000). (2) In England, a million millions (1,000,000,000,000).

BI-MONTH'LY, adj. and adv. Every two months.

BI'NA-RY SCALE. The number scale in which numbers are written with the number base two. See BASE—base of a system of numbers.

BI-NO'MI-AL, n. A polynomial of two terms, such as $2x+5y$ or $2-(a+b)$.

binomial coefficients. The coefficients of the variables in the expansion of $(x+y)^n$. The $(r+1)$th binomial coefficient of order n (n an integer) is equal to $n!/[r!(n-r)!]$, the number of combinations of n things r at a time, and is denoted by $\binom{n}{r}$, $_nC_r$, $C(n, r)$, or C_r^n. See below, binomial theorem.

binomial differential. A differential of the form $x^m(a+bx^n)^p dx$, where a and b are any constants and the exponents m, n, and p are rational numbers.

binomial distribution (binomial frequency distribution). The distribution of the various possible number of successes in a given number of trials; the distribution of probabilities of successes exhibited by the quotients of the coefficients in the binomial expansion and their sum. E.g. if two coins be thrown, the probability that both will be heads is 1/4, that one will be heads and the other tails is 2/4, and that both will be tails is 1/4. If x represents heads only, y tails only, and xy head and tails, then in the expression $(x^2+2xy+y^2)/4$, $x^2/4$ denotes that the probability of getting 2 heads is 1/4, $2xy/4$ that the probability of getting a head and a tail is 2/4, and $y^2/4$ that the probability of getting 2 tails is 1/4. Again if three coins be thrown, the probability that all will be heads, two heads and one tail, etc., is well represented by $(x^3+3x^2y+3xy^2+y^3)/8$. In general, the probability of getting $(n-m)$ heads and m tails when n coins are thrown is

$$n!/[2^n m!(n-m)!].$$

binomial equation. An equation of the form $x^n-a=0$.

binomial expansion. The expansion given by the binomial theorem.

binomial formula. The formula given by the binomial theorem.

binomial series. A binomial expansion which contains infinitely many terms. That is, the expansion of $(x+y)^n$, where n is not a positive integer or zero. Such an expansion converges and represents the function for all powers provided $|y|<|x|$. E.g.

$$\sqrt{3}=(2+1)^{1/2}=2^{1/2}+\tfrac{1}{2}(2)^{-1/2}$$
$$-(\tfrac{1}{8})^2 2^{-3/2}+\cdots.$$

binomial surd. See SURD.

binomial theorem. A theorem (or rule) for the expansion of a power of a binomial. The theorem can be stated thus: The first term in the expansion of $(x+y)^n$ is x^n; the second term has n for its coefficient, and the other factors are x^{n-1} and y; in subsequent terms the powers of x decrease by unity for each term and those of y increase by unity, while any coefficient can be obtained from the previous coefficient by multiplying the latter by the exponent of x in the previous term and dividing by the number of terms to and including the previous term. E.g. $(x+y)^3 = x^3+3x^2y+3xy^2+y^3$. In general,

$$(x+y)^n = x^n+nx^{n-1}y$$
$$+[n(n-1)/2!]x^{n-2}y^2+\cdots+y^n$$

if n is a positive integer. The general term, say the rth term, is

$$[n(n-1)\cdots(n-r+2)/(r-1)!]\ x^{n-r+1}y^{r-1}.$$

This coefficient is also written

$$\frac{n!}{(r-1)!(n-r+1)!}.$$

The $(r+1)$th term is often used since it is simpler. See above, binomial coefficients. The binomial theorem holds for any exponent whatever under certain restrictions on x and y. See above, binomial series.

sum of the binomial coefficients. Equal to 2^n, obtained by putting unity for each of x and y in $(x+y)^n$.

BI-NOR'MAL, *n.* See OSCULATING—osculating plane.

BI-PAR'TITE, *n.* **bipartite cubic.** The locus of the equation

$$y^2=x(x-a)(x-b),\quad 0<a<b.$$

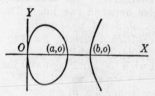

The curve is symmetric about the x-axis and intersects the x-axis at the origin and at the points $(a, 0)$ and $(b, 0)$ It is said to be bipartite because it has two entirely separate branches.

BI-QUAD-RAT'IC, *adj.* **biquadratic equation.** An algebraic equation of the fourth degree. *Syn.* Quartic.

BI-REC-TANG'U-LAR, *adj.* **birectangular triangle.** A spherical triangle, two of whose angles are right angles.

BI-SECT', *v.* To divide in half.

bisect an angle. To draw a line through the vertex dividing the angle into two equal angles.

bisect a line segment. To find the point equally distant from the two extremities of the segment.

bisect a line segment analytically. To find the coordinates of its middle point. They are the arithmetic means or averages of the corresponding coordinates of the two end points. See POINT—point of division. If $P_1(x_1, y_1)$

and $P_2(x_2, y_2)$ are the end points of a line segment, the coordinates of the mid-point are

$$x = (x_1 + x_2)/2, \quad y = (y_1 + y_2)/2.$$

BI-SECT′ING, *adj.* bisecting point of a line segment. Same as MID-POINT of a line segment.

BI-SEC′TOR, *n.* bisector of an angle. The straight line which divides the angle into two equal angles.

 bisector of the angle between two intersecting planes. A plane containing all the points equi-distant from the two planes. There are two such bisectors for any two such planes. Their equations are obtained by equating the distances of a variable point from the two planes—first giving these distances like signs, and then unlike signs. See DISTANCE—distance from a plane to a point.

 equations of the bisectors of the angles between two lines. The equations obtained by equating the distances from a variable point to each of the lines (the distances being taken first with the same sign and then with opposite signs). See DISTANCE—distance from a line to a point.

BI-WEEK′LY, *adj.* and *adv.* Occurring every two weeks.

BOARD-MEASURE. The system of measuring used in measuring lumber. See MEASURE—board measure.

BOND, *n.* A written agreement to pay interest (dividends) on a certain sum of money and to pay the sum in some specified manner, unless it be a perpetual bond.

 accrued dividend on a bond. See DIVIDEND.

 accumulation of discount on a bond. See ACCUMULATION.

 amortization of a premium on a bond. See AMORTIZATION.

 "and interest price" of a bond. See PRICE.

 annuity bond. A bond redeemed in equal installments which include the interest on the unpaid balance and sufficient payment of the face of the bond to redeem it by the end of a specified time.

 bond rate. See DIVIDEND—dividend rate.

 bond table. A table showing the values of a bond at a given bond rate for various investment rates, and for various periods. Most tables are based on interest computed semi-annually (the usual practice) and on the assumption that the bonds will be redeemed at par.

 book value of a bond. See VALUE.

 book value of a debt. See VALUE—book value of a debt on any date.

 callable, or optional, bonds. Bonds redeemable prior to maturity at the option of the payer, usually under certain specified conditions.

 collateral trust bonds. Bonds secured (guaranteed) by collateral placed in the hands of a trustee.

 coupon bonds. Bonds on which the interest is paid to the owner upon his surrender of the proper *coupon*. See COUPON.

 debenture bond. See DEBENTURE.

 dividend on a bond. See DIVIDEND—dividend on a bond.

 effective bond rate. See YIELD—yield of a bond.

 guaranteed bonds. Bonds, redemption of which is guaranteed by a third party.

 investment rate of a bond. See YIELD—yield of a bond.

 mortgage bonds. Bonds secured by mortgages or deeds of trust.

 par value of a bond. The principal named in the bond. *Syn.* Face value.

 perpetual bonds. See PERPETUAL—perpetual bonds.

 premium bonds. See PREMIUM—premium bonds.

 purchase price of a bond. See PURCHASE.

 purchase price of a bond between interest dates. The sum of the price of the bond at the last interest date and interest thereon, at the yield rate, over the expired part of the interest period. There are other definitions, but this is the market usage.

 redemption price of a bond. The price that is paid or must be paid to redeem the bond. See REDEEM.

 registered bond. A bond registered

in the holder's name by the debtor, who then pays the interest to the registered owner of the bond. When the bond is sold the registration is changed.

serial bonds. Bonds redeemable in installments.

serial issue of bonds. Bonds redeemable in uniform amounts at uniform intervals.

straight issue bonds. Bonds which have the same maturity date.

valuation of bonds. Computing the *present value*, at the investor's rate of interest, of the face value of the bond and of the interest payments (an annuity whose rental is equal to the dividend payments on the bond).

$$P = C(1+i)^{-n} + R[1-(1+i)^{-n}]/i,$$

where P denotes the value of the bond, C its redemption value, R the interest payments (coupon value if a coupon bond), n the number of periods before redemption, and i the investor's (purchaser's) rate per period.

yield of a bond. See YIELD.

BO'NUS, *n.* A sum paid in addition to a sum that is paid periodically, as bonuses added to dividends, wages, etc.

compound reversionary bonus. (*Insurance.*) A reversionary bonus which is the sum of a percentage of the original cost of the insurance and any bonuses already credited to the policy. See below, reversionary bonus.

discounted bonus policy. See DISCOUNTED.

guaranteed bonus participating insurance policy. See GUARANTEED.

reversionary bonus. The earnings of a participating life insurance policy paid when the policy is paid.

uniform reversionary bonus. (*Insurance.*) A reversionary bonus which is a percentage of the original amount of the insurance.

BOOK VALUE. See VALUE.

BOR'DER-ING, *v.* bordering a determinant. Annexing a column and a row. Usually refers to annexing a column and a row which have unity as a common element—all the other elements of either the column or row being zero. This increases the order of the determi-

nant by unity but does not change its value.

BOUND, *n.* an upper (lower) bound, or limit, of a sequence. See SEQUENCE.

greatest lower bound of a set of numbers having a lower bound. Either the least number in the set (if this exists) or the greatest number less than all the numbers in the set. In the latter case the greatest lower bound is called a **limiting** or **limit number** (or a **limit point** if one is thinking of the geometric representation of the number scale). The set of numbers $1/2, 1/3, 1/4, 1/5, \cdots$, has a greatest lower bound, zero, which is also a *limit point*.

least upper bound of a set of numbers having an upper bound. Either the largest of the set (if this exists) or the least number greater than any number in the set. In the latter case the least upper bound is called a **limiting** or **limit number** (or a **limit point**, if one is thinking of the geometrical representation of the number scale). E.g. the set of numbers $.3, .33, .333, \cdots$, has the *limit number* $\frac{1}{3}$.

lower (upper) bound of a set of numbers. See LOWER, and UPPER.

"the" upper (lower) bound of a sequence. See SEQUENCE.

BOUND'ED, *adj.* **bounded quantity, or function.** A quantity whose numerical value is always less than or equal to some properly chosen constant. The ratio of a leg of a right triangle to the hypotenuse is a bounded quantity since it is always less than or equal to 1; that is, the functions $\sin x$ and $\cos x$ are bounded functions since they are always equal to or less than 1. The function $\tan x$ in the interval $(0, \frac{1}{2}\pi)$ is not bounded.

bounded (limited) sequence. See SEQUENCE—bounded sequence.

bounded set of numbers. A set of numbers all of which are between two definite numbers; being greater than the one and less than the other, or equal to or greater than the one and equal to or less than the other.

BOYLE'S LAW. At a given temperature the product of the volume of a gas and the pressure, (pv), is constant; also called **Boyle and Mariott's** law. Approximately true for moderate pressures.

BRACE, *n.* See AGGREGATION.

BRACK′ET, *n.* See AGGREGATION.

BRANCH, *n.* **branch of a curve.** Any section of a curve separated from the other sections of the curve by discontinuities or special points such as vertices, maximum or minimum points, cusps, nodes, etc. One would speak of the two *branches* of an hyperbola, or even of four *branches* of an hyperbola; or of two *branches* of the semi-cubical parabola, or of the *branch* of a curve above (or below) the x-axis.

    infinite branch. See INFINITE.

BREADTH (of a plane figure), *n.* The length of a cross section of a plane figure all of whose cross sections are equal. If all cross sections are not equal, *breadth* is sometimes understood to mean the *longest cross section*. *Syn.* Width.

BRIGG'S LOGARITHMS. Logarithms using 10 as a base. *Syn.* Common logarithms.

B. T. U., British thermal unit. The heat required to raise the temperature of 1 lb. of water 1°F., when the water is at its maximum density, which is at 4°C. or 39.2°F.

BROKEN LINE. A line consisting of segments of lines joined end to end and not forming a continuous straight line.

BRO′KER, *n.* One who buys and sells stocks and bonds on commission, that is, for pay equal to a given percent of the value of the paper. *Broker* is sometimes applied to those who sell any kind of goods on commission, but commission merchant, or commission man, is more commonly applied to those who deal in staple goods.

BRO′KER-AGE, *n.* A commission charged for selling or buying stocks, bonds, notes, mortgages, and other financial contracts. See BROKER.

BUILDING AND LOAN ASSOCIATION. A financial organization whose objective is to loan money for building homes. One plan, called the *individual account plan*, is essentially as follows: Members may buy shares purely as an investment, usually paying for them in monthly installments at an annual nominal rate; or they may borrow money (shares) from the company with which to build, securing (guaranteeing) this money with mortgages on their homes. In both cases the monthly payments are called dues. Failure to meet monthly payments on time is sometimes subjected to a fine which goes into the profits of the company. The profits of the company are distributed to the share purchasers, thus helping to mature (complete the payments on) their shares. In practice, the interest rate is usually figured so that it returns all profits automatically. See GUARANTEED—guaranteed stock plan of building and loan association, DAYTON OHIO PLAN, TERMINATING—terminating plan of building and loan association, and SERIAL.

BUSINESS CYCLE. The period between successive periods of prosperity.

C

C. G. S. UNITS. Centimeter—gram—second systems of units. Centimeter measures the distance (length); gram, mass; and second, time. See ERG, and FORCE—unit of force.

CABLE, *n.* **parabolic cable.** See PARABOLIC.

CAL′CU-LATE, *v.* To carry out some mathematical process; to supply theory or formula and secure the results (numerical or otherwise) that are required; a looser and less technical term than compute. One may say, "Calculate the volume of a cylinder with radius 4′ and altitude 5′"; he may also say, "Calculate the derivative of $\sin (2x+6)$." *Syn.* Compute.

CALCULATING-MACHINE. Same as COMPUTING MACHINE.

CAL′CU-LUS, *n.* **differential calculus.** The study of the variation of a function with respect to changes in the independent variable, or variables, by means of the concepts of derivative and differential; in particular the study of slopes of curves, non-uniform velocities, accelerations, forces, approximations to the values of a function, maximum and minimum values of quantities, etc.

fundamental theorem of the integral calculus. See FUNDAMENTAL—fundamental theorem of the integral calculus.

infinitesimal calculus. Ordinary calculus; so called because of its use of infinitesimal quantities; sometimes refers only to that part of the calculus which deals with differentials and sums of infinitesimals.

integral calculus. The study of integration as such and its application to finding areas, volumes, centroids, equations of curves, solutions of differential equations, etc.

CALL'A-BLE, *adj.* See BOND—callable or optional bonds.

CALLING PRICE of a bond. The price that must be paid for a bond on any interest date, if the bond is called (redeemed) at that time.

CAL'O-RIE (or CAL'O-RY), *n.* The amount of heat required to raise one gram of water one degree Centigrade. The calorie thus defined varies slightly for different temperatures. A standard calorie is usually defined as the amount of heat required to raise one gram of water from 14.5° to 15.5°C. This unit is about the average amount required to raise one gram of water one degree at any point between 0° and 100°C.

CAN'CEL, *v.* (1) To divide numbers (or factors) out of the numerator and denominator of a fraction;

$$\frac{6}{8} = \frac{2 \times 3}{2 \times 4} = \frac{3}{4},$$

the number 2 having been *cancelled out.* (2) Two quantities of opposite sign but numerically equal are said to *cancel* when added; $2x + 3y - 2x$ reduces to $3y$, the terms $2x$ and $-2x$ having *cancelled* out.

CAN'CEL-LA'TION, *n.* The act of dividing like factors out of numerator and denominator of a fraction; sometimes used of two quantities of different signs which cancel each other.

CAN'TI-LE'VER BEAM. A beam supported at one end only and extending horizontally.

CAP'I-TAL, *adj.* **capital stock.** The money invested by a corporation to carry on its business; wealth used in production, manufacturing, or business of any sort, which having been so used is available for use again. Capital stock may be disseminated by losses but is not consumed in the routine process of a business.

circulating capital. Capital consumed, or changed in form, in the process of production or of operating a business—such as that used to purchase raw materials.

fixed capital. Capital invested permanently—such as that invested in buildings, machinery, etc.

CAPITALIZED COST. The sum of the first cost of an asset and the present value of replacements to be made perpetually at the ends of given periods.

CARDAN'S (correctly Ferro's) formula. Same as CARDAN'S SOLUTION OF THE CUBIC. See SOLUTION—Cardan's solution of the cubic.

CAR'DI-NAL, *adj.* **cardinal number.** A number which designates the manyness of a set of things; the number of units, but not the order in which they are arranged; used in distinction to signed numbers. E.g. when one says 3 dolls, the 3 is a cardinal number; but when he says 3 or − 3 miles, he means 3 miles in a given direction, 3 signed or ordinal units.

CAR'DI-OID, *n.* The locus (in a plane) of a fixed point on a given circle which rolls on an equal but fixed circle. If *a* is the radius of the fixed circle, ϕ the vectorial angle, and *r* the radius vector —where the pole is on the fixed circle

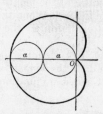

and the polar axis is on a diameter of the fixed circle—the polar equation of the cardioid is $r = 2a \sin^2 \frac{1}{2}\phi = a(1 - \cos \phi)$. A *cardioid* is an epicycloid of one loop and a special case of the limaçon.

CAR-TE'SIAN, *adj.* **Cartesian coordinates in the plane.** Numbers used to locate a point relative to two intersecting straight lines. The point is located by its distances from each line, measured along a parallel to the other line. The two intersecting lines are called **axes** (*x*-axis and *y*-axis), **oblique axes** when they are not perpendicular, and **rectangular axes** when they are perpendicular. In the latter case, the coordinates are called **rectangular Cartesian coordinates.** The coordinate measured from the *y*-axis parallel to the *x*-axis is called the **abscissa** and the other coordinate is called the **ordinate.**

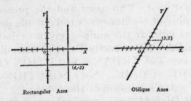

Rectangular Axes   Oblique Axes

Cartesian coordinates in space. See COORDINATE—coordinate planes.

CASH, *n.* Money of any kind; usually coin or paper money, but frequently includes checks, drafts, notes, and other sorts of commercial paper, which are immediately convertible into currency.

cash equivalent of an annuity. Same as PRESENT VALUE. See VALUE.

cash surrender value. Same as SURRENDER VALUE. See SURRENDER.

CAS-SIN'I. ovals of Cassini. The locus of the vertex of a triangle when the product of the sides adjacent to the vertex is a constant and the length of the opposite side is fixed. When the constant is equal to one-fourth the square of the fixed side, the curve is called a **lemniscate.** If k^2 denotes the constant and a one-half the length of the fixed side, the Cartesian equation takes the form

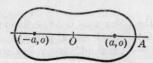

$$[(x+a)^2+y^2][(x-a)^2+y^2]=k^4.$$

If k^2 is less than a^2, the curve consists of two distinct ovals; if k^2 is greater than a^2, it consists of one, and if k^2 is equal to a^2, it reduces to the lemniscate. The figure illustrates the case in which $k^2 > a^2$.

CASTING OUT NINES. A method used to check multiplication (and sometimes division); based on the fact that the *excess of nines* in the product equals the excess in the product of the excesses in the multiplier and multiplicand. See EXCESS. E.g. to check the multiplication, $832 \times 736 = 612,352$ add the digits in 612,352, subtracting 9 as the sum reaches or exceeds 9. This gives 1. Do the same for 832, and for 736, the results are 4 and 7. Now multiply 4 by 7, getting 28. Then add 2 and 8 and subtract 9. This leaves 1—which is the same excess that was gotten for the product.

CAT'E-NA-RY, *n.* The plane curve in which a uniform cable hangs when suspended from two fixed points. Its equation in rectangular coordinates is $y = (a/2)(e^{x/a} + e^{-x/a})$, where a is the *y*-intercept.

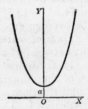

CAUCHY. Cauchy's integral test for convergence of an infinite series. Let $f(x)$ be a function which, for x greater than some positive number, is a monotonically increasing (or decreasing) function of x and such that $f(n) = a_n$ (the nth term of the series) for all n sufficiently large. Then a necessary and sufficient condition for convergence of the series, $\sum a_n$, is that there exists a number a such that

$$\int_a^\infty f(x)dx \text{ converges.}$$

In the case of the p series,

$$\sum 1/n^p, \quad f(x)=1/x^p,$$

$$\int_1^\infty x^{-p}dx=x^{1-p}/(1-p)\Big]_1^\infty \quad \text{if} \quad p\neq 1,$$

$$=\log x\Big]_1^\infty, \quad \text{if} \quad p=1,$$

$$\lim_{x\to\infty}\frac{x^{1-p}}{1-p}=0 \quad \text{if} \quad p>1, \quad =\infty \quad \text{if} \quad p<1$$

and

$$\lim_{x\to\infty}\log x=\infty.$$

Hence the p series converges for $p>1$ and diverges for $p\leqq 1$.

Cauchy's mean value formula. See MEAN—second mean value theorem.

Cauchy's necessary and sufficient condition for convergence of a sequence. See SEQUENCE.

Cauchy's necessary and sufficient condition for convergence of a series (Cauchy's Theorem): The sum of any number of terms can be made as small as desired by starting sufficiently far out in the series. *Tech.* a necessary and sufficient condition for convergence of a series is that given any $\epsilon>0$, there exists an N, dependent on ϵ, such that

$$|S_{n+h}-S_n|<\epsilon \quad \text{for all} \quad n>N$$

and all $h>0$, where S_n denotes the sum of the first n terms and S_{n+h} the sum of the first $n+h$ terms of the series.

Cauchy's ratio test. See RATIO—ratio test for convergence (or divergence) of an infinite series.

CAUCHY-LIPSCHITZ CONDITION on a function, $f(x)$: The *absolute value* of

$$\frac{f(x+\Delta x)-f(x)}{\Delta x}$$

is *bounded* for Δx small (less than some positive number).

CAVALIERI'S THEOREM: If two solids have equal altitudes and all plane sections parallel to their bases and at equal distances from their bases are equal, the solids have the same volume.

CE-LES'TIAL, *adj.* Of or pertaining to the skies or heavens.

altitude of a celestial point. See ALTITUDE.

celestial equator. See HOUR—hour angle and hour circle, and EQUATOR.

celestial horizon. See HOUR—hour angle and hour circle.

celestial meridian. See HOUR—hour angle and hour circle.

celestial point. A point on the celestial sphere.

celestial pole. See HOUR—hour angle and hour circle.

celestial sphere. The conceptual sphere on which all the celestial objects are seen in projection and appear to move.

declination of a celestial point. See DECLINATION and HOUR—hour angle and hour circle.

CEN'TER, *n.* **center of attraction.** See ATTRACTION.

center of a circle. See CIRCLE.

center of curvature. See CURVATURE—curvature of a plane curve.

center of a curve. The point (if it exists) about which the curve is symmetrical. Curves such as the hyperbola, which are not closed, but are symmetrical about a given point, are said to have this point as a center, but the term center commonly refers to closed curves such as circles and ellipses. *Syn.* Center of symmetry. See SYMMETRY—symmetry of a geometric configuration.

center of an ellipse. See ELLIPSE.

center of gravity of a mass. See ATTRACTION—center of attraction.

center of mass. See CENTROID.

center of pressure of a surface submerged in a liquid. That point at which all the pressure could be applied and produce the same effect as when the pressure is distributed.

center of a regular polygon. The center of its inscribed and circumscribed circles.

center of a sheaf. See SHEAF—sheaf of planes.

center of similarity (or similitude) of two configurations. See RADIALLY—radially related figures.

radical center. See RADICAL.

CEN-TES'I-MAL, *adj.* **centesimal system of measuring angles.** The system in which the right angle is divided into 100 equal parts, called *grades*, a *grade* into 100 *minutes* and a *minute* into 100 *seconds*. Not in common use.

CENTIGRADE THERMOMETER. A thermometer on which 0° and 100°, respectively, indicate the freezing and boiling points of water: See CONVERSION—conversion from Centigrade to Fahrenheit.

CEN'TI-GRAM, *n.* One hundredth of a gram. See DENOMINATE NUMBERS in the appendix.

CEN'TI-ME'TER, *n.* One hundredth part of a meter. See DENOMINATE NUMBERS in the appendix.

CEN'TRAL, *adj.* **central angle in a circle.** An angle whose sides are radii. An angle with its vertex at the center. See figure under CIRCLE.

central death rate, during one year. The ratio of the number of persons dying during that year to the number living at some particular time during the year; denoted by M_x, where x is the year. Usually M_x is defined as $d_x/[\frac{1}{2}(l_x+l_{x+1})]$, where d_x is the number of the group dying during the year x, l_x is the number living at the beginning of the year and l_{x+1} the number living at the end. Compare RATE—rate of mortality, death rate.

central projection. See PROJECTION.

central type of conics. Ellipses and hyperbolas.

measures of central tendency. See MEASURE—measures of central tendency.

CEN-TRIF'U-GAL FORCE. (1) The force which a mass, constrained to move in a circular path, exerts on the constraint in a direction along the radius. (2) In mechanics, the fictitious force, which must be introduced as acting along the radius on a mass moving in a circle in order to reduce the problem to one in statics. The force operating in the opposite direction is called **centripetal force.**

CEN-TRIP'E-TAL force. The force which restrains a body, in rotation, from going in a straight line. It is directed toward the center of rotation. A force equal, but opposite in sign, to the **centrifugal force.**

CEN'TROID, *n.* **centroid of a configuration.** The point whose coordinates are the *mean values* of the coordinates of the points in the configuration. This means, for configurations over which integration can be performed, that the coordinates of the centroid, $\bar{x}$, $\bar{y}$, and $\bar{z}$, are given by $\bar{x} = [\int_s x \, ds]/s$, $\bar{y} = [\int_s y \, ds]/s$ and $\bar{z} = [\int_s z \, ds]/s$; where $\int_s$ denotes the integral over the configuration, ds denotes an element which can be inclosed in an infinitesimal sphere, such as an element of area, arc length, or solid, whose largest dimension approaches zero, and s denotes a given area, arc length, or volume. See ELEMENT. ($\bar{x}$ may be looked upon as the weighted mean of the x coordinates of all points in the configuration, and similarly for $\bar{y}$ and $\bar{z}$.) See INTEGRAL—definite integral, and MEAN—mean value of a function over a given range.

centroid of mass, or center of mass, of an area. A point at which the area could all be concentrated and the moment about any line in the plane not be altered. Its coordinates are usually denoted by $\bar{x}$ and $\bar{y}$. Area, as used here, is thought of as having unit density. The centroid is sometimes called the **center of area.** The center of a circle, a square, or an ellipse, or the intersections of the medians of a triangle are centroids of these areas. See above, centroid of a configuration.

centroid of (center of mass of) a solid. The point at which its entire mass may be concentrated and not affect its moment about any plane (or any line); the point in the body which has the same motion that a particle possessing the mass of the whole body would have if the resultant of all the forces acting on the body were applied to it; a point whose position vector r is defined as follows: $r = (\sum m_s r_s)/M$, where m_s is the mass of a particle, r_s is the position vector of m_s (of some point in m_s), M is the mass of the body and $\sum$ denotes a vector sum. See ATTRACTION—center of attraction, and above, centroid of a configuration. Center of gravity and centroid are the same point. The difference in terminology is due to the fact that moment enters in the former as moment of attraction of gravitation, and in the latter as moment of mass.

CERTAIN, *adj.* **deferred annuity certain.** See DEFERRED—deferred annuity certain.

CHAIN, *n.* **surveyor's chain.** A chain 66 feet long containing 100 links, each link 7.92 inches long. Ten square chains equal one acre. See DENOMINATE NUMBERS in the appendix.

CHAIN DISCOUNTS. See DISCOUNT —discount series.

CHANCE, *n.* Same as PROBABILITY; has considerable popular but little technical usage.

CHANGE, *n.* **change of base in logarithms.** See BASE—change of base in logarithms.

change of coordinates. See TRANS-FORMATION—transformation of coordinates.

change of independent variable in a derivative (in differentiation). See DE-RIVATIVE—derivative of a function of a function.

change of variable in integration. See INTEGRATION—integration by substitution.

change of variables. See TRANS-FORMATION—transformation of coordinates.

changing signs of the roots of an algebraic equation. Replacing the unknown by its negative; e.g. the roots of the equation $x^3 + x^2 - 2x + 3 = 0$ are changed in sign by the substitution $x = -x'$, resulting in $x'^3 - x'^2 - 2x' - 3 = 0$.

cyclic change of variables. Same as CYCLIC PERMUTATION. See PERMUTATION.

CHAR'AC-TER-IS'TIC, *n.* **characteristic of the logarithm of a number.** The integral part of the logarithm. E.g. since log 100 is 2 and log 1000 is 3, the logarithm of any number between 100 and 1000 is 2 plus some decimal; 2,

then, is the **characteristic** of all numbers less than 1000 and equal to or greater than 100; e.g. log 134 = 2.1271. In general, when the base is 10, and the number is greater than or equal to 1, the characteristic is always one less than the number of digits to the left of the decimal point. When the number is less than 1, the characteristic is **negative** and numerically one greater than the number of zeros immediately following the decimal point; e.g. .1 has the characteristic -1, .01 has the characteristic -2. If a logarithm has the mantissa .7519 and the characteristic 2, it is written either 2.7519 or 12.7519 − 10 or 12.7519 $\overline{10}$; if it has the characteristic -1, it is written $\overline{1}$.7519 or 9.7519 − 10 or 9.7519 $\overline{10}$.

characteristic of a one-parameter family of surfaces. The limiting curve of intersection of two neighboring members of the family as they approach coincidence—that is, as the two values of the parameter determining the two members of the family of surfaces approach each other. The equations of a given characteristic curve are the equation of the family taken with the partial derivative of this equation with respect to the parameter, each equation being evaluated for a particular value of the parameter. The locus of the characteristic curves, as the parameter varies, is the envelope of the family of surfaces. E.g. if the family of surfaces consists of all spheres of a given, fixed radius with their centers on a given line, the characteristic curves are circles having their centers on the line, and the envelope is the cylinder generated by these circles.

characteristic rule. Rule for finding the characteristic of the logarithm of a number. See above, characteristic of the logarithm of a number.

CHARGE, *n.* **depreciation charge.** See DEPRECIATION.

surrender charge. See SURRENDER.

CHECK, *n.* A draft upon a bank, usually drawn by an individual.

check on a solution of an equation. The substitution of the calculated root in the original equation (the equation before any changes have been made in it, such as squaring, transposing terms, etc.). If the root is correct, the result of this substitution should be an identity which takes the form $0 = 0$ after all terms have been transposed to the same side and combined.

CHECK, *v.* To verify a solution or a proof by repetition or some other device.

CHORD, *n.* A chord of any curve (or surface) is a segment of a secant between two points of intersection of the secant and the curve (surface). If there are more than two such intersections, the chord is not unique. See CIRCLE, SPHERE, etc.

   chord of a circle, sphere, etc. See the specific configuration.

   chord of contact with reference to a point outside of a circle. The chord joining the points of contact of the tangents to the circle from the given point.

   focal chords of conics. See FOCAL.

   supplemental or supplementary chords in a circle. See SUPPLE-MENTAL.

CI'PHER (or CYPHER), *n.* The symbol 0, denoting *zero. Syn.* Zero, naught.

CI'PHER, *v.* To compute with numbers; to carry out one or more of the fundamental operations of arithmetic.

CIR'CLE, *n.* (1) A plane curve consisting of all points equally distant from a fixed point in the plane, called the **center**; the locus of all points equidistant from a fixed point (the center). (2) A section of a plane all points of whose periphery are equidistant from a fixed point. See below, equation of a circle in the plane.

   arc of a circle. A segment of its circumference.

   area of a circle. Pi times the square

of the radius, πr^2, or in terms of the diameter, $\frac{1}{4}\pi d^2$. See PI.

   chord of a circle. A segment cut off on a secant by the circumference. See figure under CIRCLE.

   circle of convergence. See CON-VERGENCE—circle of convergence of a power series.

   circle of curvature. See CURVA-TURE—curvature of a plane curve.

   circumference of a circle. A term used to emphasize the fact that one is concerned with the curve itself and not with its radius, diameter or what not. Used also for the length of a circle. The circumference of a circle is equal to $2\pi r$, where r is the radius and π is 3.1416−. See PI.

   circumscribed circle. See CIRCUM-SCRIBED.

   diameter of a circle. Twice the radius; the segment, intercepted by the circle, on any straight line passing through the center of the circle. See figure under CIRCLE.

   eccentric circles of an ellipse. See ELLIPSE—parametric equations of an ellipse.

   equation of a circle in the plane. *In rectangular Cartesian coordinates,* $(x-h)^2+(y-k)^2=r^2$, where r is the radius of the circle and the center is at the point (h, k). When the center is at the origin, this becomes: $x^2+y^2=r^2$. (See DISTANCE—distance between two points.) *In polar coordinates,* the equation is

$$\rho^2+\rho_1{}^2-2\rho\rho_1 \cos (\phi-\phi_1)=r^2,$$

where ρ is the radius vector, ϕ the vectorial angle, (ρ_1, ϕ_1) the polar coordinates of the center, and r the radius. When the center of the circle is at the origin this equation becomes $\rho = r$.

   equations of a circle in space. The equations of any two surfaces whose intersection is the circle; a sphere and a plane, each containing the circle, would suffice.

   escribed circle. See ESCRIBED.

   family of circles. All the circles whose equation can be obtained by assigning particular values to an essential constant in the equation of a circle.

E.g. $x^2+y^2=r^2$ is the family of circles with their centers at the origin, r being the essential constant in this case. See PENCIL—pencil of circles.

great circle. See GREAT CIRCLE.

hour circle of a celestial point. The great circle on the celestial sphere that passes through the point and the north and south celestial poles. See HOUR—hour angle and hour circle.

imaginary circle. The name given to the set of points which satisfy the equation $x^2+y^2=-r^2$, or $(x-h)^2+(y-k)^2=-r^2$. Although there are no points (in the real plane) with such coordinates this terminology is desirable because of the algebraic properties common to these imaginary coordinates and the real coordinates of points on real circles.

inscribed circle. See INSCRIBED.

nine-point circle. The circle through the mid-points of the sides of a triangle, the feet of the perpendiculars from the vertices upon the sides, and the mid-points of the line segments between the vertices and the point of intersection of the altitudes.

null circle. A circle with radius zero; the point $(0, 0)$ which is the locus of (the only point that satisfies) $x^2+y^2=0$, or, in general, (h, k) which is the only point that satisfies $(x-h)^2+(y-k)^2=0$.

osculating circle. See OSCULATING.

parallel circle. See SURFACE—surface of revolution.

parametric equations of a circle. The equations: $x=a\cos\theta$, $y=a\sin\theta$, where θ is the angle between the positive x-axis and the radius from the origin to the given point, and a is the radius of the circle.

pencil of circles. See PENCIL.

quadrature of a circle. See QUADRATURE—quadrature of a circle.

radius of a circle. The distance from the center to the circumference (see figure under CIRCLE).

secant of a circle. A line of unlimited length cutting the circumference.

small circle. A section of a sphere by a plane that does not pass through the center of the sphere.

squaring a circle. See QUADRATURE.

unit circle. See UNIT—unit circle.

CIR'CU-LAR, *adj.* **circular cone.** A cone whose base is a circle.

circular cylinder. A cylinder whose right section is a circle. *Syn.* Right-circular cylinder.

circular functions. The trigonometric functions.

circular (or cyclic) permutations. See PERMUTATION.

Napier's rules of circular parts of a right spherical triangle. See NAPIER'S RULES.

uniform circular motion. See UNIFORM.

CIRCULATING DECIMAL. See DECIMAL—repeating decimal.

CIR'CUM-CEN'TER of a triangle. The center of the circumscribed circle (the circle passing through the three vertices of the triangle); the point of intersection of the perpendicular bisectors of the sides; point O in figure.

CIR'CUM-CIR'CLE, *n.* Same as circumscribed circle. See CIRCUMSCRIBED.

CIR-CUM'FER-ENCE, *n.* (1) The boundary line of a circle; (2) the boundary line of any closed curvilinear figure. *Syn.* Periphery, perimeter.

circumference of a sphere. The circumference of any great circle on the sphere.

CIR'CUM-SCRIBED', *adj.* **circumscribed circle about a polygon.** A circle passing through the vertices of the polygon. See below, radius of a circle circumscribed about a regular polygon.

circumscribed prism. See PRISM.

cone circumscribed about a pyramid. A cone in which the pyramid is inscribed. See INSCRIBED—inscribed pyramid of a cone.

cylinder circumscribed about a prism. See PRISM—inscribed prism of a cylinder.

polygon circumscribed about a cir-

cle. A polygon having its sides tangent to the circle. If the polygon is regular its area is

$$nr^2 \tan \frac{180°}{n},$$

and its perimeter is

$$2nr \tan \frac{180°}{n},$$

where r is the radius of the circle and n the number of sides of the polygon.

pyramid circumscribed about a cone. A pyramid having its base circumscribed about the base of the cone and its vertex coincident with that of the cone. See figure below.

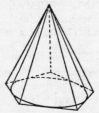

radius of a circle circumscribed about a regular polygon. If s is the length of a side and n the number of sides, the radius is

$$\frac{s}{2} \csc \frac{180°}{n}.$$

radius of a circle circumscribed about a triangle. If the sides are a, b, c, the radius is

$$\frac{abc}{4\sqrt{s(s-a)(s-b)(s-c)}},$$

where $s = \frac{1}{2}(a+b+c)$.

CIS'SOID (cissoid of Diocles), n. The plane locus of a variable point on a variable line passing through a fixed point on a circle, where the distance of the variable point from the fixed point is equal to the distance from the line's intersection with the circle to its intersection with a fixed tangent to the circle at the extremity of the diameter through the fixed point; the locus of the foot of the perpendicular from the vertex of a parabola to a variable tangent. If a is taken as the radius of the circle in the first definition, the polar equation of the cissoid is $r = 2a \tan \phi \sin \phi$; its Cartesian equa-

tion is $y^2(2a-x) = x^3$. The curve has a cusp of the first kind at the origin, the x-axis being the double tangent. The

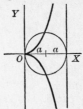

cissoid was first studied by Diocles about 200 B.C., who gave it the name "Cissoid" (meaning *ivy*).

CIVIL YEAR. A year of 365 days, as contrasted to the **commercial year** of 360 days.

CLAIRAUT'S EQUATION. A differential equation of the type $y = px + f(p)$. It can be solved by differentiating and obtaining an equation in

$$x,\ p(=dy/dx)\ \text{ and }\ p'(=dp/dx).$$

CLASS, n. **class interval.** See FREQUENCY—frequency distribution.

class marks. (*In statistics.*) The property or quality of individuals according to which they are thrown into classes—the number in each class being called the **frequency of the class,** or **class frequency.** E.g. if a group of men are arranged according to height and there are twelve between sixty-one and sixty-two inches tall and fifty between sixty-two and sixty-three inches, the inch intervals are called the *class marks* and the numbers 12 and 50 are called the *class frequencies.*

class of a plane algebraic curve. The greatest number of tangents that can be drawn to it from any point in the plane not on the curve.

number-class. See NUMBER.

sub-class. Same as SUBSET. See SET and NUMBER.

CLOCK'WISE', *adj.* In the same direction of rotation as that in which the hands of a clock move around the dial.

counter clock-wise. In the direction of rotation opposite to that in which the hands of a clock move around the dial.

CLOSED, *adj.* **closed curve.** A curve which, in its entirety, completely bounds a finite section of a plane or surface. A section of a curve which completely incloses a section of a plane or surface is called a **loop of the curve.** See below, closed plane figure.

closed interval. See INTERVAL.

closed plane figure. A figure such as the triangle, circle, or polygon which bounds a finite portion of the plane; a figure such that a particle starting at any point in the figure can move continuously over every line segment in the figure once and only once and return to the starting point without passing over any line segment not in the figure.

CO-AL′TI-TUDE, *n.* **coaltitude of a celestial point.** Ninety degrees minus the altitude; the complementary angle of the altitude. Also called zenith distance.

CO-AX′I-AL, *adj.* **coaxial circles.** Circles such that all pairs of the circles have the same radical axis.

co-axial planes. Planes which pass through the same straight line. The line is called the **axis.**

CO-DEC′LI-NA′TION, *n.* **codeclination of a celestial point.** Ninety degrees minus the declination; the complementary angle of the declination. Also called polar distance.

CO′EF-FI′CIENT, *n.* In elementary algebra, the numerical part of a term, usually written before the literal part, as 2 in $2x$ or $2(x+y)$. (See PARENTHESIS.) In general, the product of all the factors of a term except a certain one (or a certain set), of which the product is said to be the *coefficient.* E.g. in $2axyz$, $2axy$ is the coefficient of z, $2ayz$ the coefficient of x, $2ax$ the coefficient of yz, etc. Most commonly used in algebra for the constant factors, as distinguished from the variables.

binomial coefficients. See BINOMIAL.

coefficients in an equation. (1) The coefficients of the variables. (2) The constant term and the coefficients of all the terms containing variables. If the constant term is not included, the phrase *coefficients of the variables* in the equation is often used.

coefficient of linear expansion. (1) The quotient of the change in length of a rod, due to one degree change of temperature, and the original length (not the same at all temperatures). (2) The change in length of a unit rod when the temperature changes one degree Centigrade beginning at 0°C.

coefficient of strain. See ONE—one dimensional strains.

coefficient of thermal expansion. A term used to designate both the *coefficient of linear expansion* and the *coefficient of volume expansion.*

coefficient of volume (or cubical) expansion. (1) The change in volume of a unit cube when the temperature changes one degree. (The coefficient thus defined is different at different temperatures.) (2) The change in unit volume due to a change of 1°C. beginning at 0°C., i.e. $(v - v_0)/(v_0 t)$, where v_0 is the volume at 0°C., v the volume after the change of temperature and t the change of temperature.

correlation coefficient between two sets of data (or numbers). A number between −1 and 1 which indicates the degree of linear relationship between the two sets of numbers. If the two sets of numbers are $(x_1, x_2, \cdots, x_n)$ and $(y_1, y_2, \cdots, y_n)$, the coefficient of correlation r measures how near the points $(x_1, y_1), (x_2, y_2), \cdots, (x_n, y_n)$ are to lying on a straight line. If $r = \pm 1$, the points lie on a line and the two sets of data are said to be in **perfect correlation.** *Tech. r* is the quotient of the sum of the products of the algebraic deviations of the corresponding numbers of the two sets and the square root of the product of the sum of the squares of the deviations of each set; i.e.

$$r = \frac{\sum_{i=1}^{n} (x_i - x)(y_i - y)}{\sqrt{\sum_{i=1}^{n} (x_i - x)^2 \sum_{i=1}^{n} (y_i - y)^2}},$$

where x and y are the corresponding *means.* Also called **Pearson's coefficient.**

detached coefficients, multiplication and division by means of. Abbreviations of the ordinary multiplication and division processes used in algebra. The coefficients alone (with their signs) are used, the powers of the variable occurring in the various terms being understood from the order in which the coefficients are written, missing powers being assumed to be present with zero coefficients. E.g. (x^3+2x+1) is multiplied by $(3x-1)$ by using the expressions: $(1+0+2+1)$ and $(3-1)$. See SYNTHETIC—synthetic division.

determinant of the cofficients (in a set of linear equations). See DETERMINANT—determinant of the coefficients of the variables.

differential coefficient. Same as DERIVATIVE.

leading coefficient. See LEADING.

Legendre's coefficients. See LEGENDRE'S POLYNOMIALS.

matrix of the coefficients of a set of linear equations. See MATRIX.

roots and coefficients, relation between. See RELATION—relation between the roots and coefficients of a quadratic equation, and relation between the roots and coefficients of an algebraic equation.

undetermined coefficients. See UNDETERMINED.

CO-FACTOR OF AN ELEMENT OF A DETERMINANT. The minor of an element with the algebraic sign that must be attached to the product of this minor and the element when the product is used in the expansion of the determinant; e.g. the *co-factor* of an element in the second row and first column is the negative of the minor obtained by striking out the second row and first column. The sign of a co-factor is positive or negative according as the sum of the number of the row and the number of the column struck out to form the minor is even or odd. Sometimes called a CO-FACTOR OF THE DETERMINANT. See MINOR—minor of an element in a determinant.

CO-FUNC'TION, *n.* See TRIGONOMETRIC—trigonometric co-functions.

CO'IN-CIDE', *v.* To be coincident.

CO-IN'CI-DENT, *adj.* coincident configurations. Two configurations which are such that any point of either one

lies on the other. Two lines (or curves or surfaces) which have the same equation are coincident. The locus of an equation of the form $[f(x, y)]^2 = 0$ is two coincident loci.

CO-LAT'I-TUDE, *n.* colatitude of a point on the earth. Ninety degrees minus the latitude; the complementary angle of the latitude.

COL-LAT'E-RAL, *adj.* collateral security. Assets deposited to guarantee the fulfillment of some contract to pay, and to be returned upon the fulfillment of the contract.

collateral trust bonds. See BOND—collateral trust bonds.

COL-LECT'ING, *part.* collecting terms. Grouping terms in a parenthesis or adding like terms. E.g. to collect terms in $(2+ax+bx)$, we write it in the form $2+x(a+b)$; to collect terms in $(2x+3y-x+y)$, we write it in the form $(x+4y)$.

COL-LIN'E-AR, *adj.* collinear planes. Planes having a common line. *Syn.* Coaxial planes.

collinear points. Points lying on the same line.

condition that three points be collinear. See CONDITION.

condition that two lines be perpendicular, parallel. See PERPENDICULAR—perpendicular lines, PARALLEL—parallel lines.

conditions that two points in the plane be collinear with the origin: That the constant term in the Cartesian equation of the straight line through the two points be zero; that their corresponding rectangular Cartesian coordinates be proportional; that the determinant, whose first row is composed of the Cartesian coordinates of one of the points and the second of those of the other, be zero; i.e. $x_1y_2-x_2y_1=0$, where the points are (x_1, y_1) and (x_2, y_2).

conditions that two points in space be collinear with the origin: That their corresponding Cartesian coordinates be proportional; the constant term in the equation of any two planes, defining the line through the two points, be zero; the *matrix,*

$$\begin{vmatrix} x_1 & y_1 & z_1 \\ x_2 & y_2 & z_2 \end{vmatrix}$$

whose columns are composed of the co-ordinates of the points, be of rank one.

COL-LIN-E-A'TION, *n.* A transformation of the plane or space which carries points into points, lines into lines, and planes into planes.

CO-LOG'A-RITHM, *n.* **cologarithm of a number.** The logarithm of the reciprocal of the number; the negative of the logarithm of the number, written with the decimal part (mantissa) positive. Used in computations to avoid subtracting mantissas and the confusion of dealing with the negatives of man-

tissas. E.g. to evaluate $\dfrac{641}{1246}$ by use of

logarithms, write $\log \dfrac{641}{1246} = \log 641$

$+ \text{colog } 1246$, where $\text{colog } 1246 = 10$ $- \log 1246 - 10 = 10 - (3.0955) - 10$ $= 6.9045 - 10.$

COL'UMN, *n.* A vertical array of terms, used in addition and subtraction and in determinants and matrices.

column in a determinant. See DE-TERMINANT.

COM'BI-NA'TION (COMBINATION OF A SET OF ELEMENTS). Any selection of one or more of these elements.

combination of n things, r at a time, when repetitions are allowed. A set of r things chosen from the given n, each being used as many times as desired. The number of such combinations is the same as the number of combinations of $n + r - 1$ different things taken r at a time, repetitions not allowed; i.e.

$$\frac{(n+r-1)!}{(n-1)!\,r!}.$$

The combinations of a, b, c two at a time, repetitions allowed, are: aa, bb, cc, ab, ac, and bc.

linear combination. See LINEAR.

number of combinations of n things r at a time. The number of sets that can be made up from the n things, each set containing r different things and no

two sets containing exactly the same r things. Equal to the number of permutations of the n things, taken r at a time, divided by the number of permutations of r things taken r at a time; that is, $_nP_r/r! = n!/[(n-r)!\,r!]$, which is denoted by $_nC_r$. E.g. the combinations of a, b, c, two at a time, are ab, ac, bc. $_nC_r$ is also the coefficient in the $(r+1)$th term of the binomial expansion, for $(x-a)^n = (x-a_1)(x-a_2)\cdots(x-a_n)$ with the a's all equal, and the coefficient of x^{n-r} is a^r times the number of combinations of the n different a's r at a time. See BINOMIAL—binomial coefficients.

total number of combinations of n different things. The sum of the number of combinations taken $1, 2, \cdots, n$ at a time, i.e. $\sum_{r=1}^{n} {_nC_r}$, which is the sum of the binomial coefficients in $(x+y)^n$ less 1, or $(2^n - 1)$. See above, number of combinations of n things r at a time.

COM-MEN'SU-RA-BLE, *adj.* **commensurable quantities.** Two quantities which have a common measure, that is, there is a number which is exactly contained in each of them. A rule, a yard long, is commensurable with a rod, for they each contain, for instance, 6 inches an integral number of times.

COM-MER'CIAL, *adj.* **commercial bank.** A bank that carries checking accounts.

commercial draft. See DRAFT.

commercial paper. Negotiable paper used in transacting business, such as drafts, negotiable notes, endorsed checks, etc.

commercial year. A year of 360 days as used in computing ordinary simple interest. See CIVIL YEAR.

COM-MIS'SION, *n.* A fee charged for transacting business for another person.

commission man or merchant. See BROKER.

COM'MON, *adj.* **common difference** in an arithmetic progression. The difference between any term and the preceding term, usually denoted by d.

common divisor. See DIVISOR.

common fraction. See FRACTION.

common limit. A single limit approached by two or more variables. The areas of polygons inscribed in, and of those circumscribed about, a given circle each approach the area of the circle when the largest of the sides of each polygon is made to approach zero.

common logarithms. Logarithms having 10 for their base. *Syn.* Brigg's logarithms.

common multiple of a set of quantities. A quantity divisible by each of the given quantities; a quantity which contains each of the given quantities as a factor. E.g. 12 is a common multiple of 2, 3, 4, and 6.

common perpendicular. See PERPENDICULAR—common perpendicular.

common stock. Stock upon which the dividends paid are determined by the net profits of the corporation after all other costs, including dividends on preferred stock, have been paid.

least (lowest) common denominator of a set of fractions. The least common multiple of their denominators. Denoted by L.C.D. The L.C.D. of $\frac{1}{2}$, $\frac{1}{3}$ and $\frac{1}{5}$ is 30.

least common multiple. See MULTIPLE—least common multiple.

COMMUTATION, *adj.* **commutation symbols in life insurance.** Symbols denoting the nature of the numbers in the columns of a commutation table. For instance, D_x and N_x. See below, commutation tables.

commutation tables (columns). Tables from which the values of certain types of insurance can be quickly computed. E.g. suppose that one has a commutation table with the values of D_x and N_x for all ages appearing in the mortality tables, where D_x is the product of the number of persons who attain the age x in any year and the present value of a sum of money x years hence, at some given rate, and N_x is the sum of the series $(D_x + D_{x+1} + \cdots$ to end of table). The value of an immediate annuity of \$1.00 at age x is the quotient N_{x+1}/D_x, and that of an annuity due is N_x/D_x. Sometimes (following Davies) N_x is defined as the sum of the series

$(D_{x+1} + D_{x+2} + \cdots)$. Using this definition, the annuity values must be N_x/D_x and N_{x-1}/D_x, respectively. Commutation tables based on the latter definition of N_x are called the **terminal form** while those based on the former definition of N_x are called the **initial form.**

COM-MUT'A-TIVE, *adj.* **commutative law for the combination of two quantities:** The result of the combination does not depend on the order in which the combination is performed. E.g. $a + b = b + a$ and $a \cdot b = b \cdot a$.

commutative law of addition: The order of addition does not affect the sum; e.g. $2 + 3 = 3 + 2$. The law is usually written: $a + b = b + a$.

commutative law of multiplication: The order of multiplication does not affect the product; e.g. $2 \cdot 3 = 3 \cdot 2$. The law is usually written: $a \cdot b = b \cdot a$.

COMMUTING OBLIGATIONS. Exchanging one set of obligations to pay a certain sum (or sums) at various times for another to pay according to some other plan. The common date of comparison at which the two sets are equivalent (equal in value at that time) is called the **focal date.**

COMPARISON DATE. See EQUATION—equation of payments.

COMPARISON TEST for convergence of an infinite series: If, after some chosen term of a series, the numerical value of each term is equal to or less than the value of the corresponding term of some convergent series of positive terms, the series converges (and converges absolutely); if the algebraic value of each term is equal to or greater than the corresponding term of some divergent series of positive terms, the series diverges.

COM'PASS, *n.* An instrument for describing circles or for measuring distances between two points. Usually

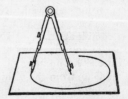

used in the plural, as **compasses.** *Syn.* Dividers.

mariner's compass. A magnetic needle which rotates about an axis perpendicular to a card (see figure) on which the directions are indicated. The needle always indicates the direction of the magnetic meridian.

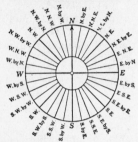

COM-PAT'I-BIL'I-TY, *n.* Same as CONSISTENCY.

COM'PLE-MEN'TA-RY, *adj.* **complementary angles.** Two angles whose sum is a right angle. The two acute angles in a right triangle are always complementary.

complementary function. See DIFFERENTIAL—linear differential equations.

complementary minor. See MINOR —minor of an element in a determinant.

complementary trigonometric functions. Trigonometric functions which are equal when the arguments are complementary, i.e. when one angle equals 90° minus the other. E.g. sin x and cos x, tan x and ctn x, sec x and csc x are pairs of complementary functions. *Syn.* trigonometric co-functions.

COMPLETE, *adj.* **complete annuity.** An annuity payable at certain regular periods, and a proportionate amount payable for any partial period, and ending with the end of the life. *Syn.* Apportionable annuity, whole life annuity.

complete expectation of life. The average number of years that the members of a given group will live after attaining a certain age.

complete induction. Same as MATHEMATICAL INDUCTION. Called **complete** in contrast to **incomplete induction** which draws a conclusion from the examination of a finite (limited) number of cases.

complete joint annuity. An annuity payable as long as two (or more) lives continue—includes a proportionate amount for any partial period over which both (all) survive. See above, complete annuity.

complete scale. See SCALE—number scale.

COMPLETING THE SQUARE. A process used in solving quadratic equations. It consists of transposing all terms to the left side of the equation, dividing through by the coefficient of the square term, then adding to the constant (and to the right side) a number sufficient to make the left member a perfect trinomial square. This method is sometimes modified by first multiplying through by a number sufficient to make the coefficient of the square of the variable a perfect square, then adding a constant to both sides of the equation, as before, to make the left side a perfect trinomial square. E.g. to complete the square in $2x^2 + 8x + 2 = 0$, divide both members of the equation by 2, obtaining $x^2 + 4x + 1 = 0$. Now add 3 to both sides, obtaining

$$x^2 + 4x + 4 = (x+2)^2 = 3.$$

Frequently, *completing* the square refers to writing any polynomial of the form $(a_1x^2 + b_1x + c_1)$ in the form $[a_1(x+b_2)^2 + c_2]$, a procedure used a great deal in reducing the equations of conics to their standard form.

COM'PLEX, *adj.* **absolute value of a complex number.** The square root of the sum of the squares of the real part (term) and the real coefficient of $i (= \sqrt{-1})$. See MODULUS.

addition, multiplication, and division of complex numbers. See ADDITION, MULTIPLICATION and below, quotient of complex numbers.

complex domain (field). The set of all complex numbers. See DOMAIN.

complex fraction. See FRACTION —complex fraction.

complex number. Any number, real or imaginary, of the form $a + bi$, where a and b are real numbers and $i = \sqrt{-1}$.

Called *imaginary numbers* when $b \neq 0$, and *pure imaginary* when $a = 0$ and $b \neq 0$.

complex plane. The plane used for graphical representation of complex numbers. See below, graphical representation of complex numbers.

complex roots of a quadratic equation $(ax^2 + bx + c = 0)$. Used in contrasting roots of the form $a + bi$ with real roots, although the latter are special cases of the former for which $b = 0$. See DISCRIMINANT—discriminant of a quadratic equation in one variable.

complex unit. A complex number whose modulus is unity; a complex number of the form $\cos \theta + i \sin \theta$; a complex number which, geometrically, is a radius of the unit circle about the pole. The products, or quotients, of unit complex numbers are unit complex numbers. See MULTIPLICATION—multiplication of complex numbers.

conjugate complex numbers. Frequently called **conjugate imaginaries:** complex numbers which are identical, except that the pure imaginary terms are opposite in sign or both zero. Numbers of the form $(a + bi)$ and $(a - bi)$ are conjugate complex numbers. When $b \neq 0$, $a + bi$ and $a - bi$ are also called *conjugate imaginary numbers*.

equality of two complex numbers. See EQUALITY.

graphical (representation of) addition of complex numbers. See ADDITION—addition of complex numbers.

graphical representation of complex numbers $a + bi$. (1) The vector from the origin of a system of rectangular coordinates to the point whose coordinates are (a, b). (2) The point indicated in (1) above, that is, the point whose rectangular Cartesian coordinates are the real term and the coefficient of i. See ARGAND DIAGRAM.

modulus of a complex number. See ABSOLUTE—absolute value of a complex number, and below, polar form of a complex number.

polar form of a complex number. The form a complex number takes when it is expressed in polar coordinates. This form is: $r(\cos \theta + i \sin \theta)$,

where r is the radius vector and θ the vectorial angle of the point represented by the complex number. The number r is called the **modulus** and the angle θ the **amplitude, argument, or phase.** *Syn.* Trigonometric form (representation) of a complex number. See COORDINATE—complex coordinates, and EULER'S FORMULA.

power of a complex number. See DE MOIVRE'S THEOREM.

quotient of complex numbers. The product of the dividend by the reciprocal of the divisor, the latter being written with its denominator rationalized, e.g.

$$(2+i) \div (1+i) = (2+i) \times \frac{1-i}{2} ;$$

the complex number whose modulus is the quotient of the modulus of the dividend by that of the divisor and whose amplitude is the amplitude of the dividend minus that of the divisor; that is

$$r_1(\cos \theta_1 + i \sin \theta_1) \div r_2(\cos \theta_2 + i \sin \theta_2)$$
$$= \frac{r_1}{r_0} [\cos (\theta_1 - \theta_2) + i \sin (\theta_1 - \theta_2)].$$

See MULTIPLICATION—multiplication of complex numbers.

root of a complex number. See ROOT.

trigonometric form (representation) of a complex number. Same as POLAR FORM. See above, polar form of a complex number.

COM-PO′NENT, *n.* **component of a force (or velocity, or acceleration).** One of a set of two or more forces (or velocities, or accelerations) which are equivalent to the given force (or velocity, or acceleration). See RESULTANT.

component of a vector in a given direction. The projection of the vector on a line in the given direction. See PROJECTION—projection of a vector on a line or plane.

direction components. See DIRECTION—direction numbers.

COM-POS′ITE, *adj.* **composite function of one variable.** (1) A function of a variable which is a function of a second variable—such as $y = f(t)$, where $t = g(x)$. The derivative of such a function, with respect to x, can be obtained by use of the formula

$$\frac{dy}{dx}=\frac{dy}{dt}\frac{dt}{dx}.$$

(2) A factorable function, one which can be written as the product of two or more functions, as x^2-1.

composite function of two variables. (1) A function in which the independent variables are functions of other independent variables; for instance, $z=f(x,y)$, where $x=u(t,s)$ and $y=v(t,s)$, is a composite function of s and t. (2) A function which is factorable (can be written as the product of two or more functions), as (x^2-y^2).

composite life of a plant. The time required for the total annual depreciation charge to accumulate, at a given rate of interest, to the original wearing value.

composite number. A number that can be factored, as 4, 6, or 10, in distinction to prime numbers like 3, 5, or 7. Refers only to integers.

composite quantity. A quantity which is factorable.

differentials of composite functions. The formulas for the total differentials of functions of one or more variables hold when the functions are composite. One may, in that case, replace the differentials of the independent variables by their total differentials in terms of the variables of which they are functions. E.g. If $z=f(x,y)$, $x=u(s,t)$ and $y=v(s,t)$, then

$$dz=\frac{\partial f}{\partial x}\,dx+\frac{\partial f}{\partial y}\,dy$$

$$=\frac{\partial f}{\partial x}\left[\frac{\partial u}{\partial s}ds+\frac{\partial u}{\partial t}dt\right]$$

$$+\frac{\partial f}{\partial y}\left[\frac{\partial v}{\partial s}ds+\frac{\partial v}{\partial t}dt\right].$$

See above, composite function of two variables, (1).

COM'PO-SI'TION, *n.* **composition in a proportion.** Passing from the statement of the proportion to the statement that the sum of the first antecedent and its consequent is to its consequent as the sum of the second antecedent and its consequent is to its consequent; i.e. passing from

$a/b=c/d$ to $(a+b)/b=(c+d)/d.$

composition and division in a proportion. Passing from the statement of the proportion to the statement that the sum of the first antecedent and its consequent is to the difference between the first antecedent and its consequent as the sum of the second antecedent and its consequent is to the difference between the second antecedent and its consequent; i.e. passing from

$a/b=c/d$ to $(a+b)/(a-b)=(c+d)/(c-d).$

See above, composition in a proportion, and DIVISION—division in a proportion.

composition of vectors. The same process as *addition of vectors*, but the term composition of vectors is used more when speaking of adding vectors which denote forces, velocities or accelerations; finding the vector which represents the resultant of forces, velocities, accelerations, etc., represented by the given vectors. See ADDITION —addition of two vectors in the plane, addition of two vectors in space.

graphing by composition of ordinates. See GRAPHING—graphing by composition.

COM'POUND, *adj.* **compound amount.** The sum of principal and compound interest on it for a given number of years. If 6% is the rate, the compound amount of $1.00 at the end of 1 year is $1.06, at the end of 2 years $(1.06)^2$, at the end of n years $(1.06)^n$. See ACCUMULATION—accumulation factor, and EXPONENT.

compound event. (1) An event the probability of whose occurrence depends upon the probability of occurrence of two or more independent events. E.g. the probability of getting two heads on each of two tosses of a coin is the product of the separate probabilities, which is $\frac{1}{2}\cdot\frac{1}{2}$. (2) An event consisting of two or more non-mutually exclusive events.

compound harmonic function. The sum of several simple harmonic functions. $\cos x+\cos 2x+\cos 3x$ is a *compound harmonic function.*

compound interest. See INTEREST.

compound number. The sum of two or more denominations of a certain kind of denominate number; e.g. 5 feet, 7 inches or 6 lbs., 3 ozs.

compound reversionary bonus. See BONUS.

compound survivorship insurance. Insurance payable at the end of a certain life, provided a group of lives, including this one, end in a certain order. Contingent insurance is the simplest case of this form of insurance.

compound survivorship probability. The probability that a set of lives will end in a certain order.

COM-PRES'SION, n. See TENSION.

compressions, simple or one-dimensional compressions. Same as ONE-DIMENSIONAL STRAINS. See ONE.

COM'PU-TA'TION, n. The act of carrying out mathematical processes; used mostly with reference to arithmetic rather than algebraic work. One might say, "Find the formula for the number of gallons in a sphere of radius r and *compute* the result for $r = 5$"; or "*Compute* the square root of 3." Frequently used to designate long arithmetic or analytic processes that give numerical results, as *computing* the orbit of a planet.

numerical computation. A computation involving numbers only, not letters representing numbers.

COM-PUTE', v. To make a computation. *Syn.* Calculate.

COMPUTING MACHINE. Any machine which works numerical problems; usually applied to machines that add and subtract integers. The other fundamental operations of arithmetic are then possible on the machine, the simplicity of carrying them out depending upon the construction of the particular machine. *Syn.* Calculating machine.

CON'CAVE, *adj.* concave toward a point (or line). Said of a curve which bulges away from (is hollow toward) the point (or line). *Tech.* an arc of a curve is concave toward a point (or line) if every segment of the arc cut off by a secant lies on the opposite side of the secant from the point (or line). If there exists a horizontal line such that the curve lies above it and is concave toward it (lies below it and is concave toward it) the curve is said to be *concave down* (*concave up*). A circle with center on the x-axis is concave toward that axis, the upper half being concave down and the lower half concave up.

concave polygon. See POLYGON.

CON-CAV'I-TY, n. The state or property of being concave.

CON-CEN'TRIC, *adj.* concentric circles. Circles lying in the same plane and having a common center. *Concentric* is applied to any two figures which have centers (that is, are symmetric about some point) when their centers are coincident. *Concentric* is opposed to *eccentric*, meaning not concentric.

CON'CHOID, n. The locus of one end point of a segment of constant length, on a line which rotates about a fixed point (O in figure) the other end-point of the segment being at the intersection Q of this line with a fixed line not containing the fixed point. If the polar axis is taken through the fixed point and perpendicular to the fixed line, the length of the segment is taken as b, and the distance from the fixed point to the fixed line as a, the polar equation

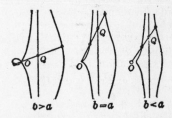

$b>a \qquad b=a \qquad b<a$

of the conchoid is $r = b + a \sec \theta$. Its Cartesian equation is

$$(x-a)^2(x^2+y^2) = b^2 x^2.$$

The curve is asymptotic to the fixed line in both directions, and on both sides of it. If the line segment is greater than the perpendicular distance from the pole to the fixed line, the curve forms a loop with a node at the pole. If these two distances are equal, it forms a cusp at the pole. The conchoid is also called the **conchoid of Nicomedes.**

CON-CLU'SION, *n.* **conclusion of a theorem.** The statement which follows (or is to be proved to follow) as a consequence of the hypotheses of the theorem.

conclusion, from a topic. An inference drawn from matters presented in the topic and the mathematical conditions involved.

CON'CRETE, *adj.* **concrete number.** A number referring to specific objects or units, as 3 people, or 3 houses. The number and its reference are denoted by *concrete number.*

CON-CUR'RENT, *adj.* Passing through a point.

concurrent lines. Three or more lines which have one point in common.

concurrent planes. Three or more planes having a single point in common.

condition that three lines (not all coincident) be concurrent. *In a plane*: that the determinant of the coefficients and constants of the equations of the three lines be zero and one second order determinant taken from the coefficients (the first two columns of the determinant) be not zero; that is, the three equations defining the lines have a common solution. *In space*: that the six linear equations defining the three lines have a common solution. See MATRIX—rank of a matrix.

CON-DI'TION, *n.* The mathematical assumption or truth that makes such and such a situation exist or certain statements be true, that is, makes these conclusions necessary if consistency in our thinking is to be maintained.

Cauchy-Lipschitz condition. See CAUCHY-LIPSCHITZ CONDITION.

condition percent of equipment. The ratio of its present wearing value to its wearing value when it was new. Present wearing value, as used here, means difference between the sale price at the present moment and the scrap value.

condition that four planes be concur-

rent: That the determinant of the system of equations of these planes be zero and not all of the third order determinants of the coefficients of the variables be zero.

condition that a line in space lie in a plane. That the plane have for its equation a linear combination of the equations of any two planes determining the line. See CONSISTENCY—consistency of three linear equations in three variables.

condition that three linear equations in three variables be consistent or inconsistent. See CONSISTENCY.

condition that three lines be concurrent. See CONCURRENT.

condition that three planes be concurrent. See CONSISTENCY—consistency of three linear equations in three variables.

condition that three planes pass through a line (or are parallel): That any one of them be a linear combination of the other two. See CONSISTENCY—consistency of three linear equations in three variables.

condition that three points in a plane be collinear: That the third order determinant whose rows are x_1, y_1, 1; x_2, y_2, 1; and x_3, y_3, 1; where the x's and y's are the coordinates of the three points, shall be zero.

condition that three points in space be collinear: That two lines through different pairs of the points have their direction numbers proportional. *Tech.* the coordinates of any one of them can be expressed as a linear combination of the other two, in which the constants of the linear combination have their sum equal to unity.

condition that two linear equations in two variables be consistent and independent, inconsistent, consistent but not independent. See CONSISTENCY—consistency of two linear equations in two variables.

condition that two non-parallel lines in space intersect. The vanishing of the fourth order determinant formed by the coefficients and constants of the four linear equations which in pairs determine the two lines.

necessary condition. A condition which is necessary to prove a desired result (or conclusion) to be true; an hypothesis which can be proved from the conclusion. A necessary condition may not be a *sufficient condition*. See below, necessary and sufficient condition.

necessary and sufficient condition. A condition which is both necessary and sufficient. A condition may be necessary but not sufficient, or sufficient but not necessary. It is necessary that a substance be sweet in order that it be called sugar, but it may be sweet and be arsenic; it is sufficient that it be granulated and have the chemical properties of sugar, but it can be sugar without being granulated. In order for a quadrilateral to be a parallelogram, it is necessary, but not sufficient, that two opposite sides be equal, and sufficient, although not necessary, that all of its sides be equal; but it is necessary and sufficient that two opposite sides be equal and parallel.

necessary and sufficient condition for convergence. See CAUCHY.

sufficient condition. A condition which is sufficient to prove a desired result (or conclusion). A *sufficient condition* may not be a *necessary condition*. See above, necessary and sufficient condition.

CON-DI'TION-AL, *adj.* **conditional convergence of series.** See CONVERGENT—conditionally convergent series.

conditional equation. See EQUATION.

conditional inequality. An inequality which is true only for certain values of the variables involved—contrasted to *unconditional* inequality, which is an inequality true for all values of the variables, or contains none. E.g. $(x+2)>3$ is a *conditional* inequality, because it is true only for x greater than 1; while $(x+1)>x$ and $3>2$ are **unconditional inequalities.**

CONE, *n.* A solid bounded by a closed conical surface and a plane cutting the surface in a closed curve. The plane section is called the **base,** and the per-

pendicular from the vertex to the plane section is called the **altitude.** See CONICAL SURFACE.

circular cone. See CIRCULAR.

cone of revolution. The surface formed by revolving a right triangle about one of its legs, or an isosceles triangle about its altitude. *Syn.* Right circular cone.

element of a cone. See ELEMENT —element of a cone.

frustum of a cone. The part of the cone bounded by the base and a plane parallel to the base (see figure). The volume of a frustum of a cone equals one-third the **altitude** (the distance between the planes) times the sum of the areas of the bases and the square root of the product of the areas of the bases; i.e.

$$\tfrac{1}{3}h(B_1+B_2+\sqrt{B_1B_2}).$$

lateral area of a frustum of a right circular cone. The area of the curved surface. It is equal to $\pi l(r+r')$, where l is the slant height and r and r' are the radii of the bases.

lateral area of a right circular cone. The area of its conical surface. Equal to one half of the product of the circumference of the base and the slant height, that is, $\pi r h$, where r is the radius of the base and h is the slant height.

oblique circular cone. A circular cone whose axis is not perpendicular to the base.

right circular cone. A cone which has a circular base perpendicular to the axis of the cone. *Syn.* Cone of revolution. Sometimes called simply **circular cone.**

rulings of a cone. See RULINGS.

spherical cone. A surface composed of the spherical surface of a spherical segment and the conical surface defined by the bounding circle of the segment and the center of the sphere (See

CONICAL SURFACE); a spherical sector whose curved base is a zone of one base. The volume of a spherical cone is $\frac{2}{3}\pi r^2 h$, where r is the radius of the sphere and h is the altitude of the zone base.

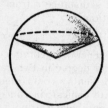

tangent cone of a quadric surface. The cone whose elements are each tangent to the quadric.

tangent cone of a sphere. Any circular cone all of whose elements are tangent to the sphere. If a ball is dropped into a cone, the cone is tangent to the ball.

tangent plane to a cone. A plane which meets the cone in one of its elements. See ELEMENT—element of a cone.

truncated cone. The portion of a cone included between two non-parallel planes whose line of intersection does not pierce the cone. The two plane sections of the cone are called the **bases** of the *truncated cone.*

volume of any cone. Equal to one-third the product of the area of the base and the altitude.

volume of a right circular cone. Equal to one-third of the product of π, the square of the radius of the base, and the altitude, i.e. $\frac{1}{3}\pi r^2 h$.

CON-FIG'U-RA'TION, *n.* A general term for any geometrical figure, or any combination of geometrical elements, such as points, lines, curves and surfaces.

CON-FO'CAL, *adj.* **confocal conics.** Conics having their foci coincident. E.g. the ellipses and hyperbolas represented by the equation $x^2/(a^2-k^2) + y^2/(b^2-k^2) = 1$, where $b^2 < a^2$, $k^2 \neq b^2$, and k takes on all other real values for which $k^2 < a^2$, are confocal. These conics intersect at right angles, forming an orthogonal system. (See point P in figure).

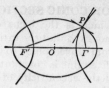

confocal quadrics. Quadrics having their foci coincident (see confocal conics). E.g. the ellipsoid,

$$\frac{x^2}{a^2-k^2}+\frac{y^2}{b^2-k^2}+\frac{z^2}{c^2-k^2}=1,$$

($k^2 < c^2$ and $c^2 < b^2 < a^2$); the hyperboloid of one sheet,

$$\frac{x^2}{a^2-e^2}+\frac{y^2}{b^2-e^2}-\frac{z^2}{e^2-c^2}=1,$$

($c^2 < e^2 < b^2 < a^2$); and the hyperboloid of two sheets,

$$\frac{x^2}{a^2-m^2}-\frac{y^2}{m^2-b^2}-\frac{z^2}{m^2-c^2}=1,$$

($c^2 < b^2 < m^2 < a^2$), are confocal. Incidentally, these form a **triply orthogonal system,** i.e. each surface is orthogonal to every member of the other two families, all along the curves in which they intersect.

CON-FOR'MAL TRANSFORMATION. A transformation which leaves the angles in any configuration unchanged. *Syn.* Isogonal or equiangular transformation.

CON'GRU-ENCE, *n.* A statement that two quantities are congruent. The congruence between a and b, with modulus c, is written: $a \equiv b \pmod{c}$, and is read "*a* is *congruent* to *b*, modulus *c*." E.g. $5 \equiv 3 \pmod 2$. (The parenthesis is not always used.) See CONGRUENT —congruent numbers.

CON'GRU-ENT, *adj.* **congruent figures in geometry.** Figures which can be superposed (placed one upon the other) so that they coincide, that is have the same appearance as either of the original figures.

congruent numbers, or quantities. Two quantities which, when each is divided by a given quantity (called the modulus), give the same remainders; two quantities whose difference is divisible by the modulus. See CONGRUENCE.

CON'IC, OR CONIC SECTION, *n.* Any curve which is the locus of a point which moves so that the ratio of its distance from a fixed point to its distance from a fixed line is constant. The ratio is called the **eccentricity of the curve;** the fixed point the **focus;** and the fixed line the **directrix.** The *eccentricity* is always denoted by *e.* When *e* is equal to unity, the conic is a parabola; when less than unity, an ellipse; and when greater than unity, a hyperbola. These are called conics since they can always be gotten by taking plane sections of a circular conical surface. See below, general equation of any conic.

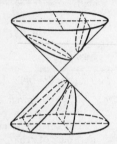

central conics. Conics which have centers—ellipses and hyperbolas.

confocal conics. See CONFOCAL.

degenerate conic. A point, a straight line, or a pair of straight lines, which is a limiting form of a conic. E.g. the parabola approaches a straight line as the plane, whose intersection with a conical surface defines the parabola, moves into a position in which it contains a single element of the conical surface; the ellipse becomes a point when the cutting plane passes through the vertex of the cone but does not contain an element; the hyperbola becomes a pair of lines when the cutting plane contains the vertex of the conical surface. All these limiting cases can be obtained algebraically by variation of the parameters in their several equations. See DISCRIMINANT—discriminant of the general quadratic.

diameter of a conic. See DIAMETER.

focal chords of conics. See FOCAL.

general equation of any conic. (1) In *polar coordinates* with the focus at the pole, and the directrix perpendicular to the polar axis and at a distance q from the pole, the equation is $\rho = (eq)/(1 + e \cos \theta)$. (2) In *Cartesian coordinates* with the focus at the origin and the directrix perpendicular to the x-axis at a distance q from the focus, the equation is

$$(1 - e^2)x^2 + 2e^2qx + y^2 = e^2q.$$

(3) The general algebraic equation of the second degree in two variables always represents a conic (including here degenerate conics); i.e. an ellipse, hyperbola, parabola, a straight line, a pair of straight lines, or a point, provided it is satisfied by any real points. See DISCRIMINANT—discriminant of a quadratic equation in one variable.

similarly placed conics. See SIMILARLY.

tangent to a general conic: (1) If the equation of the conic in *Cartesian* coordinates is $ax^2 + 2bxy + cy^2 + 2dx + 2ey + f = 0$, then the equation of the tangent at the point

(x_1, y_1) is $ax_1x + b(xy_1 + x_1y)$

$$+ cy_1y + d(x + x_1) + e(y + y_1) + f = 0$$

(2) If the equation of the conic in *homogeneous* Cartesian coordinates is written

$$\sum_{i,j=1}^{3} a_{ij}x_ix_j = 0, \quad \text{(where } a_{ij} = a_{ji}),$$

then the equation of the tangent at the point (b_1, b_2, b_3) is:

$$\sum_{i,j=1}^{3} a_{ij}b_ix_j = 0.$$

See COORDINATE—homogeneous coordinates in the plane.

CON'I-CAL SURFACE. A surface which can be generated by a line which always passes through a fixed point and intersects a fixed curve. The fixed point is called the **vertex,** or **apex,** of the conical surface, the fixed curve the **directrix,** and the moving line the **generator** or **generatrix.**

circular conical surface. A conical surface whose directrix is a circle and whose vertex is on the line perpendicular to the plane of the circle and passing through the center of the circle. If

the vertex is at the origin and the directrix in a plane perpendicular to the
z-axis, its equation in rectangular Cartesian coordinates is $x^2 + y^2 = k^2 z^2$.

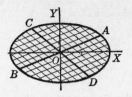

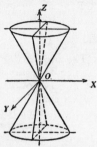

**equation of a conical surface with
vertex at the origin.** Any homogeneous equation in rectangular Cartesian
coordinates. See HOMOGENEOUS—
homogeneous equation.

quadric conical surfaces. Conical
surfaces whose directrices are conics.

CON′I-COID, *n.* An ellipsoid, hyperboloid, or paraboloid; usually does not
refer to limiting (degenerate) cases.

CON′JU-GATE, *adj.* **conjugate algebraic
numbers.** Any set of numbers which
are roots of the same irreducible algebraic equation with rational coefficients, an equation of the form:

$$a_0 x^n + a_1 x^{n-1} + \cdots + a_n = 0.$$

E.g. the roots of $x^2 + x + 1 = 0$, which
are $\frac{1}{2}(-1 + i\sqrt{3})$ and $\frac{1}{2}(-1 - i\sqrt{3})$, are
conjugate algebraic numbers (in this
case conjugate imaginary numbers).

conjugate angles. See ANGLE—conjugate angles.

conjugate arcs. Two arcs whose sum
is a complete circle.

conjugate axis of an hyperbola. See
HYPERBOLA.

conjugate complex numbers. See
COMPLEX—conjugate complex numbers.

conjugate diameters. A diameter
and the diameter which occurs among
the parallel chords that define the
given diameter. The conjugate diameters in a circle are perpendicular. The
axes of an ellipse are conjugate diameters. But, in general, conjugate diameters are not perpendicular. See
DIAMETER—diameter of a conic.

**conjugate elements of a determi-
nant.** Elements which are interchanged
if the rows and columns of the determinant are interchanged; e.g. the element
in the second row and third column is
the conjugate of the element in the
third row and second column. In gen-
eral, the elements a_{ij} and a_{ji} are conjugate elements, a_{ij} being the element
in the ith row and jth column and a_{ji}
the element in the jth row and ith column. See DETERMINANT—deter-
minant of any order.

conjugate functions. Two functions,
$u(x, y)$ and $v(x, y)$, which satisfy the
condition $D_x u = D_y v$ and $D_y u = -D_x v$.
This condition is both necessary and
sufficient in order that the function
$u + iv$, where u and v are functions of x
and y, should have a derivative with
respect to $x + iy$, $(= z)$.

conjugate imaginaries. Imaginary
numbers $a + bi$ and $a - bi$, $b \neq 0$. See
COMPLEX—conjugate complex num-
bers.

conjugate point. See POINT—isolated point.

conjugate points relative to a conic.
Two points such that one of them lies
on the line joining the points of contact
of the two tangents drawn to the conic
from the other; two points which are
harmonic conjugates of the two points
of intersection of the conic and the line
drawn through the points; a point and
any point on the polar of the point.
Tech. if the conic is written in the form

$$\sum_{i,j=1}^{3} a_{ij} x_i x_j, \text{ where } x_1, x_2 \text{ and } x_3$$

are *homogeneous rectangular Cartesian
coordinates* and $a_{ij} = a_{ji}$, then two
points, (x_1, x_2, x_3) and (y_1, y_1, y_3), are
conjugate points if and only if

$$\sum_{i,j=1}^{3} a_{ij} x_i y_j = 0.$$

See below, harmonic conjugates with respect to two points.

conjugate radicals. (1) Conjugate binomial surds (see SURD). (2) Radicals which are conjugate algebraic numbers.

conjugate roots. (1) Roots of an equation which are conjugate imaginary numbers. (2) See above, conjugate algebraic numbers.

harmonic conjugates with respect to two points. Any two points which divide the line through the two points internally and externally in the same numerical ratio; two points (the 3rd and 4th) which with the given two (the 1st and 2nd) have a cross-ratio equal to -1 (see RATIO). If two points are harmonic conjugates with respect to two others, the latter two are harmonic conjugates with respect to the first two.

isogonal conjugate lines. See ISOGONAL—isogonal lines.

CO'NOID, n. (1) Any surface generated by a straight line moving parallel to a given plane and always intersecting a given line and given curve. (2) A paraboloid of revolution, a hyperboloid of revolution, or an ellipsoid of revolution. (3) General parabaloid and hyperboloid, but not the general ellipsoid.

CON'SE-QUENT, n. The second term of a ratio; the quantity to which the first term is compared, i.e. the divisor. E.g. in the ratio $\frac{2}{3}$, 3 is the *consequent*, and 2 the *antecedent*.

CONSERVATIVE FIELD. A force field in which the work done in moving a particle around a closed curve is zero. The total work done in such a field in moving a particle from one point to another is independent of the path since the sum of the work done in going from A to B and that in going from B to A is zero. If the work be expressed as a line integral, then the integrand is exact. See INTEGRAL—line integral of the first kind. The gravitational field is a conservative field, while the magnetic field generated by a current flowing in a wire is not conservative.

conservative force. The force forming a conservative field.

CON-SIGN', v. to consign goods, or any property. To send it to some one to sell,

usually at a fixed fee, in contrast to selling on commission.

CON'SIGN-EE', n. A person to whom goods are consigned.

CON-SIGN'OR, n. A person who sends goods to another for him to sell; a person who consigns goods.

CON-SIST'EN-CY, n. **consistency of equations.** The property possessed by equations, when they are all satisfied by at least one set of values of the variables, when their loci all have one or more common points. If they are not all satisfied by any one set of values of the variables, they are said to be **inconsistent**. E.g. the equations $x+y=4$ and $x+y=5$ are inconsistent; the equations $x+y=4$ and $2x+2y=8$ are consistent, but are not independent (see INDEPENDENT); and the equations $x+y=4$ and $x-y=2$ are *consistent and independent*. The first pair of equations represents two parallel lines, the second represents two coincident lines, and the third represents two distinct lines intersecting in a point, the point whose coordinates are $(3, 1)$.

consistency of homogeneous linear equations. See HOMOGENEOUS.

consistency of n linear equations in m variables. See MATRIX—rank of a matrix.

consistency of three linear equations in three variables. The property they possess when they are satisfied by the same set or sets of values of their variables. Eliminating the variables, two at a time, from the equations:

$$a_1x+b_1y+c_1z=d_1,$$
$$a_2x+b_2y+c_2z=d_2,$$
$$a_3x+b_3y+c_3z=d_3,$$

gives $Dx=K_1$, $Dy=K_2$ and $Dz=K_3$, where K_1, K_2, and K_3 are the determinants resulting from substituting the d's in the determinant of the coefficients, D, in place of the a's, b's, and c's, respectively. Three cases arise: I. If $D\neq0$, it can be divided out and a unique set of values for x, y and z obtained; i.e. the three planes, representing the three equations, then intersect in a point and the equations are *consistent* (and also independent). II. If $D=0$ and at least one of K_1, K_2, and K_3 is not zero, there is no solution; the three planes do not have any point in common and the three equations are *inconsistent*. III. If $D = 0$ and $K_1 = K_2 = K_3 = 0$, three cases arise: a). Some second order determinant in D is not zero, in which case the equations have infinitely many points in common; the planes (the loci of the equations) intersect in a line and the equations are *consistent*. b). Every second order minor in D is zero and a second order minor in K_1, K_2, or K_3 is not zero. The planes are then parallel, but at least one pair do not coincide; the equations are *inconsistent*. c). All the second order minors in D, K_1, K_2 and K_3 are zero. The three planes then coincide and the equations are *consistent* (but not independent).

consistency of two linear equations in two variables. See CONSISTENCY. *Tech.* consider the equations: (1) $a_1x + b_1y = c_1$, (2) $a_2x + b_2y = c_2$. Multiply the first equation by b_2 and the second by b_1, then subtract. This gives $(a_1b_2 - a_2b_1)x = (b_2c_1 - b_1c_2)$; similarly $(a_1b_2 - a_2b_1)y = (a_1c_2 - a_2c_1)$;

or $\quad x \begin{vmatrix} a_1 & b_1 \\ a_2 & b_2 \end{vmatrix} = \begin{vmatrix} c_1 & b_1 \\ c_2 & b_2 \end{vmatrix}$

and $\quad y \begin{vmatrix} a_1 & b_1 \\ a_2 & b_2 \end{vmatrix} = \begin{vmatrix} a_1 & c_1 \\ a_2 & c_2 \end{vmatrix}.$

Three cases follow: I. If the determinant of the coefficients

$$\begin{vmatrix} a_1 & b_1 \\ a_2 & b_2 \end{vmatrix}$$

is not zero, one can divide by it and secure unique values for x and y. The equations are then consistent and independent. In the last example under CONSISTENCY, the determinant of the coefficients is

$$\begin{vmatrix} 1 & 1 \\ 1 & -1 \end{vmatrix} = -2.$$

II. If the determinant of the coefficients is zero and one of the determinants formed by replacing the coefficients of x (or of y) by the constant terms is not zero, there is no solution;

i.e. the equations are *inconsistent*. In the first example under CONSISTENCY, the determinant of the coefficients is

$$\begin{vmatrix} 1 & 1 \\ 1 & 1 \end{vmatrix} = 0,$$

and the determinants gotten by introducing the constants are

$$\begin{vmatrix} 4 & 1 \\ 5 & 1 \end{vmatrix} = -1, \text{ and } \begin{vmatrix} 1 & 4 \\ 1 & 5 \end{vmatrix} = 1,$$

which give the impossible statements $0 \cdot x = -1$ and $0 \cdot y = 1$.
III. If all three determinants entering are zero, there results $0 \cdot x = 0$ and $0 \cdot y = 0$. The equations are then consistent, but not independent. In the second example under CONSISTENCY, these determinants are

$$\begin{vmatrix} 1 & 1 \\ 2 & 2 \end{vmatrix}, \begin{vmatrix} 4 & 1 \\ 8 & 2 \end{vmatrix} \text{ and } \begin{vmatrix} 1 & 4 \\ 2 & 8 \end{vmatrix}$$

all of which are zero. An infinite number of pairs of values of x and y can be found which satisfy both of the two equations, which are identical.

CON-SIST'ENT, *adj.* **consistent assumptions, hypotheses, postulates.** Assumptions, hypotheses, postulates, which do not contradict each other.

consistent equations. See CONSISTENCY.

CONSOLIDATED ANNUITIES. British government bonds irredeemable except at the pleasure of the government.

CON'SOLS, *n.* The same as CONSOLIDATED ANNUITIES.

CON'STANT, *n.* A quantity whose value is not determined by, or cannot change under, the conditions of the discussion at hand. See VARIABLE, UNKNOWN, and below, arbitrary constant.

absolute constant. A constant that never changes in value, such as numbers in arithmetic.

arbitrary constant. A constant which may be assigned different values. See below, constant of integration.

constant of integration. An arbitrary constant that must be added to any function arising from integration, to obtain all the primitives. The integral, $\int 3x^2 dx$, evaluates into $x^3 + c$ where c is constant, not merely x^3, because the derivative of a constant is zero.

constant motion. A state of motion that does not change either in direction or magnitude. See VELOCITY—constant velocity.

constant of proportionality. See FACTOR—factor of proportionality.

constant speed. The speed of a particle when it passes over equal distances in equal intervals of time.

constant term in an equation or function. A term which does not contain a variable. *Syn.* Absolute term.

constant velocity. See VELOCITY.

derivative of the product of a constant and a variable. The derivative of an expression like cx or in general $cf(x)$. It is equal to the constant times the derivative of the variable (function). See DIFFERENTIATION FORMULAS in the appendix.

essential constants: number of essential constants in an equation. The number of conditions, that is the number of sets of values of the variables that must be given to determine the unknown constants in the equation. There are two essential constants in $ax + by + c = 0$. a, b and c cannot all be zero, hence one of them can be divided out and two sets of values of x and y suffice to find the two resulting ratios.

gravitational constant. See GRAVITATIONAL CONSTANT.

CONSTRAINING FORCES (Constraints). (1) Those forces which tend to prevent a particle's remaining at rest or moving at a uniform velocity in a straight line (according to Newton's first law of motion). (2) Those forces which are exerted perpendicularly to the direction of motion of a particle.

CON-STRUCT′, *v.* To draw a figure so that it meets certain requirements; usually consists of drawing the figure and proving that it meets the requirements. E.g. to construct a line perpendicular to another line, or to construct a triangle having given three sides.

CON-STRUC′TION, *n.* (1) The process of drawing a figure that will satisfy certain given conditions. See CONSTRUCT. (2) Construction in proving a theorem; drawing the figure indicated by the theorem and adding to the figure any additional parts that are needed in the proof. Such "additional" lines, points, etc., are usually called **construction lines, points, etc.**

CON′TACT, *n.* chord of contact. See CHORD.

order of contact. See ORDER—order of contact of two curves.

point of contact. See TANGENT—tangent to a curve.

CONTINGENT, *adj.* **contingent insurance.** Insurance payable upon the death of the insured provided some other life continues. The latter is called the **counter life**; the former, the **policy life.**

contingent payment of any kind. A payment to be made if some given event takes place, such as death in life insurance.

contingent probability. (*In insurance.*) The probability that one life will end before another and within a certain number of years.

contingent reversionary annuity. An annuity payable upon the death of the insured, provided some life (not necessarily the beneficiary) survives, and payable to the beneficiary during his life.

contingent reversionary life interest. A life interest to be transferred to the beneficiary upon the death of the insured provided some life (not necessarily the beneficiary) survives.

CONTINUATION NOTATION. Three center dots or dashes following a few indicated terms. In case there is an infinite number of terms, the most common usage is to indicate a few terms at the beginning of the set, follow these with three center dots, write the general term, and add three center dots as follows:

$$1 + x + x^2 + \cdots + x^n + \cdots .$$

CONTINUATION OF SIGN in a polynomial. Repetition of the same algebraic sign before successive terms.

CON-TIN′UED, *adj.* **continued equality.** See EQUALITY.

continued fraction. See FRACTION —continued fraction.

continued product. A product of an infinite number of factors, denoted by Π, that is, capital pi.

E.g. $(1/2)(2/3)(3/4) \cdots$

$$[n/(n+1)] \cdots = \Pi[n/(n+1)],$$

is a continued product.

CON′TI-NU′I-TY, *n.* The property of being continuous.

axiom of continuity. See AXIOM.

principle of continuity. See AXIOM —axiom of continuity.

CON-TIN′U-OUS, *adj.* **continuous annuity.** An annuity payable continuously. Such an annuity cannot occur, but has theoretical value. Formulas for this sort of annuity are limiting forms of the formulas for non-continuous annuities, when the number of payments per year increases without limit while the nominal rate and annual rental remain fixed. The results differ very little from annuities having a very large number of payments per year. Approximate present values for a single life continuous annuity of one dollar is that of a single life annuity payable annually at the end of the year plus $\frac{1}{2}$ of a dollar; or that of a single life annuity payable annually at the beginning of the year minus $\frac{1}{2}$ of a dollar.

continuous conversion of compound interest. Finding the limit of the amount, at the given rate of interest, as the length of the period approaches zero. That is

$$\lim_{m \to \infty} (1+j/m)^m$$

where j is the fixed nominal rate and m the number of interest periods per year. This limit is e^j. See e.

continuous function of one variable at a point, that is for a given value of the variable. A function whose change in value for changes in the independent variable can be made as small as one pleases by restricting the value of the latter to values sufficiently near the given value. *Tech.* $f(x)$ is continuous for $x = a$ if $f(a+\alpha)$ and $f(a)$ are defined for

small α's and $\lim_{\alpha \to 0} f(a+\alpha) = f(a)$, where α may be positive or negative; or $f(x)$ is continuous for $x = a$ if $f(x)$ is defined in the neighborhood of, and at, $x = a$ and if for every $\epsilon > 0$ there exists a δ such that

$$|f(x) - f(a)| < \epsilon \quad \text{if} \quad |x - a| < \delta.$$

continuous function of two variables in a region. A function of two variables which is continuous at every point in the region. See below, continuous single-valued function of two variables at a point.

continuous function over an interval. A function whose graph has no breaks in it in the interval; a function that is continuous for every value of the variable on the interval.

continuous in the neighborhood of a point [whose coordinates are $(x_1, y_1, z_1, \cdots)$]. Continuous for all points whose coordinates $(x, y, z, \cdots)$ are such that $|x - x_1|, |y - y_1|, |z - z_1|$, etc., are each less than some positive number ϵ.

continuous single-valued function of any number of variables at a point (i.e. for any given set of values of these variables). A function, uniquely defined for, and in a neighborhood of, the given values of the variables and having for its limit, as the several variables approach their several given values in any way whatever, the value it has for the given values of the variables. The function is said to be *continuous in a region* if it is continuous for all sets of values of the variables in that region.

continuous single-valued function of two variables at a point. A function $f(x, y)$ uniquely defined for $x = a$ and $y = b$ and in the neighborhood of (a, b), is said to be continuous and single valued at the point (a, b) if $f(x, y)$ approaches $f(a, b)$ when x and y approach a and b, respectively, in any way whatever.

continuous surface in a given region. The graph of a continuous function of two variables; the locus of the points whose rectangular coordinates satisfy an equation of the form $z = f(x, y)$, where $f(x, y)$ is a continuous function of x and y in the region of the x, y plane which is the projection of the surface on that plane. E.g. a sphere about the origin is a continuous surface, for $z = \sqrt{r^2 - (x^2 + y^2)}$ is a continuous function on, and within, the circle $x^2 + y^2 = r^2$. To get the entire sphere, both signs of the radical must be considered. Thought of in this way, the sphere is a multiple (two) valued surface.

CON-TIN'U-UM, *n.* [*pl.* continua]. **real continuum of numbers.** The totality of rational and irrational real numbers.

CON'TOUR, *adj.* **contour lines.** (1) Projections on a plane of all the sections of a surface by planes parallel to this given plane and equidistant apart; (2) lines on a map which pass through points of equal elevation. Useful in showing the rapidity of ascent of the surface, since the contour lines are thicker where the surface rises faster. *Syn.* Level lines.

CON'TRA-VA'RI-ANT, *adj.* **contravariant indices.** See TENSOR.

contravariant tensor. See TENSOR.

contravariant vector. A contravariant tensor of order one. See TENSOR.

CON-VERGE', *v.* To draw near to. (1) A series is said to converge when the sum of n of its consecutive terms approaches a limit as n increases without bound (see LIMIT). (2) A curve is said to converge to its asymptote, or to a point, when the distance from the curve to the asymptote, or point, approaches zero; e.g. the polar spiral, $r = 1/\theta$, converges to the origin; the curve $xy = 1$ converges to the x-axis as y increases and to the y-axis as x increases. (3) A line is said to converge to another line if it will meet the line when produced far enough. (4) A variable is sometimes said to converge to its limit.

CON-VER'GENCE, *n.* (1) The property possessed by a function when it approaches a limit. (2) See below, convergence of an infinite series.

absolute convergence of an infinite series. The property that the sum of the absolute values of the terms of the series form a convergent series. Such a series is said to **converge abso-**lutely and to be **absolutely convergent.** $1 - 1/2 + 1/2^2 - 1/2^3 + \cdots (-1)^{n-1} 1/2^{n-1} + \cdots$ is absolutely convergent. See CONVERGENT—conditionally convergent series.

Cauchy's ratio test for convergence of an infinite series. See RATIO—ratio test.

circle of convergence of a power series in the complex domain. The circle within which the series converges absolutely and outside of which it diverges, either converging or diverging at points on the circumference of the circle. E.g. $\sum_{n=0}^{\infty} (3z)^n$ converges absolutely within the circle whose radius is $\frac{1}{3}$ and whose center is the origin, and diverges outside this circle. See SERIES—infinite series of complex terms.

conditional convergence. See CONVERGENT.

convergence of an infinite series. The property the series possesses when the sum of n consecutive terms approaches a limit as n increases without bound (becomes infinite). E.g. the geometric progression, $\frac{1}{2} + \frac{1}{4} + \frac{1}{8} + \cdots$, converges to 1, for the sum of the first n terms is $[1 - (\frac{1}{2})^n]$ and

$$\lim_{n \to \infty} [1 - (\frac{1}{2})^n] = 1 - \lim_{n \to \infty} (\frac{1}{2})^n = 1.$$

convergence of an integral. The property that an integral possesses when it approaches a limit as the variable (or variables) which enters into its limits runs through some sequence of values; e.g. the integral

$$\int_2^y (1/x^2)dx, \quad = (-1/y + 1/2)],$$

approaches $1/2$ as y increases without bound.

convergence of a sequence. See SEQUENCE—convergence of a sequence.

interval of convergence. See INTERVAL—interval of convergence of a series of variable terms.

tests for convergence of infinite series. See ALTERNATING SERIES, CAUCHY, COMPARISON TEST, RAABE'S RATIO TEST, RATIO.

uniform convergence, in an interval, of a series whose terms are functions of a variable. Convergence such that the numerical value of the remainder after the first n terms is as small as desired *throughout the given interval* for n greater than a sufficiently large chosen number. *Tech.* if the sum of the first n terms of a series is $s_n(x)$ the series converges uniformly to $f(x)$ in (a, b) if for arbitrary positive ϵ there exists an N (dependent upon ϵ) such that

$$| f(x) - s_n(x) | < \epsilon$$

for all n greater than N and all x in the interval (a, b). More generally, $s_n(x)$ converges uniformly on (a, b) if for arbitrary positive ϵ, there exists an N (dependent upon ϵ) such that $|s_{n+p}(x) - s_n(x)| < \epsilon$ for all $n > N$, for all p, and for all x in the interval (a, b). E.g. the series

$$1 + x/2 + (x/2)^2 + \cdots + (x/2)^{n-1} + \cdots ,$$

converges uniformly for x in any closed interval contained in the interval $(-2, 2)$; but does not converge uniformly for $-2 < x < 2$, since the absolute value of the difference of

$$f(x), = 1/(1 - x/2), \text{ and}$$
$$s_n(x), = [1 - (x/2)^n]/(1 - x/2),$$

is $|(x/2)^n/(1 - x/2)|$ which (for any fixed n) becomes infinite as x approaches 2.

CON-VER'GEN-CY, n. The same as CONVERGENCE.

CON-VER'GENT, *adj.* Possessing the property of convergence.

conditionally convergent series. A convergent series which contains both positive and negative terms and which becomes divergent when the signs are all made positive. E.g. the series $1 - \frac{1}{2} + \frac{1}{3} - \frac{1}{4} + \cdots$ is conditionally convergent because it converges and the series $1 + \frac{1}{2} + \frac{1}{3} + \cdots$ diverges.

convergent series, sequence, or integral. See CONVERGENCE.

permanently convergent series. Series which are convergent for all values of the variable, or variables, involved in its terms; e.g. the exponential series, $1 + x + x^2/2! + x^3/3! + \cdots = e^x$ for all values of x, hence the series is *permanently* convergent.

CON-VER'GENT, n. **convergent of a continued fraction.** The fraction terminated at one of the quotients. See FRACTION—continued fraction.

CON'VERSE (converse of a theorem). The theorem resulting from interchanging the hypothesis and conclusion. If only a part of the conclusion makes up the new hypothesis, or only a part of the old hypothesis makes up the new conclusion, the new theorem is not spoken of as the converse but as *a* converse of the old.

converse of the factor theorem: If $(x - a)$ is a factor of the polynomial $f(x)$, then a is a root of the equation $f(x) = 0$. See FACTOR—factor theorem.

CON-VER'SION, *adj.* (*Finance.*) **conversion formula.** See FORMULA—conversion formulas.

conversion interval, or period. The length of the time that elapses between successive computations of interest in compound interest problems. *Syn.* INTEREST PERIOD.

conversion tables. Tables giving the insurance premiums (annual or single), at various rates of interest, which are equivalent to a given annuity.

CON-VER'SION, n. **continuous conversion of compound interest.** See CONTINUOUS—continuous conversion of compound interest.

conversion from Centigrade to Fahrenheit (or Fahrenheit to Centigrade). Expressing a given temperature as recorded by one scale in terms of the other scale. The formulas for doing this are:

$$T_f = (9/5)T_c + 32$$
and
$$T_c = (5/9)(T_f - 32).$$

frequency of conversion. See FREQUENCY—frequency of conversion.

CON'VEX, *adj.* **convex curve in a plane.** A curve such that any straight line cutting the curve cuts it in just two points.

convex polygon. See POLYGON.

convex surface. A surface such that any plane section of it is a convex curve.

convex toward a point (or a given

line). Said of a curve which bulges toward the point (or line). *Tech.* an arc of a curve is convex toward a point (or line) when every segment of it, cut off by a secant, lies on the same side of the secant as does the point (or line). If there exists a horizontal line such that a curve lies above (below) it and is convex toward it, the curve is said to be *convex down* (*convex up*). A necessary and sufficient condition that a curve, whose equation is $y = f(x)$, be convex upward (or downward) in a given interval is that the second derivative of the function, d^2y/dx^2, be negative (or positive) throughout the interval. A surface is said to be convex toward (or away from) a plane when every plane perpendicular to this plane cuts it in a curve which is convex toward (or away from) the line of intersection of the two planes.

CO-OR′DI-NATE, *n.* One of a set of numbers which locate a point in space. If the point is known to be on a given line, only one coordinate is needed; if in a plane, two are required; if in space, three. See CARTESIAN, and POLAR.

Cartesian coordinates. See CARTESIAN.

complex coordinates. Coordinates used in the Argand diagram, in graphing in the complex plane. The figure shows the graphic representation of the complex number $z = x + iy$ $= r(\cos\theta + i\sin\theta)$.

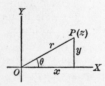

coordinate paper. Paper ruled with graduated rulings to aid in plotting points and drawing the loci of equations. See CROSS—cross-section paper and LOGARITHMIC—logarithmic coordinate paper.

coordinate planes. Three mutually perpendicular planes (XOY, XOZ, and YOZ in the figure) used to locate points in space by giving their distances from the three planes. The distances are

called the **rectangular Cartesian coordinates** of the point in space, or the **rectangular** or **Cartesian coordinates.** The three intersections of these three planes are called the **axes of coordinates** and are usually labeled the x-axis, y-axis and z-axis. Their common point is called the origin. The three axes are called a **coordinate trihedral** (see TRIHEDRAL). The x-axis and y-axis are conventionally taken in the horizontal plane, and the z-axis perpendicular to this plane. The coordinate planes divide space into eight compartments, called octants. The octant containing the three positive axes as edges is called 'the **1st octant** (or **coordinate trihedral**). The other octants are numbered 2, 3, 4, 5, 6, 7, 8; 2, 3 and 4 are reckoned counter-clockwise around the positive z-axis (or clockwise if the coordinate system is left-handed), then the quadrant vertically beneath the first quadrant is labeled 5, and the remaining quadrants 6, 7, and 8, taken

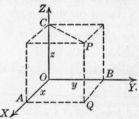

in counter-clockwise (or clock-wise) order as before. A space coordinate is quite commonly thought of as the projection of the line from the origin to the point upon the axis perpendicular to the plane from which the coordinate is measured; i.e. $x = OA$, $y = OB$, and $z = OC$ in the figure.

coordinate system. Any set of numbers which locate a point, line (or any geometric element) in space. See COORDINATE, CARTESIAN, and POLAR.

coordinate trihedral. See TRIHEDRAL.

curvilinear coordinates. See PARAMETRIC—parametric equations of a surface.

cylindrical coordinates. See CYLINDRICAL—cylindrical coordinates.

geographical coordinates. See SPHERICAL—spherical coordinates.

homogeneous coordinates in the plane. The homogeneous coordinates of a point, whose Cartesian coordinates are x and y, are any three numbers (x_1, x_2, x_3) for which $x_1/x_3 = x$ and $x_2/x_3 = y$. See LINE—line at infinity. The coordinates are called homogeneous since any equation in Cartesian coordinates becomes homogeneous when the transformation to homgeneous coordinates is made; e.g. $x^3 + xy^2 + 9 = 0$ becomes $x_1^3 + x_1 x_2^2 + 9x_3^3 = 0$.

left-handed coordinate system. A coordinate system in which the axes (positive direction of) form a left-handed trihedral. See LEFT—left-handed trihedral.

logarithmic coordinates. Coordinates using the logarithmic scale; used in plotting points on logarithmic paper. See LOGARITHMIC—logarithmic coordinate paper.

oblique coordinates. Cartesian coordinates in which the axes (or planes) are not mutually perpendicular, the coordinates being measured parallel to the corresponding axes. See CARTESIAN.

polar coordinate paper. Paper ruled with concentric circles about the point which is to serve as the pole and with radial lines through this point at graduated angular distances from the initial line. Used to graph functions in polar coordinates. See POLAR—polar coordinates in the plane.

polar coordinates in a plane. See POLAR.

polar coordinates in space. See SPHERICAL—spherical coordinates.

rectangular Cartesian coordinates. See CARTESIAN, and above, coordinate planes.

right-handed coordinate system. A coordinate system in which the positive directions of the axes form a right-handed trihedral. See RIGHT—right-handed trihedral.

spherical coordinates. See SPHERICAL—spherical coordinates.

transformation of coordinates. See TRANSLATION, and TRANSFOR-MATION—transformation of coordinates.

CO-PLA'NAR, *adj.* Lying in the same plane.

condition that four points in space be coplanar. The vanishing of the fourth order determinant whose rows consist of the coordinates of the points and unity, namely

$$\begin{vmatrix} x_1 & y_1 & z_1 & 1 \\ x_2 & y_2 & z_2 & 1 \\ x_3 & y_3 & z_3 & 1 \\ x_4 & y_4 & z_4 & 1 \end{vmatrix}.$$

coplanar lines. Lines which lie in the same plane.

coplanar points. Points lying in the same plane.

CO-PUNCTUAL PLANES. Three or more planes having a point in common.

CORD, *n.* A stack of wood (with the sticks parallel, each to each) 8 feet long, 4 feet high, and 4 feet wide. See DENOMINATE NUMBERS in the appendix.

COR'OL-LA-RY, *n.* A theorem which follows so obviously from the proof of some other theorem that no, or almost no, proof is necessary; a by-product of another theorem.

COR-RECT', *adj.* Without error in principle or computation. One speaks of a correct proof, correct solution, correct answer or correct computation. See ACCURATE.

COR-REC'TION in interpolation in a logarithmic (or trigonometric) table. The number added to a tabular logarithm (trigonometric function) to give the logarithm (trigonometric function) of a number (angle) which is not in the tables; equally applicable when interpolating in any table. (When working with tables of trigonometric functions the *correction* is negative in the case of the decreasing functions, namely the cosine, cotangent and cosecant.)

COR'RE-LA'TION, *n.* (1) In pure mathematics: A linear transformation which, in the plane, carries points into lines and lines into points and, in space, carries points into planes and planes into points. (2) In statistics: the inter-dependence between two sets of numbers; a relation between two quantities, such that when one changes the other does (simultaneous increasing or decreasing is called **positive correlation** and one increasing, the other decreasing, **negative correlation**), a relation similar to that denoted by the functional concept, but usually not as explicitly defined.

correlation coefficient. See COEFFICIENT—correlation coefficient.

COR′RE-SPOND′ENCE, *n.* **one-to-one correspondence.** A correspondence (relation) between two sets of things such that pairs can be removed, one member from each group, until both groups have been simultaneously exhausted; e.g. (*a, b, c, d*) and (1, 2, 3, 4) can be put into one-to-one correspondence in many ways. *Tech.* A one-to-one correspondence is said to have been set up between two classes of elements, *C* and *D*, when a pairing has been set up between them such that each element of *D* has been made to correspond to one and only one element of *C*, and each element of *C* has been made to correspond to one and only one element of *D*.

COR′RE-SPOND′ING, *adj.* **corresponding angles, lines, points, etc.** Points, angles, lines, etc., in different figures, similarly related to the rest of the figures. E.g. in two right triangles the hypotenuses are *corresponding* sides.

corresponding angles of two lines cut by a transversal. See ANGLE —angles made by a transversal.

corresponding polyhedral angle in a spherical pyramid. The polyhedral angle, at the center of the sphere, made by the plane faces of the pyramid. It *corresponds* to the spherical polygon which forms the base of the pyramid.

corresponding rates. Rates producing the same amount on the same principal in the same time with different conversion periods. The nominal rate of 6%, money being converted semiannually, and the effective rate of 6.09%, are corresponding rates. *Syn.* Equivalent rates.

CO-SE′CANT, *n.* **cosecant of an angle.**

See TRIGONOMETRIC—trigonometric functions.

cosecant curve. The graph of $y = \mathrm{cosec}\ x$; the same as the curve obtained by moving the secant curve $\pi/2$ radians to the right, since $\mathrm{cosec}\ x = \sec(x - \pi/2)$. See SECANT—secant curve.

CO′SINE, *n.* **cosine of an angle.** See TRIGONOMETRIC — trigonometric functions.

cosine curve. The graph of $y = \cos x$ (see figure). The curve has a *y* intercept 1, is concave toward the *x*-axis, and cuts this axis at odd multiples of $\tfrac{1}{2}\pi$ (radians).

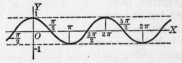

cosine law for a triangle. A relation between the sides and one of the angles of the triangle, which may be used to solve a triangle when two sides and an angle, or three sides, are given. If *a, b, c* are the sides and *C* the angle opposite *c*, the law can be stated $c^2 = a^2 + b^2 - 2ab \cos C$. Also see LAW.

direction cosine (in space). See DIRECTION—direction cosines.

exponential values of sin *x* and cos *x*. See EXPONENTIAL—exponential values of sin *x* and cos *x*.

COST, *n.* **capitalized cost.** First cost plus the *present value* of the perpetual replacements to be made at the end of regular periods.

first cost. The amount paid for an article, not including the expense of holding or handling.

percent profit on cost. See PERCENT.

replacement cost. See REPLACEMENT.

CO-TAN′GENT, *n.* **cotangent of an angle.** See TRIGONOMETRIC—trigonometric functions.

cotangent curve. The graph of $y = \cot x$; the same as the curve obtained by *reciprocating* the tangent curve. It is asymptotic to the lines $x = 0$ and $x = n\pi$ and cuts the *x*-axis at odd multiples of $\pi/2$ (radians).

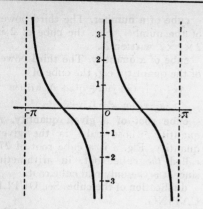

CO-TER'MI-NAL, *adj.* **coterminal angles in trigonometry.** Angles having the same terminal line and the same initial line; two angles generated by the revolution of two lines about the same point in the initial line in such a way that the final positions of the revolving lines are identical; e.g. 30°, 390°, and −330° are coterminal angles.

COUNT, *v.* To name a set of consecutive integers in order of their size, usually beginning with 1.

count by twos (threes, fours, fives, etc.). To name, in order, a set of integers that have the difference 2(3, 4, 5, etc.); e.g. when counting by twos, one says "2, 4, 6, 8, · · · "; when counting by threes, "3, 6, 9, 12, · · · ."

COUN'TER-CLOCK'WISE, *adj.* In the direction of rotation opposite to that in which the hands move around the dial of a clock.

COUNTER LIFE. See CONTINGENT —contingent insurance.

COUPON, *n.* **bond coupons.** Certificates attached to a bond, showing the amount of dividend due at the end of each interest period, and to be surrendered when the dividend is paid.

coupon rate. Same as DIVIDEND RATE.

COURSE, *n.* **course of a ship.** See SAILING—plane sailing.

CO-VA'RI-ANT, *adj.* **covariant indices.** See TENSOR.

covariant tensor. See TENSOR.

covariant vector. A covariant tensor of order one. See TENSOR.

CO-VERSED SINE. *One minus* the *sine* of an angle; geometrically the difference between the radius and the sine of an angle constructed in a unit circle. See TRIGONOMETRIC—trigonometric functions of an acute angle.

CO-VERSINE. Same as CO-VERSED SINE.

CRAMER'S RULE for the solution of any given number of linear algebraic equations in the same number of unknowns. A simple rule for writing out, in determinant form, the value of each of the variables. The rule for *n* equations is: Each variable is equal to the fraction in which the denominator is the determinant of the coefficients of the *n* unknowns and the numerator is the same determinant, except that the coefficients of the unknown which is being found are replaced by the constant terms if these appear as the right-hand members of the system of equations and by their negatives if they appear in the left members. E.g. the values of x and y which satisfy

$$x+2y=5$$
$$2x+3y=0 \quad \text{are}$$

$$x=\begin{vmatrix} 5 & 2 \\ 0 & 3 \end{vmatrix} \div \begin{vmatrix} 1 & 2 \\ 2 & 3 \end{vmatrix} = -15,$$

$$y=\begin{vmatrix} 1 & 5 \\ 2 & 0 \end{vmatrix} \div \begin{vmatrix} 1 & 2 \\ 2 & 3 \end{vmatrix} = 10.$$

See DETERMINANT—determinant of the second order, and CONSISTENCY.

CRED'IT, *adj.* **credit business.** A retail or wholesale business in which goods are sold without immediate payment, but with a promise to pay later, generally at some specified time.

CRED'I-TOR, *n.* One who accepts a promise to pay in the future in place of immediate payment; a term most commonly applied to retail merchants who do a *credit* business.

CRI-TE'RI-ON, *n.* [*pl.* **cri-te'ri-a.**] The same as CONDITION.

criteria for divisibility. See DIVISIBILITY.

CRITICAL VALUE or POINT. (1) A point at which a curve has a maximum, a minimum, or a point of inflection.

(2) A point at which a curve has a maximum or a minimum. (3) A point at which dy/dx is either zero or infinite.

CROSS, *n.* **cross product.** See MULTIPLICATION—multiplication of two vectors.

cross ratio. See RATIO—cross ratio.

cross section of an area or solid. A plane section perpendicular to the axis of symmetry or to the longest axis, if there be more than one; rarely used except in cases where all cross sections are equal, as in the case of a circular cylinder or rectangular parallelepiped.

cross-section paper. Paper ruled with vertical and horizontal lines equally spaced; used in graphing equations in rectangular coordinates. *Syn.* Ruled paper, squared paper.

CRU'CI-FORM, *adj.* **cruciform curve.** The locus of the equation

$$x^2y^2 - a^2x^2 - a^2y^2 = 0.$$

The curve is symmetric about the origin and the coordinate axes, has four branches, one in each quadrant, and is asymptotic to each of the four lines $x = \pm a$, $y = \pm a$. It is called the *cruciform curve* because of its resemblance to a cross.

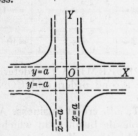

CRU'NODE, *n.* A point on a curve through which there are two branches of the curve with distinct tangents.

CUBE, *n.* A solid bounded by six planes, with its twelve edges all equal and its face angles all right angles.

cube of a number. The third power of the number. E.g. the cube of 2 is $2 \times 2 \times 2$, written 2^3.

cube of a quantity. The third power of the quantity; e.g. the cube of

$(x+y)$ is $(x+y)(x+y)(x+y)$, written

$(x+y)^3$ or $x^3 + 3x^2y + 3xy^2 + y^3$.

cube root of a given quantity. A quantity whose cube is the given quantity. E.g. 3 is a cube root of 27; called *the* cube root, in arithmetic, since it is the only real cube root.

duplication of the cube. See DUPLICATING.

CU'BIC, *adj.*, *n.* **Cardan's solution of the cubic.** See SOLUTION—Cardan's solution of the cubic.

bipartite cubic. See BIPARTITE.

cubic curve. See CURVE—algebraic plane curve.

cubic equation. An equation of the third degree, such as

$$2x^3 + 3x^2 + x + 5 = 0.$$

reduced cubic. See REDUCED.

resolvent cubic. See FERRARI'S solution of the general quartic.

CU'BI-CAL, *adj.* **coefficient of volume (cubical) expansion.** See COEFFICIENT.

cubical expansion. Same as VOLUME EXPANSION.

cubical parabola. The plane locus of an equation of the form $y = kx^3$. When k is positive the x-axis is an inflectional tangent, the curve passes through the origin and has infinite branches in the 1st and 3rd quadrants, and is concave up in the first and concave down in the 3rd quadrant. When k is negative the curve is the graph of $y = |k|x^3$ reflected in the y-axis.

semi-cubical parabola. See SEMI—semi-cubical parabola.

CU'MU-LA'-TIVE, *adj.* **cumulative frequency.** The sum of all preceding frequencies, a certain order having been established. E.g. if the number of students making the grades of 60% to 70%, 70% to 80%, 80% to 90%, and 90% to 100% are, respectively, 2, 4, 7, and 3 (which are called the frequencies), then the *cumulative frequencies* are 2, 6, 13, and 16.

cumulative frequency curve. The curve whose ordinates are the cumulative frequencies and whose abscissas are the class intervals. *Syn.* Orgive curve.

CURL, *n.* **curl of a vector function,** $F(x, y, z)$. It is written $\nabla \times F$ and defined as

$$i \times \frac{\partial F}{\partial x} + j \times \frac{\partial F}{\partial y} + k \times \frac{\partial F}{\partial z}$$

where ∇ is the operator,

$$i \frac{\partial}{\partial x} + j \frac{\partial}{\partial y} + k \frac{\partial}{\partial z} .$$

If, for example, F is the velocity at a point $P(x, y, z)$ in a moving fluid, $\frac{1}{2} \nabla \times F$ is the vector angular velocity of an infinitesimal portion of the fluid about P. See VECTOR—vector components.

CUR'RENT, *adj.* **current rate.** The same as PREVAILING INTEREST RATE. See INTEREST.

CUR'TATE, *adj.* **curtate annuity.** An annuity payable at certain regular intervals during the life of the insured, nothing being paid for the partial period from the last payment to the end of the life.

curtate expectation of life. The average number of entire years lived, after a given age, by the members of a group of a given number of persons attaining that age.

CUR'VA-TURE, *n.* **average curvature of a curve in a plane.** The ratio of the change in inclination of the tangent, over a given arc, to the length of the arc. The limit of the *average curvature* as the length of the arc approaches zero is the *curvature*.

curvature of a plane curve. The rate of change of the inclination of the tangent with respect to change of arc length; that is, the derivative of $\tan^{-1} (dy/dx)$ with respect to the arc

(see average curvature). In Cartesian coordinates the curvature, K, is given by

$$K = (d^2y/dx^2)/[1 + (dy/dx)^2]^{3/2}.$$

The numerical value of the curvature of a circle is constant and equal to the reciprocal of its radius. The circle tangent to a curve on the concave side and having the same curvature at the point of tangency is called the **circle of curvature** of the curve (at that point). Its radius is the numerical value of the **radius of curvature,** and its center is the **center of curvature.** The curvature at A is the limit of $\Delta\theta/\Delta s$ as Δs approaches zero (where $\Delta s = AB$ and θ is measured in radians). The sign of K depends upon that of $\Delta\theta$, which is positive or negative according as the curve is convex or concave down (according as d^2y/dx^2 is positive or negative). Some writers define the curvature to be $|K|$.

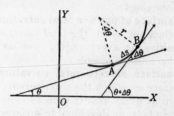

curvature (first curvature) of a space curve, at a given point. The rate of turning, with respect to the length of the arc, of the tangent to the curve; the limit of the ratio of the angle between two tangents and the arc joining their points of tangency as these points of tangency move up to the given point. The reciprocal of the first curvature is the **radius of first curvature.**

mean normal curvature of a surface. See MEAN—mean curvature of a surface.

normal curvature of a surface. See NORMAL.

radius of curvature. The reciprocal of the curvature. See above, curvature of a plane curve. In Cartesian coordinates the radius of curvature is

$$[1 + (dy/dx)^2]^{3/2}/(d^2y/dx^2).$$

radius of curvature in parametric co-ordinates. See above, curvature of a plane curve. Explicitly, it is

$$\frac{[(dx/dt)^2+(dy/dt)^2]^{3/2}}{(dx/dt)(d^2y/dt^2)-(dy/dt)(d^2x/dt^2)}$$

where $y = h(t)$, $x = g(t)$.

radius of curvature in polar coordinates: See above, curvature of a plane curve. Explicitly, it is

$$\frac{[r^2+(dr/d\theta)^2]^{3/2}}{r^2+2(dr/d\theta)^2-r(d^2r/d\theta^2)}.$$

radius of second curvature (torsion) of a space curve at a point. The reciprocal of the *torsion* at the given point.

surface of negative curvature. A surface on which the *total curvature* is negative at every point. Such a surface lies part on one side and part on the other side of the tangent plane in the neighborhood of a point; e.g. the inner surface of a torus, and the hyperboloid of one sheet.

surface of positive total curvature. A surface on which the *total curvature* is positive at every point, such as the sphere and ellipsoids.

surface of zero total curvature. A surface on which the total curvature is zero at every point; such as cylinders or, in fact, all developable surfaces.

total curvature of a surface at a point. The product of the curvatures of the two normal sections which have respectively the maximum and minimum curvatures at the given point. *Syn.* Total normal curvature. See NORMAL—normal curvature of a surface.

CURVE, *n.* The locus of a point which moves under one restriction, that is, has one degree of freedom. E.g. a straight line is the locus of points whose coordinates satisfy a linear equation, and a circle with radius 1 is the locus of points which satisfy $x^2+y^2=1$.

algebraic plane curve. A curve whose equation is expressible as a polynomial equation in the coordinates. If the equation is of the nth degree, the curve is said to be an **algebraic curve of degree** n. If n is one, the curve is a straight line, if n is two, the curve is called a **conic**; and if it is of the third, fourth, fifth, sixth degree, etc., it is called a **cubic, quartic, quintic, sextic,** etc. When n is greater than 2, the curve is called a **higher plane curve.**

angle between two intersecting curves. See ANGLE—angle between two intersecting curves.

curve fitting. Determining empirical curves. See EMPIRICAL.

curve length. The length of a curve between two fixed points; the limit of the sum of a set of non-overlapping chords, completely covering the arc between the two points, as the length of the longest chord approaches zero. This limit is the integral, between the points, of the differential of the arc; in rectangular coordinates it is

$$\int_{x_1}^{x_2}[1+(dy/dx)^2]^{1/2}dx$$

or

$$\int_{y_1}^{y_2}[1+(dx/dy)^2]^{1/2}dy$$

where the points have the coordinates (x_1, y_1) and (x_2, y_2). See ELEMENT—element of arc of a curve.

curve in a plane, or plane curve. A curve all points of which lie in a plane; the locus of an equation (in Cartesian coordinates of the form $y=f(x)$ or $f(x, y) =0$). See above, CURVE.

curves through the origin. Usually refers to algebraic curves whose equations contain no constant term, for the substitution of zero for both variables satisfies the equation if and only if the constant term is zero. More generally, any curve whose Cartesian equation is satisfied by $x=y=0$, as $y=\sin x$.

curve tracing. Plotting or graphing a curve by finding points on the curve and, in a more advanced way, by investigating such matters as symmetry, extent, and asymptotes and using the derivatives to determine critical points, slope, change of slope and concavity and convexity.

derived curve. See DERIVED.

empirical curves. See EMPIRICAL.

integral curves. See INTEGRAL—integral curves.

normal frequency curve. See FRE-QUENCY.

parabolic curve. An algebraic curve in which one variable appears in a term of the first degree, and in no other term. It is of the form:

$$y = a_0 + a_1 x + \cdots + a_n x^n.$$

parallel curves (in a plane). Two curves which have their points paired on the same normals, always cutting off the same length segments on these normals. Their tangents at points where they cut a common normal are parallel. See INVOLUTE.

path curves. See PATH.

pedal curve. See PEDAL.

periodic curves. See PERIODIC.

primitive curve. See PRIMITIVE.

quadric (or quadratic) curve. A curve whose equation is of the 2nd degree. *Syn.* Conic. See above, algebraic plane curve.

space curve. The intersection of two surfaces in space.

turning-points on a curve. See TURNING POINT.

CUR'VI-LIN'E-AR, *adj.* curvilinear co-ordinates. See PARAMETRIC—parametric equations of a surface.

curvilinear motion. See MOTION.

CUSP, *n.* A *double point* at which the two tangents to the curve are coincident. *Syn.* Spinode.

cusp of first kind, or simple cusp. A cusp in which there is a branch of the curve on each side of the double tangent in the neighborhood of the point of tangency; e.g. the semi-cubical parabola, $y^2 = x^3$, has a cusp of the *first kind* at the origin.

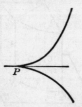

cusp of the second kind. A cusp in which the two branches of the curve lie on the same side of the tangent in the neighborhood of the point of tan-gency; the curve $y = x^2 \pm \sqrt{x^5}$ has a cusp of the second kind at the origin.

double cusp. The same as OSCULA-TION POINT and TACNODE.

hypocycloid of four cusps. See HY-POCYCLOID.

CY'CLIC, *adj.* cyclic change of objects (variables). See PERMUTATION—cyclic permutation.

cyclic interchange. Same as CY-CLIC PERMUTATION. See PER-MUTATION.

cyclic permutation. See PERMUTA-TION.

CY'CLOID, *n.* The plane locus of a point which is fixed on the circumference of a circle, as the circle rolls upon a straight line. E.g. the path described by a point on the rim of a wheel. The cycloid is a special case of the trochoid, although the two words are sometimes used synonymously. If a is the radius of the rolling circle and θ is the central angle of this circle, which is subtended by the arc (OP) that has contacted the line upon which the circle rolls, the parametric equations of the cycloid are:

$$x = a(\theta - \sin\theta), \quad y = a(1 - \cos\theta).$$

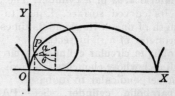

The cycloid has a cusp at every point where it touches the *base line*. The distance from cusp to cusp is $2\pi a$, and the distance traveled by the point, as the center of the circle moves between two positions, is independent of a, provided the point starts and finishes at a cusp; i.e. the length of the path traced out by a point on the rim of a large wheel is the same as the length of the path traced out by a point on the rim of a small wheel, provided the hubs travel over the same distance and both paths have cusps at the beginning and finishing point.

base of cycloid. The line upon which the generating circle rolls.

curtate cycloid. A *trochoid* which has no *loops*. See TROCHOID.

prolate cycloid. See TROCHOID.

CYCLO-SYMMETRY. See ABSOLUTE —absolute symmetry.

CYL'IN-DER, *n.* A solid bounded by two parallel planes and a cylindrical surface whose directrix is a closed curve; sometimes used for a cylindrical surface.

altitude of a cylinder. The perpendicular distance between its bases.

axis of a cylinder. The line joining the centers of the bases of a right circular cylinder; the axis (line) of symmetry of any cylinder which is symmetrical about a line.

base of a cylinder. See BASES.

circular cylinder. A cylinder whose bases are circles.

cylinder of revolution. See below, right circular cylinder.

element of a cylinder. A straight line in the cylindrical surface, joining points in the perimeters of the bases.

elliptic cylinder. A cylinder whose bases are ellipses. See CYLINDRICAL—cylindrical surface.

hyperbolic cylinder. A cylinder whose right section is an hyperbola.

lateral area of a cylinder. The area of its curved surface. Equal to the length of one of its elements times the perimeter of a right section.

oblique circular cylinder. A circular cylinder whose elements (and axis) are not perpendicular to its bases.

parabolic cylinder. See PARABOLIC—parabolic cylinder.

right circular cylinder. A cylinder whose right sections are circles; the surface generated by revolving a rectangle about one of its sides. (The equation of the cylindrical surface in the figure is $x^2 + y^2 = a^2$, where a is the radius of a cross-section.) Its volume is $\pi a^2 h$ and its lateral area is $2\pi a h$, where h is its altitude and a the radius of the base. *Syn.* Cylinder of revolution.

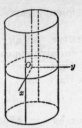

rulings of a cylinder. See RULINGS.

similar right circular cylinders. Cylinders for which the ratio between the radius of the base and the length of an element in any one cylinder is the same as the corresponding ratio in any of the other cylinders.

volume of a cylinder. The product of the area of its base by its altitude. If its base is a circle, the volume is $\pi r^2 h$, where r is the radius of the base and h is the altitude of the circular cylinder.

CY-LIN'DRI-CAL, *adj.* **cylindrical coordinates.** Space coordinates making use of polar coordinates in one coordinate plane, usually the x, y plane, the third coordinate being simply the rectangular coordinate measured from this plane. These are called cylindrical coordinates because when r is fixed and z and θ vary, they develop a cylinder; i.e. $r = c$ is the equation of a cylinder. The locus of points for which θ has a fixed value is a plane, PNO, containing the z-axis; the points for which z is constant define a plane parallel to the x, y plane. The three surfaces for r, θ, and z constant, respectively, locate the point $P(r, \theta, z)$ as their intersection.

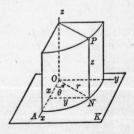

cylindrical surface. The surface generated by a straight line moving always parallel to a given straight line, and intersecting a given curve (if the curve is a plane curve with its plane parallel to the given line, the cylinder is a plane). The line is called the **generator** or **generatrix**. The curve is called the **directrix**. The generator in any one fixed position is called an **element**. A cylindrical surface is not necessarily closed, since the directrix is not restricted to being a closed curve. See, for an example, PARABOLIC—parabolic cylinder. A cylindrical surface is named after its right sections; e.g. if the right section is an ellipse, it is called an **elliptical cylindrical surface**, or simply an **elliptic cylinder** (the word cylinder not always being restricted to the solid bounded by a cylindrical surface and two parallel cutting planes).

equations of a cylindrical surface when one of the coordinate planes is perpendicular to the elements. The equation of the trace of the cylinder in this plane. E.g. (1) the equation $x^2+y^2=1$ is the equation of a right circular cylindrical surface since for every pair, (x, y), of numbers which satisfies this equation, z may take all values; (2) similarly, $y^2=2x$ is a parabolic cylindrical surface with its elements parallel to the z-axis; and

$$\frac{x^2}{a^2}+\frac{y^2}{b^2}=1$$

an elliptical cylindrical surface with its elements parallel to the z-axis.

transformation of cylindrical into rectangular coordinates, formulas for: $x=r\cos\theta$, $y=r\sin\theta$, $z=z$.

CYL'IN-DROID, *n.* (1) A cylindrical surface whose sections perpendicular to the elements are ellipses. (2) The surface which is the locus of a straight line moving so as to intersect two curves and remain always parallel to a given plane.

D

D'ALEMBERT'S TEST for convergence (or divergence) of an infinite series. Same as the *generalized ratio test*. See RATIO—generalized ratio test.

DAMPED HARMONIC MOTION. Harmonic motion having its amplitude continually reduced. See HARMONIC.

DARBOUX'S THEOREM. If $f(x)$ is bounded on (a, b), $M_1, M_2, \cdots M_n$ and $m_1, m_2, \cdots m_n$ are the upper and lower limits of $f(x)$ on the intervals $(a, x_1), (x_1, x_2), \cdots (x_{n-1}, b)$, and the lengths of these subintervals converge to zero uniformly as n increases, then

$$\lim_{n\to\infty} [M_1(x_1-a)+M_2(x_2-x_1)+ \cdots$$
$$+M_n(b-x_{n-1})$$

and

$$\lim_{n\to\infty} [m_1(x_1-a)+m_2(x_2-x_1)+ \cdots$$
$$+m_n(b-x_{n-1})]$$

both exist. The former is called the *upper* Darboux integral of $f(x)$ and written

$$\int_a^{\overline{b}} f(x)dx;$$

the latter is called the *lower* Darboux integral of $f(x)$ and written

$$\int_{\underline{a}}^{b} f(x)dx.$$

The necessary and sufficient condition that $f(x)$ be Riemann integrable is that these two integrals be equal.

DATE, *n.* after date draft. See DRAFT.

average date. Same as EQUATED DATE.

dividend date. See DIVIDEND—dividend date.

due date of a note or other promise to pay. The date when it is to be paid.

equated date. See EQUATED.

focal date. See COMMUTING OBLIGATIONS.

DAYTON OHIO PLAN of building and loan association. A plan by which payments on shares are made at any time. See BUILDING AND LOAN ASSOCIATION.

DEATH RATE. See RATE—rate of mortality.

central death rate. See CENTRAL.

DE-BEN'TURE, *n., adj.* A written recognition of a debt or loan; usually carries the seal of a corporation or other firm and represents funds raised in addition to ordinary stocks and bonds.

debenture bond. Usually refers to a bond which is not secured by a mortgage.

debenture policies. Policies, the payments of the benefits of which are deferred for a stated number of years, bearing a given rate of interest during those years.

DEBT, *n.* An obligation to pay a certain sum of money.

DEBT'OR, *n.* One who owes a debt.

DEC'ADE, *n.* Ten years.

DEC'A-GON, *n.* A polygon having ten sides.

regular decagon. A *regular polygon* having ten sides.

DEC'A-ME'TER, *n.* A term used in the metric system; 10 meters or approximately 32.808 feet. See DENOMINATE NUMBERS in the appendix.

DE-CEL'ER-A'TION, *n.* Negative acceleration. See ACCELERATION—acceleration for motion in a straight line.

DEC'I-MAL, *adj.* accuracy to a certain decimal place. See ACCURATE.

decimal equivalent of a common fraction. A decimal fraction equal to the common fraction. E.g. $1/8 = .125$; $1/3 = .333 \cdots$.

decimal fraction (or **decimal**). A proper fraction whose denominator (not written) is a power of 10, the power being the number of digits on the right-hand side of a dot, called the **decimal point.** If the number of digits in the numerator of a fraction, whose denominator is a power of 10, is not as large as the power, the required number is obtained by inserting zeros immediately to the right of the decimal point; e.g. 2/10 is written as a decimal in the form .2, 23/100 as .23, and 23/1000 as .023.

decimal measure. Any system of measuring in which each unit is derived from some standard unit by multiplying or dividing the latter by some power of 10. See METRIC SYSTEM.

decimal number. A decimal fraction or any number containing a decimal point, as .23 or 5.23. *Tech.* any number with base 10.

decimal place. The position of a digit to the right of the decimal point; e.g. in 2.357, 3 is in the *first decimal place*, 5 in the *second*, and 7 in the *third*.

decimal point. See above, decimal fraction.

decimal system. (1) The number system which uses ten as its base, the ordinary number system. (2) A number system in which all fractions are expressed as **decimal numbers.** (3) Any system of decimal measurement; the metric system for instance.

DEC'I-MAL, *n.* A decimal fraction. Sometimes used of any decimal number.

addition of decimals. See ADDITION—addition of decimals.

mixed decimal. An integer plus a decimal, as 23.35.

recurring decimal. Same as repeating decimal.

repeating decimal. A decimal in which all the digits (after a certain one) consist of a set of one or more digits repeated indefinitely. E.g. $.333 \cdots$, $.030303 \cdots$, and $.235235 \cdots$ are repeating decimals, while π and the square root of 2 can not be so represented. A repeating *decimal* can always be written as a geometric series having the ratio 1/10, or 1/100, or 1/1000, etc. E.g. $.333 \cdots = .3 + .03 + .003 + \cdots$, while $.030303 \cdots = .03 + .0003 + \cdots$, and $.235235 \cdots = .235 + .000235 \cdots$. Using this property any repeating decimal can be shown to be equal to an ordinary fraction (a quotient of integers) and is therefore a rational number. See SERIES—geometric series. *Syn.* Circulating decimal.

similar decimals. Decimals having the same number of decimal places, as 2.361 and .253. Any decimals can be made similar by annexing the proper number of zeros; e.g. .36 can be made similar to .321 by writing it .360. See DIGIT—significant digits.

DEC'I-ME'TER, *n.* A term used in the metric system; one-tenth of a meter; approximately 3.937 inches. See DENOMINATE NUMBERS in the appendix.

DEC'LI-NA'TION, *n.* **declination of a celestial point.** Its angular distance north or south of the celestial equator, measured along the hour circle passing through the point. See HOUR—hour angle and hour circle.

north declination. The celestial declination of a point which is north of the celestial equator. It is always regarded as *positive*.

south declination. The celestial declination of a point which is south of the celestial equator. It is always regarded as *negative*.

DECOMPOSITION OF A FRACTION. Breaking a fraction up into **partial fractions.**

DE-CREAS'ING, *adj.* **decreasing function of one variable.** A function whose value decreases as the independent variable increases; a function whose graph falls as the abscissa increases. If the function possesses a derivative, the derivative is negative when and only when the function decreases as the independent variable increases, for then Δy is negative when Δx is positive. See DERIVATIVE.

decreasing the roots of an equation. See DIMINUTION.

monotonic decreasing. See MONOTONIC.

DEC'RE-MENT, *n.* The decrease, at a given age, of the number of lives in a given group—such as the number in the service of a given company.

DEDEKIND CUT, *n.* A postulate defining irrational numbers. Divide the rational numbers into two sets, which will be called A and B, such that: (a) All numbers in B are greater than any of those in A; (b) set A contains no largest number; (c) set B contains no smallest number. (I.e. no matter what number is selected in A (or B) another number can be found in A (or B) which is greater than (less than) the selected one.) The Dedekind cut postulate then determines a number which is the least upper bound of A and the greatest lower bound of B. This number is called an irrational number.

DE-DUC'TIVE, *adj.* **deductive method or proof.** The method which makes inferences (arrives at conclusions) from accepted principles. *Syn.* Synthetic method.

DEFAULTED PAYMENTS. (1) Payments made on principal after the due date; occurs most frequently in installment plan paying. (2) Payments never made.

DE-FEC'TIVE, *adj.* **defective equation.** See EQUATION—defective equation.

defective number. A number which is greater than the sum of all its proper divisors. See NUMBER—perfect number, and redundant number. *Syn.* Deficient number.

DE-FERRED', *adj.* **deferred annuity.** An annuity in which the first payment is made after a certain period has lapsed.

deferred annuity certain. An annuity certain which is also a deferred annuity.

deferred annuity due. An annuity due which is also a deferred annuity.

deferred reversionary annuity. An annuity to be paid to one person at the expiration of a given period after the death of another person.

deferred temporary annuity. A temporary annuity whose first payment is deferred. *Syn.* Intercepted temporary annuity.

deferred temporary (or term) insurance. Insurance payable at the end of the life insured, if this occurs during a certain period after some future date.

deferred whole life insurance. Insurance payable at the end of the life of the insured, provided this occurs after a specified period; insurance not payable if the insured dies before the expiration of a certain number of years and then payable only upon his death.

DE-FI'CIEN-CY, *n.* **premium deficiency reserves.** See RESERVE.

DEF'I-NITE, *adj.* **definite integral.** See INTEGRAL—definite integral.

definite integration. The process of finding definite integrals.

partial definite integral. One of the definite integrals constituting an ITERATED INTEGRAL.

DE-GEN'ER-ATE, *adj.* **degenerate conics.** See CONIC—degenerate conic.

DE-GREE', *n.* (1) A unit of angular measure; one of the angles resulting when a perigon is divided into 360 equal angles. A number of degrees, say

ninety degrees, is indicated thus: 90°.
(2) A unit of measure of temperature.
(3) Sometimes used in the same sense as *period* in arithmetic. See SEXA-GESIMAL—sexagesimal measure of an angle.

changing degrees to radians. Writing the measure of the angle in radians instead of degrees. The relation used is $180° = \pi$ radians or $1° = \pi/180$ radians; e.g.

$$30° = 30(\pi/180) = \pi/6 \text{ radians.}$$

degree of a curve. See CURVE—algebraic plane curve.

degree of a differential equation. The degree of the equation with respect to its highest order derivative; the greatest power to which the highest order derivative occurs. The degree of

$$\left(\frac{d^2y}{dx^2}\right)^2 + 2\left(\frac{dy}{dx}\right)^3 = 0$$

is two.

degree of a polynomial, or equation. The degree of its highest degree term. The equation $x^4 + 2x^2 + 1 = 0$ is of the fourth degree.

degree of a polynomial, or equation, with respect to a certain variable. The exponent of the highest power of the variable that occurs in the polynomial, or equation; e.g. the degree in x of $(3xyz + 4x^2 + y^3)$ is two.

degree of a term. The sum of the exponents of its unknowns (or variables); i.e. the number of unknowns (or variables) with unit exponents that can be found in it. E.g. x^2 is of second degree, and xyz^2 is of the fourth.

degree of a term in (or with respect to) a certain variable, or variables. The exponent of that variable, or the sum of the exponents of the several variables. The degree of xy^2 is one in x, two in y, three in x and y.

general equation of the nth degree. See GENERAL—general rational integral equation.

spherical degree. See SPHERICAL.
DELAMBRE'S ANALOGIES. Same as GAUSS'S FORMULAS.
DELTA METHOD. See FOUR-STEP RULE (or METHOD).

DEMAND NOTE. See NOTE.
DE MOIVRE'S HYPOTHESIS of equal decrements. (*In life insurance.*) The hypothesis that, for practical purposes, monetary computations can be made on the assumption that the number of a given group that die is the same during each year; in other words, if births are ignored, the numbers of members of a group which are living at the beginnings of successive years form a decreasing arithmetical progression. (Not a sufficiently accurate hypothesis to meet present day demands.) See MAKEHAM'S LAW.
DE MOIVRE'S THEOREM. A rule for raising a complex number to a power when the number is expressed in polar form. The rule is: Raise the modulus to the given power and multiply the amplitude by the given power; i.e.

$$[r(\cos\theta + i\sin\theta)]^n = r^n(\cos n\theta + i\sin n\theta).$$
E.g. $(\sqrt{2} + i\sqrt{2})^2 = [2(\cos 45° + i\sin 45°)]^2$
$$= 4(\cos 90° + i\sin 90°) = 4i.$$

DE-NOM'I-NATE, *adj.* **denominate number.** A number whose unit represents a unit of measure—such as 3 inches, 2 pounds, or 5 gallons.

addition, subtraction or multiplication of denominate numbers. The process of reducing them to the same denomination and then proceeding as with ordinary (abstract) numbers. E.g. to find the number of square yards in a room 17 ft. 6 in. by 12 ft. 4 in., the length in yards is $5\frac{5}{6}$ and the width is $4\frac{1}{9}$. The required number of square yards is $5\frac{5}{6} \times 4\frac{1}{9}$. See MULTIPLICATION—multiplication of mixed numbers.

DE-NOM'I-NA'TION, *n.* **denomination of a number.** The kind of unit to which it refers—as pounds, feet, gallons, tenths, hundredths, etc.

denomination of a bond. Its par value.

DE-NOM'I-NA'TOR, *n.* The term below the line in a fraction; the term which divides the numerator. The denominator of $\frac{2}{3}$ is 3.

common denominator. A quantity divisible by all the denominators under consideration.

DENSE, *adj.* **dense set of numbers, or points.** A set such that every member of the set is a *limit point* of the set. The set of rational numbers, of all real numbers, and of all complex numbers are all dense sets.

DEN′SI-TY, *n.* The mass or amount of matter per unit volume. Since the mass of 1 c.c. of water at 4°C. is one gram, density in the *metric system* is the same as *specific gravity.* See SPECIFIC.

   mean density. The mass divided by the volume. *Tech.*

$$\int_v \rho\, dv \div \int_v dv,$$

where ρ is the density and $\int_v$ denotes the integral taken over the total volume, V.

   unit density. The density when mass is numerically equal to volume. See above, DENSITY.

DE-PAR′TURE, *n.* **departure between two meridians on the earth's surface.** The length of the arc of the parallel of latitude subtended by the two meridians. This grows shorter the nearer the parallel of latitude is to a pole. Used in parallel sailing.

DE-PEND′ENT, *n.* **dependent event.** See EVENT.

   dependent functions. A set of functions, one of which can be expressed as a function of the others; e.g.

$$u=(x+1)/(y+1) \text{ and } v=\sin\,[(x+1)/(y+1)]$$

are dependent functions, for $v = \sin u$. *Syn.* Interdependent functions. Functions that are not *independent* are said to be *dependent.* See INDEPENDENT.

   dependent variable. See FUNCTION—function of one variable.

   linearly dependent. See LINEAR—linearly dependent quantities.

DE-PLE′TION. Same as DEPRECIATION.

DE-PRE′CI-A′TION, *n.* (1) The loss in value of equipment; the difference between the cost value and the *book value.* (2) The decrease in amount of a substance, such as radium or gasoline. *Syn.* Depletion, wasting assets.

   book value of depreciating equipment. See VALUE—book value of depreciating assets, equipment.

   depreciation charge, constant percentage plan. A decrease made in the book value, usually annually, equal to a constant percentage of that value and such that the fund consisting of these decreases, without interest, will equal the cost minus the scrap value at the end of a certain number of years. The percentage decrease is $(1 - \sqrt[n]{R/C})$, where C is the cost, R the scrap value, and n the number of years.

   depreciation charges. Deductions from the income of a firm to provide a fund to pay replacement costs.

   depreciation charges, sinking fund plan. Equal depreciation charges invested periodically, usually annually, at a given rate of compound interest.

   depreciation charges, straight line method. The plan by which an equal part of the estimated replacement cost is put in a fund each year, during the years preceding the replacement.

   total depreciation. See TOTAL.

DEPRESSED EQUATION. The equation resulting from reducing the number of roots in an equation, i.e. by dividing out the difference of the unknown and a root; e.g. $x^2 - 2x + 2 = 0$ is the *depressed* equation obtained from $x^3 - 3x^2 + 4x - 2 = 0$ by dividing the left member of the latter by $(x - 1)$.

DE-PRES′SION, *n.* See ANGLE—angle of depression.

DE-RIV′A-TIVE, *n.* The instantaneous rate of change of a function with respect to the variable; in Cartesian coordinates, the slope of the graph of the function with reference to the axis of the independent variable. See ACCELERATION, and below, derivative of a function of one variable. *Syn.* Differential coefficient.

   change of variable in a derivative. See below, derivative of a function of a function.

   derivative of an equation. The equation formed by replacing the terms by their derivatives.

derivative of a function of a function, say $F(u)$, where $u = f(x)$. The product of the derivative of the first function with respect to its argument, u, and the derivative of the second function with respect to the independent variable, x. Explicitly,

$$\frac{dF(u)}{dx} = \frac{dF(u)}{du}\,\frac{df(x)}{dx}.$$

E.g. the derivative of $(x^2+1)^5$ is

$$\frac{du^5}{du}\,\frac{du}{dx}, \quad \text{where} \quad u = x^2+1,$$

or $\qquad 5(x^2+1)^4 2x.$

Syn. Derivative of a *composite function*. See COMPOSITE—composite function of one variable.

derivative of a function of one variable. *Tech.* If delta x, written Δx, denotes the change in x, then the derivative is defined as the limit of the quotient of the corresponding change in the function of x and Δx, when Δx approaches zero, provided that limit exists; written

$$\lim_{\Delta x \to 0} \frac{f(x+\Delta x) - f(x)}{\Delta x}$$

or $\qquad \lim\limits_{\Delta x \to 0} \dfrac{\Delta y}{\Delta x}, \quad \text{where} \quad y = f(x).$

This limit, that is, the derivative, is denoted by

$$y',\ D_x y,\ \frac{dy}{dx},\ f'(x),\ D_x f(x),\ \frac{d}{dx}f(x) \text{ or } \frac{df(x)}{dx}.$$

The derivative, evaluated at a point, $x = a$, is written

$$f'(a) \text{ or } D_x f(x)_{x=a} \text{ or } \left[\frac{df(x)}{dx}\right]_{x=a}.$$

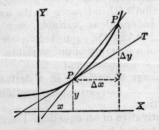

See DIFFERENTIATION—differen-

tiation formulas, and FOUR-STEP RULE or METHOD. *Syn.* Differential coefficient. In the figure $\Delta y/\Delta x$ is the slope of the secant PP'. This quantity approaches the derivative at P and the secant approaches the tangent PT as Δx approaches zero. Hence dy/dx is the slope of the tangent PT.

derivatives of higher order. Derivatives of other derivatives, the latter being considered as functions of the independent variable just as was the function of which the first derivative was taken. E.g. $y = x^3$ has its first derivative $y' = 3x^2$ and its second derivative $y'' = 6x$, gotten by taking the derivative of $3x^2$; similarly $y''' = 6$, and $y^{[4]} = 0$.

derivative from parametric equations. See PARAMETRIC—differentiation of parametric equations.

derivative of a position vector. The vector whose projections on the coordinate axes are the derivatives of the corresponding projections of the original vector; the vector whose magnitude is the rate of change of arc-length of a curve and whose direction is that of the tangent to the curve. E.g. the position vector $t^2 i + t^3 j$ (where $x = t^2$, $y = t^3$ are parametric equations of a curve) has for its derivative, at the point t, the vector $2ti + 3t^2 j$.

derivative as the slope of the graph of a function. See above, derivative of a function of one variable.

derivative of a sum, of a constant times a variable, of a power of a variable, of a quotient, of trigonometric functions, of logarithms, and of exponentials, etc. See DIFFERENTIATION FORMULAS in the appendix.

derivative of a vector: Let t be the arc-length of a curve and suppose that corresponding to each point of the curve there is a vector. Let $v(t)$ denote the vector at the point t of the curve. Then

$$\lim_{\Delta t \to 0} \frac{v(t+\Delta t) - v(t)}{\Delta t}.$$

is the derivative of the vector, relative to the arc-length of the curve, at the point t, provided this limit exists. See above, derivative of a position vector.

directional derivative. See DIRECTIONAL.

normal derivative. See NORMAL—normal derivative.

partial derivative. See PARTIAL.

sign of the derivative at a point, significance of. Enables one to tell whether a curve is increasing or decreasing as the variable increases. The derivative at a point is positive if the function is increasing and negative if the function is decreasing. See above, derivative of a function of one variable.

total derivative. The rate of change of a function of two or more variables with reference to a parameter on which these variables are dependent. If $z = f(x, y)$, $x = \phi(t)$ and $y = \theta(t)$, the total derivative of z with reference to t, written dz/dt, is given by

$$\frac{dz}{dt} = f_x(x, y)\ \phi_t\ (t) + f_y\ (x, y)\ \theta_t\ (t).$$

See PARTIAL—partial derivative. *Syn.* Total differential coefficient.

DE-RIVED′, *n.* **derived curve** (first derived curve). The curve whose ordinates, corresponding to given abscissas, are equal in sign and numerical value to the slope of some given curve for the same values of the abscissas. E.g. the curve whose equation is $y = 3x^2$ is the derived curve of the curve whose equation is $y = x^3$. The derived curve of the first derived curve is called the **second derived curve,** etc.

derived equation. (1) *In algebra*, an equation obtained from another one by transposing terms, powering both sides, or multiplying or dividing by some quantity. A derived equation is not always equivalent to the original, i.e. does not always have the same set of roots. (2) *In calculus*, the equation resulting from differentiating the given equation. See above, derived curve.

DESARGUES'S THEOREM on perspective triangles: If the lines joining corresponding vertices of two triangles pass through a point, the intersections of the three pairs of corresponding sides lie on a line, and conversely.

DESCARTES, folium of Descartes. See FOLIUM.

DESCARTES' RULE OF SIGNS. A rule determining an upper bound to the number of positive roots and to the number of negative roots of an equation. The rule as ordinarily used states that an algebraic equation, $f(x) = 0$, cannot have a greater number of positive roots than it has variations in sign, nor a greater number of negative roots than the equation $f(-x) = 0$ has variations in sign. For instance the equation

$$x^4 - x^3 - x^2 + x - 1 = 0$$

has three variations in sign and hence cannot have more than three positive roots. Since $f(-x) = 0$ takes the form $x^4 + x^3 - x^2 - x - 1 = 0$, in which there is only one variation of sign, the original equation cannot have more than one negative root. Descartes' Rule of Signs in full shows more than is indicated above, the complete criteria being: The number of positive real roots of an equation with real coefficients is either equal to the number of its variations of sign, or is less than that number by an even integer, a root of multiplicity m being counted as m roots. As before the equation can be tested for negative roots by applying this rule to the equation $f(-x) = 0$.

DE-TACHED′, *adj.* **detached coefficient.** See COEFFICIENT—detached coefficients.

DE-TER′MI-NANT. *n.* A square array of quantities, called **elements,** symbolizing the sum of certain products of these **elements.** The number of **rows** (or **columns**) is called the **order** of the determinant. The diagonal, from the upper left corner to the lower right corner, is called the **principal** (or **leading**) **diagonal.** The diagonal from the lower left corner to the upper right corner is called the **secondary diagonal.** The value of a determinant can be found by combining the *elements* according to the first rule for determinants of the third order, extended to a determinant of any order (see below, determinant of the third order); *Tech.* the rule of combination may be stated: Form the algebraic sum of all products obtained by taking one and only one factor from each row and each column and attach the positive or negative sign to each product according as the number of inversions of the column (or row) indices of the factors of a product are even or odd when the row (or column) indices are in natural order (1, 2, 3, etc.). The elements of a general determinant are usually indicated by some such form as a_{ij}, where i denotes the number of the row, and j the number of the column in which the element appears. The i and j are called the **row** and **column indices.**

cofactor of an element in a determinant. See COFACTOR.

conjugate elements of a determinant. See CONJUGATE—conjugate elements of a determinant.

determinant of the coefficients of the variables in n linear equations in n variables. The determinant obtained by writing the equations so that the terms which contain the same variable form a column, then deleting the variables. The determinant of the coefficients of the variables of

$$2x+3y-1=0 \quad \text{is} \quad \begin{vmatrix} 2 & 3 \\ 4 & -7 \end{vmatrix}.$$
$$\text{and } 4x-7y+5=0$$

determinant of the second order. Written

$$\begin{vmatrix} a_1 & b_1 \\ a_2 & b_2 \end{vmatrix},$$

and defined as $a_1b_2 - a_2b_1$. This form appears in the solution of the equations

$$a_1x + b_1y = c_1$$
$$a_2x + b_2y = c_2,$$

from which

$$x = \frac{c_1b_2 - c_2b_1}{a_1b_2 - a_2b_1}$$

$$= \frac{\begin{vmatrix} c_1 & b_1 \\ c_2 & b_2 \end{vmatrix}}{\begin{vmatrix} a_1 & b_1 \\ a_2 & b_2 \end{vmatrix}}.$$

determinant of the third order. Written:

$$\begin{vmatrix} a_1 & b_1 & c_1 \\ a_2 & b_2 & c_2 \\ a_3 & b_3 & c_3 \end{vmatrix}$$

and defined as

$$(a_1b_2c_3 + a_2b_3c_1 + a_3b_1c_2 - a_3b_2c_1 - a_2b_1c_3 - a_1b_3c_2).$$

(This expression appears in the solution of three simultaneous equations in three unknowns. See above, determinant of the second order, and CRAMER'S RULE.) There are two easy ways for combining the elements in the third order determinant so as to obtain this expression. One, which is applicable to determinants of any order, is as follows: Form the sum of the products of each element in the first column by its *minor*, taking each product positive or negative according as the element is in an odd or even numbered row. In fact, any column or any row can be used, instead of the first column, provided the sign attached to the product of any element by its minor is determined by counting along rows and columns from the element in the first row and first column to the given element and making the sign positive or negative according as the number of the given element is odd or even. E.g. b_2 would be in an odd position and have a positive sign, since we go a_1 to b_1 to b_2 or from a_1 to a_2 to b_2. The second definition, which is not applicable to determinants of higher order than the third, is as follows: Form the sum of the triple products of the elements which lie on the principal diagonal, and on pairs of lines parallel to it, and those which lie on the secondary diagonal, and on pairs of lines parallel to it. Take the latter negative and add all triple products in these sets. For instance, the product $a_1b_2c_3$ is positive while the product $a_3b_2c_1$ is negative.

development of a determinant. Same as EXPANSION OF A DETERMINANT. See below, expansion of a determinant.

division of a determinant by a constant. See DIVISION.

evaluation of a determinant. (1) Finding its numerical value. (2) Same as EXPANSION OF A DETERMINANT.

expansion of a determinant. (1) The act of writing the determinant in the algebraic form to which it is equivalent. *Syn.* Development of a determinant. (2) The algebraic form to which the determinant is equivalent by definition.

functional determinant. Same as JACOBIAN.

leading elements in a determinant. See LEADING.

minor of an element in a determinant. See MINOR.

multiplication of determinants. See MULTIPLICATION—multiplication of two determinants.

numerical determinant. A determinant whose elements are numbers (absolute numbers).

properties of determinants. Refers to such properties as the following, which are often useful in short-cutting the expansion of a determinant: (1) If all the elements of a column (or row) are zero, the value of the determinant is zero. (2) If two columns (or rows) have their corresponding elements alike, the determinant is zero. (3) The value of a determinant is unaltered if the same multiple of the elements of any column (row) are added to the corresponding elements of any other column (row). (4) If two columns (or rows) of a determinant are interchanged, the sign of the determinant is changed. (5) The value of a determinant is unaltered when all the corresponding rows and columns are interchanged.

skew-symmetric determinant. See SKEW.

symmetric determinant. See SYMMETRIC—symmetric determinant.

DE′VI-A′TION, *n.* (*In statistics.*) (1) The variation from the trend. (2) The difference between the particular number and the average of the set of numbers under consideration. *Syn.* Measure of dispersion. See RESIDUAL.

algebraic deviation. (*In statistics.*) Deviation which is counted positive if the magnitude is greater than the average or trend, and negative if less. See DEVIATION.

mean or average deviation. The arithmetic mean of the *numerical* values of the deviations from the average. (The mean of the *algebraic* deviations would be zero.)

median deviation. Median of a set of deviations.

probable deviation. A special name given to the quartile deviation when the distribution is normal.

quartile deviation. One half of the difference between the two quartile magnitudes.

standard deviation. Denoted by sigma, σ; the square root of the arithmetic mean of the squares of the deviations from the mean. *Syn.* Root mean square deviation.

DI-AG′O-NAL, *n. adj.* **diagonal of a determinant.** See DETERMINANT.

diagonal of a parallelepiped. A line segment joining two vertices which are not in the same face. There are four of these, all equal to $\sqrt{a^2+b^2+c^2}$, where a, b, c are the edges of the parallelepiped. They are usually called the principal diagonals, the other diagonals being the diagonals of the faces.

diagonal of a polygon. A line connecting two non-adjacent vertices. In *elementary geometry* it is thought of as the **line segment** between non-adjacent vertices; in *projective geometry* it is the straight line (of infinite length) passing through two non-adjacent vertices.

diagonal of a polyhedron. A line segment between any two vertices which do not lie in the same face.

DIAGRAM 72 DIFFERENCES

diagonal scale, for a rule. A scale in which the rule is divided crosswise and diagonally by systems of parallel lines. E.g. suppose that there are 11 longitudinal (lengthwise of the ruler) lines per inch (counting the lines at the beginning and end of the inch interval) and one diagonal line per inch. Then the intersections of the diagonal lines with the longitudinal lines are 1/10″ apart longitudinally, for the 10 segments cut off on any one diagonal by the horizontal lines are equal, and hence the 10 corresponding distances measured along the longitudinal lines must be equal. Thus the inch is divided into 10 equal parts. Similarly one diagonal per 1/10″ scales the ruler in 1/100″, etc.

DI'A-GRAM, n. A drawing representing certain data and, perhaps, conclusions drawn from the data; a drawing representing pictorially (graphically) a statement or a proof; used to aid readers in understanding algebraic explanations.

   Argand diagram. See ARGAND.

   indicator diagram. See INDICATOR.

DIALYTICAL METHOD OF SYLVESTER. See SYLVESTER'S DIALYTIC METHOD.

DI-AM'E-TER, n. conjugate diameters. See CONJUGATE—conjugate diameters.

   diameter of a circle. See CIRCLE.

   diameter of a conic. Any straight line which is the locus of the midpoints of a family of parallel chords; a chord joining the points of tangency of two parallel tangents to the conic. Any conic has infinitely many diameters. In the central conics, ellipses and hyperbolas, they form a pencil of lines through the center of the conic.

DI-AM'E-TRAL, adj. conjugate diametral planes. Two diametral planes, each of which is parallel to the set of chords defining the other.

   diametral line in a conic (ellipse, hyperbola or parabola). Same as DIAMETER.

   diametral plane of a quadric surface. A plane containing the middle points of a set of parallel chords.

DIDO'S PROBLEM. The problem of finding the curve, with a given perimeter, which incloses the maximum area. The required curve is a circle.

DIF'FER-ENCE, n. The result of subtracting one quantity from another. Syn. Remainder.

   difference of like powers of two quantities, factorability of. If the power is odd, the difference of like powers of two quantities is divisible by the difference of the two quantities; while if the power is even, the difference is divisible by both the sum and the difference of the two quantities. E.g.

$$x^3 - y^3 = (x-y)(x^2 + xy + y^2) \quad \text{while}$$
$$x^4 - y^4 = (x-y)(x+y)(x^2 + y^2).$$

See SUM—sums of like powers of two quantities.

   difference of two squares. The result of subtracting the square of one number from the square of another. If a and b denote the numbers, the difference of the squares, $(a^2 - b^2)$, is equal to $(a+b)(a-b)$.

   difference quotient. The increment of the function, corresponding to an increment of the independent variable, divided by the latter; e.g. if the function, $f(x)$, is x^2, the difference quotient is

$$\frac{f(x+\Delta x) - f(x)}{\Delta x} = \frac{(x+\Delta x)^2 - x^2}{\Delta x} = 2x + \Delta x.$$

See DERIVATIVE—derivative of a function of one variable.

   tabular difference. See TABULAR.

DIF'FER-EN-CES, n. differences of the first order or first order differences. The sequence formed by subtracting each term of a sequence from the next succeeding term. The first order differences of the sequence $(1, 3, 5, 7, \cdots)$ would be $(2, 2, 2, \cdots)$.

   differences of the second order or second order differences. The first order differences of the first order differences; e.g. the first order differences of the sequence $(1, 2, 4, 7, 11, \cdots)$ are $(1, 2, 3, 4, \cdots)$, while the second order differences are $(1, 1, 1, \cdots)$. Similarly, the *third order differences* are the first order differences of the second order; and, in general, the rth *order differences* are the first order differences of the $(r-1)$th order. If the sequence is $(a_1, a_2, a_3, \cdots a_n, \cdots)$, the 1st order differences are a_2-a_1, a_3-a_2, a_4-a_3, $\cdots$, the 2nd order are $a_3-2a_2+a_1$, $a_4-2a_3+a_2$, and the rth order are:

$$[a_{r+1}-ra_r+\{r(r-1)/2!\}a_{r-1}-\cdots \pm a_1]$$
$$[a_{r+2}-ra_{r+1}+\{r(r-1)/2!\}a_r-\cdots$$
$$\pm a_2], \cdots .$$

finite differences. The differences gotten from the sequence of values obtained from a given function by letting the variable change by arithmetic progression. If $f(x)$ is the given function, the arithmetic progression $(a, a+h, a+2h, \cdots)$ gives the sequence of values: $f(a)$, $f(a+h)$, $f(a+2h)$, $\cdots$. The differences may be of any given order. The first order differences are $f(a+h)-f(a)$, $f(a+2h)-f(a+h)$, $\cdots$. The successive differences of order one, two, three, etc. are written: $\Delta f(x)$, $\Delta^2 f(x)$, $\Delta^3 f(x)$, etc.

method of differences. A method of finding the sum of a given number of terms of certain series by use of the differences of the terms.

DIF'FER-ENC-ING, *p.* **differencing a function.** Taking the successive differences. See DIFFERENCES—finite differences.

DIF'FER-EN'TIAL, *adj.* or *n.* **binomial differentials.** See BINOMIAL.

degree of a differential equation. See DEGREE—degree of a differential equation.

differential of an arc. An approximation to the length or *increment* of arc between the points corresponding to the abscissas x and $(x+\Delta x)$; the differential of this arc is defined to be $\sqrt{(dx)^2+(dy)^2}$. Geometrically this is the length of the segment of the tangent to the curve at the point whose abscissa is x, which lies between this point and the ordinate of the point where the abscissa is $x+\Delta x$. This segment of the tangent approaches coincidence with the arc of the curve as

Δx approaches zero. See ELEMENT—element of arc of a curve.

differential of area, attraction, mass, moment, moment of inertia, pressure, volume, and work. Same as ELEMENT OF AREA, ATTRACTION, etc.

differential calculus. See CALCULUS.

differential coefficient. See DERIVATIVE.

differential coefficient from parametric equations. See PARAMETRIC.

differential of a composite function. See COMPOSITE—differentials of composite functions.

differential equations (ordinary) in two variables. Equations containing at most two variables, and derivatives of the first or higher order of one of the variables with respect to the other, such as $y(dy/dx)+2x=0$. When an equation contains only derivatives of the first order it is frequently written in terms of differentials. This is permissible because the first derivative may be treated as the quotient of the differentials. Thus the equation above may be written $ydy+2xdx=0$.

differential equations reducible to the homogeneous form. Equations of the type

$$\frac{dy}{dx}=\frac{ax+by+c}{dx+ey+f},$$

which can be reduced by the substitutions: $x=x'+h$, $y=y'+k$, where h and k are to be chosen so as to remove the constant terms in the numerator and denominator of the fraction.

differential equations with variables separable. Ordinary differential equations which can be written in the form $P(x)dx+Q(y)dy=0$, by means of algebraic operations performed on the given equation. Its general solution is obtainable directly by integration.

differential of a function of one variable. If $y=f(x)$, then differential y is the derivative of $f(x)$ times differential x, written

$$dy=f'(x)dx.$$

dy differs from Δy, the change in the

ordinate when x makes a change of Δx, by an *infinitesimal of higher order* than Δx; for since

$$\lim_{\Delta x \to 0} \frac{\Delta y}{\Delta x} = f'(x),$$

$$\frac{\Delta y}{\Delta x} = f'(x) + \epsilon,$$

where ϵ is an infinitesimal (see LIMIT). Hence

$$\Delta y = f'(x)\Delta x + \epsilon \Delta x,$$

from which dy is obtained by dropping

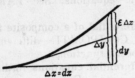

the infinitesimal, $\epsilon \Delta x$, and writing dx in the place of Δx. $\epsilon \Delta x$ is of higher order than Δx. See INFINITESIMAL and APPROXIMATION—approximation by differentials.

differential of a function of several variables. Same as TOTAL DIFFERENTIAL.

differential of an independent variable. An increment of the variable.

differential mass. The product of an *element* (differential element) of volume and the density at a point within this element.

differential operator in differential equations. A polynomial in the operator D, where D stands for d/dx and Dy for dy/dx. E.g. $(D^2 + xD + 5)y = d^2y/dx^2 + x(dy/dx) + 5y$. Symbols of the form $1/f(D)$, where $f(D)$ is a polynomial in D, are called **inverse differential operators.** E.g. the symbol $1/(D-a)$ arises from the equation $dy/dx - ay = f(x)$. The equation is written in the form $(D-a)y = f(x)$. Then

$$y = \frac{1}{(D-a)} f(x)$$

is a solution, where

$$\frac{1}{(D-a)} f(x) = Ce^{ax} + e^{ax} \int e^{-ax} f(x) dx.$$

exact differential. The total differential of some function; one of the forms

$$f'(x)dx \quad dz = \frac{\partial z}{\partial x} dx + \frac{\partial z}{\partial y} dy,$$

and similar forms for any number of variables. See below, exact differential equation.

exact differential equation in three variables. An equation which is the total differential of some function of the three variables, set equal to zero. If the equation be in the form

$$Pdx + Qdy + Rdz = 0,$$

the necessary and sufficient conditions that it be exact are that $D_y P = D_x Q$, $D_z Q = D_y R$ and $D_x R = D_z P$, where $D_y P$, etc. denote partial derivatives. This can be generalized to any number of variables.

exact differential equation in two variables. A differential equation which is the total differential of some function of the two variables, set equal to zero; i.e. an equation which can be put in the form:

$$[\partial f(x \; y)/\partial x]dx + [\partial f(x \; y)/\partial y]dy = 0.$$

The necessary and sufficient condition that any equation of the form $Mdx + Mdy = 0$ be exact is that the partial derivative of M with respect to y be equal to the partial derivative of N with respect to x; i.e. $D_y M = D_x N$. The equation

$$(2x + 3y)dx + (3x + 5y)dy = 0$$

is exact.

general solution of a differential equation. See SOLUTION—general solution of a differential equation.

homogeneous differential equation. A name usually given to a differential equation of the first degree and first order which is homogeneous in the variables (the derivatives not being considered) such as

$$y^2 + (xy + x^2)\frac{dy}{dx} = 0$$

and

$$\frac{x}{y} + \left(\sin \frac{x}{y}\right)\frac{dy}{dx} = 0.$$

Solvable by use of the substitution $y = ux$. See HOMOGENEOUS—homogeneous equation.

homogeneous linear differential equation. A *linear differential equation* which does not contain a term involving only the independent variable. E.g. $y' + yf(x) = 0$.

integrable differential equations. Differential equations that are exact, or that can be easily made so by multiplying through by an integrating factor.

intermediate differential. See INTERMEDIATE.

Laplace's differential equation. See LAPLACE'S DIFFERENTIAL EQUATION.

linear differential equation of first order. A technical name given to an equation of the form

$$\frac{dy}{dx} + P(x)y = Q(x).$$

See example above, under differential operator in differential equations.

linear differential equations. Differential equations of any order and of the first degree in y and its derivatives; the coefficients of y and its derivatives being functions of x only. The *general solution* is found by equating to zero the sum of all terms containing y or its derivatives, finding as many particular solutions of this **auxiliary equation** as there are units in its order, multiplying each of these solutions by an arbitrary parameter, and adding to the sum of these products (called the **complementary function**) some particular solution of the original differential equation. Another method of finding a general solution, after having the complementary function, consists in assuming that the arbitrary parameters in the complementary function are undetermined functions of x, then substituting the complementary function in the original differential equation and determining these undetermined functions of x so that the result is an identity. This method is called **variation of parameters.**

order of a differential equation. The order of its highest order derivative.

partial differential. The product of the partial derivative of a function, with respect to an independent variable, and the differential of the variable; one of the terms of the total differential.

partial differential equations. Equations involving more than one independent variable and partial derivatives with respect to these variables.

primitive of a differential equation. See PRIMITIVE—primitive of a differential equation.

simultaneous (or systems of) differential equations. Two or more differential equations involving the same number of dependent variables, taken as a system in the sense that solutions are sought which will satisfy them simultaneously.

total differential of a function of several variables. The sum of all the partial differentials, taken with respect to the several variables. Written, in the case of a function of two variables,

$$df(x, y) = \frac{\partial f}{\partial x} \, dx + \frac{\partial f}{\partial y} \, dy.$$

DIF'FER-EN'TI-A'TION, *n.* The process of finding the derivative, or differential coefficient.

change of variable in differentiation. See DERIVATIVE—derivative of a function of a function.

differentiation of exponential, hyperbolic, inverse, logarithmic and trigonometric functions; of powers, products, quotients, and sums, etc. See DIFFERENTIATION FORMULAS in the appendix.

differentiation formulas. Formulas which give the derivatives of functions or enable one to reduce the finding of their derivatives to the problem of finding the derivatives of simpler functions. See DIFFERENTIATION FORMULAS in the appendix.

differentiation of a function of a function. See DERIVATIVE—derivative of a function of a function.

differentiation of an implicit function of two variables. The process of finding the derivative of one of two variables with respect to the other by differentiating all the terms of a given equation in the two variables, leaving the derivative of the dependent variable (with respect to the independent variable) in indicated form, and solving the resulting identity for this derivative. E.g. if

$$x^3+x+y+y^2=4,$$

then $\quad 3x^2+1+y'+3y^2y'=0,$

whence $\quad y'=-(3x^2+1)/(3y^2+1).$

In cases where an equation cannot be solved for one of the variables, this method is indispensable; and it generally facilitates the work even when the equation can be so solved. For the equation $f(x, y) = 0$ one may also use the formula:

$$dy/dx=-D_xf(x, y)/D_yf(x, y),$$
if $\quad D_yf(x, y)\neq0,$

which is easily seen to be equivalent to the above method. See DIFFEREN-TIAL—total differential (when the point (x, y, z) moves along a curve parallel to the xy plane, i.e. if z is constant, $dz=df(x, y)$ is zero and the above formula results). *Syn.* Implicit differentiation.

differentiation of an infinite series of variable terms. Differentiation of each term in the sense that a new series is defined by the derivative of the general term. If the given series has the sum $S(x)$ for all x on the interval (a, b), the new series has the sum $S'(x)$ on the same interval, provided it converges uniformly on that interval. See CONVERGENCE—uniform convergence, and INTEGRA-TION—integration of an infinite series.

differentiation of parametric equations. See PARAMETRIC.

differentiation of a power series. See above, differentiation of an infinite series of variable terms. Differentiation of a power series results in a series which converges uniformly on an interval within the interval of convergence of the original series; that is, the resulting series has the same interval of convergence, except possibly for the *end-points* of the interval, and defines a function which is the derivative of the function defined by the given series. See above, differentiation of an infinite series of variable terms.

differentiation under the integral sign (with respect to a variable other than the one with respect to which the integration is to be performed): If the limits of integration are constant, the derivative is the integral of the derivative of the integrand. If the limits are functions of the variable with respect to which one is differentiating, the derivative is the integral, with the integrand differentiated, plus the product of the derivative of the upper limit and the integrand, with the variable of integration replaced by the upper limit, minus the product of the derivative of the lower limit and the integrand with the variable of integration replaced by the lower limit. E.g. the derivative of

$$\int_1^2 (x^2+y)dx,$$

with respect to y, is

$$\int_1^2 dx,$$

and the derivative, with respect to y, of

$$\int_y^{y^2} (x^2+y)dx$$

is

$$\int_y^y dx+(y^4+y)2y-(y^2+y).$$

A sufficient condition that differentiation under the integral sign be permissible is that the integrand and its derivative with respect to the variable with respect to which the integral is being differentiated be continuous functions of the variable of integration between the limits of integration.

implicit differentiation. Same as DIFFERENTIATION OF AN IMPLICIT FUNCTION.

indirect differentiation. See INDIRECT.

logarithmic differentiation. Finding derivatives by the use of logarithms. Consists of taking the logarithm of both sides of an equation and then differentiating. It is used for finding the derivatives of variable powers of variable bases, such as x^x, and to simplify certain differentiation processes. E.g.

if $y = x^x$, one can write log $y = x$ log x, and find the derivative of y with respect to x from the latter equation by means of the usual method of *implicit differentiation*.

successive differentiation. The process of finding higher order derivatives by differentiating lower order derivatives.

DIG'IT, *n.* A term applied to any of the integers 0, 1, 2, 3, 4, 5, 6, 7, 8, 9 occurring in a number. The number 23 has the digits 2 and 3.

significant digits. (1) The digits of a number which have a significance; the digits of a number beginning with the first digit on the left that is not zero and ending with the last digit to the right. E.g. the significant digits in 230 are 2, 3, and 0. The significant digits in .230 are 2, 3, and 0, the 0 meaning that, to third place accuracy, the number is .230. In 0.23, the 0 is not significant. (2) The digits which determine the mantissa of the logarithm of the number; the digits of a number beginning with the first digit on the left that is not zero and ending with the last digit on the right that is not zero.

DI-HE'DRAL, *adj.* **dihedral angle.** The angle between two planes. If the planes are parallel, the angle is said to be zero. A dihedral angle is measured by the plane angle formed by the lines of intersection of the two planes with a plane perpendicular to their line of intersection. The planes α and β form a dihedral angle, which is measured by the angle drawn at A, or at A'.

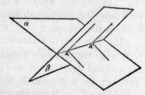

DI-MEN'SION, *n.* Refers to those properties called length, area and volume. A configuration having length only is said to be of one dimension; area and not volume, two dimensions; volume, three dimensions. *Tech.* a configuration

has 1, 2, 3, or in general, n dimensions when the equation describing it analytically contains 1, 2, 3, or n essential constants. See CONSTANT—essential constants. A space is said to have n dimensions when n numbers (coordinates) are necessary to fix the position of a point in the space.

DI-MEN'SION-AL, *adj.* **one, two, three or n dimensional.** Possessing the given number of dimensions. See DIMENSION.

DI-MEN'SION-AL'I-TY, *n.* The number of dimensions of a quantity. See DIMENSION.

DIM'I-NU'TION of the roots of an equation. Replacing the equation by one whose roots are those of the original equation, each reduced by the same constant; transforming the equation by the substitution $x = x' + a$, $a > 0$, where x is the unknown in the given equation. If the old equation has the root x_1, the new one has a root $x_1' = x_1 - a$. The substitution of $x = x' + 2$ in $x^2 - 3x + 2 = 0$, whose roots are 1 and 2, results in the equation $(x')^2 + x' = 0$ whose roots are -1 and 0.

DI-O-PHAN'TINE ANALYSIS. A method for finding *integral* solutions of certain algebraic equations. Depends mostly upon an ingenious use of arbitrary parameters.

DIOPHANTINE EQUATIONS. See EQUATION—indeterminate equation.

DI-RECT' trigonometric functions. The trigonometric functions *sine, cosine, tangent,* etc., as distinguished from the *inverse trigonometric functions*. See TRIGONOMETRIC—trigonometric functions.

DI-RECT'ED, *adj.* **directed angle.** An angle that has been indicated as positive or negative. See ANGLE.

directed line, or line segment. A line (or line segment) on which the direction from one end to the other has been indicated as positive, and the reverse direction as negative.

directed numbers. Numbers having signs, positive or negative, indicating that the negative numbers are to be measured, geometrically, in the direction opposite to that in which the positive are measured. *Syn.* Signed numbers, algebraic numbers. See POSITIVE—positive number.

DI-REC′TION, *n.* The relation between two points which is independent of the distance between them.

direction angle of a line in the plane. The smallest positive (or zero) angle that the line makes with the positive *x*-axis. See below, direction of a line in a plane.

direction angles. The three positive angles which a line makes with the positive directions of the coordinate axes. There are two such sets for an undirected line, one for each direction which can be assigned to the line. Direction angles are not independent (see PYTHAGOREAN—Pythagorean relation between direction cosines). In the figure, direction angles of the line *L* are the angles, α, β and γ, which the parallel line *L′* makes with the coordinate axes.

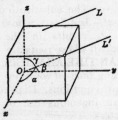

direction cosines. The cosines of the *direction angles.* They are usually denoted by *l*, *m*, and *n*, where, if α, β, γ are the direction angles with respect to the *x*-axis, *y*-axis and *z*-axis, respectively, $l = \cos \alpha$, $m = \cos \beta$, and $n = \cos \gamma$. *Direction cosines* are not independent. When two of them are given, the third can be found, except for sign,

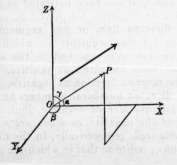

by use of the *Pythagorean relation*, $\cos^2 \alpha + \cos^2 \beta + \cos^2 \gamma = 1$. See below, direction numbers.

direction of a curve (at a point). The direction of the tangent to the curve at the point. See below, direction of a line in a plane, and direction of a line in space.

direction of a line in a plane. Its inclination; the angle it makes with the *x*-axis (which is defined as the smallest positive angle obtainable by revolving the positive *x*-axis, counterclockwise, until it is parallel to the line).

direction of a line in space. Its direction angles.

direction numbers (or ratios) of a line in space. Any three numbers proportional to the *direction cosines* of the line. *Syn.* Direction components. If a line passes through the points (x_1, y_1, z_1) and (x_2, y_2, z_2), its direction numbers are proportional to $x_2 - x_1$, $y_2 - y_1$, $z_2 - z_1$, and its direction cosines are

$$\frac{x_2 - x_1}{D}, \quad \frac{y_2 - y_1}{D}, \quad \frac{z_2 - z_1}{D},$$

where

$$D = \sqrt{(x_2 - x_1)^2 + (y_2 - y_1)^2 + (z_2 - z_1)^2},$$

the distance between the points.

DI-REC′TION-AL, *adj.* **directional derivative of a function of three variables,** $u = F(x, y, z)$. The rate of change of *u* with respect to arc length, *s*, as the point $P:(x, y, z)$ moves in a given direction (i.e., along a given curve with arclength *s*). It is expressed as the sum of the directed projections, upon the tangent line to the path of *P*, of the rates of change in *u* in directions parallel to the three axes. Explicitly, du/ds equals the partial derivative of $F(x, y, z)$ with respect to *x* times dx/ds, plus the partial derivative of $F(x, y, z)$ with respect to *y* times dy/ds, plus the partial derivative of $F(x, y, z)$ with respect to *z* times dz/ds. Since dx/ds, dy/ds and dz/ds are the direction cosines of the tangent to the curve,

$$du/ds = lF_x(x, y, z) + mF_y(x, y, z) + nF_z(x, y, z),$$

where *l*, *m* and *n* are the direction cosines of the tangent to the curve followed by the point $P(x, y, z)$.

directional derivative of a function of two variables, $u = f(x, y)$. The rate of change of u with respect to arc length s as the point $P(x, y)$ moves along a given curve. It is the sum of the projections, on the tangent to the curve, of the rates of change of u as P moves in the directions parallel to the x- and y-axes. Explicitly, it is written du/ds and is equal to the partial derivative of $f(x, y)$ with respect to x times dx/ds plus the partial derivative of $f(x, y)$ with respect to y times dy/ds. If θ is the angle which the tangent to the curve (directed in the direction of motion of P) makes with the directed x-axis, then $dx/ds = \cos\ \theta$, $dy/ds = \sin\ \theta$ and $du/ds = f_x(x, y) \cos\theta + f_y(x, y) \sin\theta$. See PARTIAL—partial derivative.

DIRECTOR-CIRCLE of an ellipse (or hyperbola). The locus of the intersection of pairs of perpendicular angents to the ellipse (or hyperbola). In the figure, the circle is the director-circle of the ellipse, being the locus of points P which are the intersections of perpendicular tangents like (1) and (2).

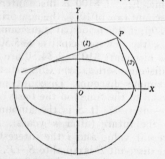

DI-REC′TRIX, *n.* directrix of a conic. See CONIC.

directrix of a cylindrical surface. See CYLINDRICAL—cylindrical surface.

directrix of a parabola, hyperbola, or ellipse. See PARABOLA, and CONIC.

directrix of a ruled surface. A curve through which a line generating the surface always passes. See CONICAL SURFACE, CYLINDRICAL—cylindrical surface, and PYRAMIDAL—pyramidal surface.

DIS-CON′TI-NU′I-TY, *n.* finite discontinuity. See FINITE.

finite, non-removable discontinuity at a point. A finite discontinuity at which the function approaches different values or no values when the independent variable approaches its value at the point from opposite directions. E.g. $y = \sin 1/x$ has such a discontinuity at the origin, since it does not approach a limit as x approaches zero (either from the right or left); $\tan^{-1} 1/x$ has such a discontinuity at $x = 0$, for if x is positive and decreases toward zero as a limit, the principal value of this function approaches $\frac{1}{2}\pi$; while if x is negative and increases toward zero, it approaches $-\frac{1}{2}\pi$ (such a point-break in a curve is also called a *jump*).

infinite discontinuity at a point. A point where the function becomes infinite; e.g. $1/x$ where $x = 0$.

ordinary discontinuity. A finite non-removable discontinuity.

point of discontinuity of a function. A point at which the function is not continuous.

removable discontinuity. A discontinuity which can be removed by re-defining (or defining) the function for a certain value of the variable; e.g. $y = x \sin 1/x$ has a removable discontinuity at the origin. It approaches zero as x approaches zero either from the left or right, although it is not defined for $x = 0$.

DIS′CON-TIN′U-OUS, *adj.* discontinuous function. A function which is not continuous. The term is usually used when speaking of the nature of a function at a given point, or set of points, although it is sometimes used loosely in the sense that a function is discontinuous on an interval when it is discontinuous at some point or points on the interval.

DIS′COUNT, *n.* bank discount. A discount equal to the simple interest on the obligation; interest paid in advance on a note or other obligation (strictly speaking the interest is made part of the face of the note and paid when the note is paid). E.g. a note for $100, discounted by the *bank rule* at 6%, would leave $94 (paying the face value of $100 at the end of the year is equivalent to paying 6.38% interest, or if the interest is to be 6%, the *true discount* would be $5.66 and the discount rate 5.66%, not 6%).

bond discount. The difference between the face value and the purchase price when the bond is bought beneath par.

cash discount, or discount for cash. A reduction in price made by the seller because the buyer is paying cash for the purchase.

chain discount. Same as DISCOUNT SERIES.

commercial discount. A reduction in the price of goods, or in the amount of a bill or debt, often given to secure payment before the due date. This discount may be computed either by means of discount rate or by means of interest rate; the former is used in discounting prices and the latter, usually, in discounting interest bearing contracts. The discount in the latter case is the face of the contract minus its present value at the given rate. When simple interest is used *present value* is $S/(1+ni)$; when compound interest is used it is $S/(1+i)^n$ where n in both cases is the number of interest periods and S the face of the contract. See below, discount rate, simple discount, compound discount.

compound discount. Discount under compound interest; the difference between face value and the present value at the given rate after a given number of years:
$$D = S - S/(1+i)^n,$$
or in terms of *discount rate*
$$D = S - A, \quad \text{where} \quad A = S(1-d)^n.$$

discount factor. The factor which, when multiplied into a sum, gives the present value over a period of n years; i.e. gives the principal which would amount to the sum at the end of n years at the given interest rate. For compound interest, this factor is $(1+i)^{-n}$, where i is the interest rate. In terms of the *discount rate, d*, this factor is $(1-d)^n$. See below, discount rate.

discount on a note. The difference between the selling value and the present value of a note.

discount on stocks. The difference between the selling value and the face value of stocks, when the former is lower than the latter.

discount problem under compound interest. Finding the present value of a given sum, at a given rate of compound interest; i.e. solving the equation $S = P(1+r)^n$ for P.

discount rate. The percent used to compute the discount. It is never the same as the interest rate on the contract. See above, bank discount, and below, true discount. If d is the discount rate and i the interest rate, the discount on a sum, S, for one interest period is $S - S/(1+i)$ or Sd, where
$$d = 1 - 1/(1+i) = i/(1+i).$$

discount series. A sequence of discounts consisting of a discount, a discount upon the discounted face value, a discount upon the discounted, discounted face value, etc. The successive discount rates may or may not be the same. E.g. if $100 is discounted at a discount rate of 10%, the new principal is $90; if this principal is discounted at 5%, the new principal is $85.50, and the discounts $10 and $4.50 are called a discount series. *Syn.* Chain discount.

simple discount. Discount proportional to the time (on the basis of simple interest). If S is the amount due in the future (after n years), P the present value and i the interest rate, the discount D is equal to $S - P$, where $P = S/(1+ni)$.

term of a discount. See TERM— term of discount.

time discount. Discount allowed if payment is made within a prescribed time; usually called *cash discount*. A vender who does credit business often prices his goods high enough to make his credit sales cover losses due to bad accounts, then *discounts* for cash or for cash within a certain period.

trade discount. A reduction from the list price to adjust prices to prevailing prices or to secure the patronage of certain purchasers, especially purchasers of large amounts.

true discount. The reduction of the face value of an agreement to pay, by the simple interest on the reduced amount at a given rate; e.g. the *true discount* on $100 for one year at 6% is $5.66, because 6% of $94.24 is $5.66. The formula for true discount is: $D = S - S/(1+ni)$, where S is face value, n time in years, and i interest rate.

DIS-COUNT'ED, *adj.* **discounted bonus policy.** An insurance policy in which the premiums are reduced by the estimated (anticipated) future bonuses.

discounted value of an annuity. Same as PRESENT VALUE. See VALUE—present value.

DIS-CRETE', *adj.* **discrete variable.** A variable which is not continuous; a variable which takes on only certain disconnected values on any interval of the continuum; a variable whose possible values form a discrete set. E.g. the integers.

discrete set. A set of numbers, or points, which has no limit points.

DIS-CRIM'I-NANT, *n.* discriminant of an equation of the form $x^n + a_1 x^{n-1} + \cdots + a_n = 0$. The product of the squares of all the differences of the roots taken in pairs. The discriminant is equal to the *resultant* of the equation and its derived equation, except possibly in sign. The discriminant is $(-1)^{n(n-1)/2}$ times this resultant.

discriminant of the cubic, $x^3 + ax^2 + bx + c = 0$. The expression $a^2b^2 + 18abc - 5b^3 - 4a^3c - 27c^2$.

discriminant of the general quadratic, $ax^2 + bxy + cy^2 + dx + ey + f = 0$. The product of $-(b^2 - 4ac)$ and the constant term in the equation obtained by translating the axes so as to remove the first degree terms, namely

$$a'x^2 + b'xy + c'y^2 - \Delta/(b^2 - 4ac) = 0.$$

The discriminant is equal to $(4acf - b^2f - ae^2 - cd^2 + bde)$, which can be written,

$$\Delta = \tfrac{1}{2} \begin{vmatrix} 2a & b & d \\ b & 2c & e \\ d & e & 2f \end{vmatrix}.$$

The discriminant and the invariant, $(b^2 - 4ac)$, provide the following criteria concerning the locus of the general quadratic in two variables. If $\Delta \neq 0$ and $b^2 - 4ac < 0$, the locus of the general quadratic is a real or imaginary ellipse; if $\Delta \neq 0$ and $b^2 - 4ac > 0$, an hyperbola; if $\Delta \neq 0$ and $b^2 - 4ac = 0$, a parabola. If $\Delta = 0$ and $b^2 - 4ac < 0$, the locus is a point ellipse; if $\Delta = 0$ and $b^2 - 4ac > 0$, two intersecting lines; and if $\Delta = 0$ and $b^2 - 4ac = 0$, two parallel or coincident lines or no (real) locus. The discriminant Δ is defined differently by different writers, but all the forms are the same except for multiplication by some constant.

discriminant of a quadratic equation in one variable. The expression, involving the coefficients, which is zero when and only when the roots are equal and negative or positive according as the roots are imaginary or real. If the quadratic equation is given in the form $ax^2 + bx + c = 0$, the discriminant is $(b^2 - 4ac)$. E.g. the discriminant of $x^2 + 2x + 1 = 0$ is 0, and the two roots are equal; the discriminant of $x^2 + x + 1 = 0$ is -3 and the roots are imaginary; the discriminant of $x^2 - 3x + 2 = 0$ is 1 and the roots, 1 and 2, are real and unequal. See QUADRATIC—quadratic formula.

DIS-PER'SION, *n.* (*In statistics.*) The variation, scatteration, of the data; the lack of tendency to concentrate or congregate.

measure of dispersion. (*In statistics.*) Usually taken as the STANDARD DEVIATION.

DISSIMILAR TERMS. Terms which do not contain the same powers or the same unknown factors. E.g. $2x$ and $5y$, or $2x$ and $2x^2$, are *dissimilar terms*. See ADDITION—addition of similar terms in algebra.

DIS'TANCE, *n.* **angular distance between two points.** The angle between the two lines drawn from the point of observation (point of reference) through the two points. *Syn.* Apparent distance.

distance between two parallel lines. The length of a perpendicular joining them; the distance from one of them to a point on the other.

distance between two parallel planes. The length of the segment which they cut off on a common perpendicular; the distance from one of them to a point on the other.

distance between two points. The length of the straight line joining the points. In analytic geometry it is found by taking the square root of the sum of the squares of the differences of the corresponding rectangular Cartesian coordinates of the two points. In the plane this is $\sqrt{(x_2-x_1)^2+(y_2-y_1)^2}$ where the points are (x_1, y_1) and (x_2, y_2); in space it is

$$\sqrt{(x_2-x_1)^2+(y_2-y_1)^2+(z_2-z_1)^2}$$

where the points are (x_1, y_1, z_1) and (x_2, y_2, z_2).

distance between two skew-lines. The length of the line segment joining them and perpendicular to both.

distance from a line to a point. The length of the perpendicular from the point to the line. It is obtained by substituting the coordinates of the point in the left member of the normal equation of the line, when the right member is zero; i.e. $D = x_1 \cos\theta + y_1 \sin\theta - p$, where the point is (x_1, y_1). This distance is positive or negative according as the point and the origin are on opposite sides or the same side of the straight line. See LINE—equation of a straight line in a plane, (5).

distance from a line to a point in space. The perpendicular distance from the line to the point. It can be found by finding the coordinates of the foot of the perpendicular from the point to the line and then finding the distance between these two points.

distance from a plane to a point. The length of the perpendicular from the point to the plane. It is obtained by substituting the coordinates of the point in the normal form of the equation of the plane. See PLANE—equation of a plane, (3).

distance of a point from the origin. In the plane, the square root of the sum of the squares of its two rectangular coordinates, $(x_1^2+y_1^2)^{1/2}$. **In space,** the square root of the sum of the squares of its three rectangular coordinates,

$$\sqrt{x_1^2+y_1^2+z_1^2}.$$

polar distance of a circle on a sphere. The shortest distance, on the surface of the sphere, from the nearer pole of the circle to a point on the circle; the length of the arc of a great circle from the nearer pole of the given circle to the intersection of the two circles.

zenith distance of a star. See ZENITH.

DISTANCE-RATE-TIME FORMULA. The formula which states that the distance passed over by a body, moving at a fixed rate for a given time, is equal to the product of the rate and time, written $d = rt$.

DIS'TRI-BU'TION, *n.* **binomial distribution.** See BINOMIAL—binomial distribution.

distribution. (*In statistics.*) The relative arrangement of a set of numbers (elements).

frequency distribution. See FREQUENCY.

normal distribution. (*In statistics.*) A distribution which follows the normal frequency curve. See FREQUENCY—normal frequency curve.

DIS-TRIB'U-TIVE, *adj.* **distributive law in algebra:** The product of a monomial by a polynomial is equal to the sum of the products of the monomial by each term of the polynomial; e.g. $2(3+x+2y) = 6+2x+4y$. When two polynomials are multiplied together, one is first treated as a monomial and multiplied by the individual terms of the other, then the results multiplied out according to the above law. E.g.

$$(x+y)(2x+3) = x(2x+3)+y(2x+3)$$
$$= 2x^2+3x+2xy+3y.$$

distributive law in general: An operation performed upon the combination of a set of quantities is equivalent to performing the operation upon each member of the set and then combining the results by the same rule of combination. E.g.

$$\frac{d(u+v)}{dx} = \frac{du}{dx} + \frac{dv}{dx},$$

the rule of combination being addition. The function sin x is not distributive, since sin $(x+y) \neq$ sin $x+$ sin y. See above, distributive law in algebra.

DI-VER'GENCE, *n.* **divergence of a series.** The property of being divergent; the property of not being convergent.

divergence of a vector function, $F(x, y, z) . \nabla \cdot F$, where ∇ is the operator

$$i \frac{\partial}{\partial x} + j \frac{\partial}{\partial y} + k \frac{\partial}{\partial z}$$

and

$$\nabla \cdot F = i \cdot \frac{\partial F}{\partial x} + j \cdot \frac{\partial F}{\partial y} + k \cdot \frac{\partial F}{\partial z} .$$

If, for instance, F is the velocity of a fluid at the point $P:(x, y, z)$, then $\nabla \cdot F$ is the rate of change of volume per unit volume of an infinitesimal portion of the fluid containing P.

DI-VER'GENT, *adj.* **divergent series.** Series whose sum to n terms either oscillates, or increases or decreases without limit, as n increases. The sum is either positively infinite or negatively infinite or oscillates between values, finite or infinite. The former are called **properly divergent series,** and the latter are called **oscillating divergent series,** or just **oscillating series** (the latter, however, is sometimes used of convergent series whose sums oscillate about the limit as they approach it—such as, $1-1/2+1/3-1/4+ \cdots$). The series $1+2+3+ \cdots$, $\quad 1+1/2+1/3+ \cdots$ and $-1-1-1-1 \cdots$ are *properly divergent*, while $1-1+1-1+ \cdots$ and $1-2+3-4+ \cdots$ are *oscillating divergent series.*

DI-VIDE', *v.* To perform a division.

DIV'I-DEND, *n.* (1) A quantity which is to be divided by another quantity. (2) *In finance,* profits of a stock company or any joint enterprise which are to be distributed among shareholders. (3) The amount of such profits as noted in (2), which accrue to each shareholder.

accrued dividend on a bond. A partial dividend; the interest on the face value of a bond from the nearest preceding dividend date to the purchase date. In bond market parlance, **accrued interest** is used synonymously with *ac-*

crued dividends. Actually, *interest* equals dividend minus amortization payment, when a bond is purchased at a premium, and dividend plus payment for accumulation of the discount, when a bond is purchased at a discount.

dividend on a bond. The periodic, usually semi-annual, interest paid on a bond.

dividend date. The date upon which the dividend is due.

dividend rate. (*Finance.*) The interest rate named in the bond. *Syn.* Bond rate.

dividend on stock. The portion of the profits of the business which is paid on each share of stock.

DI-VID'ERS, *n.* Same as COMPASS.

DI-VIS'I-BIL'I-TY, *n.* **special criteria for divisibility in arithmetic:** A number is divisible by 3 (or 9) when, and only when, the sum of the digits is divisible by 3 (or 9); e.g. 35,712 is divisible by both 3 and 9, since the sum of the digits is 18. A number is divisible by 2 if the last digit is divisible by 2. A number is divisible by 4 if the number consisting of the last two digits on the right is divisible by 4. A number is divisible by 8 if the number formed by the last three digits is divisible by 8. A number is divisible by 5 if it ends in 0 or 5.

DI-VI'SION, *n.* (division of one quantity by a second quantity). The process of finding the other factor (the **quotient**) when the product of two factors (the **dividend**) and one of the factors (the **divisor**) are given; the inverse of multiplication, when multiplication has a unique inverse (division by zero is impossible, since the product of any number by zero is zero). E.g. 6 divided by 3 is 2, because 3 times 2 is 6.

division of complex numbers. See COMPLEX—quotient of complex numbers.

division by a decimal. See above, division of one quantity by a second quantity. Accomplished by multiplying dividend and divisor by a power of 10 that makes the divisor a whole number (i.e. moving the decimal point to the right in the dividend as many places as there are decimal places in the divisor), then dividing as with whole numbers, placing a decimal point in the quotient in the place arrived at before using the first digit after the decimal place in the dividend. E.g.

$$28.7405 \div 23.5 = 287.405 \div 235 = 1.223.$$

division of a determinant by a constant. Division of the value of the determinant by the constant. The division is effected by dividing each element of any *one* row (or any *one* column) by the constant. See DETERMINANT.

division by a fraction. See above, division of one quantity by a second quantity. Accomplished by inverting the fraction and multiplying by it, or by writing the quotient as a complex fraction and simplifying. See FRACTION—complex fraction.

division of a fraction by an integer. See above, division of one quantity by a second quantity. Accomplished by dividing the numerator (or multiplying the denominator) by the integer;

$$\tfrac{1}{4} \div 2 = \tfrac{2}{8} \text{ or } \tfrac{1}{16}; \quad \tfrac{1}{3} \div 2 = \frac{\tfrac{1}{3}}{3} \text{ or } \tfrac{1}{6}.$$

division of mixed numbers. See above, division of one quantity by a second quantity. Accomplished by reducing the mixed numbers to improper fractions and dividing these results. See above, division by a fraction.

division in a proportion. Passing from a proportion to the statement that the first antecedent minus its consequent is to its consequent as the second antecedent minus its consequent is to its consequent, i.e. from $a/b = c/d$ to $(a-b)/b = (c-d)/d$. See COMPOSITION—composition in a proportion.

division by use of logarithms. Looking up the logarithms of the dividend and the divisor, subtracting the latter from the former, and finding the number (antilogarithm) whose logarithm is this difference. This number is the desired quotient. See LOGARITHM —fundamental laws of logarithms.

division by zero. An undefined operation, since division is the inverse of multiplication and any number

(quotient) multiplied by zero gives zero. That is, the product of the quotient and divisor is not the dividend unless the dividend be zero, and in that case the quotient would be indeterminant, because any number whatever times zero gives zero.

point of division. See POINT— point of division.

ratio of division or **division ratio.** See POINT—point of division.

synthetic division. See SYNTHETIC.

the division transformation. Same as LONG DIVISION. Rarely used.

DI-VI′SOR, *n,* The quantity by which the dividend is to be divided.

common divisor. A quantity which is a factor of each of two or more quantities. It is sometimes called a **common measure.** A common divisor of 10 and 15 is 5.

greatest common divisor. The greatest (largest) quantity which is a common divisor of two or more quantities. It is written G. C. D. The G. C. D. of 30 and 42 is 6. *Tech.* the G. C. D. of two quantities is a common divisor of the two quantities which is divisible by any one of their common divisors. *Syn.* Greatest common measure.

DO-DEC′A-GON, *n.* A polygon having twelve sides.

regular dodecagon. See REGULAR —regular polygon.

DO′DEC-A-HE′DRON, *n.* A polyhedron having twelve faces.

regular dodecahedron. A dodecahedron whose faces are regular pentagons and whose polyhedral angles are congruent. See figure under POLYHEDRON—regular polyhedron.

DO-MAIN′, *n.* A set of (at least two) numbers such that the sum, difference, product and quotient (excluding division by zero) of any two numbers in the set are in the set. All rational numbers form a *domain;* but all integers do not, because the quotients would not all be present. Likewise, all real numbers form a domain; and if $i, (=\sqrt{-1})$, be introduced (*adjoined*), the new domain contains all complex numbers. *Syn.* Field or number field.

DOT, *n.* dot product. See MULTIPLI-CATION—multiplication of two vectors.

DOU'BLE, *adj.* double-angle formulas. See FORMULA.

double cusp. A name sometimes given to a point on a curve where two branches have a common tangent and each branch extends in both directions of the tangent. Sometimes called a *point of osculation* or a *tacnode*.

double endowment insurance. A policy which guarantees payment of a certain amount if the insured dies within the period, and double that amount at the close of the period if the insured lives that long.

double integral. An integral involving two integrations;

$$\iint dx dy = \int [\int dx] dy$$

is the simplest *double integral*. See INTEGRAL—iterated integral.

double law of the mean. See MEAN—second mean value theorem.

double ordinate. See ORDINATE.

double point. See POINT—double point.

double root of an algebraic equation. A root that is repeated, or occurs twice in the equation; a root such that $(x-r)^2$, where r is the root, is a factor of the left member when the right is zero. *Syn.* Repeated root, root of multiplicity two, coincident roots, equal roots. See MULTIPLE—multiple root of an equation.

double subscript. Two subscripts on a letter, as on e_{ij}. Used, for example, in writing determinants with general terms, the first subscript denoting the row number and the second the column number.

double tangent. (1) A tangent which has two *non-coincident* points of tangency with the curve. (2) Two coincident tangents, as the tangents at a cusp. See POINT—double point.

DRAFT, *n.* An order written by one person and directing another to pay a certain amount of money.

after date draft. An accepted draft,

for which the time during which discount is reckoned (if there be any) begins on the date of the draft.

after sight draft. An accepted draft for which the time during which discount is reckoned begins with the date of acceptance.

bank draft. A draft drawn by one bank upon another.

commercial draft. A draft made by one firm on another to secure the settlement of a debt.

DRAWING TO SCALE. See SCALE—drawing to scale.

DU'AL, *adj.* dual formula. Same as DUAL THEOREM.

dual theorems. See PRINCIPLE—principle of duality of projective geometry, and principle of duality in a spherical triangle. Sometimes called RECIPROCAL THEOREMS.

DU-AL'I-TY, *n.* principle of duality. See PRINCIPLE.

DUE DATE. See DATE—due date.

DUHAMEL'S THEOREM. If the sum of n infinitesimals (each a function of n) approaches a limit as n increases (becomes infinite), then the same limit is approached by the sum of the infinitesimals formed by adding to each of these infinitesimals other infinitesimals which are *uniformly* of higher order than the ones to which they are added. E.g. the sum of n terms, each equal to $1/n$, is equal to 1 for all n. Hence this sum approaches (is) 1 as n increases. The sum of n terms, each equal to $(1/n)+(1/n^2)$, must, by *Duhamel's Theorem*, also approach 1 as n increases. This is seen to be true, from the fact that this sum is $1+1/n$, which certainly approaches 1 as n increases. See INTEGRAL—definite integral. *Tech.* If

$$\lim_{n \to \infty} \sum_{i=1}^{n} \alpha_i(n) = L$$

then

$$\lim_{n \to \infty} \sum_{i=1}^{n} [\alpha_i(n) + \beta_i(n)] = L$$

provided that for any $\epsilon > 0$ there exists an N such that $|\beta_i(n)/\alpha_i(n)| < \epsilon$ for all i's and for all $n > N$. (When β_i/α_i satisfies this restriction the ratios

$\beta_i/\alpha_i(i=1, 2, 3, \cdots)$ are said to *converge uniformly* to zero). This is a sufficient, but not a necessary, condition for the two limits to be the same. All that is necessary is that the sum of the n betas approach zero as n becomes infinite, which can happen, for example, when any finite number of the betas are larger than the alphas, provided each of them approaches zero and the other betas are such that all β_i/α_i formed from them converge uniformly to zero. See UNIFORM—uniform convergence of a set of functions.

DU'O-DEC'I-MAL, *adj*. duodecimal system of numbers. A system of numbers in which twelve is the base, instead of ten. E.g. in the *duodecimal system*, 24 would mean two twelves plus four, which would be 28 in the decimal system. See BASE—base of a system of numbers.

DUPIN INDICATRIX. See INDICATRIX.

DUPLICATING (DUPLICATION OF) THE CUBE. The problem of finding the edge of a cube whose volume is twice that of a given cube; the problem of solving the equation, $y^3 = 2a^3$, for y, using only ruler and compasses. This is impossible since the cube root of 2 cannot be expressed in terms of radicals of index 2, and square roots are the only kind of irrationals that can be evaluated by means of ruler and compasses alone.

DU'TY, *n*. A tax levied, by a government, on imported (sometimes on exported) merchandise at the time of entering (or leaving) the country.

ad valorem duty. A duty which is a certain percent of the value of the goods.

DY-NAM'ICS, *n*. The study of masses and forces; the study of the effect of forces in causing or modifying the motions of masses and producing strains in elastic bodies. It is usually treated under two heads, *statics* and *kinematics*.

DYNE, *n*. The unit of force in the c.g.s. system of units (centimeter-gram-second system). See FORCE—unit of force.

E

e. The base of the natural system of logarithms; the limit of $(1+1/n)^n$ as n increases without limit. Its numerical value is $2.7182818284\cdots$. The binomial form, $(1+1/n)^n$, occurs in the process of deriving the formula for the derivative of log x with respect to x. Its limit can be approximated by expanding by the binomial theorem (see BINOMIAL—binomial theorem) and adding the limits of successive terms, giving $e = 1+1/1!+1/2!+1/3!+\cdots$.

EC-CEN'TRIC, *adj*. eccentric angle of an ellipse. See ELLIPSE—parametric equations of an ellipse.

eccentric circles of an ellipse. See ELLIPSE—parametric equations of the ellipse.

eccentric, or excentric, configurations. Configurations with centers which are not coincident. The term is used mostly with reference to two circles.

EC'CEN-TRIC'I-TY, *n*. eccentricity of a parabola, ellipse, or hyperbola. See CONIC.

E-CLIP'TIC, *n*. The great circle in which the plane of the earth's orbit cuts the celestial sphere; the path in which the sun appears to move.

EDGE, *n*. A line which is the intersection of two plane faces of a solid.

edge of a dihedral angle. The intersection of the faces of the dihedral angle.

edge of a polyhedral angle. See ANGLE—polyhedral angle.

edge of a polyhedron. See POLYHEDRON.

lateral edge of a prism. See PRISM.

EFFECTIVE INTEREST RATE. See INTEREST—nominal rate of interest.

E'LAS-TIC'I-TY, *n*. The power to recover from stretching, straining, pressure, etc. In bodies which are homogeneous and isotropic there are two principal kinds of elasticity, that in virtue of which the body resists change of volume and that resisting change of shape. Elasticity is measured by the ratio of the stress to the corresponding strain.

volume elasticity, or bulk modulus. The quotient of the increase in pressure and the change in unit volume; the negative of the product of the volume and the rate of change of the pressure with respect to the volume, i.e. $E = -Vdp/dV$.

Young's modulus of elasticity. A measure of the elasticity of stretching or compression; the ratio of the stress to the resulting strain.

ELECTROMOTIVE FORCE. Denoted by E. M. F. (1) That which causes current to flow. (2) The energy added per unit charge due to the mechanical (or chemical) action producing the current. (3) The open circuit difference in potential between the terminals of a cell or generator.

EL'E-MENT, *n.* **conjugate elements of a determinant.** See CONJUGATE—conjugate elements of a determinant.

element of arc of a curve. The infinitesimal arc, denoted by ds, which, when summed (integrated) between certain limits, gives the length of the arc of the curve between those limits. Explicitly,

$$ds = \sqrt{(dx)^2 + (dy)^2} = \sqrt{1 + (dy/dx)^2}\, dx$$
$$= \sqrt{(dx/dy)^2 + 1}\, dy,$$

where dy/dx is to be determined in terms of x before integrating, and dx/dy in terms of y, from the equation of the curve. It can be seen from the figure that $ds = MP$, is an approximation of the arc-length $MN = \Delta s$, which results from an increase of Δx in the independant variable. **In polar form:**

$$ds = \sqrt{\rho^2 + (d\rho/d\theta)^2}\, d\theta.$$

Syn. Differential of arc of a curve.

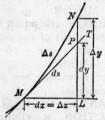

element of area of a curved surface. See SURFACE—surface area.

element of area of a surface of revolution. See SURFACE—surface of revolution.

element of attraction of a mass on a unit particle. The element kdm/r^2, where k is the proportionality constant, dm is the element of mass, and r is the distance from the unit particle to an arbitrary point in the element of mass. *Unit particle* is used here as meaning a particle of unit mass, concentrated at a point. *Syn.* Differential attraction.

element of a cone. A straight line joining the vertex and a point in the base. See CONICAL SURFACE.

element of a cylinder. See CYLINDER—element of a cylinder.

element of a cylindrical surface. See CYLINDRICAL—cylindrical surface.

element of a determinant. See DETERMINANT.

element of mass. $dm = \rho dV$, where dV is the geometric magnitude of a particle, element of arc, area or volume, and ρ is the density at some point in dV (ρ may, of course, be constant). To calculate the mass, ρ and dV must both be expressed in terms of the same variable (or variables) and the integration (or integrations) performed just as in finding the geometric magnitude.

element of moment. The product of an element of mass, dm, and the perpendicular distance from any point in the mass to the line (or plane) with respect to which the moment is to be found. To find the moment of an entire body, the limits are determined and the integration carried out just as when finding the mass; see above, element of mass.

element of moment of inertia. See MOMENT—moment of inertia.

element of plane area. An infinitesimal area, denoted by dA, which, when summed (integrated) between the proper limits, gives a required area. When the area is bounded by the curve $y = f(x)$, the x-axis, and the lines $x = a$ and $x = b$, the element is usually taken in the form $f(x)dx$. The area is then equal to

$$\int_a^b f(x)dx.$$

See INTEGRAL. In polar coordinates, dA is usually taken as $\frac{1}{2}r^2 d\theta$, or $\frac{1}{2}\rho^2 d\theta$.

Then

$$A = \frac{1}{2} \int_{\theta_1}^{\theta_2} \rho^2 d\theta.$$

When $\rho = f(\theta)$ is the polar equation of the curve, the differential element may be expressed in terms of θ by means of this equation. In double integration, the element of area in rectangular Cartesian coordinates is $dx\,dy$, and in polar coordinates, it is $\rho d\rho d\theta$.

element of pressure. See PRESSURE—fluid pressure.

element of volume. In Cartesian coordinates, $dx\,dy\,dz$. The volume then equals

$$\int_{z_1}^{z_2} \int_{y_1}^{y_2} \int_{x_1}^{x_2} dx\,dy\,dz,$$

where z_1 and z_2 are constants, y_1 and y_2 may be functions of z, and x_1 and x_2 may be functions of y, or z, or of both y and z, these functions depending upon the particular shape of the surface that bounds the volume. The order of integration may, of course, be changed (the proper change in limits being made) to best suit the volume under consideration. The figure shows an element of volume in rectangular coordinates and illustrates the process of finding the volume by an integral of the form

$$\int_{x_1}^{x_2} \int_{y_1}^{y_2} \int_{z_1}^{z_2} dz\,dy\,dx.$$

In cylindrical coordinates, the element of volume is $dv = rdrd\theta dz$, and in polar (spherical) coordinates it is $dv = r^2 \sin\theta\,(dr\,d\theta\,d\phi)$.

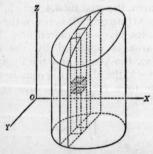

element of volume of a solid of revolution. The element $\pi r^2 dh$, where r is the numerical distance from a point on the surface of the solid to the axis of revolution and h and dh are measured parallel to this axis. Obviously $\pi r^2 dh$ is the volume of a small cylinder, with radius r and altitude dh. The limit of the sum of these cylinders, from h_1 to h_2 (where h_1 and h_2 are the values of h at the ends of the solid of revolution), as dh approaches zero, is the desired volume of the solid of revolution. This limit is

$$\int_{h_1}^{h_2} \pi r^2 dh.$$

If the revolution is, in particular, about the x-axis, the volume is given by

$$\int_{x_1}^{x_2} \pi y^2 dx,$$

where $y = f(x)$ is the curve revolved.

element of work. The element $f\,ds$, where f is the force and s the distance passed over. The work done in moving a body a distance s is, then,

$$\int_0^s f\,ds,$$

where the force f is in the direction of motion of the body.

elements of geometry, calculus, etc. The fundamental assumptions and propositions of the subject.

geometrical element. (1) A point, line, or plane. (2) Any of the parts of a configuration, as the sides and angles of a triangle.

leading elements in a determinant. See LEADING.

minor of an element of a determinant. See MINOR.

EL'E-VA'TION, n. (elevation of a given point.) The height of the point above a given plane, above sea-level unless otherwise indicated.

angle of elevation. See ANGLE—angle of elevation.

E-LIM'I-NANT, n. See RESULTANT.

E-LIM'I-NA'TION, n. elimination by addition or subtraction. The process of putting a set of equations in such a form that when they are added or subtracted in pairs one or more of the variables disappears, then adding or subtracting them as the case may require to secure a system (or perhaps one equation) containing at least one less variable. E.g. (a) given $2x+3y+4 =0$ and $x+y-1=0$, x can be eliminated by multiplying the latter equation by 2 and subtracting the result from the first equation, giving $y+6=0$; (b) given,

(1) $\qquad 4x+6y-z-9=0,$

(2) $\qquad x-3y+z+1=0$

(3) $\qquad x+2y+z-4=0,$

y can be eliminated by multiplying (2) by 2 and adding the result to (1), and (3) by -3 and adding to (1). The results are $6x+z-7=0$ and $x-4z+3 =0$.

elimination by comparison. The process of putting two equations in such forms that their left (or right) members are identical and the other members don't contain one of the variables, then equating the right (or left) members. E.g. $x+y=1$ and $2x+y=5$ can be written $x+y=1$ and $x+y =5-x$, respectively. Hence $5-x=1$.

elimination by substitution. The process of solving one of a set of equations for one of the unknowns (in terms of the other unknowns), then substituting this expression in place of this unknown in the other equations. E.g. in solving $x-y=2$ and $x+3y=4$, one might solve the first equation for x, getting $x=y+2$, and substitute in the second, getting

$$y+2+3y=4 \quad \text{or} \quad y=\tfrac{1}{2}.$$

elimination of an unknown from a set of simultaneous equations in two or more unknowns. The process of deriving from these equations another set of equations which do not contain the unknown which was to be eliminated and are satisfied by any values of the remaining unknowns which satisfy the original equations.

elimination of n variables from $n+1$ equations. The process of finding a relation (the **eliminant** or **resultant**) between the coefficients in the $n+1$ equations which must hold if the equations can all be satisfied by the same values of the variables; the process of solving any n of the equations for the n variables (if this be possible) and substituting their values in the unused equation. In case the equations are linear this can be accomplished expeditiously by equating to zero the determinant (of order $n+1$) whose columns are the coefficients of the respective variables and the constant terms. E.g. the result of eliminating x and y from:

$$ax+by+c=0 \qquad \begin{vmatrix} a & b & c \\ d & e & f \\ g & h & k \end{vmatrix}=0.$$
$$dx+ey+f=0$$
$$gx+hy+k=0$$

EL-LIPSE′, *n.* A sort of elongated circle, like a longitudinal section of a football; any plane section of a circular conical surface, which is a closed curve (i.e. a section whose plane is not parallel to any element of the conical surface); the plane curve which is the locus of a point moving so that the sum of its distances from two fixed points (called the **foci**) is constant; a conic whose eccentricity is less than unity. The ellipse is symmetric with respect to two lines, called its **axes**. *Axes* usually refer to the segments cut off on these lines by the ellipse, and are called the **major** (larger) and **minor** (smaller) axis. If the major and minor axes lie on the x- and y-axes, respectively, the center is then at the origin and the equation of the ellipse, in Cartesian coordinates, is

$$\frac{x^2}{a^2}+\frac{y^2}{b^2}=1,$$

where a and b are the lengths of the

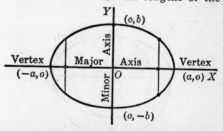

semi-major and **semi-minor** axes. This is the **standard form** of the equation of the ellipse, and is the equation of the ellipse in the position illustrated. The intersection of the axes is called the **center** of the ellipse, the points where the ellipse cuts its major axis are called its **vertices,** and the chords through its foci and perpendicular to its major axis are called the **latera recta** (plural of **latus rectum**). If the center of the ellipse is at the point (h, k) and its axes are parallel to the coordinate axes, its Cartesian equation is

$$\frac{(x-h)^2}{a^2}+\frac{(y-k)^2}{b^2}=1.$$

See CONIC and DISCRIMINANT—discriminant of the general quadratic.

area of an ellipse. The product of π and the lengths of the semi-major and semi-minor axes (i.e. πab). This reduces to the formula for the area of a circle (πr^2) when the major and minor axes of the ellipse are equal, when the ellipse is a circle.

diameter of an ellipse. The locus of the mid-points of a set of parallel chords. Any diameter must pass through the center of the ellipse and always belongs to a set of parallel chords defining some other diameter. Two diameters in this relation to each other are called **conjugate diameters.**

director-circle of an ellipse. See DIRECTOR-CIRCLE.

parametric equations of an ellipse. When the ellipse has its center at the origin and its axes on the coordinate axes (in a system of rectangular Cartesian coordinates), the parametric equations are usually taken as

$$x=a \cos \alpha, \quad y=b \sin \alpha,$$

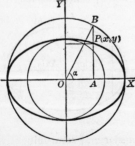

where a and b are the lengths of the semi-major and semi-minor axes, and

α is the angle (at the origin) in the right triangle whose legs are the abscissa, OA, of the point $P(x, y)$ on the ellipse, and the ordinate, AB, to the circle with radius a and center at the origin. The angle, α, is called the **eccentric angle** of the ellipse. The two circles in the figure are called the **eccentric circles** of the ellipse.

point ellipse. The locus of an equation which has the form of an equation of an ellipse, but is satisfied by the coordinates of only one point; the loci of $x^2/a^2+y^2/b^2=0$, and $(x-h)^2/a^2+(y-k)^2/b^2=0$, are point ellipses, satisfied, respectively, by $(0, 0)$ and (h, k), but by no other points. Geometrically, a point ellipse is thought of as the limit of an ellipse as the lengths of its axes approach zero.

reflection property of the ellipse. See REFLECTION—reflection property of the ellipse.

similar ellipses. See SIMILAR.

EL-LIP'SOID, *n.* A surface whose plane sections are all either ellipses or circles. An ellipsoid is symmetrical with respect to three mutually perpendicular lines (called the **axes**), and with respect to the three planes determined by these lines. The intersection of these lines is called the **center.** Any chord through the center is called a **diameter.** The standard equation of the ellipsoid, with center at the origin and intercepts on the axes, $a,-a,\ b,-b,$ and $c,-c,$ is

$$x^2/a^2+y^2/b^2+z^2/c^2=1.$$

If $a>b>c$, a is called the **semi-major** axis, b the **semi-mean** axis, and c the **semi-minor** axis. If $a=b=c$, the equation becomes the equation of a sphere.

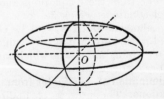

ellipsoid of revolution. A surface (ellipsoid) generated by revolving an ellipse about one of its axes; an ellipsoid whose sections by planes perpendicular to one of its axes are all circles. See SURFACE—surface of revolution. The axis passing through the centers of these circular sections is called the **axis of revolution**. The largest circular section is called the **equator** of the ellipsoid of revolution. The extremities of the axis of revolution are called the **poles** of the ellipsoid of revolution. The ellipsoid of revolution is said to be **prolate** if the diameter of its equatorial circle is less than the length of the axis of revolution, and **oblate** if this diameter is greater than the length of the axis of revolution. *Syn.* Spheroid.

imaginary ellipsoid. A term used when speaking of the *locus* of the equation $x^2/a^2+y^2/b^2+z^2/c^2 = -1$, because there are no real values of the coordinates that satisfy this equation. See CIRCLE—imaginary circle.

volume of an ellipsoid. If a, b and c are the semi-axes, the volume is $\frac{4}{3}\pi abc$. When $a=b=c$ the ellipsoid is a sphere and this formula becomes $\frac{4}{3}\pi a^3$.

EL-LIP′TIC, or EL-LIP′TI-CAL, *adj.* **elliptic conical surface.** A conical surface whose directrix is an ellipse. When the vertex is at the origin and the axis coincident with the z-axis in a system of rectangular Cartesian coordinates, its equation is

$$x^2/a^2+y^2/b^2-z^2/c^2=0.$$

When $a=b$, this is a **circular cone.**

elliptic cylinder. See CYLINDER.

elliptic function. The inverse of an *elliptic integral.*

elliptic integral. The most familiar elliptic integrals are of the forms

$$\int \frac{dx}{\sqrt{ax^4+bx^2+c}},$$

$$\int \frac{x^2 dx}{\sqrt{ax^4+bx^2+c}}$$

and

$$\int \frac{dx}{(x^2+h)\sqrt{ax^4+bx^2+c}}.$$

These are called elliptic integrals of the **first, second,** and **third kinds,** respectively. Elliptic integrals are so named because they were first encountered in the problem of finding the length of the circumference of an ellipse.

elliptic paraboloid. See PARABOLOID.

elliptic point on a surface. A point whose *Dupin indicatrix* is an ellipse.

ELONGATIONS and COMPRESSIONS. Same as ONE DIMENSIONAL STRAINS. See ONE.

EM-PIR′I-CAL, *adj.* **empirical formula, assumption, or rule.** A statement whose reliability is based upon a limited number of observations (such as laboratory experiments) and is not necessarily supported by any established theory or laws; formulas based upon immediate experience rather than logical (or mathematical) conclusions.

empirical curve. A curve which is drawn to approximately fit a set of statistical data. It is usually assumed to represent, approximately, additional data of the same kind. See METHOD —method of least squares, and GRAPHING—statistical graphing.

END POINT, *n.* **end point of a curve.** A point at which a branch of the curve ends; e.g. the curve $y=x \log x$ has an end point at the origin.

end point of an interval. The last point in a given direction. If the interval from 2 to 8 is closed, i.e. if it includes 2 and 8, then 2 and 8 are *end points.* If the interval is open, it has no end points, for there is no largest number less than 8 and no smallest number greater than 2.

EN-DORSE′, *v.* Same as INDORSE.

ENDOWMENT INSURANCE. Insurance in which the benefits are payable (usually to the insured) after a definite period, or (to the beneficiary) at the death of the insured if that occurs before the end of the period.

EN′ER-GY, *n.* The capacity for doing work.

energy integral. (1) An integral which arises in the solution of the particular differential equation of motion, $d^2s/dt^2 = \pm k^2 s$, describing simple harmonic motion. The integral is $v^2/2 = \pm k^2 \int s ds$ and is called the energy integral, because when it is multiplied by m it is equal to the *kinetic* *energy,* $\frac{1}{2}mv^2$. (2) An integral stating that the sum of the potential and kinetic energies is constant, in a dynamic system in which this is true.

kinetic energy. See KINETIC.

potential energy. The energy a body possesses by virtue of its position.

EN-TIRE', *adj.* entire function. A function which can be written as a polynomial (with a finite or infinite number of terms); a function which can be expanded in a Maclaurin's Series, valid for all finite values of the variables. *Tech.* a function which is analytic for all finite values of the variables. Also called INTEGRAL FUNCTION.

entire series. A power series which converges for all values of the variable. The exponential series,

$$1+x+x^2/2!+x^3/3!+\cdots+x^n/n!+\cdots$$

is an entire series.

EN'VEL-OPE, *n.* envelope of a one-parameter family of curves. A curve which is tangent to (has a common tangent with) every curve of the family. Its equation is obtained by eliminating the parameter between the equation of the curve and the partial derivative of this equation with respect to this parameter. The envelope of the circles $(x-a)^2+y^2-1=0$, is $y=\pm1$. See SOLUTION—singular solution of an ordinary differential equation.

envelope of a one-parameter family of straight lines. The curve which is tangent to every member of the family of lines. Any curve is the envelope of its tangents.

envelope of a one-parameter family of surfaces. The surface which is tangent to (has a common tangent plane with) each of the surfaces of the family along their characteristics; the locus of the characteristic curves of the family. The cylinder $x^2+y^2=1$ is the envelope of the spheres $x^2+y^2+(z-a)^2=1$. See CHARACTERISTIC—characteristic of a one-parameter family of surfaces.

EP-I-CY'CLOID, *n.* The plane locus of a point fixed on the circumference of a circle as the circle rolls on the outside of a fixed circle (remaining in the same plane as the fixed circle). If *b*

(*OB* in the figure) is the radius of the fixed circle with center at the origin, a (*BC*) is the radius of the rolling circle,

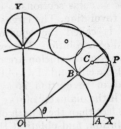

and θ is the angle at the origin subtended by the arc, AB, which has already contacted the rolling circle when the point is in the position $P:(x, y)$, the parametric equations of the curve are:

$$x=(a+b)\cos\theta-a\cos[(a+b)\theta/a],$$
$$y=(a+b)\sin\theta-a\sin[(a+b)\theta/a].$$

The curve has one arch when $a=b$, two arches when $a=b/2$, and n arches when $a=b/n$. It has a cusp of the first kind at every point at which it touches the fixed circle.

EP-I-TRO'CHOID, *n.* A generalization of an epicycloid, in which the describing point may be at any fixed point on the radius of the rolling circle, or this radius extended. Letting h denote the distance from the center of the rolling circle to the describing point, and using a, b, and θ as in the discussion of the epicycloid, the parametric equations of the *epitrochoid* are:

$$x=(a+b)\cos\theta-h\cos[(a+b)\theta/a],$$
$$y=(a+b)\sin\theta-h\sin[(a+b)\theta/a].$$

The cases for $h<a$ and $h>a$ are analogous to the corresponding cases ($b<a$ and $b>a$) in the discussion of the *trochoid*. See figure under TROCHOID.

E'QUAL, *adj.* In *geometry,* **equal** is used to denote exact agreement with respect to some particular property, but not necessarily actual *congruence.* E.g. triangles with equal altitudes and equal bases are said to be equal because their areas are the same, but they may not be congruent. Equality and congruence are **synonymous** in some cases; two equal angles are congruent. Congruent figures are equal in every respect

Equal is sometimes, although rarely, used in the same sense as *congruent*. In *analysis*, **equal** is used in describing a relation between two quantities which are alike in any or all senses, the sense in which they are alike being specified; e.g. if two functions of a variable are equal numerically for all values of the variable the relation is an identity; if they are equal for only certain values, the relation is an equation. *Tech.* An *equals relation* is a relation which is *reflexive, symmetric*, and *transitive*. Equality is then defined by means of the particular equals relation which applies to the case at hand.

equal roots of an equation. See MULTIPLE—multiple root of an equation.

equal roots of a quadratic equation. See DISCRIMINANT—discriminant of a quadratic equation in one variable.

E-QUAL′I-TY, *n.* The state of being *equal*; the statement, usually in the form of an equation, that two things are equal.

continued equality. Three or more quantities set equal by means of two or more equality signs in a continuous expression, as $a = b = c = d$, or $f(x, y) = g(x, y) = h(x, y)$. The last expression is equivalent to the equations $f(x, y) = g(x, y)$ and $g(x, y) = h(x, y)$.

equality of two complex numbers. The property of having their real parts equal, and their pure imaginary parts equal $(a + bi = c + di$ means $a = c$ and $b = d)$; the property of having equal amplitudes and equal moduli.

E-QUATE′, *v.* to equate one expression to another. To form the algebraic statement of equality which says that the two expressions are equal. The statement may be either an *identity* or a *conditional equation* (commonly called simply an *equation*). E.g. one may *equate* $(x+1)^2$ to $x^2 + 2x + 1$, getting the identity $(x+1)^2 = x^2 + 2x + 1$; or he may *equate* $\sin x$ and $2x + 1$; or he may *equate* coefficients in $ax + b$ and $2x + 3$, getting $a = 2$, $b = 3$.

E-QUAT′ED, *adj.* equated date (for a set of payments). The date upon which they could all be discharged by a single payment equal to the sum of their values when due, taking into account accumulations of payments due prior to that date and present values, at that date, of future payments. *Syn.* Average date.

equated time. (*In finance.*) The time from the present to the equated date.

E-QUA′TION, *n.* A statement of equality between two quantities. Equations are of two types, *identities* and *conditional* equations (or usually simply *equations*). A *conditional equation* is true only for certain values of the unknown quantities involved (see IDENTITY); e.g. $x + 2 = 5$ is a true statement only when $x = 3$; and $xy + y - 3 = 0$ is true when $x = 2$, and $y = 1$, but for many pairs of values of x and y it is false.

a-form of the general algebraic equation. See A-FORM.

algebraic equation. See POLYNOMIAL—polynomial equation.

amortization equation. See AMORTIZATION.

auxiliary equation. See DIFFERENTIAL—linear differential equations.

Bessel's equation. See BESSEL'S EQUATION.

biquadratic equation. An algebraic equation of the fourth degree. *Syn.* Quartic equation.

complete equation of the *n*th degree. A numerical (or general) equation of the *n*th degree, in which the coefficients and constant terms are all different from zero.

cubic equation. See CUBIC.

defective equation. An algebraic equation which has fewer roots than some equation from which it has been obtained. Roots may be lost, for instance, by dividing both members of an equation by a function of the variable. If $x^2 + x = 0$ is divided by x, the result, $x + 1 = 0$, is defective; it lacks the root 0.

degree of an algebraic equation. See DEGREE—degree of a polynomial or equation.

differential equation. See DIFFERENTIAL—differential equations.

differential equation with variables

EQUATION 94 **EQUATION**

separable. See DIFFERENTIAL—differential equation with variables separable.

equal roots of an equation. See MULTIPLE—multiple root of an equation.

equation (equating) of accounts. The process of finding *equated time*.

equation of a circle in space. See CIRCLE.

equation of a curve in a plane. An equation satisfied by all values of the variables which are coordinates of points on the curve and only by those values. See CURVE.

equation of a cylinder. See CYLINDRICAL—equations of a cylindrical surface.

equation of a line. See LINE—equation of a straight line.

equation of motion. An equation, usually a differential equation, stating the law by which a particle moves.

equation of the normal line to a plane curve. See NORMAL—normal line to a plane curve.

equation of the nth degree. See below, general equation of the nth degree in one variable.

equation in the p-form. An algebraic equation in one variable, in which the coefficient of the highest degree term is unity and the other coefficients are all integers.

equation of payments. An equation stating the equivalence of two sets of payments on a certain date, each payment in each set having been accumulated or discounted to that certain date, called the **comparison,** or **focal, date.**

equation of a plane. See PLANE.

equation of a surface. An equation satisfied by those, and only those, values of its variables which are coordinates of points on the surface. See PARAMETRIC—parametric equations of a surface.

equation of value. An equation of payments stating that a set of payments is equivalent to a certain single payment, at a given time. Some authors use only the term **equation of value** and others use only **equation of**

payments, making no distinction between the cases in which there are two sets of several payments and those in which one set is replaced by a single payment. See above, equation of payments.

equations of a curve in space (space curve). The equations of any two surfaces which intersect in the curve. See PARAMETRIC—parametric equations of a curve.

equivalent algebraic equations. Algebraic equations which have exactly the same roots. Ordinarily only applied to equations in one variable (unknown).

exact differential equation. See DIFFERENTIAL.

exponential equation. An equation in which the unknown letter (or letters) occurs in an exponent. Usually refers to an equation in which the unknown appears only in the exponent, but is sometimes used for equations having the unknown in the exponent and elsewhere; an equation of the form $2^x - 5 = 0$ would always be called an exponential equation.

fractional equations. See FRACTIONAL.

general equation of the nth degree in one variable. A rational, integral equation (polynomial equation) of the nth degree whose coefficients are literal constants. Usually written in the form

$$a_0 x^n + a_1 x^{n-1} + \cdots + a_n = 0.$$

Often called an *equation of the nth degree*. See below, solution of an algebraic equation of the nth degree.

general equation of the second degree. An equation of the form

$$ax^2 + by^2 + cxy + dx + ey + f = 0.$$

See DISCRIMINANT—discriminant of the general quadratic.

general solution of a differential equation. See GENERAL—general solution of a differential equation.

homogeneous equation. See HOMOGENEOUS.

incomplete equation of the nth degree. An algebraic equation of the nth degree in which the coefficient of one or more of the powers of the unknown

EQUATION 95 **EQUATION**

(less than n), or the constant term, is zero.

inconsistent equations. See CONSISTENCY.

indeterminate equation. An equation containing more than one variable, such as $x+2y=4$. The equation is indeterminate because there are, in general, an unlimited number of sets of values which satisfy it. Historically, this kind of equation has been of particular interest when the coefficients are integers and it is required to find expressions for the sets of integral values of the variables which satisfy the given equation. Under these restrictions, the equations are called **Diophantine equations.**

indeterminant system of equations. A system of equations having fewer equations than unknowns.

integrable differential equations. See DIFFERENTIAL—integrable differential equations.

inverse trigonometric equation. See INVERSE—inverse trigonometric equations.

irrational (or radical) equation. An equation containing the unknown, or unknowns, under radical signs or with fractional exponents. The equations

$$\sqrt{x^2+1}=\sqrt{x+2} \quad \text{and} \quad x^{1/2}+1=3$$

are both irrational equations.

Legendre's equation. See LEGENDRE'S EQUATION.

linear differential equation of first order. See DIFFERENTIAL—linear differential equation of first order.

linear differential equations. See DIFFERENTIAL—linear differential equations.

linear equation. See LINEAR.

logarithmic equation. An equation containing the logarithm of the unknown. It is usually called logarithmic only when the unknown occurs only in the arguments of logarithms; $\log x+2 \log 2x+4=0$ is a logarithmic equation.

multiple root of an equation. See MULTIPLE.

non-linear equation representing straight lines. An equation which can be factored into two or more linear factors. Each linear factor, equated to zero, then represents a straight line which is a part of the locus of the original equation.

normal form of the equation of a plane. See PLANE—equation of a plane.

normal form of the equation of a straight line. See LINE—equation of a straight line in the plane.

numerical equation. An equation in which all the coefficients and the constant term are numbers, not literal constants. The equation $2x^2+3+5x=0$ is a numerical equation.

partial differential equations. See DIFFERENTIAL—partial differential equations.

polynomial equation. See POLYNOMIAL—polynomial equation.

primitive of a differential equation. See PRIMITIVE—primitive of a differential equation.

quadratic equation. See QUADRATIC.

reciprocal equation. See RECIPROCAL.

redundant equation. An algebraic equation containing roots which have been introduced by operating upon a given equation; for instance, such roots may be introduced by multiplying both members by the same function of the unknown, or by raising both members to a power. The introduced roots are called **extraneous roots.** The equation $x-1=\sqrt{x+1}$, when squared and simplified, becomes $x^2-3x=0$, which has the roots 0 and 3, hence is *redundant*, because 0 does not satisfy the original equation.

simultaneous equations. See SIMULTANEOUS.

solution of an algebraic equation of the nth degree. (1) A root of the equation. (2) Finding the roots. Unless the equation can be factored, the method of solution consists essentially of trial substitutions based upon the fact that if $f(a)<0$ (>0) and $f(a+\epsilon)>0$ (<0) a root of $f(x)=0$ lies between a and $a+\epsilon$. Horner's and Newton's methods offer systematic approximations. If the equation has only imaginary roots, one can substitute $u+iv$ for the variable, equate the real and imaginary parts to zero, and solve these equations for u and v. These methods are commonly used on equations of higher degree than the second, but are not in general applicable when an equation has literal coefficients. See SOLUTION—Cardan's solution of the cubic, FERRARI'S solution of the general quartic, and QUADRATIC—quadratic formula.

systems of linear equations. See SIMULTANEOUS—simultaneous linear equations.

theory of equations. See THEORY.

transformation of an equation. See TRANSFORMATION.

trigonometric equation. An equation which states a relation between trigonometric functions of the unknown angles, such as $\cos\beta - \sin\beta = 0$. See SOLUTION—solution of trigonometric equations.

E-QUA′TOR, *n.* **celestial equator.** The great circle in which the plane of the earth's equator cuts the celestial sphere. See HOUR—hour angle and hour circle.

equator of an ellipsoid of revolution. See ELLIPSOID—ellipsoid of revolution.

geographic equator (earth's equator). The great circle which is the section of the earth's surface by the plane through the center of the earth and perpendicular to the earth's axis. See ELLIPSOID—ellipsoid of revolution.

E′QUI-AN′GU-LAR, *adj.* **equiangular hyperbola.** Same as RECTANGULAR HYPERBOLA. See HYPERBOLA.

equiangular polygon. A polygon having all of its interior angles equal. An equiangular triangle is necessarily equilateral, but this is not true for a polygon of more than three sides.

equiangular spiral. Same as *logarithmic* spiral. Called equiangular because the angle between the tangent and radius vector is a constant. See LOGARITHMIC—logarithmic spiral.

mutually equiangular polygons. See MUTUALLY.

E′QUI-LAT′ER-AL, *adj.* **equilateral hy-**

perbola. See HYPERBOLA—rectangular hyperbola.

equilateral polygon. A polygon having all of its sides equal. An equilateral triangle is necessarily equiangular, but this is not true for polygons of more than three sides.

equilateral spherical triangle. A spherical triangle which has all of it sides equal.

mutually equilateral polygons. See MUTUALLY.

E′QUI-LIB′RI-UM, *n.* **equilibrium of forces.** The property of having their resultant zero. See RESULTANT.

equilibrium of a particle or a body. A particle is in equilibrium when the resultant of all forces acting on it is zero. A body is in equilibrium when it has no acceleration, either of translation or rotation; a rigid body is in equilibrium when its center of mass has no acceleration and the body has no angular acceleration. The conditions for a body to be in equilibrium are: (1) That the resultant of the forces acting on it be equal to zero. (2) That the sum of the moments of these forces about every axis be equal to zero (about each of three mutually perpendicular axes suffices).

E-QUIV′A-LENT, *adj.* **cash equivalent of an annuity.** Same as PRESENT VALUE. See VALUE—present value.

equivalent equations. Equations in one variable that have exactly the same roots.

equivalent figures. Equal figures. Some writers always use *equivalent* where others use *equal*, and *equal* for *congruent*.

equivalent sets. Sets that can be put into one-to-one correspondence. See CORRESPONDENCE.

ERG, *n.* A unit of work; the work done by a force of one dyne operating over a distance of one centimeter.

ER′ROR, *n.* The difference between a result obtained by some specific method and the correct result, taken positive or negative according as the former is the larger or smaller. In practice the exact result is not usually known; hence only the upper and lower limits (bounds) to the errors are found; e.g. if the square root of 2 has been approximated to 1.41, the error must lie between zero and .09, since 1.4 is too small and 1.5 too large. Also used as a synonym for mistake.

percent error. The quotient of the error by the correct result, multiplied by 100.

relative error. The quotient of the error by the correct result.

ES-CRIB'ED, *adj.* **escribed circle of a triangle.** A circle tangent to one side of the triangle and to the extensions of the other sides. *Syn.* Excircle. In the figure, the circle is an excircle of the triangle ABC, being tangent to BC at L and to AB and AC, extended, at N and M, respectively. The bisector of angle BAC passes through the center of the circle.

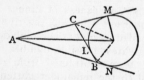

ES-SEN'TIAL, *adj.* **essential constants.** See CONSTANT—essential constants.

ES'TI-MATE, *v.* **to estimate a desired quantity.** To pass judgment based upon very general considerations, as contrasted to finding the quantity by exact mathematical procedure. One might *estimate* the square root of any number to the nearest integer, but he would *compute* it systematically, by some rule for extracting roots, if he wanted it accurate to three or four decimal places.

EU-CLID'E-AN, *adj.* **Euclidean algorithm.** See ALGORITHM.

Euclidean geometry. See GEOMETRY—elementary or Euclidean geometry.

EUCLID'S algorithm, axioms, postulates. See ALGORITHM, AXIOM, POSTULATE.

EULER'S ANGLES. The three angles usually chosen to fix the directions of a new set of rectangular space coordinate axes with reference to an old set. They are the angle between the old and the new z-axis, the angle between the new x-axis and the intersection of the new xy-plane with the old xy-plane, and the angle between this intersection and the old x-axis. This intersection is called the **nodal line** of the transformation.

EULER'S CONSTANT (or Mascheroni's constant). The constant defined as

$$\lim_{n\to\infty} (1+1/2+1/3+ \cdots +1/n-\log n)$$
$$=0.5772157 \cdots .$$

It has been calculated to 260 decimal places.

EULER'S FORMULA. The formula $e^{ix}=\cos x +i \sin x$. It can be verified by expanding each of the functions e^{ix}, $\cos x$, and $\sin x$ in a Maclaurin's series and substituting the three series in the formula. Interesting special cases are those in which $x=\pi$ and 2π, for which $e^{\pi i}=-1$ and $e^{2\pi i}=1$, respectively.

EULER'S THEOREM on homogeneous functions. A homogeneous function of degree n in the variables x_1, x_2, x_3, $\cdots x_n$, multiplied by n, is equal to x_1 times the partial derivative of the function with respect to x_1, plus x_2 times the partial derivative of the function with respect to x_2, etc.

E.g. if $f(x, y, z)=x^2+xy+z^2$, then
$$2(x^2+xy+z^2)=x(2x+y)+y(x)+z(2z).$$

EULER'S THEOREM on polyhedrons. In any polyhedron the number of edges is two less than the sum of the number of vertices and the number of faces.

EULER'S Φ FUNCTION. See INDICATOR—indicator of an integer.

E-VAL'U-ATE, *v.* To find the value of. E.g. to evaluate $8+3-4$ means to reduce it to 7; to evaluate x^2+2x+2 for $x=3$ means to replace x by 3 and collect the results (giving 17); to evaluate an integral means to carry out the integration and, if it is a definite integral, substitute the limits of integration. See also, DETERMINANT—evaluation of a determinant.

E-VAL'U-A'TION, *n.* The act of evaluating.

E'VEN, *adj.* **even number.** A number that is divisible by 2. All even numbers can be written in the form $2n$, where n is an integer.

even function. See FUNCTION—even function.

E-VENT′, *n.* **compound event.** See COMPOUND.

dependent events. Two events such that the occurrence, or non-occurrence, of one of them affects the occurrence, or non-occurrence, of the other. E.g. drawing a ball from a bag of different colored balls, the ball not being replaced, affects the probability of drawing any specified color in a second drawing.

independent events. Two or more events such that the occurrence or non-occurrence of any one in a given trial does not affect the occurrence or non-occurrence of any of the other events. E.g. the probability of drawing a certain ball from one bag is not affected by the drawing of a certain ball from another bag, nor from the same bag if the ball first drawn is replaced before the second drawing.

mutually exclusive events. Two or more events such that the occurrence of any one precludes the occurrence of all the others; if a coin is tossed, the coming up of heads and the coming up of tails on a given throw are mutually exclusive events.

simple event. An event whose probability can be obtained from consideration of a single occurrence; an event whose probability can be deduced from direct observation. The tossing of a coin for heads (or tails) is a simple event.

EV′O-LUTE, *n.* **evolute of a plane curve.** The curve whose *involute* is the given curve; the locus of the center of curvature of the given curve. The family of straight lines normal to the given curve are tangent to the evolute, and the change in length of the radius of curvature is equal to the change in length of arc of the evolute as the point on the curve moves continuously in one direction along the curve. The equation of the *evolute* is obtained by eliminating the coordinates of the point on the curve between the equation of the curve and equations expressing the coordinates of the center of curvature in terms of the coordinates of the point on the curve.

EV′O-LU′TION, *n.* The extraction of a root of a quantity; e.g. finding a square root of 25. *Evolution* is the inverse of finding a power of a number, or involution.

EX-ACT′, *adj.* **exact differential equation.** See DIFFERENTIAL.

exact division. Division in which the remainder is zero.

exact divisor. A quantity that divides another without a remainder, i.e. with the remainder zero.

exact interest. See INTEREST.

EX-CENTER of a triangle. The center of an *escribed* circle; the intersection of the bisectors of two exterior angles of the triangle.

EX-CESS′, *n.* **excess of nines.** The remainder left when any positive integer is divided by nine; the remainder when the greatest possible number of nines have been subtracted from it. It is equal to the remainder gotten by dividing the sum of the digits by 9. It is customary, but not necessary, to restrict the process to positive integers. The excess of nines in 237 is 3, since $237 = 26 \times 9 + 3$ (or $2+3+7 = 9+3$). See CASTING OUT NINES.

spherical excess. See SPHERICAL—spherical excess.

EX-CHANGE′, *n.* Payment of obligations other than by direct use of money; by use of checks, drafts, money orders, exchange of accounts, etc.

foreign exchange. Exchange carried on with other countries (between countries). The **rate of foreign exchange** is the value of the foreign money in terms of American money (or vice versa).

EX-CIRCLE of a triangle. See ESCRIBED—escribed circle of a triangle.

EX-CLU′SIVE, *adj.* **mutually exclusive events.** See EVENT.

EX′ER-CISE, *n.* A problem which is designed primarily for drill on the use of formulas, theorems, or mathematical concepts. *Syn.* Problem.

EX-PAN'SION, *n.* (1) The form a quantity takes when written as a sum of terms, or as a continued product, or in general in any type of expanded (extended) form. (2) The act, or process, of obtaining the expanded form of a quantity. (3) Increase in size.

binomial expansion. The expansion given by the binomial theorem. See BINOMIAL—binomial theorem.

coefficient of linear expansion. See COEFFICIENT.

coefficient of thermal expansion. See COEFFICIENT.

coefficient of volume (or cubical) expansion. See COEFFICIENT.

cubical expansion. Same as VOLUME EXPANSION.

expansion of a determinant. See DETERMINANT—expansion of a determinant.

expansion (of a function) in a series. Writing a series which converges to the function for certain values of the variables. The series itself is also spoken of as the *expansion* of the function.

linear expansion. See LINEAR—linear expansion.

thermal expansion. Expansion due to a rise in temperature.

volume expansion. Increase in volume. See COEFFICIENT—coefficient of volume expansion.

EX-PEC-TA'TION, *n.* **complete expectation of life.** See COMPLETE—complete expectation of life.

curtate expectation of life. See CURTATE—curtate expectation of life.

expectation of life. The average number of years that a man of a given age may be expected to live, according to mortality tables.

joint expectation of life. See JOINT.

mathematical expectation. The amount of money that an individual may expect to receive if a given sum is offered him on the condition that a given event (or events) occurs. It is equal to the product of the sum offered and the probability of the occurrence of the event; if a man is to receive one dollar for tails-up throw of a coin, his expectation is $\$1 \times \frac{1}{2}$, or 50 cents.

EX-PENS'ES, *n.* **overhead expenses.** Administrative expenses, such as salaries of officers and employees, cost of supplies, losses by credit, and rent and plant depreciation. (It sometimes includes some of the selling expenses.)

selling expenses. Expenses such as: insurance, taxes, advertising, and salesman's wages.

EX-PLIC'IT, *adj.* **explicit function.** See IMPLICIT—implicit function.

EX-PO'NENT, *n.* **exponent in elementary algebra.** A positive integer at the right and above a letter or quantity indicating that the letter or quantity is to be taken as a factor as many times as there are units in this integer. E.g. $3^2 = 3 \times 3$; $x^3 = x \times x \times x$. *Syn.* Index.

fractional exponent. A fraction at the right and above a quantity, the denominator denoting a principal root of the quantity and the numerator a power of this root, or the reverse (the two being equivalent for positive numbers). E.g.

$$8^{2/3} = (\sqrt[3]{8})^2 = \sqrt[3]{(8)^2} = 4; \text{ but } [(-2)^{1/2}]^2 = -2,$$

while if -2 is squared first one obtains $4^{1/2} = 2$. This difficulty is avoided by always combining and simplifying fractional exponents before operating with them. One then has only such forms as $(-a)^{n/m}$ where n and m are not both even; hence the order in which they are applied does not affect the result. See LAW—laws of fractional exponents.

irrational exponent. See IRRATIONAL—irrational power.

laws of exponents. See LAWS.

negative exponent. A negative number to the right and above a quantity, indicating that in addition to the opertions indicated by the numerical value of the exponent, the quantity is to be reciprocated. Whether the reciprocating is done before or after the other exponential operations have been carried out is immaterial. E.g. $3^{-2} = (3^2)^{-1} = (9)^{-1} = 1/9$, or $3^{-2} = (3^{-1})^2 = (1/3)^2 = 1/9$.

zero exponent. A small zero written above and to the right of a quantity, indicating the result of subtracting exponents when dividing a quantity by itself, $x^2/x^2 = x^0 = 1$; the power of a quantity, which is defined to be unity.

EX'PO-NEN'TIAL, *adj.* **derivative of an exponential.** See DIFFERENTIATION FORMULAS in the appendix.

exponential curve. The plane locus of $y = a^x$ (or, what is the same, $x = \log_a y$). It can be obtained geometrically by revolving the logarithmic curve, $y = \log_a x$, about the line $y = x$, i.e. reflecting it in this line. The curve is asymptotic to the negative x-axis and has its y intercept unity.

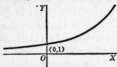

exponential equation. See EQUATION—exponential equation.

exponential function of a variable. See FUNCTION—exponential function.

exponential laws. See LAW.

exponential series. The series

$$(1 + x + x^2/2! + x^3/3! + \cdots + x^n/n! + \cdots).$$

This is the Maclaurin expansion of e^x. It converges to e^x for every value of x.

exponential values of sin x and cos x.

$$\text{Sin } x = \frac{e^{ix} - e^{-ix}}{2i} \quad \text{and} \quad \cos x = \frac{e^{ix} + e^{-ix}}{2},$$

where $i = \sqrt{-1}$. These can be proven by use of EULER'S FORMULA.

EX-PRES'SION, *n.* A very general term used to designate any symbolic mathematical form, such as a polynomial, an equation, etc.

EX-SE'CANT, *n.* See TRIGONOMETRIC—trigonometric functions of an acute angle.

EX-TEND'ED, *adj.* **extended insurance.** Insurance extended (because of default in payment or some other exigency) over a period of such length that the *net single premium* is equal to the *surrender value* of the policy.

extended mean value theorem. (1) Same as TAYLOR'S THEOREM. (2) Same as the SECOND MEAN VALUE THEOREM.

EX-TENT', *n.* Extent of a curve, or sur-

face. The regions of the plane, or space, which it occupies.

EX-TE'RI-OR, *adj.* **alternate exterior angles.** See ALTERNATE.

exterior angle of a polygon. The angle between any side produced and the adjacent side (not produced).

exterior angle of a triangle. The angle between one side produced and the adjacent side (not produced).

exterior-interior angles. See ANGLE—angles made by a transversal.

EX-TER'NAL, *adj.* **external ratio.** See POINT—point of division.

EX-TER'NAL-LY, *adj.* **externally tangent.** See TANGENT.

EX-TINC'TION of debts. The payment of debts.

EX-TRACT', *v.* **extract a root of a number.** To find a root of the number; usually refers to finding the positive real root, or the real negative root if it be an odd root of a negative number. E.g. one extracts the square root of 2 when he finds it to be $1.4142 \cdots$, or the cube root of -8 when he finds it to be -2. *Syn.* Find, compute, or estimate a root.

EX-TRA'NE-OUS, *adj.* **extraneous root.** A root gotten in the process of solving an equation, but not belonging to the equation given to be solved. It is generally introduced either by squaring the original equation, or clearing it of fractions. E.g. (1) the equation $(x^2 - 3x + 2)/(x - 2) = 0$ has only one root, 1; but if one multiplies through by $x - 2$ the resulting equation has the root 2 also; (2) the equation $1 - \sqrt{x - 1} = x$ has only one root, 1; but if one transposes the radical and squares, thus getting rid of the radical, the resulting equation is $x^2 - 3x + 2 = 0$, which has the two roots 1 and 2. The root, 2, is an extraneous root of the original equation, since its substitution in that equation gives $1 - 1 = 2$.

EX'TRA-PO-LA'TION, *n.* Estimating (approximating) the value of a function (quantity) for a value of the argument which is either greater than, or less than, all the values of the argument which are being used in the estimating (approximating). Using log 2 and log 3 one might find an approximate value of log 3.1 by extrapolation, using the formula

$$\log 3.1 = \log 3 + \tfrac{1}{10}(\log 3 - \log 2).$$

See INTERPOLATION.

EX-TREME′, *adj.* **extreme terms, or extremes.** The first and last terms in a proportion; the antecedent in the first ratio, and the consequent in the second.

extreme or extremum of a function. A *maximum* or *minimum* value of the function. See MAXIMUM and MINIMUM.

F

FACE, *n.* **face amount of an insurance policy.** The amount that the company is contracted to pay when the exigency stated in the policy occurs.

face of a dihedral angle. One of the planes that form the dihedral angle.

face of a polyhedral angle. One of the planes that form the polyhedral angle.

face of a polyhedron. See POLYHEDRON.

face-value. See PAR.

lateral face of a pyramid. See PYRAMID.

FAC′TOR, *n.* **accumulation factor.** See ACCUMULATION.

factor of an algebraic polynomial. One of two or more polynomials whose product is the given polynomial. Usually, in elementary algebra, a polynomial with rational coefficients is considered factorable only when it has two or more polynomial factors, other than unity, whose coefficients are rational (sometimes it is required that they be integers). *Tech.* One of a set of polynomials whose product gives the polynomial to be factored and whose coefficients lie in a given *field* (*domain*). (See DOMAIN.) Unless a field is specified, the field of the coefficients of the given polynomial is understood. *Factor* is sometimes used of any quantity whatever that divides a given quantity. E.g. $(x^2 - y^2)$ has the factors $(x - y)$ and $(x + y)$ in the ordinary (elementary) sense; $(x^2 - 2y^2)$ has the factors $(x - \sqrt{2}y)$ and $(x + \sqrt{2}y)$ in the field of real numbers; $(x^2 + y^2)$ has the factors

$(x - iy)$ and $(x + iy)$ in the complex field.

factor of an integer. An integer whose product with some integer is the given integer. E.g. the factors of 12 are 12, 2, 3, 4, 6, 1. However when speaking of the *factors of a number*, it is not usually intended that unity and the number itself should be included.

factor of proportionality. The constant value of the ratio of two proportional quantities. This relation is usually written in the form $y = kx$, where k is the *factor of proportionality*. E.g. the distance passed over is proportional to the time when the velocity is constant, i.e. $s = kt$, where k is the *factor of proportionality*. *Syn.* Constant of proportionality.

factor of a term. Any exact divisor of the term.

factor theorem: An algebraic polynomial in x is exactly divisible by $(x - a)$ if it reduces to zero when a is substituted for x. See REMAINDER —remainder theorem.

integrating factor. (*In differential equations.*) A factor which, when multiplied into a differential equation, makes it integrable. E.g. If the differential equation

$$\frac{dy}{x} + \frac{y}{x^2}\, dx = 0$$

be multiplied by x^2, there results

$$x\,dy + y\,dx = 0,$$

which has the solution $xy = c$.

monomial factor. See MONOMIAL.

FAC′TOR, *v.* To resolve into factors. One factors 6 when he writes it in the form 2×3.

FAC′TOR-A-BLE, *adj.* *In arithmetic*, containing factors other than unity and itself (referring to integers). *In algebra*, containing factors other than constants and itself (referring to polynomials). $x^2 - y^2$ is factorable, $x^2 + y^2$ is not, in the real domain.

FAC-TO′RI-AL, *adj.* **factorial of a positive integer.** The product of all the positive integers less than or equal to the integer. *Factorial n* is denoted by either one of the symbols $n!$ or $\underline{|n}$. E.g.

$1! = 1$, $2! = 1 \cdot 2$, $3! = 1 \cdot 2 \cdot 3$, and in general, $n! = 1 \cdot 2 \cdot 3 \cdots n$. This definition of factorial leaves the case when n is zero meaningless. In order to make certain formulas work in all cases, **factorial zero** is arbitrarily defined to be unity. Despite the fact that this is the value of factorial 1, there is considerable to be gained by using this definition; e.g. this makes the general binomial coefficient, $n!/[r!(n-r)!]$, valid for the first and last terms, which are the terms for which $r = 0$ and $r = n$ respectively.

factorial notation. The notation $n!$ or $\underline{n}$ used in writing the factorials of a positive integer or zero. See above, factorial of a positive integer.

factorial series. See SERIES—factorial series.

FAC'TOR-ING, type forms for:

(1) $\qquad x^2 + xy = x(x+y);$

(2) $\qquad x^2 - y^2 = (x+y)(x-y);$

(3) $\qquad x^2 + 2xy + y^2 = (x+y)^2;$

(4) $\qquad x^2 - 2xy + y^2 = (x-y)^2;$

(5) $\quad x^2 + (a+b)x + ab = (x+a)(x+b);$

(6) $acx^2 + (bc+ad)x + bd = (ax+b)(cx+d);$

(7) $\quad x^3 \pm 3x^2y + 3xy^2 \pm y^3 = (x \pm y)^3;$

(8) $\quad x^3 \pm y^3 = (x \pm y)(x^2 \mp xy + y^2).$

(In (7) and (8) either the upper, or the lower, signs are to be used throughout.)

FAC-TO-RI-ZA'TION, n. The process of factoring.

factorization of a transformation. Finding two or more transformations which, when made successively, have the same effect as the given transformation. See AFFINE TRANSFORMATION.

FAHRENHEIT THERMOMETER. A thermometer so graduated that water freezes at 32° and boils at 212° on its scale. See CONVERSION, n—conversion from Centigrade to Fahrenheit (or Fahrenheit to Centigrade).

FALLING BODY; acceleration of a falling body. In the English system of units, approximately 32 feet per second per second. The distance traveled (in feet) in time t is then $s = \frac{1}{2}gt^2 = 16t^2$, where it is assumed that the body was at rest at time $t = 0$.

FALSE, *adj*. **method of false position.** (1) Same as REGULA FALSI. (2) A method for approximating the roots of an algebraic equation. Consists of making a fairly close estimate, say r, then substituting $(r+h)$ in the equation, dropping the terms in h of higher degree than the first (since they are relatively small), and solving the resulting linear equation for h. This process is then repeated, using the new approximation $(r+h)$ in place of r. E.g. the equation $x^3 - 2x^2 - x + 1 = 0$ has a root near 2 (between 2 and 3). Hence we substitute $(2+h)$ for x. This gives (when the terms in h^2 and h^3 have been dropped) the equation $3h - 1 = 0$; whence $h = 1/3$. The next estimate will then be $2 + 1/3$ or $7/3$.

FAM'I-LY, n. **family of lines in a plane.** All the lines obtained by assigning values to some single parameter (arbitrary constant) which is an *essential constant* in the equation of some line. E.g. all the lines through a point in a plane, and all the lines tangent to a circle are *families* of lines.

n-parameter family of plane curves. A set of curves whose equations can be gotten from the equation of a given curve by varying n essential constants which occur in the given equation; a set of curves whose equations are non-singular solutions (special cases of the general solution) of a differential equation of the nth order. E.g. all the circles in a plane constitute a three-parameter family and all the conics in a plane a five parameter family.

one parameter family of plane curves. All the plane curves whose equations are gotten from a given equation of a curve by assigning values to a single parameter (arbitrary constant) which is an essential constant in the given equation. A set of concentric circles constitutes a family of circles, the radius being the arbitrary parameter. In general, all curves whose equations are non-singular solutions, special cases of the general solutions, of a given differential equation of the first order form a one parameter family of curves.

one parameter family of surfaces.

All surfaces whose equations can be obtained from the equation of some given surface by assigning values to an essential constant which occurs in the equation. All spheres with the same center, and all circular cylindrical surfaces with a given axis, are families of surfaces. See also CONFOCAL—confocal quadrics.

two parameter family of plane curves. All curves whose equations can be obtained from the equation of a given curve by varying two arbitrary parameters (essential constants) which occur in the given equation; the set of curves whose equations are non-singular solutions of a differential equation of the second order. All circles in the plane having a given radius, and all central conics with centers at the origin and foci on the x-axis are two parameter families of plane curves.

FERMAT'S LAST THEOREM: The equation $x^n + y^n = z^n$, where n is an integer greater than 2, has no solution in positive integers. This theorem has never been proved, although it has been proved that it cannot have a solution, in the so-called first case in which neither x, y, nor z has a factor in common with n, unless n is greater than 253,547,889 and the least of x, y and z is greater than $(111/77)n(2n^2+1)^n$; and that it cannot have a solution in the second case, namely when either x, y, or z has a factor in common with n, unless n is greater than 600.

FERMAT'S SPIRAL. See PARABOLIC —parabolic spiral.

FERMAT'S THEOREM. (*In number theory*.) If p is a prime and a is prime to p, then a^{p-1}, divided by p, leaves a remainder of unity. *Tech.* $a^{p-1} \equiv 1$ (mod p); e.g. $2^4 \equiv 1$ (mod 5), where $p = 5$ and $a = 2$. See CONGRUENCE.

FERRARI'S solution of the general quartic. A solution of the general quartic equation which depends upon the possibility of expressing one member of the equation as a perfect square of a quadratic and the other member as a perfect square of a linear expression (in the unknown). This requires the solution of a certain cubic, which is called the resolvent cubic.

FIELD, *n.* field of study. A group of subjects which deal with closely related material, such as the field of analysis, the field of pure mathematics or the field of applied mathematics.

number field. Same as DOMAIN.

tensor field. See TENSOR.

FIG'URE, *n.* (1) A character or symbol denoting a number, as 1, 5, 12; sometimes used in the same sense as digit. (2) A drawing, diagram or cut used to aid in presenting subject matter in text books and scientific papers.

geometrical figure. See GEOMETRIC.

plane figure. See PLANE.

reciprocal polar figures. See RECIPROCAL.

FI'NITE, *adj.* finite differences. See DIFFERENCES—finite differences.

finite discontinuity. A point of discontinuity such that the function is bounded (does not become infinite) in the neighborhood of the point. See DISCONTINUITY.

finite quantity. Any quantity which is *bounded*.

finite set (group or assemblage). A set which contains a finite (limited) number of members. *Tech.* a set which cannot be put into one-to-one correspondence with a part of itself; all the integers between 0 and 100 constitute a finite set. See INFINITE—infinite set.

FIRST MERIDIAN. See MERIDIAN—principal meridian.

FIT'TING, *adj.* curve fitting. See EMPIRICAL—empirical curve, and METHOD—method of least squares.

FIXED, *adj.* fixed assets. See ASSETS.

fixed investment. See INVESTMENT.

fixed line, circle, plane, or other figure. A relative term meaning that the fixed configuration, or *fixed* part of a configuration, does not change in position, shape, size, or any other way during a given discussion.

fixed value of a letter or quantity. A value that does not change during a given discussion or series of discussions; not arbitrary. In an expression containing several letters, some may be *fixed* and others subjected to being assigned certain values or to taking on certain values by virtue of their place in the expression; e.g. if in $y = mx + b$, b is *fixed*, m arbitrary and x and y variables, the equation represents the pencil of lines through the point whose coordinates are (o, b). When m has also been assigned a particular value, x and y are then thought of as taking on all pairs of values which are coordinates of points on a particular line.

FLAT, *adj.* **flat angle.** Same as *straight angle*, that is, an angle of 180°.

flat price of a bond. The *purchase price*; the price actually paid for the bond.

FLEC′NODE, *n.* A *node* which is also a point of inflection on one of the branches of the curve that touch each other at the node.

FLEX, *n.* Same as INFLECTION.

FLEX′ION, *n.* A form sometimes used for the rate of change of the slope of a curve; the second derivative of a function.

FLU′ENT, *n.* Newton's name for a varying, or *"flowing,"* function.

FLU′ID, *adj.* **fluid pressure.** See PRESSURE—fluid pressure.

FLUX′ION, *n.* Newton's name for the rate of change or derivative of a *"fluent."* It is denoted in Newton's writing by a letter with a dot over it.

FO′CAL, *adj.* **focal chords of a conic.** Chords passing through a focus of the conic.

focal date. See COMMUTING OBLIGATIONS.

FO′CUS, *n.* [*pl.* foci.] **focus of a parabola, hyperbola, or ellipse.** See PARABOLA, HYPERBOLA, and ELLIPSE.

FO′LI-UM of DESCARTES. A plane

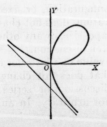

cubic curve consisting of a single loop, a node, and two branches asymptotic to the same line. Its rectangular Cartesian equation is $x^3 + y^3 = 3axy$, where the curve passes through the origin and is asymptotic to the line $x + y + a = 0$.

FOOT, *n.* A unit of linear measure, equal to 12 inches. See DENOMINATE NUMBERS in the appendix.

foot of a line cutting a plane. The point where the line intersects the plane.

foot of a perpendicular to a line. The point of intersection of the perpendicular and the line.

foot of a perpendicular to a plane. The point in which the perpendicular cuts the plane.

FOOT-POUND, *n.* A unit of work; the work done when a body weighing one pound is lifted one foot. This unit varies with the latitude and the distance from sea level. See HORSEPOWER.

FORCE, *n.* That which pushes, pulls, compresses, distends, or distorts in any way; that which changes the state of rest or state of motion of a body. *Tech.* The vector equal to ma, where m is the mass of the body and a its vector acceleration.

conservative force. See CONSERVATIVE FIELD.

electromotive force. See ELECTROMOTIVE FORCE.

force function. A function $u(x, y, z)$ such that $\partial u/\partial x$, $\partial u/\partial y$, $\partial u/\partial z$ are equal, respectively, to the components X, Y, Z of a force vector $Xi + Yj + Zk = F$. Such a function is also called a POTENTIAL.

force of interest. See INTEREST.

force of mortality. (*In insurance.*) The annual rate of mortality under the assumption that the intensity of mortality is constant throughout the age-year which is under consideration and has the value it had at the moment after the beginning of the age-year.

force vector. A vector equal in numerical length to a given force and having its direction parallel to the line of action of the force. See PARALLELOGRAM—parallelogram of forces.

moment of a force. See MOMENT.

parallelogram of forces. See PARALLELOGRAM—parallelogram of forces.

unit of force. The force which will give unit acceleration to a unit mass. The force which acting on a mass of one gram for one second increases its velocity by one centimeter per second is called a force of one *dyne*. The force which acting on a mass of one pound for one second will increase the velocity of the mass one foot per second is called a force of one *poundal*.

FORCED VIBRATIONS. The motion resulting from harmonic motion being disturbed by a certain periodic force; oscillation of a body, maintained by an external periodic force, in a period other than its natural period.

FOREIGN EXCHANGE. See EXCHANGE.

FORM, *n.* (1) A mathematical expression of a certain type; see STANDARD—standard form of an equation. (2) A homogeneous polynomial expression in two or more variables.

initial form. See COMMUTATION—commutation tables.

p-form of the quadratic. Same as REDUCED FORM; see REDUCED.

standard form. See STANDARD—standard form of an equation.

terminal form. See COMMUTATION—commutation tables.

FOR'MU-LA, *n.* A general answer, rule or principle stated in mathematical language.

addition and subtraction formulas of trigonometry. Formulas expressing the sine, cosine, tangent, etc., of the sum or difference of two angles in terms of functions of the angles. They answer the need created by the fact that functions of sums and differences of angles are not distributive; i.e. $\sin (x \pm y) \neq \sin x \pm \sin y$. The most important of these formulas are:

$$\sin (x \pm y) = \sin x \cos y \pm \cos x \sin y;$$

$$\cos (x \pm y) = \cos x \cos y \mp \sin x \sin y;$$

and $\quad \tan (x \pm y) = \dfrac{\tan x \pm \tan y}{1 \mp \tan x \tan y}.$

(The upper signs, and the lower signs, are to be taken together throughout.)

conversion formulas. A name sometimes given to the addition and subtraction formulas of trigonometry and formulas immediately derivable from them, such as double and half angle formulas and product formulas.

double-angle formulas. Formulas expressing the sine, cosine, tangent, etc., of twice an angle in terms of functions of the angle. These are easily obtained by using equal angles in the ADDITION FORMULAS. The most important are:

$$\sin 2x = 2 \sin x \cos x,$$

$$\cos 2x = \cos^2 x - \sin^2 x,$$

and $\quad \tan 2x = 2 \tan x/(1 - \tan^2 x).$

empirical formula. See EMPIRICAL.

Euler's formula. See EULER'S FORMULA.

formulas of integration. See INTEGRATION and the appendix.

Gregory-Newton formula for interpolation. See GREGORY-NEWTON.

half-angle formulas, of plane trigonometry. Formulas expressing trigonometric functions of half an angle in terms of functions of the angle. They are the inverses of certain double angle formulas (with the double angle, $2A$, replaced by a single angle, A, and the single angle, A, replaced by $\frac{1}{2}A$). The most important are:

$$\sin \tfrac{1}{2}A = \sqrt{(1 - \cos A)/2};$$

$$\cos \tfrac{1}{2}A = \sqrt{(1 + \cos A)/2};$$

and $\quad \tan \tfrac{1}{2}A = \sin A/(1 + \cos A),$

$$= (1 - \cos A)/\sin A.$$

half-angle formulas, for the solution of plane triangles. Relations between the sides and one of the angles of a triangle; used in place of the *cosine law* because they are better adapted to calculation by logarithms. The half-angle formulas are:

$$\tan \tfrac{1}{2}A = r/(s-a),$$

$$\tan \tfrac{1}{2}B = r/(s-b),$$

$$\tan \tfrac{1}{2}C = r/(s-c),$$

where A, B, C are the angles of the triangle, a, b, c the sides opposite A, B, C, respectively, $s = \frac{1}{2}(a+b+c)$, and

$$r = \sqrt{(s-a)(s-b)(s-c)/s}.$$

half-angle formulas of spherical trigonometry. See HALF—half-angle formulas of spherical trigonometry.

half-side formulas of spherical trigonometry. See HALF—half-side formulas of spherical trigonometry.

Huygen's formula. See HUYGEN'S FORMULA.

reduction formulas in integration. See REDUCTION—reduction formulas in integration.

product formulas. (*Trigonometry*.) The formulas:

$$\sin x \cos y = \frac{1}{2}[\sin (x+y) + \sin (x-y)],$$
$$\cos x \sin y = \frac{1}{2}[\sin (x+y) - \sin (x-y)],$$
$$\cos x \cos y = \frac{1}{2}[\cos (x+y) + \cos (x-y)],$$
$$\sin x \sin y = \frac{1}{2}[\cos (x-y) - \cos (x+y)].$$

These can be easily derived from the *addition* and *subtraction formulas*.

rotation formulas. See ROTATION—rotation of rectangular axes in the plane.

subtraction formulas of trigonometry. See above, addition and subtraction formulas of trigonometry.

translation formulas. See TRANSLATION.

Wallis's formulas. See WALLIS'S FORMULAS.

FOUR-COLOR PROBLEM. The problem of proving that any map can be colored with four colors so that no two countries having a common boundary line will have the same color. It has been proved for 5 colors; and 3 colors have been proved insufficient. It is assumed that each country is connected, i.e. that it is possible to go between any two points of a given country without leaving that country.

FOURIER SERIES. A series of the form

$$\frac{1}{2}a_0 + (a_1 \cos x + b_1 \sin x) + (a_2 \cos 2x + b_2 \sin 2x)$$
$$+ \cdots = \frac{1}{2}a_0 + \sum_{n=1}^{\infty} (a_n \cos nx + b_n \sin nx)$$

where there exists $f(x)$ such that for all n

$$a_0 = \frac{1}{\pi} \int_{-\pi}^{\pi} f(x)dx,$$

$$a_n = \frac{1}{\pi} \int_{-\pi}^{\pi} f(x) \cos nx \, dx$$

and $$b_n = \frac{1}{\pi} \int_{-\pi}^{\pi} f(x) \sin nx \, dx.$$

The marked characteristic of a Fourier Series is that it can be used to represent functions that ordinarily are represented by different expressions in different parts of the interval, the functions being subject only to certain very general restrictions (see FOURIER'S THEOREM). Since the sine and cosine each have a period of 2π, the Fourier Series has a period of 2π. E.g. if $f(x)$ is defined by the relations $f(x) = 1$ when $-\pi \le x \le 0$, $f(x) = 2$ when $0 < x \le \pi$; then

$$\pi a_0 = \int_{-\pi}^{\pi} f(x)dx = \int_{-\pi}^{0} dx + \int_{0}^{\pi} 2dx = 3\pi,$$

from which $a_0 = 3$. Similarly, $a_n = 0$ for all n, $b_n = 0$ for n even and equals $[2/(n\pi)]$ for n odd. Whence

$$f(x) = 3/2 + (2/\pi) \sin x + [2/(3\pi)] \sin 3x$$
$$+ [2/(5\pi)] \sin 5x + \cdots.$$

Series on ranges other than $(-\pi, \pi)$, derived from the above type of Fourier's Series, are also called FOURIER SERIES.

Fourier's half-range series. A *Fourier Series* of the form

$$\frac{1}{2}a_0 + a_1 \cos x + a_2 \cos 2x \cdots$$
$$= \frac{1}{2}a_0 + \sum_{n=1}^{\infty} a_n \cos nx$$

or $$b_1 \sin x + b_2 \sin 2x \cdots = \sum_{n=1}^{\infty} b_n \sin nx.$$

These are also called the **cosine** and **sine** series, respectively. Since the cosine is an *even* function, the cosine series can represent a function, $f(x)$, on the whole interval $-\pi < x < \pi$ only if $f(x)$ is an even function, i.e. $f(-x) = f(x)$. Likewise, since the sine is an *odd* function, the sine series can represent a function, $f(x)$, on the whole interval $-\pi < x < \pi$ only if $f(x)$ is an odd function, i.e. $f(-x) = -f(x)$.

FOURIER'S THEOREM. A theorem concerning the possibility of expanding a function in a Fourier Series. The theorem, as proved by Dirichlet, is as follows: If $f(x)$ is defined and bounded on the range $(-\pi, \pi)$ and has only a finite number of maxima and minima and a finite number of discontinuities on this range and if

$$\pi a_n = \int_{-\pi}^{\pi} f(x) \cos nx dx,$$

and

$$\pi b_n = \int_{-\pi}^{\pi} f(x) \sin nx dx$$

the series

$$\tfrac{1}{2}a_0 + \sum_{n=1}^{\infty} (a_n \cos nx + b_n \sin nx)$$

converges to $f(x)$ for all x in the interval $(-\pi < x < \pi)$ for which $f(x)$ is continuous and to $\tfrac{1}{2}[f(x+0) + f(x-0)]$ at points for which $f(x)$ is discontinuous, $f(a+0)$ denoting the limit of $f(x)$ as x approaches a from the right, and $f(a-0)$ the limit of $f(x)$ as x approaches a from the left. (These conditions are more restrictive on $f(x)$ than is necessary.)

FOUR-LEAFED ROSE. The graph of the equation $r = a \sin 2\theta$, or $r = a \cos 2\theta$. The graph of the first equation (shown in the figure) has the four petals symmetric by pairs about each of the lines

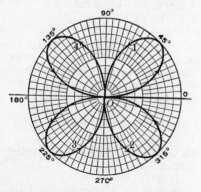

$\theta = 45°$ and $\theta = 135°$, and tangent to the coordinate axes in the several quadrants. The length of the line of sym-

metry of each petal, from the pole to the intersection with the curve, is a. The graph of the second equation is the same, except that the petals are symmetric about the coordinate axes and tangent to the lines $\theta = 45°$ and $\theta = 135°$. See THREE—three-leafed rose, and N-LEAFED ROSE.

FOUR-STEP RULE (or METHOD). A rule for finding the derivative of a function: (1) add an increment Δx to x in the function, giving $f(x+\Delta x)$; (2) subtract the function, giving $f(x+\Delta x) - f(x)$; (3) divide by Δx, obtaining

$$\frac{f(x+\Delta x) - f(x)}{\Delta x},$$

and simplify (usually by expanding the numerator and cancelling out Δx); (4) find the limit as Δx approaches 0 (usually found by putting $\Delta x = 0$). This is the mechanization of the definition of the derivative. It is used in simple examples to fix in one's mind the concept of a derivative, and then to derive general formulas for taking the derivative. If $f(x) = x^2$, the process gives:

(1) $\qquad f(x+\Delta x) = (x+\Delta x)^2$;

(2) $f(x+\Delta x) - f(x) = (x+\Delta x)^2 - x^2$;

(3) $\dfrac{f(x+\Delta x) - f(x)}{\Delta x} = \dfrac{(x+\Delta x)^2 - x^2}{\Delta x} = 2x+\Delta x$

(4) $\lim\limits_{\Delta x \to 0} (2x+\Delta x) = 2x = \dfrac{dx^2}{dx}$.

FRACTION, *n.* An indicated quotient of two quantities. See below, common fraction.

clearing of fractions. Multiplying both members of an equation by a common denominator of the fractions. See EXTRANEOUS.

common fraction. An integral number of equal parts of unity; any indicated quotient of two whole numbers, such as $\tfrac{1}{2}$, $\tfrac{3}{4}$, $\tfrac{6}{9}$. The number above the line is called the **numerator** and the number below the **denominator** of the fraction. *Syn.* Vulgar fraction.

complex fraction. A fraction whose numerator or denominator or both are fractions. See DIVISION—division by a fraction. E.g. $(\tfrac{1}{2})/4$ and $(a/b + d/c) / [1/(a-b)]$. To simplify such a fraction, invert its denominator and multiply, or better, multiply numerator and denominator by the least common multiple of all denominators in the complex fraction; e.g.

$$\tfrac{1}{3}/(\tfrac{1}{2}+\tfrac{1}{4})=\tfrac{1}{3}/\tfrac{3}{4}=\tfrac{1}{3}\times\tfrac{4}{3}=\tfrac{4}{9},$$
$$\tfrac{1}{3}/(\tfrac{1}{2}+\tfrac{1}{4})=(12\times\tfrac{1}{3})/[12(\tfrac{1}{2}+\tfrac{1}{4})]=\tfrac{4}{9}.$$

continued fraction. A number plus a fraction whose denominator is a number plus a fraction, etc. such as:

$$a_1+\cfrac{b_2}{a_2+\cfrac{b_3}{a_3+\cfrac{b_4}{a_4+\cfrac{b_5}{a_5,\text{ etc.}}}}}$$

A continued fraction may have either a finite or an infinite number of terms. In the former case it is said to be a **terminating** continued fraction; in the latter, **non-terminating.** If a certain sequence of the a's and b's occurs periodically, the continued fraction is said to be **recurring** or **periodic.** The terminating continued fractions

$$a_1,\quad a_1+\cfrac{b_2}{a_2,}\quad a_1+\cfrac{b_2}{a_2+\cfrac{b_3}{a_3}},\text{ etc.}$$

are called **convergents** of the continued fraction. The quotients b_2/a_2, b_3/a_3, etc., are called **partial quotients.**

decimal fraction. See DECIMAL.

decomposition of fractions. See DECOMPOSITION.

division by a fraction. See DIVISION—division by a fraction.

improper fraction. A fraction which is not a proper fraction. *In arithmetic,* a fraction whose numerator is greater than its denominator; 3/2 is an improper fraction. *In algebra,* a fraction whose numerator is of equal or higher degree than its denominator in the variable or variables with respect to which the fraction is being described; $x^2/(x+1)$ is an improper fraction.

integration of rational fractions. See RATIONAL.

partial fraction. See PARTIAL—partial fractions.

proper fraction. *In arithmetic,* a fraction whose numerator is smaller than its denominator; $\tfrac{2}{3}$ is a proper fraction. *In algebra,* a fraction whose numerator is of lower degree than its denominator in the variable or variables with respect to which the fraction is being described; $x/(x^2+1)$ is a proper fraction in x, and $(x-y)/xy$ is a proper fraction in x and y, but not in x or y alone.

radix fraction. See RADIX—radix fractions.

rational fraction. A fraction whose numerator and denominator are rational.

similar fractions. Fractions having a common denominator or, if decimals, having the same number of decimal places.

simple fraction. A fraction whose numerator and denominator are both integers, as contrasted to complex fractions which have a fraction for the numerator or denominator or both.

simplified fraction. See SIMPLIFIED—simplified fraction.

unit fraction. A simple fraction whose numerator is unity.

vulgar fraction. Same as COMMON FRACTION.

FRAC'TION-AL, *adj.* **fractional equation.** (1) An equation containing fractions of any sort, such as $\tfrac{1}{2}x+2x=1$. (2) An equation containing fractions in the variable, such as $x^2+2x+1/x^2=0$.

fractional exponent. See EXPONENT.

FRAME, *n.* **frame of reference.** Any set of lines or curves *in a plane,* by means of which the position of any point *in the plane* may be uniquely described; any set of planes or surfaces by means of which the position of a point *in space* may be uniquely described.

FRENCH HORSEPOWER. See HORSEPOWER.

FRE'QUEN-CY, *n.* **binomial frequency distribution.** See BINOMIAL—binomial distribution.

cumulative frequency. See CUMULATIVE.

frequency of conversion of compound interest. The number of times a year that interest is compounded.

frequency distribution. (*Statistics.*) A classification showing the number of individuals in each of certain groups, such as the number of students making grades from 60% to 70%, 70% to 80%, 80% to 90%, and 90% to 100%. If these grades are marked at equal intervals in ascending order on the axis of abscissas (x-axis), and the number in each class is indicated by a horizontal line segment drawn above the x-axis at a height equal to the number in the class (the number making a grade within the particular interval), the diagram is called a **histogram.** The common spacing on the x-axis is called the **class interval.** If the upper ends of the ordinates at the middle of the interval are connected by line segments, the resulting figure is called a **frequency polygon.**

frequency of a periodic function. The number of times the function repeats itself in a certain interval. If an interval of length 2π is being considered, the frequency of sin x is 1; of sin $2x$, 2, and of sin $3x$, 3.

normal frequency curve. The graph of $y=[N/(\sigma\sqrt{2\pi})]e^{-(x-A)^2/(2\sigma^2)}$, where N is the total number of observations, A is the average of the observations, σ the *standard deviation*, and e the base of natural logarithms. *Syn.* Normal distribution curve, probability curve.

relative frequency of the occurrence of an event. The ratio of the number of times that an event happens to the number of trials in which the event can happen or fail to happen. The ratio of the number of times the event occurs to the total possible times it could have occurred. See PROBABILITY—empirical probability.

FRUS′TUM, *n.* **frustum of any solid.** The part of the solid between two parallel planes cutting the solid. See PYRAMID, and CONE.

FUL′CRUM, *n.* The point at which a lever is supported. See LEVER.

FUNC′TION, *n.* A quantity which takes on a definite value, or values, when special values are assigned to certain other quantities, called the arguments or independent variables of the func-

tion. Any mathematical quantity, constant or variable, is sometimes spoken of as a *function*, but this term is used mostly to point out dependence on some certain variable or variables. See below, function of one variable, and function of several variables.

algebraic function. A function containing only algebraic terms and symbols. See ALGEBRAIC.

analytic function at a point x_0. A function which can be represented by a power series in $(x-x_0)$, valid in a neighborhood of the point x_0.

$$1+(x-1)+(x-1)^2+\cdots+(x-1)^{n-1}+\cdots$$

represents the function

$$\frac{1}{2-x} \text{ for } |x-1|<1.$$

Bessel functions. See BESSEL.

complementary function. See DIFFERENTIAL—linear differential equations.

composite function. See COMPOSITE.

compound harmonic function. See COMPOUND—compound harmonic function.

conjugate function. See CONJUGATE—conjugate functions.

continuous function. See CONTINUOUS.

decreasing function. See DECREASING.

dependent functions. See DEPENDENT.

derivative of a function. See DERIVATIVE.

differential of a function. See DIFFERENTIAL—differential of a function of one variable.

entire function. See ENTIRE.

Euler's ϕ-function. See INDICATOR—indicator of an integer.

even function. A function whose value does not change when the sign of the independent variable is changed; i.e. a function such that $f(-x)=f(x)$; x^2 and cos x are even functions, for $(-x)^2=x^2$ and cos $(-x)=$cos x.

exponential function. (1) The function e^x, where e is the base of Napierian logarithms. (2) The function a^x, where a is a constant. (3) A function in which the variable or variables appear in exponents and possibly also as a base, such as 2^{x+1} or x^x.

ϕ-function. See INDICATOR—indicator of an integer.

frequency of a periodic function. See FREQUENCY—frequency of a periodic function.

function of one variable. An expression involving one variable; $2x$ and $(1-x^2)$ are functions of the one variable x. *Tech.* One quantity is said to be a function of another if one or more values of the first (the *dependent variable*) are determined by every value of the second (the *independent variable*) on some range. The range is either explicitly stated, or understood to be the entire range for which the function is defined. The area of a circle is a function of the radius; the sine of an angle is a function of the angle; the logarithm of a number is a function of the number. The symbols used for a general function are $f(x)$, $F(x)$, $\phi(x)$, etc., and called the f function, the F function, the ϕ function, etc. of x. Such symbols are used when making statements that are true for several different functions, in other words, statements that are not concerned with a specific form of the function; e.g. (1) $[f(x) - F(x)]\,[f(x) + F(x)] = f^2(x) - F^2(x)$ for any specific functions whatever; (2) if $f(x)$ and $F(x)$ are each continuous on (a, b) then $f(x) + F(x)$ is continuous on (a, b). A symbol like $f(x)$ is entirely general unless otherwise specified as in $f(x) = 0$ in algebra where $f(x)$ is understood to be a polynomial. The notations $f(x)$, $F(x)$, etc. are also used as abbreviations for specific functions under consideration. See FUNCTIONAL—functional notation.

function of several variables. A quantity (called the *dependent variable*) which takes on a value or values corresponding to every set of values of the several variables (called the *independent variables*). The binomial $2x + xy$ is a function of x and y. A *function of two variables* is written in the form $f(x_1, x_2)$, $F(x, y)$, etc. A function of n variables is written in the form $f(x_1, x_2, \cdots, x_n)$, etc. See above, function of one variable, and FUNCTIONAL—functional notation.

function theory. See THEORY.

gamma function. See GAMMA—gamma function.

harmonic function. (1) A solution of Laplace's differential equation which has continuous first and second partial derivatives. (2) Same as *compound* and *simple harmonic functions*.

hyperbolic functions. See HYPERBOLIC.

implicit function. See IMPLICIT—implicit function.

increasing function. See INCREASING.

increment of a function. See INCREMENT.

independent functions. See INDEPENDENT.

integral function. (1) A function in which the variable or variables do not appear in any denominator or under any negative exponent. (2) Same as ENTIRE FUNCTION.

inverse function. See INVERSE.

logarithmic function. A function of the form $\log f(x)$.

maximum and minimum of a function. See MAXIMUM (MINIMUM).

mean value of a function. See MEAN.

monotonic decreasing function. See MONOTONIC.

monotonic functions. Functions which are either monotonic increasing or monotonic decreasing. See MONOTONIC.

monotonic increasing function. See MONOTONIC.

notation of a function. See FUNCTIONAL—functional notation.

odd function. A function whose sign changes when the sign of the dependent variable is changed; i.e. a function such that $f(-x) = -f(x)$; x^3 and $\sin x$ are odd functions, for
$$(-x)^3 = -x^3 \text{ and}$$
$$\sin(-x) = -\sin x.$$

periodic function. A function that repeats its values periodically; a function for which there is a p such that $f(x+p) = f(x)$ for all x. See PERIOD—period of a function. Sin x is a periodic function, because

$$\sin (x+2\pi) = \sin x.$$

principal part of an increment of a function. See PRINCIPAL—principal part of an increment of a function.

· **rational integral function** of a variable. Same as POLYNOMIAL IN ONE VARIABLE. See POLYNOMIAL.

simple harmonic function. A function used to describe simple harmonic motion. The sine and cosine. See HARMONIC—simple harmonic motion.

transcendental function. See TRANSCENDENTAL.

trigonometric function. See TRIGONOMETRIC—trigonometric functions.

unbounded function. See UNBOUNDED.

vector function of two or more variables. A vector of the form $f_1 i + f_2 j + f_3 k$, where f_1, f_2, and f_3 are scalar functions of the variables. See VECTOR.

FUNC'TION-AL, *adj.* Of, relating to, or affecting a function.

functional determinant. See JACOBIAN.

functional notation. A notation used to denote the general concept *function* and often as an abbreviation of some specific function. The notation consists of a letter placed before parentheses containing a number of letters representing the independent variable or variables of the function, followed by the interval or intervals over which the variable or variables range; e.g. one writes $f(x)$ on (a, b) or $f(x)$, $a < x < b$, and $f(x, y)$, $a \leq x \leq b$, $c \leq y \leq d$. (The interval is commonly omitted when obtainable from the context or the nature of the function.) See FUNCTION—function of one variable, function of several variables.

FUND, *n.* Money (sometimes other assets immediately convertible into money) which is held ready for immediate demands.

endowment fund. A fund permanently appropriated for some objective, such as carrying on a school or church.

reserve fund. (1) *In insurance.* See RESERVE. Used to take care of additional cost of policy in later years. (2) *In business,* a sum held ready to meet emergencies or take advantage of opportunities to purchase at low prices.

sinking fund. A fund accumulated by periodic investments for some specific purpose such as retiring bonds, replacing equipment, providing pensions, etc. (The amount of the sinking fund is the amount of the annuity formed by the payments.)

FUN'DA-MEN'TAL, *adj.* **four fundamental operations of arithmetic.** Addition, subtraction, multiplication and division.

fundamental assumption. See ASSUMPTION.

fundamental identities of trigonometry. See TRIGONOMETRIC—relations between the trigonometric functions.

fundamental relations of trigonometry. See TRIGONOMETRIC—relations between the trigonometric functions.

fundamental theorem of algebra. Every polynomial equation in one variable has at least one root; there exists at least one value of the variable of a polynomial for which the polynomial is zero. See GAUSS' PROOF.

fundamental theorem of the integral calculus. A theorem giving a method of summing elements of area, volume, etc. (finding the area, volume, etc.) by the use of anti-derivatives. If

$$\int_a^b f(x)dx$$

is defined as $F(b) - F(a)$, where $F(x)$ is a function such that

$$\frac{dF(x)}{dx} = f(x),$$

then the fundamental theorem of the integral calculus states: If $f(x)$ is continuous and single valued,

$$\lim_{n \to \infty} [f(x_1)\Delta_1 x + f(x_2)\Delta_2 x + f(x_3)\Delta_3 x + \cdots$$

$+f(x_n)\Delta_n x] = \lim\limits_{n\to\infty} \angle_1 f(x_i)\Delta_i x = \int_a f(x)dx,$

where $\Delta_1 x, \Delta_2 x, \Delta_3 x, \cdots \Delta_n x$ are n non-overlapping subintervals of the interval (a, b), whose sum is $(b-a)$, the largest of which approaches zero as n becomes infinite (i.e. they approach zero uniformerly. See UNIFORM—uniform convergence of a set of functions), and x_i is some value of x in the interval $\Delta_i x$. If

$$\int_a^b f(x)dx$$

is defined as the above limit, then the *fundamental theorem of calculus* is stated thus: If $f(x)$ is continuous and single-valued,

$$\int_a^b f(x)dx = F(b) - F(a), \text{ where } \frac{dF(x)}{dx} = f(x).$$

The fundamental theorem of the integral calculus is sometimes taken as the statement that the above summation has a limit under the given hypothesis. (The requirement that $f(x)$ be continuous is a *sufficient* condition which is much more restrictive than is necessary.) See DARBOUX'S THEOREM, INTEGRAL, and ELEMENT—element of area, volume, etc.

fundamental theorems on limits. See LIMIT.

FUTURE value of a sum of money. See AMOUNT.

G

GAME OF NIM. See NIM.

GAM'MA, *n*. The third letter of the Greek alphabet, written γ, capital, Γ. See the appendix.

gamma function. Gamma of x is written $\Gamma(x)$ and is defined to be

$$\int_0^\infty t^{x-1}e^{-t}dt$$

(for $x>0$, or the real part of x greater than zero if x is complex). It can easily be shown that $\Gamma(x+1) = x\Gamma(x)$ and $\Gamma(1) = 1$, and from these results that $\Gamma(n) = (n-1)!$, when n is any positive integer.

GAUSS' FORMULAS or DELAMBRE'S ANALOGIES. Formulas stating the relations between the sine (or cosine) of half of the sum (or difference) of two angles of a spherical triangle and the other angle and the three sides. If the angles of the triangle are A, B, and C and the sides opposite these angles are a, b, and c respectively, then Gauss' formulas are:

$\cos\frac{1}{2}c \sin\frac{1}{2}(A+B) = \cos\frac{1}{2}C \cos\frac{1}{2}(a-b),$

$\cos\frac{1}{2}c \cos\frac{1}{2}(A+B) = \sin\frac{1}{2}C \cos\frac{1}{2}(a+b),$

$\sin\frac{1}{2}c \sin\frac{1}{2}(A-B) = \cos\frac{1}{2}C \sin\frac{1}{2}(a-b),$

$\sin\frac{1}{2}c \cos\frac{1}{2}(A-B) = \sin\frac{1}{2}C \sin\frac{1}{2}(a+b).$

GAUSS' PROOF of the fundamental theorem of algebra. The first known proof. A geometrical proof consisting essentially of substituting a complex number, $a+bi$, for the unknown of the equation, separating the real and imaginary parts of the result, and then showing that the two resulting functions of a and b are zero for some pair of values of a and b.

GEN'ER-AL, *adj*. Not specific or specialized; covering all known special cases.

general equation of the second degree. See EQUATION—general equation of the second degree.

general formula for all angles having the same sine, cosine, etc. All angles having the same sine are given (in radians) by $n\pi+(-1)^n\theta$; all having the same cosine by $2n\pi\pm\theta$; all having the same tangent by $n\pi+\theta$, where θ is an angle having the given sine, cosine, or tangent, respectively, and n is any positive or negative integer or zero. $\pi/6$, $5\pi/6$, $13\pi/6$, $\cdots$ all have the same sine; $\pi/6$, $11\pi/6$, $13\pi/6$, $\cdots$ all have the same cosine; and $\pi/6$, $7\pi/6$, $13\pi/6$, $\cdots$ all have the same tangent. The general formula for all angles having the same cotangent, same secant, or the same cosecant, are identical with those for the tangent, cosine and sine, respectively, since each of the latter set is the reciprocal of the corresponding function in the former set.

general rational integral equation of the nth degree in m variables. An equation, with literal coefficients, containing all possible rational integral terms of the nth degree, and all possible terms of lower degrees in the m variables. For a discussion of the general equation of the second degree in two variables, see DISCRIMINANT —discriminant of the general quadratic.

general solution of a differential equation. A solution, the number of whose independent arbitrary (essential) constants is equal to the order of the differential equation.

general term. See TERM—general term.

GEN′ER-AL-IZED, *adj.* **generalized mean value theorem.** (1) Same as TAYLOR'S THEOREM. (2) Same as SECOND MEAN VALUE THEOREM. See MEAN.

generalized ratio test. See RATIO.

GEN′ER-A′TOR. Same as GENERATRIX (the feminine form of *generator*).

rectilinear generators. See RULED —ruled surface, HYPERBOLOID— hyperboloid of one sheet, and PARABOLOID—hyperbolic paraboloid.

GEN′ER-A′TRIX, *n.* **generatrix of a surface.** A straight line which forms the surface by moving according to some law. The elements of a cone are different positions of its generatrix. (Any surface thus generatable is called a **ruled surface.**) *Syn.* Generator.

GE′O-GRAPH′I-CAL, *adj.* Pertaining to the surface of the earth.

geographic coordinates. Same as SPHERICAL COORDINATES. Spherical coordinates use the longitude and colatitude of a point on a sphere of radius r.

geographic equator. See EQUATOR.

GE′O-MET′RIC, or GE′O-MET′RI-CAL, *adj.* Pertaining to geometry; according to rules or principles of geometry; done by geometry.

geometric average. See AVERAGE —geometric average.

geometric figure. Any combination of points, lines, planes, circles, etc.

geometric locus. Any system of points, curves, or surfaces defined by certain general conditions or equations, such as the *locus of points* equidistant

from a given point, or the *locus* of the *equation* $y = x$.

geometric magnitude. Any magnitude having a geometric interpretation; length, area, volume, angle, etc.

geometric mean. See MEAN—geometric mean between two numbers.

geometric progression. See PROGRESSION.

geometric series. See SERIES.

geometric solid. Any portion of space which is occupied conceptually by a physical solid; e.g. a cube, or a sphere.

geometric solution. The solution of a problem by strictly geometric methods, as contrasted to algebraic or analytic solutions.

geometric surface. Same as SURFACE.

method of geometric exhaustion. See METHOD.

GE-OM′E-TRY, *n.* The science that treats of the shape and size of things.

analytic geometry. The geometry in which position is represented analytically (by coordinates) and algebraic methods of reasoning are used for the most part.

elementary or Euclidean geometry. The branch of geometry based upon the axioms (common notions) and postulates of Euclid and using essentially his methods, assuming no previous knowledge of geometry.

modern analytic geometry. Projective geometry treated by analytic methods.

plane analytic geometry. Analytic geometry in the plane (in two dimensions), devoted primarily to the graphing of equations in two variables and finding the equations of loci in the plane.

plane (elementary) geometry. The branch of geometry which treats of the properties and relations of plane figures (such as angles, triangles, polygons, circles) which can be drawn with ruler and compasses.

solid analytic geometry. Analytic geometry in three dimensions; devoted primarily to the graphing of equations (in three variables) and finding the equations of loci in space.

solid (elementary) geometry. The branch of geometry which studies figures in space (three dimensions) whose plane sections are the figures studied in plane elementary geometry, such as angles between planes, cubes, spheres, polyhedrons.

synthetic geometry. See SYNTHETIC—synthetic geometry.

GIRTH, *n.* The length of the perimeter of a cross-section of a surface when that length is the same for all cross-sections.

GOMPERTZ'S LAW. The force of mortality (risk of dying) increases geometrically; is equal to a constant multiple of a power of a constant, the exponent being the age for which the force of mortality is being determined. See MAKEHAM'S LAW.

GRADE, *n.* (1) The slope of a path or curve. (2) The inclination of a path or curve, the angle it makes with the horizontal. (3) The sine of the inclination of the path, vertical rise divided by the length of the path. (4) An inclined path. (5) A class of things relatively equal. (6) A division or class in an elementary school. (7) A rating, given students on their work in a given course. (8) One hundredth part of a right angle. See CENTESIMAL.

GRA'DI-ENT, *n.* (*In physics.*) The rate at which a variable quantity, such as temperature or pressure, changes in value; in these instances, called thermometric *gradient*, and barometric *gradient*, respectively.

gradient of a function. (*Vector analysis.*) The vector whose components along the axes are the partial derivatives of the function with respect to the variables. Written: grad $f = \nabla f = if_x + jf_y + kf_z$, where f_x, f_y and f_z are the partial derivatives of f, a function of x, y, and z. Grad $f(x, y, z)$ is a vector whose component in any direction is the derivative of f in that direction. Its direction is that in which the derivative of f has its maximum, and its absolute value is equal to that maximum. Grad f, evaluated at a point $P: (x_1, y_1, z_1)$, is normal to the surface

$f(x, y, z) = c$ at P, where c is the constant $f(x_1, y_1, z_1)$.

GRAD'U-AT'ED, *adj.* Divided into intervals, by rulings or other marks, such as the graduations on a ruler, a thermometer or a protractor.

GRAM, *n.* A unit of weight in the metric system; one-thousandth of a standard kilogram of platinum preserved in Paris. It was intended to be the weight of one cubic centimeter of water at 4°C. (the temperature at which its density is a maximum), and this is very nearly true. See DENOMINATE NUMBERS in the appendix.

GRAPH, *n.* A drawing that shows the relation between certain sets of numbers. *Tech.* A drawing which depicts a functional relation.

bar graph. A graph consisting of parallel bars (see figure) whose lengths are proportional to certain quantities given in a set of data. Used to convey a better idea of the meaning of the data than is gotten directly from numbers.

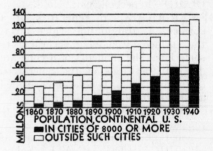

broken line graph. A graph formed by segments of straight lines which join the points representing certain data. The days during a certain period

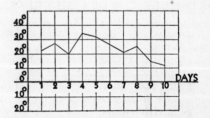

of time might be indicated by successive, equally spaced points on the *x*-

axis and ordinates drawn at each point proportional in length to the highest temperature on those days. If the upper ends of these ordinates be connected by line segments, a broken line graph results.

circular graph. A compact scheme for geometrically comparing parts of a whole to the whole. The whole is represented by the area of a circle, while the parts are represented by the areas of sectors of the circle.

graph of a complex number. See COMPLEX—graphical representation of complex numbers.

graph of an equation in three variables. A surface which contains those points and only those points whose coordinates satisfy the equation.

graph of an equation in two variables. *In the plane*, the curve which is the locus of those points, and only those points, whose coordinates satisfy the given equation. *In space*, the cylinder whose right section is the graph in a plane of the given equation. See CURVE—curve in a plane, and CYLINDRICAL—equation of a cylindrical surface.

graph of a first degree linear equation in Cartesian coordinates. *In the plane*, a straight line. *In space*, a plane. See LINE, and PLANE.

graph of a simultaneous set of equations. (1) The graphs of all the equations, showing their intersections. (2) The intersection of the graphs of the equations.

GRAPH, *v.* To draw the graph of. See above, bar graph, broken line graph, etc.

GRAPH'IC-AL, or GRAPH'IC, *adj.* Pertaining to graphs, or drawings-to-scale; working by drawings-to-scale rather than with algebraic tools.

graphical addition of complex numbers. See ADDITION—addition of complex numbers.

graphical representation of complex numbers. See COMPLEX—graphical representation of complex numbers.

graphical solution of an equation, $f(x) = 0$. Estimating the real roots from the graph of the equation $y = f(x)$. The real roots are the values of the variable

for which the function is zero, hence they are the abscissas of the points at which the graph crosses the x-axis. See HORNER'S and NEWTON'S method of approximating the roots of an equation.

graphical solution of inequalities. Finding the region in the plane or space where the inequality, or inequalities, hold true. E.g. (1) $x > 2$ has for its solution all points in the region to the right of the line whose equation in rectangular coordinates is $x = 2$; (2) the inequality $x^2 + y^2 + z^2 < 1$ has for its solution all points within the sphere $x^2 + y^2 + z^2 = 1$.

GRAPH'ING, *p.* Drawing the graph of an equation or the graph representing a set of data. See CURVE—curve tracing, and below, statistical graphing.

graphing by composition. A method of graphing which consists of writing the given function as the sum of several functions whose graphs are easier to draw, plotting each of these functions, then adding the corresponding ordinates. The graph of $y = e^x - \sin x$ can be readily drawn by drawing the graphs of each of the equations $y = e^x$ and $y = -\sin x$, then adding the ordinates of these two curves, which correspond to the same values of x. *Syn.* Graphing by composition of ordinates.

statistical graphing. Representing a set of statistics diagrammatically. E.g. (1) a curve or broken line may be drawn through points whose ordinates represent the statistical values obtained at time intervals which are indicated on the axis of abscissas. (2) Adjoining bars may be drawn, from a common line, representing (in length) certain statistical values. This is called a **bar graph.** Many other schemes for representing statistics diagrammatically are employed. The fundamental idea in all of them is to enable the reader to study the statistics better than he could were they presented as a mere collection of numbers. See GRAPH—bar graph, broken line graph, and FREQUENCY—normal frequency curve.

GRAV'I-TA'TION, *n.* See ATTRACTION—attraction of gravitation.

GRAVITATIONAL CONSTANT. The constant, G, in Newton's law of gravitation $F = Gm_1m_2/r^2$, where F denotes the force of gravitation, m_1 and m_2 the masses of two particles and r the distance between them. In the c.g.s. system, $G = (6.664 \pm .002)10^{-8}$ dynes, which is the attraction between two particles of one gram each when the distance between them is one centimeter.

GRAV'I-TY, *n.* acceleration of gravity. The acceleration of a particle toward the earth's center caused by gravitation and diminished by the centrifugal force due to the earth's rotation. Acceleration of gravity at the poles is 32.25 feet per second per second, at sea level at the equator about 32.09, decreasing about 1/500 of an inch for every mile of altitude.

    center of gravity. See ATTRACTION—center of attraction.

GREAT CIRCLE. A section of a sphere by a plane which passes through its center; a circle (on a sphere) which has its diameter equal to that of the sphere.

GREAT'ER, *adj.* One **cardinal number** is greater than a second when the set of units represented by the second is a part of that represented by the first; one cardinal number is greater than a second if, when undertaking to pair their units one-to-one, the latter is exhausted before the former. One ordinal (real algebraic) number is greater than a second when the number that must be added to the second to make them equal is positive; one ordinal (real algebraic) number is greater than a second when it is to the right of the second in the number scale: $\cdots$ $-4, -3, -2, -1, 0, 1, 2, 3, 4, \cdots$. Thus 3 is greater than 2 (written $3 > 2$); and $-2 > -3$, because 1 must be added to -3 to make -2.

GREAT'EST, *adj.* **greatest common divisor.** See DIVISOR.

    greatest common measure. Same as GREATEST COMMON DIVISOR.

    greatest lower bound. See BOUND.

    greatest value of a function in an interval. The largest algebraic value it takes on in the interval, if it takes on a largest value. E.g. (1) the greatest value of the function $x^3 - 3x^2$ on the interval $(-4, 4)$ is 16, while its maximum is 0; (2) the function $\tan x$ has no greatest value on $(0, \frac{1}{2}\pi)$, for it becomes infinite as x approaches $\frac{1}{2}\pi$; (3) the function $1 - 1/x$ has no greatest value for $x > 0$, since it approaches 1 as a limit as x increases without limit, never being equal to 1.

GREEK ALPHABET. See the appendix.

GREEN'S THEOREM. (1) *For a function of two variables*: The line integral of $P dx + Q dy$ around a closed curve C in a direction such as to keep the interior of C always on the left (see LINE—line integral) is equal to the integral, over the area bounded by the curve, of the partial derivative of Q with respect to x minus the partial of P with respect to y. (2) *For a function of three variables*: The integral of $P dy dz + Q dx dz + R dx dy$ over a closed surface is equal to the integral, over the enclosed solid, of the partial derivative of P with respect to x plus the partial derivative of Q with respect to y plus the partial derivative of R with respect to z.

GREGORY-NEWTON FORMULA. A formula for interpolation. If $x_0, x_1, x_2, x_3, \cdots$ are successive values of the argument, and $y_0, y_1, y_2, y_3, \cdots$ the corresponding values of the function, the formula is:

$$y = y_0 + k\Delta_0 + \frac{k(k-1)}{2!}\Delta_0^2 + \frac{k(k-1)(k-2)}{3!}\Delta_0^3 + \cdots,$$

where $k = (x - x_0)/(x_1 - x_0)$, x (the value of the argument for which y is being computed) lies between x_0 and x_1,

$$\Delta_0 = y_1 - y_0,$$
$$\Delta_0^2 = y_2 - 2y_1 + y_0,$$
$$\Delta_0^3 = y_3 - 3y_2 + 3y_1 - y_0,$$

etc., the coefficients in Δ_0^n being the binomial coefficients of order n. If all the terms in the formula except the first two are dropped, the result is the ordinary interpolation formula used with logarithmic and trigonometric tables and in approximating roots of an equation, namely

$$y = y_0 + [(x - x_0)/(x_1 - x_0)](y_1 - y_0).$$

(This is,, incidentally, the two point form of the equation of a straight line.)

GROSS, *adj.* **gross capacity, price, profit, etc.** The totality before certain parts have been deducted to leave the balance designated by the term *net*. E.g. the *gross profit* is the sale price minus the initial or first cost. When the overhead charges have been deducted the remainder is the *net profit*.

gross premium. See PREMIUM.

gross tonnage. See TONNAGE.

GROSS, *n.* Twelve dozen; 12×12.

GROUP, *n.* A set of elements subject to some rule of combination (usually called multiplication) such that: (1) the product of any two elements (alike or different) is unique and is in the set; (2) the set contains a unique element (called the **identity** element) such that its product with any element, in either order, does not change that element; (3) for every element in the set there is an element (called the **inverse**) such that the product of the two, in either order, is the identity element; (4) the *associative law* holds. The number of elements in a group is called its order. The cube roots of unity form a group under ordinary multiplication. The positive and negative integers and zero form a group under ordinary addition, the identity being zero and the inverse of an element its negative.

Abelian or commutative group. A group which (in addition to the four assumptions listed above) satisfies the commutative law. I.e. $ab = ba$, where a and b are any two elements of the group. Any group where all elements are powers of one element is Abelian. The examples under GROUP are Abelian groups.

finite group. A group containing only a finite number of elements. The cube roots of unity (or the nth roots of unity) form a finite group under ordinary multiplication. See GROUP.

group theory. The study of groups.

grouping terms. A method of factoring consisting of rearranging terms, when necessary, inserting parentheses and taking out a factor;

e.g. $x^3 + 4x^2 - 8 - 2x = x^3 + 4x^2 - 2x - 8$
$$= x^2(x+4) - 2(x+4) = (x^2 - 2)(x+4).$$

infinite group. A group containing an unlimited number of elements. All positive real numbers (with the exception of zero) form an infinite group under ordinary multiplication, unity being the identity element and the reciprocal of a number being its inverse.

subgroup. A group contained within a group. The group consisting of the cube roots of unity is a sub-group of the group consisting of the sixth roots of unity, the combination operation being ordinary multiplication. (The product of any two elements within a subgroup is in the subgroup, but the product of one within the subgroup by one not in it is not in the subgroup.)

GUAR′AN-TEED′, *adj.* **guaranteed bonus, participating insurance policies.** Policies which carry a guarantee of a certain rate of profit-sharing (bonus); really non-participating since the bonuses assured are determined at the policy date.

guaranteed stock plan of building and loan association. The plan in which certain investors provide certain funds and guarantee the payment of certain dividends on all shares, any surplus over this guarantee being divided among these basic stockholders.

GU-DER-MANN′I-AN, *n.* The function u of the variable x defined by the relation of $\tan u = \sinh x$; u and x also satisfy the relations $\cos u = \mathrm{sech}\ x$ and $\sin u = \tanh x$. The Gudermannian of x is written $gd\, x$.

GY-RA′TION, *n.* **radius of gyration.** See RADIUS.

H

HALF, *adj.* **half-angle formulas of plane trigonometry.** See FORMULA—half-angle formulas of plane trigonometry.

half-angle formulas of spherical trigonometry. Formulas giving the tangents of half of an angle of a spherical triangle in terms of functions of the sides. If α, β, γ are the angles, a, b, c, respectively, the opposite sides and $s = \frac{1}{2}(a+b+c)$, then

$$\tan \tfrac{1}{2}\alpha = \frac{r}{\sin (s-a)}$$

where

$$r = \sqrt{\frac{\sin (s-a) \sin (s-b) \sin (s-c)}{\sin s}}.$$

Formulas for $\tan \frac{1}{2}\beta$ and $\tan \frac{1}{2}\gamma$ are obtained from this formula by a cyclic change between a, b, c.

half-line. A line terminated by a finite point in one direction and extending indefinitely (without limit) in the opposite direction.

half-side formulas of spherical trigonometry. Formulas giving the tangents of one-half of each of the sides in terms of functions of all the angles. See above, half-angle formulas of spherical trigonometry. If α, β, γ are the angles, a, b, c, respectively, the sides opposite these angles and $S = \frac{1}{2}(\alpha+\beta+\gamma)$, then

$$\tan \tfrac{1}{2}a = R \cos (S-\alpha)$$

where

$$R = \sqrt{\frac{-\cos S}{\cos (S-\alpha) \cos (S-\beta) \cos (S-\gamma)}}.$$

Formulas for $\tan \frac{1}{2}b$ and $\frac{1}{2}c$ are obtained by a cyclic change between α, β and γ.

HAR-MON'IC, *adj.* **compound harmonic function.** See COMPOUND.

damped harmonic motion. The motion of a body which would have simple harmonic motion except that it is subjected to a resistance proportional to its velocity. The equation of motion is $x = ae^{-ct} \cos (kt+\phi)$. The exponential factor continuously reduces the amplitude. The differential equation of the motion is

$$\frac{d^2x}{dt^2} = -(c^2+k^2)\, x - 2c \frac{dx}{dt}.$$

harmonic conjugate. See CONJUGATE—harmonic conjugates with respect to two points.

harmonic division of a line. A line segment is said to be divided *harmoni-*

cally when it is divided externally and internally in the same numerical ratio. See RATIO—harmonic ratio.

harmonic mean between two numbers. Denoted by H. M. The middle term of three successive terms in an harmonic progression; the reciprocal of the arithmetic mean of their reciprocals; e.g. the harmonic mean between 1 and $\frac{1}{3}$ is the reciprocal of the arithmetic mean between 1 and 3, which is $\frac{1}{2}$. Stated algebraically, the H. M. between a and b is the reciprocal of $\frac{1}{2}(1/a+1/b)$, which is $2ab/(a+b)$.

harmonic progression. A sequence of quantities whose reciprocals form an arithmetic progression; denoted by H. P. In *music*, strings of the same material, same diameter, and the same tension, whose lengths are proportional to the terms in a harmonic progression, produce harmonic tones. The sequence $1, 1/2, 1/3, \cdots, 1/n, \cdots$, is an harmonic progression.

harmonic ratio. See RATIO—harmonic ratio.

harmonic series. See SERIES.

simple harmonic function. See FUNCTION—simple harmonic function, and below, simple harmonic motion.

simple harmonic motion. Motion like that of the projection upon a diameter of a circle of a point moving with uniform speed around the circumference; the motion of a particle moving on a straight line under a force proportional to the particle's distance from a fixed point and directed toward that point. If the fixed point is the origin and the x-axis the line, the acceleration of the particle is $-k^2x$, where k is a constant. I.e. the equation of motion of the particle is

$$\frac{d^2x}{dt^2} = -k^2x.$$

The general solution of this equation is $x = a \cos (kt+\phi)$. The particle moves back and forth (oscillates) between points at a distance a on either side of the origin. The time for a complete oscillation is $2\pi/k$. The distance a is called the **amplitude** and $2\pi/k$ the

period. The angle $\phi + kt$ is called the **phase** and ϕ the initial phase.

HA'VER-SINE. See TRIGONOMET-RIC—trigonometric functions of an acute angle.

HEL'I-COID, *n.* A surface shaped like a propeller screw; a surface whose parametric equations are $x = u \cos t$, $y = u \sin t$, $z = bt$, where u and t are variable parameters. If u is held constant, the equations define a helix (the intersection of the helicoid and the cylinder $x^2 + y^2 = u^2$).

HE'LIX, *n.* [*pl.* **helices.**] A curve on a right circular cylinder cutting all the elements of the cylinder at the same angle. Its equation, in parametric form, is

$$x = a \sin \theta, \quad y = a \cos \theta, \quad z = b\theta,$$

where a and b are constants and θ is the parameter. The thread of a bolt is a helix. This helix, technically called the **circular helix,** is a special case of the **cylindrical helix,** which is a curve on any type of cylinder which cuts the elements of the cylinder at a constant angle.

HEM'I-SPHERE, *n.* A half of a sphere.

HEP'TA-GON, *n.* A polygon having seven sides.

 regular heptagon. A heptagon whose sides are all equal and whose interior angles are all equal.

HERON'S FORMULA. Same as HERO'S FORMULA. The latter name is usually given to it.

HERO'S FORMULA. A formula expressing the area of a triangle in terms of the sides, a, b, c. It is:

$$A = \sqrt{s(s-a)(s-b)(s-c)},$$

where $\quad s = \frac{1}{2}(a+b+c)$.

HEX'A-GON, *n.* A polygon of six sides.

 regular hexagon. A hexagon whose sides are all equal and whose interior angles are all equal.

 simple hexagon. Six points, no three of which are collinear, and the six lines determined by them in pairs.

HEXAGONAL PRISM. A prism having hexagons for bases. See PRISM.

HEX'A-HE'DRON, *n.* A polyhedron having six faces.

 regular hexahedron. See POLYHE-DRON—regular polyhedron.

HIGH'ER, *adj.* **higher degree terms.** Terms of *higher degree* relative to other terms under consideration. One would say "dropping terms of *higher degrees* than the second in $1 + x + x^2 + x^3 \cdots$, leaves $1 + x + x^2$."

 higher plane curve. An algebraic curve of degree higher than the second.

 higher terms. A phrase used to describe the fraction resulting from multiplying the numerator and denominator of a fraction by a constant different from zero. The fraction $1/2$ becomes $3/6$, a fraction in *higher terms*, when its numerator and denominator are multiplied by 3.

HIGHEST COMMON FACTOR. Same as GREATEST COMMON DIVISOR. See DIVISOR.

HIS'TO-GRAM. See FREQUENCY—frequency distribution.

HOLD'ER, *n.* (*Finance.*) The one who owns a note, not necessarily the payee named in the note. See NEGOTIA-BLE.

HO'MO-GE'NE-OUS, *adj.* **consistency of n homogeneous linear equations in m unknowns:** (1) If $n < m$, the equations have a non-trivial solution (not all unknowns zero). (2) If $n = m$, the equations have a non-trivial solution if, and only if, the determinant of the coefficients is equal to zero. (3) If $n > m$, the equations have a non-trivial solution if, and only if, the *rank* of the *matrix* of the coefficients is equal to $(m - 1)$. These are simply the special case of the results for n linear equations in m unknowns when the constant terms are all zero. See MATRIX—rank of a matrix.

 homogeneous affine transformation. See AFFINE TRANSFORMATION.

 homogeneous algebraic polynomial. A polynomial whose terms are all of the same degree with respect to all the variables; $x^2 + 3xy + 4y^2$ is homogeneous.

 homogeneous coordinates. See CO-ORDINATE—homogeneous coordinates.

homogeneous differential equation. See DIFFERENTIAL.

homogeneous equation. An equation such that if it is written with no terms in the right hand member, the left member is a homogeneous function of the variables involved; an equation such that if t times each variable is substituted for that variable, t factors out of the equation entirely.

homogeneous function. A function such that if each of the variables is replaced by t times the variable, t can be completely factored out of the function. The functions $(\sin x/y + x/y)$ and $(x^2 \log x/y + y^2)$ are homogeneous. See above, homogeneous algebraic polynomial.

homogeneous solid. (1) A solid whose density is the same at all points. (2) A solid such that if congruent pieces be taken from different parts of it they will be alike in all respects.

homogeneous strains. See STRAIN.

homogeneous transformation. See TRANSFORMATION—homogeneous transformation.

HO-MOL'O-GOUS, *adj.* **homologous elements** (such as terms, points, lines, angles). Elements that play similar roles in distinct figures or functions. The numerators or the denominators of two equal fractions are *homologous terms*. The vertices of a polygon and those of a projection of the polygon on a plane are *homologous points* and the sides and their projections are *homologous lines*. *Syn.* Corresponding.

HO-MO-THET'IC, *adj.* **homothetic figures.** Figures so related that lines joining corresponding points pass through a point and are divided in a constant ratio by this point.

homothetic transformation. See SIMILITUDE—transformation of similitude.

HOOKE'S LAW. (*In physics.*) The elongation due to stretching is proportional to the tension, written $E = cT$, where E is the elongation, T the tension, and c a constant. The law applies approximately (within limits for the tension) to springs, rods, etc.

HO-RI'ZON, *n.* **horizon of an observer on the earth.** The circle in which the earth, looked upon as a plane, appears to meet the sky; the great circle on the celestial sphere which has its pole at the observer's zenith. See HOUR—hour angle and hour circle.

HOR'I-ZON'TAL, *adj.* Parallel to the earth's surface looked upon as a plane; parallel to the plane of the horizon. *Tech.* In a plane perpendicular to the plumb line.

HORNER'S METHOD. A method for approximating the real roots of an algebraic equation. Its essential steps are as follows: (1) Locate a positive root between two successive integers (if the equation has only negative real roots, *transform* it to one whose roots are the negatives of those of the given equation). (2) *Transform* the equation into an equation whose roots are decreased by the lesser of the integers between which the root lies, by the substitution $x' = x - a$. The root of the new equation will lie between zero and unity. (3) Locate the root of the new equation between successive tenths. (4) *Transform* the last equation into an equation whose roots are decreased by the smaller of these tenths and locate the root of this equation between hundredths. Continue this process to one decimal place more than the place to which the answer is to be correct. The root sought is then the total amount by which the roots of the original equation were reduced; namely the lesser integer, plus the lesser tenth, plus the lesser hundredth, etc., the last decimal being rounded off to make the result accurate to the desired decimal place. Fractions may be avoided in locating the roots by transforming the equation in step (4) to one whose roots are ten times as large, and repeating the same transformation each time another digit in the root is sought. Synthetic division is generally used to expedite the work of substituting values for the variable. Roots can be located very quickly after the first step by solving the equation obtained by dropping the terms of higher degree than the first. See RE-

MAINDER—remainder theorem, IN-
TERPOLATION, and REGULA
FALSI.

HORSEPOWER. A unit of power; a
measure of how fast work is being
done. Several values have been assigned to this unit. The one used in England and America is the *Watts horsepower*. It is defined as 550 foot pounds
per second, at sea level and 50° latitude. The Watts horsepower is 1.0139
times the French horsepower. See
FOOT-POUND.

HOUR, *n.* One twenty-fourth of the time
required for the earth to make one
complete revolution about its axis. See
TIME.

   hour angle and hour circle: In the
figure, let *O* be the place of the observer, *NESW* the circle in which the
plane of the observer's horizon cuts
the celestial sphere, *EKW* the circle
in which the plane of the earth's equator cuts the celestial sphere, *NS* the
north and south line, and *EW* the east
and west line. The circles *NESW* and
EKW are called respectively the astronomical **horizon** and the **celestial equator.** *Z* is the zenith and *P* the **north
celestial pole.** *SZPN* is called the **celestial meridian** or **meridian** of *O.* Let
M be any celestial object, and draw
great circles *ZR, PL* perpendicular to
the horizon and the equator respectively. *RM* is the **altitude** of *M*, and
NR its **azimuth.** *LM* is the **declination**
of *M*, and *KOL* is its **hour angle.** *LP* is
called the **hour circle** of *M*. If *M* is
north of the equator the declination is

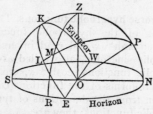

taken as positive; if south, as negative.
The hour angle is positive if *M* is west
of the meridian, negative if it is east of
the meridian. The hour angle of a celestial object changes at the rate of 15°
an hour or 360° a day, the hour circle

passing through it appearing to rotate
in the opposite direction to that of the
earth, that is to the west.

   kilowatt hour. See KILOWATT.

HUNDRED'S PLACE. See PLACE—
place value.

HUN'DREDTH, *adj.* **hundredth part of
a number.** The quotient of the number and 100, or 1/100 times the number.

HUYGEN'S FORMULA: The length of
an arc of a circle is approximately equal
to twice the chord subtending half the
arc plus one third of the difference between twice this chord and the chord
subtending the entire arc; or eight-
thirds of the chord subtending half the
arc minus one-third of the chord subtending the whole arc.

HY-PER'BO-LA, *n.* A curve with two
branches which is a plane section of
a circular conical surface; the locus of
a point whose distances from two fixed
points, called the **foci,** have a constant
difference. The standard form of the
equation in rectangular Cartesian coordinates is

$$x^2/a^2 - y^2/b^2 = 1,$$

where the hyperbola is symmetric
about the *x*- and *y*-axes and cuts the
x-axis in the points whose coordinates
are (*a*, 0) and (−*a*, 0), as in the figure
below. The intercepts on the *y*-axis are
imaginary. The axes of symmetry of
the hyperbola are called the **axes** of the
hyperbola (regardless of whether they
coincide with the coordinate axes). The
segment (of length 2*a*) of the axis which
cuts the hyperbola is called the **transverse** (real) axis and the **conjugate axis**
is the line segment of length 2*b* (as illustrated). The line segments *a* and *b* are
called the **semi-transverse** and **semi-
conjugate** axes, respectively. (Transverse and conjugate axes are also used
in speaking of the entire axes of symmetry.) The extremities of the transverse axes are called the **vertices** of the
hyperbola; the double ordinate at a
focus, i.e. the chord through a focus
and perpendicular to the transverse
axis, is called a **latus rectum.** See
CONIC.

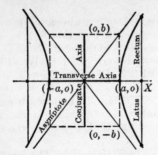

asymptote to an hyperbola. See ASYMPTOTE.

conjugate diameters of a hyperbola. See CONJUGATE—conjugate diameters.

conjugate hyperbolas. Hyperbolas for which the real (transverse) and conjugate axes of one are, respectively, the conjugate and real axes of the other. Their standard equations are $x^2/a^2 - y^2/b^2 = 1$ and $x^2/a^2 - y^2/b^2 = -1$. They have the same asymptotes.

diameter of an hyperbola. A line through the mid-points of a family of parallel chords.

director-circle of an hyperbola. See DIRECTOR-CIRCLE.

equiangular hyperbola. Same as RECTANGULAR HYPERBOLA.

equilateral hyperbola. Same as RECTANGULAR HYPERBOLA.

rectangular hyperbola. An hyperbola whose major and minor axes are equal. Its equation, in standard form, is $x^2 - y^2 = a^2$. The equations of the asymptotes are $y = x$ and $y = -x$. *Syn.* Equiangular hyperbola, equilateral hyperbola.

similar hyperbolas. See SIMILAR.

HY'PER-BOL'IC, *adj.* **hyperbolic cylinder.** See CYLINDER—hyperbolic cylinder.

hyperbolic functions. A set of functions related to the hyperbola in a manner somewhat similar to the way the trigonometric functions are related to the circle and bearing relations to each other similar to those between trigonometric functions. The hyperbolic functions are: *hyperbolic sine* of x, *hyperbolic cosine* of x, etc.; written $\sinh x$, $\cosh x$, etc. *Tech.* they are defined by the relations: $\sinh x = (e^x - e^{-x})/2$, $\cosh x$

$= (e^x + e^{-x})/2$, $\tanh x = \sinh x/\cosh x$, $\coth x = 1/\tanh x$, $\operatorname{sech} x = 1/\cosh x$, and $\operatorname{csch} x = 1/\sinh x$. The hyperbolic and trigonometric functions are connected by the relations: $\sinh ix = i \sin x$, $\cosh ix = \cos x$, $\tanh ix = i \tan x$, where $i = \sqrt{-1}$. Some of the properties of the hyperbolic functions are:

$$\sinh (-x) = -\sinh x$$
$$\cosh (-x) = \cosh x,$$
$$\cosh^2 x - \sinh^2 x = 1,$$
$$\operatorname{sech}^2 x + \tanh^2 x = 1,$$
$$\coth^2 x - \operatorname{csch}^2 x = 1.$$

See EXPONENTIAL—exponential values of $\sin x$ and $\cos x$.

hyperbolic logarithms. Another name for *natural logarithms.* See LOGARITHM.

hyperbolic paraboloid. See PARABOLOID.

hyperbolic point of a surface. A point whose Dupin indicatrix is an hyperbola.

hyperbolic (or reciprocal) spiral. A plane curve whose radius vector varies inversely with the vectorial angle. Its polar equation is $\rho\theta = a$, where a is the constant of proportionality. It is asymptotic to a straight line parallel to the polar axis and at a distance a above it.

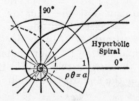

inverse hyperbolic functions. The inverses of the hyperbolic functions; written $\sinh^{-1} x$ and read inverse hyperbolic sine of x, also called **arc-hyperbolic functions,** $\cosh^{-1} x$, etc. The explicit forms of the functions can be gotten from the definitions of the hyperbolic functions; they are

$$\sinh^{-1} x = \log (x + \sqrt{x^2 + 1}),$$
$$\cosh^{-1} x = \log (x \pm \sqrt{x^2 - 1}),$$
$$\tanh^{-1} x = \tfrac{1}{2} \log \frac{1+x}{1-x},$$

$$\operatorname{ctnh}^{-1} x = \tfrac{1}{2} \log \frac{x+1}{x-1},$$

$$\operatorname{sech}^{-1} x = \log \frac{1 \pm \sqrt{1-x^2}}{x},$$

$$\operatorname{csch}^{-1} x = \log \frac{1+\sqrt{1+x^2}}{x}$$

See INVERSE—inverse function.

HY-PER'BO-LOID, *n.* A quadric surface having a (finite) center and some of its plane sections hyperbolas; a term referring to the so called hyperboloids of one sheet and of two sheets.

hyperboloid of one sheet. An hyperboloid that is cut in an ellipse or hyperbola by every plane parallel to a coordinate plane. If its equation is written in the form

$$\frac{x^2}{a^2}+\frac{y^2}{b^2}-\frac{z^2}{c^2}=1,$$

planes parallel to the xy-plane cut the surface in ellipses, while planes parallel to the xz or yz plane cut it in hyperbolas (see figure). The surface is a *ruled surface*. It contains two sets of rulings (two families of straight lines), and through each point of the surface there passes one member of each family. The equation of the two families of lines are:

$$x/a - z/c = p(1 - y/b)$$
$$p(x/a+z/c) = 1 + y/b$$
an
$$x/a - z/c = p(1+y/b),$$
$$p(x/a+z/c) = 1 - y/b,$$

where p is an arbitrary parameter. The product of the two equations in either set gives the original equation of the hyperboloid. Therefore the lines represented by these sets must lie on the

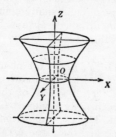

hyperbola. Either set of rulings is called a set of **rectilinear generators**

since it may be used to generate the surface; see RULED—ruled surface.

hyperboloid of revolution of one sheet. The hyperboloid of one sheet whose elliptical sections (see above, hyperboloid of one sheet, for equation), parallel to the xy-plane, when in the position illustrated above, are circles. The parameters a and b are equal in this case and the surface can be generated by revolving the hyperbola, $x^2/a^2 - z^2/c^2 = 1$, about the z-axis.

hyperboloid of revolution of two sheets. An hyperboloid of two sheets whose elliptical sections are circles (see below, hyperboloid of two sheets, for equation). The parameters b and c (in the equation of the hyperboloid of two sheets) are equal in this case, and the *hyperboloid of revolution of two sheets* can be generated by revolving the hyperbola, $x^2/a^2 - y^2/c^2 = 1$, about the x-axis.

hyperboloid of two sheets. A surface whose sections by planes parallel to two of the three coordinate planes (see figure) are hyperbolas and whose sections by planes parallel to the third plane are ellipses, except for a finite interval where there is no intersection (the intersection is imaginary). When the surface is in the position illustrated, its equation is of the form $x^2/a^2 - y^2/b^2 - z^2/c^2 = 1$.

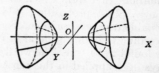

HY-PER-GE-O-MET'RIC, *adj.* **hypergeometric series.** A series of the form

$$1 + \sum_{n=1}^{\infty} \frac{a(a+1)\cdots(a+n-1)b(b+1)\cdots(b+n-1)z^n}{n!\,c(c+1)(c+2)\cdots(c+n-1)}$$

where c is not a negative integer. The series converges absolutely for $|z| < 1$. A necessary and sufficient condition for it to converge when $z = 1$ is that $a+b-c$ shall be negative (or that its real part be negative if it is complex). Also called *Gaussian Series.*

HY-PO-CY'CLOID, *n.* The plane locus of a point, P, fixed on a circle which rolls on the inside of a given fixed circle. If a is the radius of the fixed circle, b the radius of the rolling circle, and θ the angle subtended by the arc which has contacted the fixed circle, the parametric equations of the hypocycloid are:

$$x = (a-b) \cos \theta + b \cos [(a-b)\theta/b],$$
$$y = (a-b) \sin \theta - b \sin [(a-b)\theta/b].$$

The criteria for the number of arches is the same as for the *epicycloid*. The hypocycloid of four cusps (which is the case shown in the figure) has the Cartesian equation $x^{2/3} + y^{2/3} = a^{2/3}$. The hypocycloid has a cusp of the first kind at every point at which it touches the fixed circle. See EPICYCLOID.

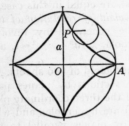

HY-POT′E-NUSE, *n.* The side opposite the right angle in a plane right triangle. See TRIANGLE—right triangle.

HY-POTH′E-SIS, *n.* [*pl.* **hypotheses.**] (1) An assumed proposition used as a premise in proving something else; a condition; that from which something follows. (2) A proposition held to be probably true because its consequences, according to known general principles, are found to be true. The word has always been applied in this sense to the theories of the planetary system.

HY-PO-TRO′CHOID, *n.* Same as *hypocycloid,* except that the describing point may lie within the circle or on the radius extended. If h is the distance from the center of the rolling circle to the describing point, and the other parameters are the same as for the *hypocycloid,* the parametric equations are:

$$x = (a-b) \cos \theta + h \cos [(a-b)\theta/b],$$
$$y = (a-b) \sin \theta - h \sin [(a-b)\theta/b].$$

The cases when h is less than b, or greater than b, are similar to the corre-

sponding cases for the *trochoid* (see TROCHOID).

I

I′CO-SA-HE′DRON, *n.* A polyhedron having twenty faces.

    regular icosahedron. An icosahedron whose faces are congruent triangles and whose polyhedral angles are congruent. See POLYHEDRON—regular polyhedron.

I-DE′AL, *adj.* **ideal point.** A point at infinity; a term used to complete the terminology of certain subjects (e.g. projective geometry) so that it is not necessary to state exceptions to certain theorems. Instead of saying that two straight lines in the same plane intersect except when they are parallel, it is said that two straight lines in a plane always intersect, intersecting in the ideal point being synonymous with being parallel. Thus an *ideal point* is thought of as a direction, the direction of a certain set of parallel lines. In *homogeneous coordinates,* the ideal points are the points for which $x_3 = 0$; the points $(x_1, x_2, 0)$, where x_1 and x_2 are not both zero. The point $(x_1, x_2, 0)$ lies on any line whose slope is equal to x_2/x_1. See COORDINATE—homogeneous coordinates in the plane.

I-DEN′TI-CAL, *adj.* **identical figures.** Figures which are exactly alike in form and size; two triangles with three sides of one equal to three sides of the other are identical. *Syn.* Congruent.

    identical quantities. Quantities which are alike in form as well as value. Quantities which form the left and right members of an *identity* are not necessarily identical, usually being different in form although always having the same values for all values of the variables.

I-DEN′TI-TY, *n.* A statement of equality, denoted by $\equiv$; a statement which is true for all values of the variables if there be any involved (see EQUATION). The two quantities which are equated are the same except possibly in form. $2+3 \equiv 5$, $2 \times 3 \equiv 6$, $(x+y)^2 \equiv x^2 + 2xy + y^2$, are identities. The equality sign, $=$, is quite commonly used in place of the sign, $\equiv$.

Pythagorean identities. See PYTHAGOREAN.

trigonometric identity. An identity involving only trigonometric functions and numbers; e.g. $\sin^2 x + \cos^2 x = 1$. See TRIGONOMETRIC—relations between the trigonometric functions.

IM-AG′I-NAR′Y, *adj.* **conjugate imaginary numbers.** See CONJUGATE—conjugate imaginaries.

imaginary axis. See AXIS.

imaginary circle. See CIRCLE.

imaginary curve (surface). A term used to provide continuity in speaking of loci of equations; the imaginary part of the curve (surface) corresponding to imaginary values of the variables which satisfy the equation. The equation $x^2 + y^2 + z^2 = 1$ has for its real locus the sphere with radius one and center at the origin, but is also satisfied by $(1, 1, i)$ and many other points whose coordinates are not all real. See CIRCLE—imaginary circle.

imaginary intersection. See INTERSECTION.

imaginary number. Any number of the form $a + bi$, $b \neq 0$, where i is the indicated square root of -1 $(i = \sqrt{-1})$ and a and b are real. See COMPLEX—complex number.

imaginary roots. (1) Roots of an equation, which are imaginary, such as the roots of $x^2 + x + 1 = 0$. (2) Roots of a number which are imaginary; even roots of negative numbers. See ROOT—nth root of a number.

pure imaginary number. An imaginary number of the form bi, $b \neq 0$; the special form of the complex number, $a + bi$, in which $a = 0$. See above, imaginary number.

IMMEDIATE ANNUITY. (1) An annuity whose payments begin immediately, as contrasted to a deferred annuity. (2) Same as ORDINARY ANNUITY. See ANNUITY.

IM-PLIC′IT, *adj.* **differentiation of implicit functions.** See DIFFERENTIATION—differentiation of an implicit function.

general implicit function theorem.

(See below, implicit function theorem for a function of two variables.) Consider a system of n equations between the $n + p$ variables

$$u_1, u_2, \cdots, u_n, \quad \text{and} \quad x_1, x_2, \cdots, x_p,$$

namely

$$f_1(x_1, x_2, \cdots, x_p; u_1, u_2, \cdots, u_n) = 0,$$
$$f_2(x_1, x_2, \cdots, x_p; u_1, u_2, \cdots, u_n) = 0,$$
$$\cdots \cdots \cdots \cdots \cdots \cdots$$
$$f_n(x_1, x_2, \cdots, x_p; u_1, u_2, \cdots, u_n) = 0.$$

Suppose that these equations are satisfied for the values $x_1 = x_1^0, \cdots,$ $x_p = x_p^0$, $u_1 = u_1^0, \cdots, u_n = u_n^0$, that the functions f_i are continuous in the neighborhood of this set of values and possess first partial derivatives and, finally, that the Jacobian of these functions does not vanish for $x_i = x_i^0$, $u_k = u_k^0$, $(i = 1, 2, \cdots p; k = 1, 2, \cdots n)$. Under these conditions there exists one and only one system of continuous functions

$$u_1 = \phi_1(x_1, x_2, \cdots, x_p)$$
$$\cdots \cdots \cdots \cdots \cdots$$
$$u_n = \phi_n(x_1, x_2, \cdots, x_p)$$

defined in some neighborhood of

$$(x_1^0, x_2^0, \cdots, x_p^0)$$

which satisfy the above equations and which reduce to

$$u_1^0, u_2^0, \cdots, u_n^0, \text{ for } x_1 = x_1^0, x_2 = x_2^0, \cdots$$
$$x_p = x_p^0.$$

implicit differentiation. See DIFFERENTIATION—differentiation of an implicit function.

implicit function. A function defined by an equation of the form $f(x, y) = 0$ (in general $f(x_1, x_2, \cdots, x_n) = 0$). If y is thought of as the dependent variable, $f(x, y) = 0$ is called an *implicit* function of x. Sometimes such equations can be solved for y, that is, written in the form $y = F(x)$. When this has been done y is called an **explicit** function of x. In $x + y^3 + 2x^2 y + xy = 0$, y is an *implicit* function of x, while in $y = x^2 + 1$, y is an *explicit* function of x.

implicit function theorem for a function of two variables. A theorem stating the conditions under which an implicit function of two variables possesses a solution for one of the variables in a neighborhood of a point whose coordinates make the given function vanish. *Tech.* If $F(x, y)$ and $D_y F(x, y)$, the partial derivative of F with respect to y, are continuous in the neighborhood of the point (x_0, y_0) and if $F(x_0, y_0) = 0$ and $D_y F(x_0, y_0) \neq 0$, then there exists one and only one function of x, continuous in a neighborhood of the point (x_0, y_0), and such that y has the value y_0 when x has the value x_0. E.g. the function $x^2 + xy^2 + y - 1$ and its partial derivative with respect to y, namely $2xy + 1$, are both continuous in the neighborhood of $(1, 0)$, and $x^2 + xy^2 + y - 1 = 0$ while $2xy + 1 \neq 0$ when $x = 1$, $y = 0$. Hence there exists a unique solution for y, in the neighborhood of $(1, 0)$, which gives $y = 0$ for $x = 1$. That solution is

$$= \frac{-1 + \sqrt{1 - 4x(x^2 - 1)}}{2x}.$$

IM-PROP'ER, *adj.* **improper fraction.** See FRACTION.

improper integral. See INTEGRAL.

IN'AC-CES'SI-BLE, *adj.* **inaccessible limit.** (1) A limit which a variable approaches but does not actually reach, as contrasted to limits which are actually reached. The limit approached by the distance traveled by a man who walks one-half as far in each second as in the preceding second is an inaccessible limit. If the distance traveled in one second is 1, the total distance traveled in n seconds is $1 + 1/2 + 1/4 + 1/8 + 1/16 + \cdots + 1/2^{n-1}$, which approaches but does not attain the value 2. (2) In geometry, a point off the paper.

INCENTER of a triangle. The center of the inscribed circle; the intersection

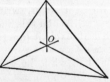

of the bisectors of the interior angles of the triangle.

INCH, *n.* A unit of measure of length, or distance; one twelfth of one foot, 2.54 centimeters. See DENOMINATE NUMBERS in the appendix.

IN-CIR'CLE, *n.* Same as INSCRIBED CIRCLE.

IN'CLI-NA'TION, *n.* **inclination of a line in the plane.** The angle from the x-axis to the line. (See ANGLE—angle between two lines in a plane, (1).); the angle whose tangent is the slope of the line.

inclination of a line in space with respect to a plane. The smaller angle the line makes with its projection in the plane.

inclination of a plane with respect to a given plane. The smaller of the angles which it makes with the given plane.

IN'COME, *n.* **income rate.** (*Finance.*) Same as YIELD.

income tax. A tax on incomes (salaries or profits), levied by the federal or state governments. The tax is determined by taking a certain percent of the remainder of the income after certain deductions (exemptions) have been made.

IN'COM-MEN'SU-RA-BLE, *adj.* **incommensurable lines.** Two lines that have no common measure, such as the hypotenuse and a leg of an isoceles right triangle; two lines whose lengths are represented by incommensurable numbers.

incommensurable numbers. Numbers which are not both integral multiples of the same number. The numbers $\sqrt{2}$ and 3 are incommensurable, for no number is contained in both an integral number of times.

IN'COM-PAT'I-BLE, *adj.* **incompatible equations.** Same as INCONSISTENT EQUATIONS.

IN'COM-PLETE', *adj.* **incomplete induction.** See COMPLETE—complete induction.

INCONSISTENT EQUATIONS. Two (or more) equations which are not satisfied by any one set of values of the variables; equations which are not consistent. E.g. $x + y = 2$ and $x + y = 3$ are inconsistent. See CONSISTENCY. *Syn.* Incompatible.

IN-CREAS'ING, *p.* **increasing function** of a single variable. A function whose value increases as the independent variable increases; a function whose graph, in Cartesian coordinates, rises as the abscissa increases. The necessary and sufficient condition that a differentiable function be increasing is that its derivative be positive.

increasing premium policy. An insurance policy on which the early premiums are smaller than the later ones.

monotonic increasing. See MONOTONIC.

IN'CRE-MENT, *n.* A change in a variable; an amount added to a given value of a variable, usually thought of as a small amount.

increment of a function of one variable. The change in the function due to the addition of an increment to the independent variable. If the function is $f(x)$ and the change in the independent variable, x, is Δx, then the increment in $f(x)$ is $f(x+\Delta x) - f(x)$. See DIFFERENTIAL—differential of a function of one variable.

total increment of a function of two or more variables. The change in the function due to adding increments to each of the variables. If, for instance, $u, = u(x, y)$, is a function of x and y, the total increment of u, written Δx, is equal to $u(x+\Delta x, y+\Delta y) - u(x, y)$. By the use of the *mean value theorem* for a function of two variables this expression can be written as the sum $(D_x u \Delta x + D_y u \Delta y) + (\epsilon_1 \Delta x + \epsilon_2 \Delta y)$, where $D_x u$ and $D_y u$ denote the partial derivatives of u with respect to x and y respectively, and ϵ_1 and ϵ_2 are infinitesimals. The first bracket is called the **principal part** of Δu, or **total differential** of u, written $du = D_x u \, dx + D_y u \, dy$. The increments of x and y, Δx and Δy, have been written dx and dy, in order to avoid confusion of notation in the cases $u = x$ and $u = y$. The increments dx and dy are called the *differentials* of the *independent* variables x and y.

IN-DEF'I-NITE, *adj.* **indefinite integral.** See INTEGRAL—indefinite integral.

IN'DE-PEND'ENT, *adj.* **independent equations.** A system of equations such that no one of them is necessarily satisfied by a set of values of the independent variables which satisfy all the others. See CONSISTENCY.

independent events. See EVENT.

independent functions. A set of functions $u_1, u_2, \cdots, u_n$, where $x_1, x_2, \cdots, x_n$ are the independent variables, such that there does not exist a relation $F(u_1, u_2, \cdots, u_n) = 0$ which does not explicitly involve any of the variables $x_1, x_2, \cdots, x_n$. The functions are independent if and only if the *Jacobian*

$$\frac{D(u_1, u_2, \cdots, u_n)}{D(x_1, x_2, \cdots, x_n)}$$

does not vanish identically. The functions $2x+3y$ and $4x+6y+8$ are dependent, since $4x+6y+8 = 2(2x+3y) + 8$. The functions

$$u_1 = 2x+3y+z, \quad u_2 = x+y-z$$

and $u_3 = x+y$, are independent. Their Jacobian does not vanish; it is

$$\begin{vmatrix} 2 & 3 & 1 \\ 1 & 1 & -1 \\ 1 & 1 & 0 \end{vmatrix}$$

which equals -1.

independent variable. See FUNCTION.

IN'DE-TER'MI-NATE, *adj.* **indeterminate equation.** See EQUATION—indeterminate equation.

indeterminate forms. Expressions of the type $\infty - \infty$, $0/0$, ∞/∞, $0 \cdot \infty$, ∞^0, 0^0, 1^∞, which are undefined. These arise from replacing different members of composite functions by their limits before combining the members properly. The correct procedure is to find the limits of the difference, quotient, etc., not the difference, quotient, etc., of the limits. See L'HOSPITAL'S RULE.

IN'DE-TER'MI-NATE-NESS, *adj.* The state of being indeterminate. See INDETERMINATE.

IN'DEX, *n.* [*pl.* indices.] A number used to point out a specific characteristic or operation.

contravariant index. See TENSOR.

covariant index. See TENSOR.

dummy index. See SUMMATION—summation convention.

free index. See SUMMATION—summation convention.

index laws. Same as exponential laws. See LAW—laws of exponents.

index of a number or quantity. Same as EXPONENT.

index of precision. The constant h in the normal frequency (probability) curve, $y = Ke^{-h^2(x-A)^2}$. See FREQUENCY—normal frequency curve.

index of a radical. An integer placed above and to the left of a radical to indicate what root is sought; e.g. $\sqrt[3]{64} = 4$. The index is omitted when it would be 2; $\sqrt{x}$ rather than $\sqrt[2]{x}$ indicates the square root of x.

index of refraction. See REFRACTION.

IN'DI-CA'TOR, n. **indicator diagram.** A diagram in which the ordinates of a curve represent a varying force, the abscissas the distance passed over, and the area beneath the curve the work done.

indicator of an integer. The number of integers not greater than the given integer and relatively prime to it. If the number is $n = a^p b^q c^r \cdots$, where a, b, c, $\cdots$ are distinct primes, then its indicator is $n(1-1/a)(1-1/b)(1-1/c) \cdots$. The indicator of 1 is 1, of 2 is 1, and of 3 is 2; the indicator of 12 is $12(1-\frac{1}{2})(1-\frac{1}{3})$ or 4. *Syn.* Totient, ϕ-function (Euler's ϕ-function).

IN-DI-CA'TRIX, n. **Dupin indicatrix of a surface (at a point).** The quadratic curve which approximates the curve of intersection of the surface and a plane parallel to and very near to the tangent plane at the point, the point being an *ordinary point*.

spherical indicatrix of a space curve. The curve traced out on a unit sphere by the end of a radius which is always parallel to a tangent that moves along the curve. If the curve is a plane curve, its spherical indicatrix is a great circle of the sphere. Hence, the amount of deviation of the spherical indicatrix from a great circle gives some idea of the amount of deviation of the curve from being a plane curve, i.e. of the amount of torsion of the curve.

IN'DI-CES, n. Plural of index. See INDEX.

IN'DI-RECT', *adj.* **indirect differentiation.** The differentiation of a function of a function by use of the formula $df(u)/dx = (df(u)/du)(du/dx)$. See DERIVATIVE—derivative of a function of a function.

indirect proof. (1) Same as REDUCTIO AD ABSURDUM PROOF. (2) Proving a proposition by first proving another theorem from which the given proposition follows.

IN-DORSE', v. **to indorse a note or other financial agreement.** To accept the responsibility for carrying out the obligation of the maker of the paper provided the maker does not meet his own obligation; to assign a paper to a new payee by signing it on the back (this makes the indorser liable for the maker's obligation unless the signature is accompanied by the statement *without recourse*).

IN-DORSE'MENT, n. The act of indorsing; that which is written when indorsing. See INDORSE.

IN-DUC'TION, n. **complete induction.** Same as MATHEMATICAL INDUCTION.

incomplete induction. See COMPLETE—complete induction.

mathematical induction. See MATHEMATICAL.

INDUCTIVE METHODS. Drawing conclusions from several known cases; reasoning from the particular to the general. See MATHEMATICAL—mathematical induction.

IN'E-QUAL'I-TY, n. A statement that one quantity is less than (or greater than) another. If the quantity a is less than the quantity b, their relation is denoted symbolically by $a < b$, and the relation a greater than b is written $a > b$. Inequalities have many of the properties of equations. They are still true after any quantities have been added or subtracted from both members and after both members have been multiplied or divided by any positive number. However multiplication or division by negative numbers changes the sense of the inequality. Since $3 > 2$,

$$3+1>2+1; \quad 3-1>2-1 \text{ and}$$
$$2\times3>2\times2; \quad \text{but} \quad -3<-2.$$

absolute inequality. An inequality which holds for all values of the variables (on their given ranges); $x^2+y^2> -1$ is an *absolute inequality* for x and y real numbers.

conditional inequality. An inequality which holds for only a restricted number of values of the variables involved. $x+xy>0$ does not hold, say, when $x=1$ and $y=-5$; it is therefore a conditional inequality.

graphical solution of inequalities. See GRAPHICAL.

sense of an inequality. See SENSE.

simultaneous inequalities. See SIMULTANEOUS.

IN-ER'TI-A, *n.* element (or differential) of moment of inertia. See MOMENT—moment of inertia.

inertia of a body. Its resistance to change of its state of motion, or rest; the property of a body which necessitates exertion of force upon the body to give it acceleration. *Syn.* Mass.

moment of inertia. See MOMENT.

IN-FE'RI-OR, *adj.* inferior limit. See LIMIT.

IN'FI-NITE, *adj.* Becoming large beyond any fixed bound. *Tech.* A function is said to *become infinite* if its absolute value becomes larger than any assigned number whatever. It is said to become *positively infinite* or to approach *plus infinity* if its value becomes larger than any assigned number; and to become *negatively infinite* or to approach *minus infinity* if its value becomes less than any assigned number. A function which becomes infinite as the argument approaches a given value is said to be **unbounded** or **infinite** in the neighborhood of the value (point).

infinite branch of a curve. A part of the curve which contains points infinitely far, measured along straight lines, from some fixed point; a part of the curve which cannot be enclosed in any finite circle with center at the origin of coordinates.

infinite integral. An integral at least one of whose limits of integration is infinite. The value of the integral is the limit it approaches as its limit (or limits) of integration becomes infinite. E.g.

$$\int_1^\infty \frac{dp}{p^2}= \lim_{h\to\infty} \int_1^h \frac{dp}{p^2}= \lim_{h\to\infty} [-1/h+1]=1.$$

infinite limit. A variable is said to have an *infinite limit* when it becomes infinite. See INFINITE.

infinite point. Same as IDEAL POINT.

infinite product. A product which contains an unlimited number of factors. An infinite product is denoted by a capital pi, Π; e.g. $\Pi[n/(n+1)]$ $=\frac{1}{2}\cdot\frac{2}{3}\cdot\frac{3}{4}\cdot\frac{4}{5}\cdots$, is an infinite product.

infinite root. See ROOT—infinite root of an algebraic equation.

infinite sequence. See SEQUENCE.

infinite series. See SERIES.

infinite set. (1) A set of numbers which is *unbounded*, i.e. there is no one number which is larger in absolute value than every number of the set. (2) A set which has an unlimited number of members; a set which can be put into one-to-one correspondence with a part of itself. E.g. (1) All positive integers constitute an infinite set. It can be put into one-to-one correspondence, for instance, with the set of positive even integers. (2) The rational fractions between 0 and 1 constitute an infinite set. It can be put into one-to-one correspondence with all rational fractions whose numerators are unity.

point at infinity. The same as IDEAL POINT.

IN'FIN-I-TES'I-MAL, *adj.* A variable whose numerical value becomes and remains smaller than any assigned value; a variable which approaches zero as a limit.

infinitesimal analysis. The study of differentials, and of integration as a process of summing an infinite set of infinitesimals; see INTEGRAL—definite integral. Sometimes used for the calculus and all subjects making use of the calculus.

infinitesimal calculus. Ordinary calculus; so-called because it is based on the study of infinitesimal quantities.

order of an infinitesimal. A relative term used to compare infinitesimals. If the limit of the quotient of two infinitesimals is a constant, not zero, they are said to be of the *same order*; if this limit is zero, the first, the numerator, is said to be of *higher order* than the second, and the second of *lower order* than the first; if the limit is infinite, the first (the numerator) is said to be of lower order than the second and the second of higher order than the first. If the ratio of the nth power of one infinitesimal to a second infinitesimal approaches a constant, not zero, the second is said to be of the nth *order* relative to the first. $(1 - \cos x)$ is of the second order relative to x, since $x^2/(1 - \cos x)$ approaches 2 as x approaches zero.

IN-FIN'I-TY, *n*. An *ideal* region used to make geometric terminology parallel algebraic concepts. Two parallel lines are said to intersect at infinity, in order to permit the use, without exceptions, of such statements as two lines always determine a point. The form, $a/0$, is sometimes spoken of as *infinity*, meaning thereby a/x as x approaches zero. See IDEAL.

approach infinity. See INFINITE.

line at infinity. See LINE—line at infinity.

order of infinities. If n and m are functions of t and both become infinite as t approaches t_0, say, n is said to be of the *same, lower,* or *higher order* than m according as $\lim_{t \to t_0} n/m$ is a constant (different from zero), zero, or infinite. If $\lim_{t \to t_0} n/m^r$ is a constant (not zero), n is said to be of the rth *order* with respect to m.

IN-FLEC'TION, *n*. **point of inflection.** A point at which a plane curve changes from concavity toward any fixed line to convexity toward it; a point at which a curve has a *stationary tangent*, that is, a point at which the tangent is changing from rotating in one direction to rotating in the opposite direction; a point at which the curvature is zero. The vanishing of the 2nd derivative, if it is continuous, is a *necessary* but not a *sufficient* condition for a point of inflection, because the second derivative may be zero without changing signs at the point. E.g. the curve $y = x^3$ has its second derivative zero at the origin, and has a *point of inflection* there; the curve $y = x^4$ also has its second derivative zero at the origin, but has a minimum there; the curve $y = x^4 + x$ has its 2nd derivative zero at the origin, but has neither a point of inflection nor a maximum or minimum there. A necessary and sufficient condition that a point be a point of inflection is that the second derivative change sign at this point, i.e. have different signs for values of the independent variable immediately less and immediately greater than at the point.

IN-FLEC'TION-AL, *adj*. **inflectional tangent to a curve.** A tangent at a point of inflection. It meets the curve in three coincident points at the point of inflection.

IN-I'TIAL, *adj*. **initial form of commutation columns.** See COMMUTATION—commutation tables.

initial reserve. (*Life insurance*.) See RESERVE.

initial side of an angle. See ANGLE.

IN-SCRIBED', *adj*. A figure having vertices (as a polygon or polyhedron) is said to be inscribed in a figure composed of lines, curves or surfaces, when every vertex of the former is incident upon the latter; a curved figure is said to be inscribed in a polygon or polyhedron when every side (in the former case) or every face (in the latter) is tangent to it. The figure shows a polygon inscribed in a circle, the circle inscribed in another polygon.

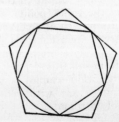

inscribed angle of a closed curve. An angle (in the interior of the curve) formed by two chords which intersect on the curve.

inscribed circle of a triangle. The circle tangent to the sides and with its center at the intersection of the bisectors of the angles of the triangle. Also called **incircle.** Its center is called the **incenter** of the triangle. Its radius is

$$\sqrt{\frac{(s-a)(s-b)(s-c)}{s}}$$

where a, b, c are the sides of the triangle and

$$s = \tfrac{1}{2}(a+b+c).$$

inscribed cone of a pyramid. The cone having its base inscribed in the base of the pyramid and its vertex in common with the vertex of the pyramid.

inscribed cylinder of a *prism*. See PRISM—circumscribed prism of a cylinder.

inscribed polygon of a circle. A polygon with its vertices on the circumference of the circle. If the polygon is *regular* and has n sides, its area is $\tfrac{1}{2}r^2n \sin 360°/n$ and its perimeter is $2rn \sin 180°/n$, where r is the radius of the circle.

inscribed prism of a cylinder. See PRISM—inscribed prism of a cylinder.

inscribed pyramid of a cone. A pyramid whose base is a polygon inscribed in the base of the cone and whose vertex coincides with the vertex of the cone.

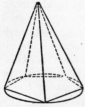

radius of a circle inscribed in a regular polygon. If s is the length of a side of the polygon and n the number of its sides, the radius is $\tfrac{1}{2}s \cot 180°/n$.

IN-STALL'MENT (or IN-STAL'MENT), *n.* **installment payments.** Payments on notes, accounts, or mortgages at regular periods. Each payment may include a fixed payment on principal and interest on the balance over the preceding period, or the interest on the entire amount may have been added to the principal at the outset and the payments made equal. The latter practice makes the actual interest practically double the quoted rate. The former method is sometimes called the **long-end interest plan.** Sometimes fixed payments plus the interest on the amount of the payment from the beginning of the contract are made periodically (monthly). This is sometimes called the **short-end interest plan.** See AMORTIZE.

installment plan of buying. Any plan under which a debt is paid in installments.

installment policies. Insurance policies whose benefits are payable in installments beginning at the death (or end of the death year) of the insured, instead of in a single payment.

installment premium. See PREMIUM.

IN'STAN-TA'NE-OUS, *adj.* **instantaneous acceleration.** See ACCELERATION—acceleration for motion in a straight line.

instantaneous velocity (or speed). The limit of the *average velocity* (or *speed*) during an interval of time, as this interval of time approaches zero; the vector derivative of the position vector. The numerical value of the velocity (i.e. the speed) is the numerical value of the derivative ds/dt, where s denotes distance passed over at time t. See VELOCITY.

IN-SUR'ANCE, *n.* **compound survivorship insurance.** See COMPOUND—compound survivorship insurance.

contingent insurance. See CONTINGENT.

deferred temporary or term insurance. See DEFERRED.

deferred whole life insurance. See DEFERRED—deferred whole life insurance.

deficiency, or premium deficiency, reserve. See RESERVE.

discounted bonus insurance. See

DISCOUNTED—discounted bonus policy.

double endowment insurance. See DOUBLE.

extended insurance. See EXTENDED—extended insurance.

increasing premium policy. See INCREASING—increasing premium policy.

initial reserve. See RESERVE.

insurance policy. See POLICY—insurance policy.

insurance with return of premiums. A policy which returns all premiums when the policy is paid, the company paying its other expenses out of the earnings on the premiums.

joint life insurance. See JOINT—joint life insurance.

last survivor insurance. See LAST.

mean reserve. See RESERVE.

mutual insurance company. See MUTUAL—mutual insurance company.

n-payment endowment insurance. See POLICY—n-payment endowment policy.

n-payment life insurance. See POLICY—n-year payment life policy.

n-year term insurance. See POLICY—n-year term policy.

option term insurance. See OPTION.

ordinary life insurance. Whole life insurance with premiums payable annually throughout life.

paid-up insurance policy. See PAID.

pure endowment insurance. See PURE.

reserve of an insurance policy. See RESERVE.

temporary contingent insurance. See TEMPORARY—temporary contingent insurance.

temporary life insurance. See LIFE—life insurance.

term life insurance. See LIFE—life insurance.

terminal reserve. See RESERVE—terminal reserve of an insurance policy.

tontine insurance. See TONTINE.

whole life insurance. See LIFE—life insurance.

IN'TE-GER, *n.* Any of the numbers 1, 2, 3, etc. These are often spoken of as **positive integers** in contradistinction to the **negative integers,** -1, -2, -3, etc.

indicator, totient or ϕ-function of an integer. See INDICATOR.

IN'TE-GRA-BLE, *adj.* **integrable function.** See INTEGRAL—definite integral, and DARBOUX'S THEOREM.

integrable differential equation. See DIFFERENTIAL—integrable differential equations.

IN'TE-GRAL, *adj.* **integral calculus.** See CALCULUS.

integral curves. The family of curves whose equations are solutions of a particular differential equation; the *integral curves* of the differential equation $y' = -x/y$ are the family of circles $x^2 + y^2 = c$, where c is an arbitrary parameter.

integral expression. An algebraic expression in which no variables appear in any denominator when the expression is written in a form having only positive exponents.

integral number. An INTEGER (positive, negative, or zero).

integral tables. Tables giving the primitives (indefinite integrals) of the more common functions and sometimes some of the more important definite integrals. See INTEGRATION TABLES in the appendix.

integral test for convergence. See CAUCHY.

rational integral function. See RATIONAL.

IN'TE-GRAL, *n.* **definite integral.** The difference between the values of the indefinite integral for two values of the independent variable. Geometrically, the definite integral is the limit, as Δx approaches zero, of the sum of the areas of the rectangles, Δx in width, formed with successive ordinates taken Δx apart throughout the interval between the two values of x (a and b in the figure). The *definite integral* from a to b of $f(x)$ with respect to x is written:

$$\int_a^b f(x)dx$$

and spoken of as the integral of $f(x)$ with respect to x between the limits a and b. It is the area between the curve $y = f(x)$, the x-axis and the lines $x = a$ and $x = b$; $f(x)$ is called the **integrand** and a and b the **lower** and **upper** **limits of integration**. *Tech.* The (Riemann) *definite integral* of a function on a given interval is the limit obtained by dividing the given interval into non-overlapping sub-intervals, multiplying the width of each sub-interval by the value of the ordinate corresponding to some abscissa within that interval (usually the largest or smallest. See Duhamel's theorem), adding all such products, and finding the limit of such sums as the number of subintervals becomes infinite in such a way that they all become arbitrarily small. The integral is said to exist if and only if this limit exists and is unique for all methods of summing which satisfy the stated restrictions. The definite integral always exists for a function which is continuous in the closed interval defined by the limits of integration; continuity is here a sufficient but not a necessary condition. See DARBOUX'S THEOREM. The definite integral does not always represent area, but may be so interpreted when evaluating it. See ELEMENT—element of arc of a curve, etc. Such symbols as $\int_e$ indicate that the integral is a definite integral whose number of integration signs and limits are to be selected to fit the case at hand; see MEAN—mean value of a function, f, over a given range, and below, iterated integral, line integral of a curve, properties of definite integrals.

double integral. See DOUBLE.

energy integral. See ENERGY.

improper integral. An integral whose limits are not both finite or one whose integrand becomes infinite in the interval between the limits of integration; an integral in which the interval of integration and the integrand are not both bounded.

indefinite integral of a function of a single variable. Any function whose derivative is the given function. If $g(x)$ is an indefinite integral of $f(x)$, then $g(x) + c$, where c is an *arbitrary constant*, is also an integral of $f(x)$; c is called the **constant of integration**. The indefinite integral of $f(x)$ with respect to x is written $\int f(x)dx$; $f(x)$ is called the **integrand**. Many basic formulas for finding integrals are listed in the appendix. More extensive tables have been published, but the list of integrals is inexhaustible.

infinite integral. See INFINITE—infinite integral.

iterated integral. An indicated succession of integrals in which integration is to be performed first with respect to one variable, the others being held constant, then with respect to a second, the remaining ones being held constant, etc.; the inverse of successive partial differentiation, if the integration is *indefinite integration*. When the integration is *definite integration*, the limits may be either constants or variables, the latter usually being functions of variables with respect to which integration is yet to be performed. (Some writers use the term *multiple* for *iterated integrals*.) E.g. (1) The iterated integral,

$$\int\int xy\,dy\,dx$$

(called the double integral of xy with respect to y and x), may be written

$$\int \left\{ \int xy\,dy \right\} dx.$$

Integrating the inner integral gives $(\frac{1}{2}xy^2 + C_1)$ where C_1 is any function of

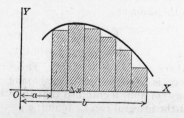

x, only. Integrating again gives

$$\tfrac{1}{4}x^2y^2 + \int C_1 dx + C_2$$

where C_2 is any function of y. The result may be written in the form $\tfrac{1}{4}x^2y^2 + \phi_1(x) + \phi_2(y)$, where $\phi_1(x)$ and $\phi_2(y)$ are any differentiable functions of x and y, respectively. The order of integration is usually from the inner differential out, as taken here. The orders are not always interchangeable. (2) The **definite iterated integral**,

$$\int_a^b \int_x^{x+1} x\,dy\,dx,$$

for example, is equivalent to

$$\int_a^b \left\{ \int_x^{x+1} x\,dy \right\} dx$$

hich is equal to

$$\int_a^b \{x(x+1) - x^2\}\,dx = \tfrac{1}{2}(b^2 - a^2)$$

See INTEGRAL—definite integral.

line integral of a curve. Let P_0, P_1, $\cdots$, P_n be successive points selected around (along) a given curve; let $\Delta_1 x$, $\Delta_2 x$, $\cdots$, $\Delta_n x$, be the projections of the arcs $P_0 P_1$, $P_1 P_2$, $\cdots$, $P_{n-1} P_n$ upon the x-axis; let x_i be any abscissa terminating in $\Delta_i x$, and let $M(x, y)$ be a continuous function of x and y for all points on the curve; then add the products $M(x_i, y_i)\Delta_i x$ $(i = 1, \cdots, n)$. The line integral is

$$\lim_{n \to \infty} \sum_{i=1}^n M(x_i, y_i)\Delta_i x, \quad \text{written} \quad \int_C M\,dx.$$

Also defined as

$$\int_C (M\,dx + N\,dy),$$

where

$\int_C N\,dy$ is defined similarly to $\int_C M\,dx$.

line integral of the first kind. A line integral,

$$\int_C (M\,dx + N\,dy),$$

where the integrand is exact; i.e.

where $\quad \dfrac{\partial M}{\partial y} = \dfrac{\partial N}{\partial x}.$

See DIFFERENTIAL—exact differential, and CONSERVATIVE FIELD.

line integral of the second kind. A line integral where the integrand is not exact. See above, line integral of the first kind.

multiple integral. A generalization of the integral of a function of a single variable as the limit of a sum. The double integral is defined over a given region, A, as follows: Divide the region into n non-overlapping subregions $\Delta_i A$, $i = 1, 2, 3, \cdots, n$, which can be inclosed in squares the largest of which converges to zero as n increases and let M_i and N_i be the absolute maximum and minimum values of $f(x, y)$ in the ith subregion. Form the sums

$$S_n = \sum_1^n M_i \Delta_i A \quad \text{and} \quad s_n = \sum_1^n N_i \Delta_i A.$$

If $\lim_{n \to \infty} S_n$ and $\lim_{n \to \infty} s_n$ exist and are equal, their common limit is called the double integral over A and written,

$$\iint_A f(x, y)\,dy\,dx.$$

If $f(x, y)$ is continuous throughout A, the double integral exists and is equal to the iterated integral of $f(x, y)$ over A. See above, iterated integral.

particular integral. See PARTICULAR.

properties of definite integrals. Some elementary properties are: (1) The value of a definite integral depends entirely upon the limits of integration and the form of the function; i.e. the value of a definite integral is independent of the variable with respect to which the integration is performed;

$$\int_a^b f(x)\,dx$$

is the same as

$$\int_\alpha^\beta f[z(t)]\,dz(t),$$

where $a = z(\alpha)$ and $b = z(\beta)$. This property is very useful in reshaping the form of an integrand so that the value of the integral can be found; e.g.

$$\int_0^{\pi/2} \sin x \cos x\, dx = \int_0^{\pi/2} \sin x\, d\sin x$$

$$= \int_0^1 u\, du.$$

(2) Interchanging the limits of integration simply changes the sign of the result. (3) A definite integral from a to b is equal to the sum of the definite integrals from a to c and c to b, written

$$\int_a^b f(x)dx = \int_a^c f(x)dx + \int_c^b f(x)dx,$$

if these exist. This fact is inherent in the definition of integration as a summation process. (4) The definite integral of a function over an interval is equal to or greater than the width of the interval times the least value of the function in that interval, and is equal to or less than the width of the interval times the greatest value of the function in that interval. (5) The definite integral of a continuous function over a given interval is equal to the product of the width of the interval by some value of the function within the interval. (Property (5) is called the **first law of the mean for integrals**.)

rationalization of integrals. See RATIONALIZATION.

surface integral. See SURFACE—surface integral.

triple integral. See TRIPLE.

IN'TE-GRAND, *n.* See INTEGRAL—definite integral.

exact integrand. An integrand which is an exact differential. See DIFFERENTIAL—exact differential.

rationalization of integrands. Same as RATIONALIZATION OF INTEGRALS.

IN'TE-GRAPH, *n.* A mechanical device for finding areas under curves; a mechanical device for performing *definite integration*.

IN'TE-GRAT'ING, *p.* **integrating factor.** See FACTOR.

integrating machine. Mechanical instruments for use in evaluating definite integrals; such instruments as the *integraph* and *polar planimeter*.

IN'TE-GRA'TION, *n.* The process of finding an indefinite or definite integral

of a given function. See INTEGRAL.

change of variable in integration. See below, integration by substitution.

definite integration. The process of finding definite integrals. See INTEGRAL—definite integral.

formulas of integration. Formulas giving the indefinite integrals or certain definite integrals of a few of the most commonly met functions.

integration of an infinite series. The derivation of a new series by integrating each term of the given series. If the given series *converges uniformly* in a given interval, the series derived by integrating it will converge and represent, in the same interval, the integral of the function represented by the given series. See CONVERGENCE—uniform convergence.

integration by partial fractions. A specific method of integration used when the integrand is a rational fraction with denominator of higher degree than the first. Consists of breaking the integrand up into *partial fractions* with simpler denominators. E.g.

$$\int \frac{dx}{1-x^2} = \frac{1}{2}\int \frac{dx}{1-x} + \frac{1}{2}\int \frac{dx}{1+x}.$$

See PARTIAL—partial fractions.

integration by parts. A process of integrating by use of the formula for the differential of a product. The formula $d(uv) = udv + vdu$ is written $udv = d(uv) - vdu$; integrating both sides of this equation gives $\int udv = uv - \int vdu$. This last formula enables one to modify the form of an integrand and simplify the process of integration, or actually integrate functions whose exact integral could not otherwise be found directly. It is especially useful in integrating such functions as xe^x, log x, $x \sin x$, etc.; e.g.

$$\int xe^x dx = xe^x - \int e^x dx,$$

where $x = u$, $e^x dx = dv$, and $v = e^x$.

integration of a power series. The derivation of a new series by integrating the given series term by term. The integral represents the integral of the function represented by the given series in any region within the region of convergence of the series, for a power series is uniformly convergent in any region within its region of convergence. The series,

$$1 - x + x^2 - \cdots (-1)^{n+1} x^{n-1} \cdots$$

converges when $|x| < 1$. Hence term by term integration is permissible between the limits 0 and $\frac{1}{2}$, for instance, or between x_1 and x_2 provided $|x_1| < 1$, and $|x_2| < 1$.

integration of rational fractions. Evaluation of an integral whose integrand is a rational fraction. See above, integration by partial fractions.

integration by substitution. The process of integrating by first transforming the integral into a form that is more easily evaluated. Typical substitutions are those which replace the variable by the square of a variable in order to rationalize indicated square roots of the variable, and the *trigonometric substitutions* by which the square roots of quadratic binomials are reduced to monomials, e.g. if one substitutes $\sin u$ for x in $\sqrt{1-x^2}$ the result is $\cos u$; similarly $\sqrt{1+x^2}$ and $\sqrt{x^2-1}$ lend themselves to the substitutions $\tan u = x$, and $\sec u = x$, respectively. In all cases when a substitution is made in the integrand, it must also be made in the differential and the proper changes must be made in the limits if the integrals are definite integrals (an equivalent and quite common practice is to integrate the new integrand as an indefinite integral, then make the inverse substitution and use the original limits). E.g.

$$\int_0^1 \sqrt{1-x^2}\, dx,$$

transformed by the substitution $x = \sin u$, becomes

$$\int_0^{\pi/2} \cos^2 u\, du = \frac{1}{2}u + \frac{1}{4}\sin 2u \Big]_0^{\pi/2} = \frac{1}{4}\pi$$

or one may write

$$\int \cos^2 u\, du = \frac{1}{2}u + \frac{1}{4}\sin 2u$$
$$= \frac{1}{2}\sin^{-1} x + \frac{1}{2}x\sqrt{1-x^2},$$

whence

$$\int_0^1 \sqrt{1-x^2}\, dx = \frac{1}{2}\sin^{-1} x + \frac{1}{2}x\sqrt{1-x^2}\Big]_0^1 = \frac{1}{4}\pi.$$

integration as a summation process. See INTEGRAL—definite integral.

integration by use of series. The expanding of the integrand in a series and integrating term by term. An upper bound to the numerical value of the remainder of the series, after any given number of terms, can be integrated to find limits to the error. See INTEGRAL—properties of definite integrals, (4).

mechanical integration. Determining the area bounded by a curve without the use of its equation, with ruler and compass or some specific mechanical device such as the *integraph* or *polar planimeter*.

reduction formulas in integration. See REDUCTION—reduction formulas in integration.

second law of the mean for integrals. See MEAN—second law of the mean for integrals.

Wallis' formulas. See WALLIS' FORMULAS.

IN'TER-CEPT', *v.*, *adj.*, or *n.* To cut off or bound some part of a line, plane, surface, or solid. Two radii intercept arcs of the circumference of a circle.

intercept form of the equation of a plane. See PLANE—equation of a plane.

intercept form of the equation of a straight line. See LINE—equation of a straight line in the plane.

intercept of a straight line, curve, or surface on an axis of coordinates. The distance from the origin to the point where the line, curve or surface cuts the axis. The intercept on the axis of abscissas, or x-axis, is called the **x-intercept**, and that on the axis of ordinates, or y-axis, the **y-intercept**. (In space, the intercept on the z-axis is likewise called the **z-intercept**.) The intercepts of the line $2x + 3y = 6$ on the x-axis and y-axis, respectively, are 3 and 2.

intercepted annuity. Same as DE-FERRED ANNUITY.

intercepted temporary annuity. See DEFERRED—deferred temporary annuity.

IN′TER-CHANG′ING, *p.* interchanging rows and columns in a determinant. See DETERMINANT—properties of determinants.

IN′TER-DE-PEND′ENT, *adj.* interdependent functions. Same as DEPENDENT FUNCTIONS.

IN′TER-EST, *n.* Money paid for the use of money.

accrued interest. See ACCRUE.

compound interest. Interest computed upon the principal for the first period, upon the principal and the first period's interest for the second period, upon the new principal and the second period's interest for the third period, etc. Thus at 6%, the interest plus principal at the end of the first, second, and nth years is respectively $P(1.06)$, $P(1.06)^2$, and $P(1.06)^n$, where P denotes the principal.

continuous conversion of compound interest. See CONTINUOUS.

effective rate of interest. The rate of interest actually earned in a year. See below, nominal rate of interest.

exact interest. Interest computed upon the basis of the exact number of days in a year (365 days except for leap year, which has 366 days). Interest for 90 days at 6% would be 90/365 of 6% of the principal. In counting days between dates the last, but not the first date, is usually included. However, both dates are sometimes included. The number of days from Dec. 25th to Feb. 2nd would be counted as 39 under the customary practice and 40 under the other. See below, ordinary interest.

force of interest. The nominal rate which converted *continuously* is equivalent to a certain effective rate.

frequency in computing compound interest. See FREQUENCY—frequency of conversion.

interest-bearing note. See NOTE.

interest period. The period over which interest is reckoned. Usually means the same as *conversion period* but is also used with reference to the time over which simple interest is computed.

interest rate. The ratio of interest to principal, times 100. *Syn.* Rate of interest, rate, rate percent.

long-end interest plan. See INSTALLMENT—installment payments.

nominal rate of interest. The yearly rate when interest is compounded over periods of less than a year. When interest is computed at the rate of 3% semi-annually, the nominal rate would be 6%. The annual rate which gives the same yield as the nominal computed over fractions of the year is called the *effective rate.* The effective rate for 6% nominal computed semi-annually is 6.09%.

ordinary interest. Interest computed on the basis of the commercial year of 360 days and 30 days to the month. Interest for 2 months at 6% would be 60/360 of 6% times the principal—when the time of a note is expressed in days, the exact number of days is counted; e.g. a note dated July 26th and due in 30 days would be due Aug. 25th, while if due in one month it would be due Aug. 26th. See above, exact interest.

prevailing interest rate (for any given investment). The rate which is common, or generally accepted, for that particular type of investment at the time under consideration. *Syn.* Current rate.

short-end interest plan. See INSTALLMENT—installment payments.

simple interest. Interest which is equal to the product of the *time, rate of interest,* and *original principal;* interest upon the principal only and not upon principal plus interest as in compound interest. E.g. the interest upon $100 at 6% for 5 years is $5 \times (6/100) \times 100 = \$30$.

sixty day method for computing interest. See SIXTY.

IN-TE′RI-OR, *adj.* alternate interior angles. See ALTERNATE—alternate interior angles.

interior and exterior-interior angles

of two lines cut by a transversal. See ANGLE—angles made by a transversal.

interior angle of a polygon. An angle between any two sides of the polygon (not produced) and lying within the polygon. When the interior of the polygon is not defined, as when sides intersect at points other than vertices, this definition of interior angle does not apply.

interior angle of a triangle. An angle lying within the triangle.

IN'TER-ME'DI-ATE, *adj*. intermediate differential. A name applied to each of the terms which appear in the several variables, at least one of which is implicitly dependent upon the others, as in

$$du = (D_x f + D_z f \cdot D_x z)dx + (D_y f + D_z f \cdot D_y z)dy,$$

where $u = f(x, y, z)$ and $z = g(x, y)$. The two terms on the right are each called *intermediate differentials*.

IN-TER'NAL, *adj*. internal ratio. See POINT—point of division.

IN-TER'PO-LA'TION, *n*. The process of finding a value of a function between two known values by a procedure other than the law which is given by the function itself. E.g. in linear interpolation the procedure is based on the assumption that the three points having these values of the function for ordinates lie on a straight line. This is approximately true when the values of the arguments are close together, and the function is continuous, i.e. its graph between the points, whose abscissas are the three values of the arguments, is a single curve with no breaks in it. If the function is $f(x)$ and its value is known for $x = x_1$ and for $x = x_2$ ($x_1 < x_2$), the formula for linear interpolation is

$$f(x) = f(x_1) + \left[f(x_2) - f(x_1) \right] \frac{x - x_1}{x_2 - x_1}.$$

correction in interpolation. See CORRECTION.

Gregory-Newton interpolation formula. See GREGORY-NEWTON FORMULA.

IN'TER-SEC'TION, *n*. The point, or locus of points, common to two (or more) geometric configurations.

imaginary intersection. A phrase used to complete the analogy between discussions of the equations of curves and of their loci; consists of the sets of imaginary values of the variables which are common solutions of the equations of the curves.

intersecting curves, angle between. See ANGLE—angle between two intersecting curves.

intersection of two curves. Their common point or points.

intersection of two lines. Their common point.

intersection of two planes. Their common line.

intersection of two surfaces. Their common curve.

IN'TER-VAL, *n*. closed number interval. A set of numbers which consists exclusively of all the numbers simultaneously greater than or equal to one fixed number and less than or equal to another. If the two numbers are a and b, the interval is indicated by (a, b), or better, $[a, b]$, and the length of the interval is $b - a$; a and b are called the end points of the interval. Such an interval is called a closed interval in distinction from the sort of interval in which one or both of the end points are missing. Intervals with no end points are called open intervals.

fixed interval. An interval whose points (or numbers) do not change during the discussion at hand.

interval of convergence of a series of variable terms. The interval containing those values of the variable for which the given series converges. E.g. the series

$$1 + x + x^2 + x^3 + x^4 \cdots + x^n + \cdots$$

has the open interval of convergence $-1 < x < 1$.

open interval. See above, closed number interval.

IN-TRAN'SI-TIVE, *adj*. intransitive relation. See TRANSITIVE.

IN-TRIN'SIC, *adj*. intrinsic properties of a curve. Properties which are not altered by any change of coordinate systems. Some of the intrinsic properties of the conics are their eccentricity, distance from focus (foci) to directrix, length of latus rectum, length of the axes (of an ellipse or hyperbola), and their reflection properties.

IN-VA′RI-ANT, *adj.* **invariant property.** A property of a function, configuration, or equation that is not altered by a particular transformation. The invariant property is used with reference to a particular transformation or type of transformation. E.g. the value of a cross ratio is not changed by a projection and hence is said to be invariant under projective transformations.

invariants of an algebraic equation. Algebraic expressions involving the coefficients which remain unaltered in value when any translation or rotation of the axes is made. For the general quadratic, $ax^2 + bxy + cy^2 + dx + ey + f = 0$, $a + c$, $b^2 - 4ac$, and the **discriminant** are invariants. See DISCRIMINANT—discriminant of the general quadratic.

IN-VERSE′, *n.* **inverse function.** The function obtained by expressing the independent variable explicitly in terms of the dependent and considering the dependent variable as an independent variable. If $y = f(x)$ results in $x = g(y)$, the latter is the inverse of the former (and vice versa). It is customary to interchange the variables in the latter, writing $y = g(x)$ as the inverse. If $y = \sin x$, $y = \sin^{-1}x$ is used to denote the inverse trigonometric sine.

inverse hyperbolic functions. See HYPERBOLIC—inverse hyperbolic functions.

inverse logarithm of a given number. The number whose logarithm is the given number. Log 100 is 2, hence 100 is inverse log 2. *Syn.* Anti-logarithm.

inverse of a number. One divided by the number. *Syn.* Reciprocal of a number.

inverse of an operation. That operation which, when performed after or before a given operation, annuls the given operation. Subtraction of a quantity is the inverse of addition of that quantity. Addition is likewise the inverse of subtraction. Any operation is the inverse of its inverse.

inverse of a point or curve. See INVERSION.

inverse or reciprocal proportion. A proportion containing one reciprocal ratio. See INVERSELY—inversely proportional quantities.

inverse or reciprocal ratio of two numbers. The ratio of the reciprocals of the numbers.

inverse substitution. See SUBSTITUTION.

inverse transformation. See TRANSFORMATION.

inverse trigonometric equations. Equations involving inverse trigonometric functions of the unknowns, such as $2 \sin^{-1}x - 1 = 0$.

inverse trigonometric function. The function whose value is the angle whose trigonometric function is the given argument. The inverse sine of x is the angle whose sine is x. The inverse sine of $\frac{1}{2}$ ($\sin^{-1}\frac{1}{2}$) is 30° or $\pi/6$ radians. The inverse functions of an angle A are written either $\sin^{-1}A$, $\cos^{-1}A$, $\tan^{-1}A$, etc., or arc sin A, arc cos A, arc tan A, etc. See VALUE—principal value of an inverse trigonometric function. *Syn.* Anti-trigonometric function.

inverse variation. See VARIATION—inverse variation.

IN-VERSE′LY, *adj.* **inversely proportional quantities.** Two quantities having their product constant; i.e. the ratio between one of them and the inverse (reciprocal) of the other is constant. The term has no significance unless the quantities are variables.

IN-VER′SION, *n.* **inversion of a point with respect to a circle.** The finding of the point on the radius through the given point such that the product of the distances of the two points from the center of the circle is equal to the square of the radius. Either of the points is called the **inverse** of the other and the center of the circle is called the **center of inversion.** Any curve whose points are the inverses of the points of a given curve is called the inverse of the given curve. E.g. the inverse of a circle which passes through the center of inversion is a straight line; the inverse of any other circle is a circle. If the equation of a curve is $f(x, y) = 0$, the equation of its inverse is

$$f[k^2x/(x^2+y^2), k^2y/(x^2+y^2)] = 0,$$

where k is the radius of the circle.

inversion of a point with reference to a sphere. The finding of a point on the radius through the given point such that the product of the distances of the two points from the center of the sphere is equal to the square of the radius of the sphere. E.g. the inverse of every sphere with respect to a fixed sphere is another sphere, except that the inverse of a sphere passing through the center of the fixed sphere is a plane.

inversion in a sequence of objects. A displacement of one of the objects by one place; the interchange of two adjacent objects. The *number of inversions* in a sequence is the minimum number of inversions which can be performed in order to put the objects in a certain *normal* order. The permutation 1, 3, 2, 4, 5 has one inversion, if the normal order is 1, 2, 3, 4, 5; while the permutation 1, 4, 3, 2, 5 has three. A permutation is said to be **odd** or **even** according as it contains an *odd* or an *even* number of inversions. The normal order is said to be even.

proportion by inversion. See PROPORTION.

IN-VER'SOR, *n.* A mechanical device which simultaneously traces out a curve and its *inverse*. A rhombus, with its sides pivoted at the vertices and a pair of opposite vertices each linked to a fixed point (the *center of inversion*) by equal links, is such a mechanism, called a *Peaucellier's cell*. When one of the unlinked vertices traces out a curve, the other traces out the inverse of the curve. See INVERSION.

IN-VEST'MENT, *n.* Money used to buy notes, bonds, etc., or put into any enterprise for the purpose of making profit.

fixed investment. An investment which yields a fixed income; the amount which must be put into a sinking fund at the end of each year to accumulate to a given sum at the end of a given term.

investment, or investor's, rate. See YIELD.

mathematics of investment. Same as MATHEMATICS OF FINANCE.

IN'VO-LUTE, *n.* an involute of a plane curve. The locus of a fixed point on a non-flexible string as it is unwound, under tension, from the curve; the locus of any fixed point on a tangent line as this line rolls, but does not slide, around the curve; a curve orthogonal to the family of tangents to a given curve; a curve whose *evolute* is the given curve. Any two involutes of the same curve are parallel, that is, the segments cut off by the two involutes on a common normal are always of the same length.

involute of a circle. The curve described by the end of a thread as it is unwound from a stationary spool. The parametric equations of the involute of a circle in the position illustrated, where θ is the angle from the x-axis to the radius marked a, are:

$$x = a(\cos \theta + \theta \sin \theta)$$
$$y = a(\sin \theta - \theta \cos \theta).$$

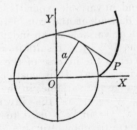

IN'VO-LU'TION, *n.* (1) Raising to a power; multiplying a quantity by itself a given number of times; the inverse of *evolution*. The process of squaring 2 is *involution*, of finding a square root of 4 is *evolution*. (2) A transformation which is its own inverse, e.g. $x = 1/x'$ is an involution. See TRANSFORMATION—inverse transformation.

involution on a line. A projective correspondence between the points of a line, which is its own inverse. Algebraically, the transformation

$$x' = \frac{ax+b}{cx-a},$$

where $a^2+bc \neq 0$. If $c \neq 0$, this can be written $x' = k/x$, by a proper choice of the origin.

involution of lines of a pencil. A correspondence between the lines, which is such that corresponding lines pass through corresponding points of an involution of points on a line which does not pass through the vertex of the pencil.

IR-RA'TION-AL, *adj.* **irrational algebraic surface.** The graph of an algebraic function in which the variable (or variables) appear under a radical sign. The loci of $z = \sqrt{y+x^2}$ and $z = x^{1/2}+xy$ are irrational algebraic surfaces.

irrational equation. See EQUATION—irrational equation.

irrational number. A number not expressible as an integer or quotient of integers; a non-rational number. See DEDEKIND CUT.

irrational power of a quantity. The quantity approximated by using rational exponents which approximate the irrational exponent; e.g. 3 with exponent $\sqrt{2}$ denotes the limit of the sequence $3^{1.4}$, $3^{1.41}$, $3^{1.414}$, $\cdots$ *Tech.* If the sequence a_1, a_2, $\cdots$, a_n, $\cdots$ approaches an irrational limit a, then c^a denotes the limit of the sequence c^{a_1}, c^{a_2}, c^{a_3}, $\cdots c^{a_n}$, $\cdots$.

IR'RE-DUC'I-BLE, *adj.* **irreducible case** in Cardan's formula for the roots of a cubic. The case in which the formula involves the extraction of the cube root of a complex number. This case occurs when the roots are all three real and distinct.

irreducible equation. A rational integral equation of the form $f(x) = 0$, where $f(x)$ is a polynomial irreducible in a certain field, usually the field of all rational numbers. See below, polynomials irreducible in a given field (domain).

irreducible radical. A radical which cannot be written in an equivalent rational form. The radicals $\sqrt{6}$ and $\sqrt{x}$ are irreducible, while $\sqrt{4}$ and $\sqrt{x^2}$ are reducible since they are equal, respectively, to 2 and x.

polynomials irreducible in a given field (domain). Polynomials which cannot be factored into factors whose coefficients are in the given domain. Unless otherwise stated, *irreducible* means irreducible in the domain of the coefficients of the polynomial under consideration. The binomial x^2+1 is *irreducible* in the domain of real numbers, although in the domain of complex numbers it can be factored into $(x+i)(x-i)$, where $i = \sqrt{-1}$. In elementary algebra an irreducible polynomial is a polynomial which cannot be factored into factors having rational coefficients.

I-SOG'O-NAL, *adj.* Having equal angles.

isogonal affine transformation. See AFFINE.

isogonal conjugate lines. See below, isogonal lines.

isogonal lines. (*In plane geometry.*) Lines through the vertex of an angle and symmetric with respect to (making equal angles with) the bisector of the angle. The lines are called **isogonal conjugates.**

isogonal transformation. A transformation which leaves all the angles in any configuration unchanged. E.g. the general similarity transformation is an isogonal transformation. *Syn.* Equiangular or conformal transformation.

I'SO-LATE, *v.* **isolate a root.** The same as locating the root. See LOCATION THEOREM or PRINCIPLE.

isolated point. See POINT—isolated point.

I'SO-LAT'ING, *p.* **isolating a root of an equation.** Finding two numbers between which the root (and usually no other root) lies. See LOCATION THEOREM or PRINCIPLE.

I'SO-MET'RIC, *adj.* **isometric surfaces.** Surfaces on which corresponding small (differential) distances (ds and ds') are equal and angles between corresponding lines are equal.

I-SO-PER-I-MET'RIC or **I-SO-PER-I-MET'RI-CAL,** *adi.* **isoperimetric figures.** Figures having equal perimeters.

I-SOS'CE-LES, *adj.* **isosceles spherical triangle.** A spherical triangle having two of its sides equal.

isosceles plane triangle. A triangle having two of its sides equal. The angles opposite these equal sides are then necessarily equal. The third side is called the *base*, and the angle opposite it the *vertex* or, sometimes, the *summit angle*.

I'SO-THERM, *n.* (*Meteorology.*) A line drawn on a map through places having equal temperatures.

I'SO-THER'MAL, *adj.* Relating to equal temperatures.

isothermal change. (*Physics.*) A change in the volume and pressure of a substance which takes place at constant temperature.

isothermal lines. Lines on a map connecting points which have the same mean (annual) temperatures. In *physics*, curves obtained by plotting pressure against volume for a gas kept at constant temperature.

I'SO-TROP'IC, *adj.* **isotropic matter.** Matter which, at any point, has the same properties in any direction (such properties, for instance, as elasticity, density, and conductivity of heat or electricity).

IS'SUE, *n.* **issue of bonds, bank notes, money, or stock.** A set of bonds, bank notes, etc., which is (or has been) issued at a certain time.

IT'ER-ATE, *v.* Repeat; do or say over again.

iterated integral. See INTEGRAL —iterated integral.

J

JA-CO'BI-AN, *n.* **Jacobian of two or more functions in as many variables.** For the n functions $f_i(x_1, x_2, \cdots, x_n)$, $i = 1, 2, 3, \cdots, n$, the Jacobian is the determinant:

$$\begin{vmatrix} \dfrac{\partial f_1}{\partial x_1} & \dfrac{\partial f_1}{\partial x_2} & \dfrac{\partial f_1}{\partial x_3} & \cdots & \dfrac{\partial f_1}{\partial x_n} \\ \dfrac{\partial f_2}{\partial x_1} & \dfrac{\partial f_2}{\partial x_2} & \dfrac{\partial f_2}{\partial x_3} & \cdots & \dfrac{\partial f_2}{\partial x_n} \\ \cdots & \cdots & \cdots & & \cdots \\ \dfrac{\partial f_n}{\partial x_1} & \dfrac{\partial f_n}{\partial x_2} & \dfrac{\partial f_n}{\partial x_3} & \cdots & \dfrac{\partial f_n}{\partial x_n} \end{vmatrix}.$$

Written:

$$\frac{D(f_1, f_2, f_3, \cdots f_n)}{D(x_1, x_2, x_3, \cdots, x_n)}.$$

For two functions, $f(x, y)$ and $g(x, y)$, the Jacobian is the determinant

$$\begin{vmatrix} \dfrac{\partial f}{\partial x} & \dfrac{\partial f}{\partial y} \\ \dfrac{\partial g}{\partial x} & \dfrac{\partial g}{\partial y} \end{vmatrix}, \quad \text{written: } \frac{D(f, g)}{D(x, y)}.$$

See INDEPENDENT—independent functions, and IMPLICIT—general implicit function theorem. *Syn.* Functional determinant.

JELLICOE'S FORMULAS. (*In insurance.*) Formulas giving the values of various types of *life interests*.

JOINT, *n.* **joint expectation of life.** The average number of additional years that two (or more) persons at a given age both (all) will live, according to the experience of large groups, i.e. according to a mortality table.

joint life annuity. A life annuity payable as long as two (or more) lives survive. See LIFE—life annuity.

joint life insurance. Insurance payable when the first of two (or more) lives end.

joint variation. See VARIATION— joint variation.

JUMP, *n.* A discontinuity in a curve of such a nature that if the point at which it occurs is approached from one direction along the curve the function approaches one value while if approached from the opposite direction the function approaches a different value. It is an example of a *finite non-removable* discontinuity.

K

KAPP'A, *n.* The Greek letter κ, K.

kappa curve. The graph of the rectangular equation $x^4 + x^2 y^2 = a^2 y^2$. The curve has the lines $x = \pm a$ as asymptotes, is symmetrical about the coordinate axes and the origin, and has a double cusp at the origin. It is called the kappa curve because of its resemblance to the Greek letter K.

KEPLER'S LAWS of planetary motion. The three laws: (1) The orbits of the planets are ellipses having the sun at one focus. (2) The areas described by the radius vectors of a planet in equal times are equal. (3) The square of the period of revolution of a planet is proportional to the cube of its mean distance from the sun. These laws can be directly derived from the law of gravitation and Newton's laws of motion as applied to the sun and one planet.

KIL′O-GRAM, *n.* One thousand grams; the weight of a platinum rod preserved in Paris as the standard unit of the metric system of weights; approximately 2.2 lbs. avoirdupois. See DENOMINATE NUMBERS in the appendix.

KIL′O-ME′TER, *n.* One thousand meters; approximately 3280 feet.

KIL′O-WATT, *n.* A unit of measure of electrical power; 1000 watts. See WATT.

kilowatt hour. A unit of energy; 1000 watt-hours; a kilowatt of power used for one hour; approximately 4/3 horsepower acting for one hour.

KIN′E-MAT′ICS, *n.* That part of *mechanics* which treats of different kinds of motion and of the modes of strains in elastic bodies without reference to the forces involved.

KI-NET′IC, *adj.* **kinetic energy.** The energy (capacity for doing work) that a body possesses by virtue of its motion; it is equal to $\frac{1}{2}mv^2$, where m is mass and v is velocity.

kinetic energy of rotation. The energy a body possesses by virtue of its rotary motion. Specifically, $\frac{1}{2}I\omega^2$, where I is the moment of inertia of the mass and ω its angular velocity in radians per second.

KI-NET′ICS, *n.* That part of *mechanics* which treats of the effect of forces in changing the motion of bodies.

KNOT, *n.* (*Naut.*) (1) Nautical miles per hour. "A ship sails 20 knots" means it sails 20 nautical miles per hour. (2) Non-technically, a nautical mile; 6080 feet as adopted by the British Admiralty; 6,080.27 feet as adopted by the United States Hydrographic Office. The latter distance is equal to one-sixtieth part of a degree on a great circle of a sphere whose surface is equal to that of the earth.

L

LAGRANGE'S FORMULA of interpolation. A formula for finding an approximation of an additional value of a function within a given interval of the independent variable, when certain values of the function within that interval are known. It is based upon the assumption that a polynomial of degree one less than the number of given values of the independent variable can be determined which will approximate the given function to the accuracy desired for the value sought. If x_1, $x_2, \cdots, x_n$ are the values of x for which the values of the function $f(x)$ are known, the formula is:

$$f(x) = \frac{f(x_1)(x-x_2)(x-x_3)\cdots(x-x_n)}{(x_1-x_2)(x_1-x_3)\cdots(x_1-x_n)}$$
$$+ \frac{f(x_2)(x-x_1)(x-x_3)\cdots(x-x_n)}{(x_2-x_1)(x_2-x_3)\cdots(x_2-x_n)}$$

$+ \cdots$, to n terms.

LAGRANGE'S METHOD OF MULTIPLIERS. A method for finding the maximum and minimum values of a function of several variables when relations between the variables are given. If it is desired to find the maximum area of a rectangle whose perimeter is a constant, k, it is necessary to find the maximum value of xy for $2x+2y-k = 0$. Lagrange's method of multipliers is to solve the three equations $2x+2y -k = 0$, $\partial u/\partial x = 0$, and $\partial u/\partial y = 0$ for x and y, where $u = xy + t(2x+2y-k)$ and t is to be treated as an unknown to be eliminated. In general: given a function $f(x_1, x_2, \cdots, x_n)$ of n variables connected by h distinct relations, $\phi_1 = 0$, $\phi_2 = 0$, $\cdots$, $\phi_h = 0$, in order to find the values of $x_1, x_2, \cdots, x_n$ for which this function may have a maximum or minimum, equate to zero the partial derivatives of the auxiliary function $f + t_1\phi_1 + \cdots + t_h\phi_h$, with respect to $x_1, x_2, \cdots, x_n$, regarding t_1, $t_2, \cdots, t_h$ as constants, and solve these n equations simultaneously with the given h relations, treating the t's as unknowns to be eliminated.

LAND MEASURE. See ACRE.

LAM'I-NA, *n.* A thin plate or sheet of uniform thickness.

LAPLACE'S DIFFERENTIAL EQUATION. The partial differential equation

$$\frac{\partial^2 v}{\partial x^2} + \frac{\partial^2 v}{\partial y^2} + \frac{\partial^2 v}{\partial z^2} = 0.$$

Under certain conditions, gravitational, electrostatic, magnetic, electric, and velocity potential satisfy Laplace's equation.

LAST, *adj.* **last survivor annuity.** An annuity payable until the last of two (or more) lives ends. It may be either complete or curtate.

    last survivor insurance. Insurance payable when the last of two or more lives ends.

LAT'ER-AL, *adj.* **lateral area of a cone, cylinder, prism,** etc. See CONE, CYLINDER, PRISM, etc.

    lateral edge of a prism. See PRISM.
    lateral face. See PYRAMID, and PRISM.

LAT'I-TUDE, *n.* **latitude of a point on the earth's surface.** The number of degrees in the arc of a meridian from the equator to the point; the angle which the plane of the horizon makes with the earth's axis; the elevation of the pole of the heavens; the angle which a plumb line at the point makes with a plumb line on the same meridian at the equator.

LA'TUS, *adj.* **latus rectum.** [*pl.* **latera recta.**] See PARABOLA, ELLIPSE, HYPERBOLA.

LAW, *n.* A general principle or rule to which all cases to which it can apply must conform.

    associative law. See ASSOCIATIVE.
    Boyle's law. See BOYLE'S LAW.
    commutative law. See COMMUTATIVE.
    Gompertz's law. See GOMPERTZ'S LAW.
    index laws. Same as the LAWS OF EXPONENTS. See below.
    law of cosines in a plane triangle. See COSINE—cosine law for a triangle.
    law of cosines in a spherical triangle. Relations between the sides and angles

of a spherical triangle. Explicitly:

$$\cos a = \cos b \cos c + \sin b \sin c \cos A,$$
$$\cos A = -\cos B \cos C + \sin B \sin C \cos a,$$

where *a*, *b*, *c* are the sides of the spherical triangle and *A*, *B*, *C* are the corresponding opposite angles.

    law of organic growth. See BACTERIAL GROWTH, law of.
    law of sines in a plane triangle. See SINE—law of sines.
    law of sines in a spherical triangle. A relation between the sides and the angles of a spherical triangle. Explicitly, the sines of the sides are proportional to the sines of the opposite angles.
    law of species in a spherical triangle. See SPECIES.
    law of tangents in plane trigonometry. See TANGENT—tangent law.
    law of uniform seniority. The following law used in evaluating joint life insurance policies: The difference between the age that can be used in computation (instead of the actual ages) and the lesser of the unequal ages is the same for the same difference of the unequal ages, regardless of the actual ages. (The age used in computation instead of the actual ages is the age which two persons of the same age would have if they were given insurance identical with that given those with the different ages.)
    laws of exponents. The rules by which exponents can be combined. The same as the *laws of integral exponents* except that laws (4) and (5) for integral exponents do not hold in general unless a convention has been made so as to uniquely define what is meant by a^x, where x is fractional or irrational. See laws of integral exponents, and laws of fractional exponents.
    laws of fractional exponents. The same as the laws of integral exponents except that laws (4) and (5) (see laws of integral exponents) sometimes fail. If $a^{1/n}$ denotes the real *n*th root of *a*, if there is only one such, and the positive one if there are two, then $a^{1/n}b^{1/n} \neq (ab)^{1/n}$ when *a* and *b* are both nega-

tive and n is even. If n is even, a positive and b negative, $(a/b)^{1/n} \neq a^{1/n}/b^{1/n}$. In order to make law (4) hold it would be necessary to have involution take precedence over multiplication in these exceptional cases. The product $(-1)^{1/2}(-1)^{1/2}$ if taken as $[(-1)^2]^{1/2}$ equals -1, whereas $(-1 \cdot -1)^{1/2}$ becomes $+1^{1/2}$, or 1, if the multiplication is performed first. In practice such difficulties are avoided by writing even roots of negative numbers as the product of the roots of -1 and the roots of the numbers; e.g.

$$\sqrt{-2}\sqrt{-3} = (\sqrt{-1})^2\sqrt{2}\sqrt{3} = -\sqrt{6}.$$

See EXPONENT—fractional exponent.

laws of integral exponents. Rules by which integral exponents are combined when different powers of the same base are multiplied and divided, when powers of powers are taken, and when powers of products and quotients are taken. They are: (1) to multiply add exponents; (2) to divide subtract exponents; (3) to raise a power to a power multiply exponents; (4) the power of a product is the product of the powers; (5) a power of a quotient is the quotient of the powers. E.g.

(1) $a^2 \cdot a^3 = a^5$;   (2) $a^5/a^2 = a^3$;
(3) $(a^2)^3 = a^6$ (4) $(ab)^2 = a^2b^2$
(5) $\qquad (a/b)^2 = a^2/b^2$.

In general the laws are stated:

(1) $a^n a^m = a^{n+m}$;   (2) $a^m/a^n = a^{m-n}$;
(3) $(a^m)^n = a^{mn}$ (4) $(ab)^n = a^n b^n$;
(5) $\qquad (a/b)^n = a^n/b^n$.

laws of quadrants for a right spherical triangle. (1) Any angle and the side opposite it are in the same quadrant; (2) when two of the sides are in the same quadrant the third is in the first quadrant and when two are in different quadrants the third is in the second. (The *first*, *second*, *third* and *fourth* quadrants mean angles from 0° to 90°, 90° to 180°, 180° to 270°, and 270° to 360°, respectively.)

Makeham's law. See MAKEHAM'S LAW.

Newton's laws. See NEWTON—Newton's laws of motion.

LEAD'ING, *p.* **leading coefficient** of a polynomial in one variable. The coefficient of the term of highest degree.

leading elements in a determinant. Elements whose row and column numbers are equal; elements in the principal diagonal; elements which are their own conjugates.

LEAST, *adj.* **least common multiple.** See MULTIPLE—least common multiple.

least upper bound. See BOUND.

least value of a function. The smallest value the function can take on, if it takes on a smallest value.

method of least squares. See METHOD—method of least squares.

LEFT, *adj.* **left-handed coordinate system.** See COORDINATE—left-handed coordinate system, and below, left-handed trihedral.

left-handed trihedral. A directed trihedral with an ordering given to the lines, which is such that if the thumb of the left hand extends along and in the positive direction of the first line, the fingers fold in the direction in which the second line could be rotated through an angle of 90° (or less than 180° if the axes are oblique) about the first line to coincide with the third.

LEG, *n.* **leg of a right triangle.** One of the sides adjacent to the right angle.

LEGENDRE'S EQUATION. The differential equation

$$(1-x^2)\frac{d^2y}{dx^2} - 2x\frac{dy}{dx} + n(n+1)y = 0.$$

See LEGENDRE'S POLYNOMIALS.

LEGENDRE'S POLYNOMIALS or LEGENDRE'S COEFFICIENTS. The coefficients in the expansion of

$$(1-2xh+h^2)^{-1/2}.$$

If $P_n(x)$ denotes the Legendre polynomial of order n, then

$$(1-2xh+h^2)^{-1/2} = P_0(x) + hP_1(x)$$
$$+ h^2P_2(x) + h^3P_3(x) + \cdots,$$

where $\quad P_0(x) = 1, \quad P_1(x) = x,$
$$P_2(x) = \tfrac{1}{2}(3x^2 - 1),$$
$$P_3(x) = \tfrac{1}{2}(5x^3 - 3x), \cdots.$$

$y = P_n(x)$ is a solution of Legendre's equation.

LEIBNIZ' THEOREM or FORMULA. A theorem for finding the nth derivative of the product of two functions; the theorem is as follows:

$$D_x{}^n(uv) = vD_x{}^n u + nD_x{}^{n-1}uD_x v$$
$$+ \tfrac{1}{2}n(n-1)D_x{}^{n-2}uD_x{}^2 v + \cdots$$
$$+ uD_x{}^n v,$$

the numerical coefficients being the coefficients in the expansion of $(u+v)^n$ and the indicated derivatives being of the same order as the corresponding powers in this expansion. Analogously the nth derivative of the product of k functions can be written out from the multinomial expansion of the nth power of the sum of k quantities.

LEM'MA, *n.* A theorem proved for use in the proof of another theorem.

LEM-NIS'CATE, *n.* The plane locus of the foot of the perpendicular from the origin to a variable tangent to the equilateral hyperbola; the locus of the vertex of a triangle when the product of the two adjacent sides is kept equal to one-fourth the square of the third side (which is fixed in length). Employing polar coordinates, if the node (see the figure) is taken as the pole, the axis of symmetry as the initial line, and the greatest distance from the pole to the curve as a, the equation of the lemniscate is $\rho^2 = a^2 \cos 2\theta$. Its corresponding Cartesian equation is

$$(x^2 + y^2)^2 = a^2(x^2 - y^2).$$

This curve was first studied by Jacques Bernoulli, hence is frequently called *Bernoulli's lemniscate*, or the *lemniscate of Bernoulli*. See CASSINI.

LENGTH, *n.* **length of arc** of a plane or space curve. The limit approached by the sum of the chords subtending a set of non-overlapping arcs covering the given arc, as the number of chords becomes infinite in such a way that the longest of the chords approaches zero. For plane curves, see ELEMENT—element of arc of a curve, and *ARC*—length of arc of a curve. If the equation of a space curve is in the parametric form, $x = f(t)$, $y = g(t)$, $z = h(t)$, the length of the curve between the points corresponding to $t = t_0$ and $t = t_1$ is

$$\int_{t_0}^{t_1} \sqrt{(dx/dt)^2 + (dy/dt)^2 + (dz/dt)^2}\, dt.$$

length of a rectangle. The length of its longer side.

length of a straight line segment. The number of times it contains a line segment of unit length.

LESS, *adj.* One *cardinal* number is said to be *less than* another when a set of units represented by the first is a part of the set of the same kind of units represented by the second. (See CARDINAL.) One *ordinal* number is said to be *less than* a second when the addition of a positive number to the first results in the second, or when the first subtracted from the second leaves a positive remainder. See GREATER.

LEV'EL, *adj.* **level lines.** See CONTOUR—contour lines.

net level premiums. See NET.

LE'VER, *n.* A rigid bar used to lift weights by placing the bar against a support called the *fulcrum*, and applying a force or weight. A lever is said to be of the *first*, *second*, or *third* type according as the fulcrum is under the bar and between the weights, under the bar at one end, or above the bar at one end.

law of the lever. If there is equilibrium for two weights (forces), the weights (forces) are to each other inversely as their lever arms, or, what is equivalent, the products of the weights by their lever arms are equal, or the sum of the moments of all the forces about the fulcrum is equal to zero.

lever arm. The distance of a weight (or line of action of a force) from the fulcrum of the lever.

L'HOSPITAL'S RULE. A rule for evaluating *indeterminant forms*: If $f(x)/F(x)$ takes one of the forms $0/0$ or ∞/∞ when $x=a$, and $f'(x)/F'(x)$, where $f'(x)$ and $F'(x)$ are the derivatives of $f(x)$ and $F(x)$, approaches a limit as x approaches a, then $f(x)/F(x)$ approaches the same limit. E.g. if $f(x) = x^2-1$, $F(x) = x-1$, and $a=1, f(a)/F(a)$ takes the form $0/0$ and

$$\lim_{x \to 1} f'(x)/F'(x) = \lim_{x \to 1} 2x = 2,$$

which is the limit approached by $(x^2-1)/(x-1)$ as x approaches 1. See MEAN—second mean value theorem.

L'HUILIER'S THEOREM. A theorem relating the spherical excess of a spherical triangle to the sides:

$$\tan \tfrac{1}{4}E$$
$$= \sqrt{\tan \tfrac{1}{2}s \, \tan \tfrac{1}{2}(s-a) \, \tan \tfrac{1}{2}(s-b) \, \tan \tfrac{1}{2}(s-c)}$$

where a, b, and c are the sides of the triangle, E is the spherical excess, and

$$s = \tfrac{1}{2}(a+b+c).$$

LI′A-BIL′I-TY, *n.* See ASSETS.

LIFE, *n.* (*In insurance.*) (1) The difference between a policy date and the death of the insured. (2) The period during which something under consideration is effective, useful, or efficient, such as: the life of a lease or contract; the life of an enterprise, or the life of a machine.

deferred temporary life insurance. See DEFERRED—deferred temporary insurance.

deferred whole life insurance. See DEFERRED—deferred whole life insurance.

life annuity. A series of payments at regular intervals during the life of an individual (a *single life annuity*) or of a combination of individuals (a *joint life annuity*).

life insurance. A contract to pay a fixed sum when a certain life ends, or when the life ends if that is within a certain period of years. The former is called **whole life insurance**; the latter, **temporary** or **term insurance.**

life interest in property or other assets. Title to the income for life from such assets. The beneficiary is called the *life tenant in possession* or simply *life tenant*. Same as an ordinary life annuity except that the amount received may vary.

most probable after lifetime. (*Life insurance.*) The difference in years between the *most probable lifetime* and the actual age of an individual.

most probable lifetime. (*Life insurance.*) The most likely length of life; the period (beginning at the time of birth) at the end of which exactly half of the persons of a given age will have died.

radix of a life insurance mortality table. The number of lives at the age with which the table starts.

reversionary life interest. A life interest which goes to another person upon the death of the *life tenant*.

LIGHT, *n.* **reflection of light.** See REFLECTION.

refraction of light. See REFRACTION.

LIKE, *adj.* **like terms.** See TERM—like terms.

LIM′A-ÇON, *n.* The locus of a point on a line, at a fixed distance from the intersection of this line with a fixed circle, as the line revolves about a point on the circle. If the diameter of the circle is taken as a (see figure), the fixed distance as b, the fixed point as the pole, the moving line as the radius vector, and the diameter through the fixed circle as the polar axis, the equation of the limaçon is $r = a \cos \theta + b$. This curve was first studied and named by Pascal, hence is usually called **Pascal's limaçon.** When b is less than the diameter of the fixed circle, the curve

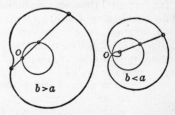

consists of two loops, one within the other; the outside loop is heart-shaped and the inside loop is pear-shaped, the curve having a node at the origin. When b is equal to a, there is one heart-shaped loop, called the **cardioid**. When b is greater than a, there is one loop, whose shape tends toward that of a circle as b increases.

LIM'IT, *n*. **limit of a variable.** A quantity such that the difference between it and the variable can be made to become and remain as near zero as one pleases; e.g. the limit of $1/x$ is 0, as x increases beyond all bounds; the same is true if x takes on numerically large negative values, and also if x takes on, alternately, large positive and numerically large negative values, such as 10, -10, 100, -100, 1000, -1000, $\cdots$. A variable is said to *approach its limit* or to *approach* a certain quantity *as a limit*. The fact that a variable function, $f(x)$, approaches a certain limit k as x approaches a given limit a is written

$$\lim_{x \to a} f(x) = k$$

and stated "limit of $f(x)$, as x approaches a, is k." *Tech*. A function $f(x)$ is said to approach k as a limit as x approaches a if for every positive number ϵ there is a number δ such that $|f(x) - k| < \epsilon$ if $0 < |x - a| < \delta$; $f(x)$ is said to approach the limit k as x *becomes infinite* if for every positive number ϵ there is a number δ such that $|f(x) - k| < \epsilon$ if $x > \delta$.

a lower limit to a sequence. See SEQUENCE—a lower limit to a sequence.

an upper limit to a sequence. See SEQUENCE—an upper limit to a sequence.

common limit. See COMMON.

fundamental theorems on limits: (1) If a variable u approaches a limit l and c is a constant, then cu approaches the limit cl. (2) If u and v approach the limits l and m, respectively, then $u + v$ approaches the limit $l + m$. (3) If u and v approach the limits l and m, respectively, then uv approaches the limit lm. (4) If u and v approach the limits l and m, respectively, and if m is not zero, then u/v approaches the limit l/m. (5) If a variable u steadily increases but never becomes greater than

a given constant, A, then u approaches a limit, U, which is not greater than A. (6) If a variable u steadily decreases but never becomes less than a given constant, B, then u approaches a limit, U, which is not less than B.

greatest limit of a sequence. Same as MAXIMUM LIMIT OF A SEQUENCE.

inaccessible limit. See INACCESSIBLE—inaccessible limit.

inferior limit to the roots of an equation. A number equal to or less than any real root of the equation. *Syn*. Lower limit, or lower bound, to the roots of an equation.

inferior limit of a set of numbers. The least number in the set, or if there be no least, then the greatest number less than all numbers in the set. The *inferior limit* of 1, 1/2, $\cdots$, 1/n, $\cdots$ is 0; of 1/2, 2/3, 3/4, $\cdots$, $n/(n+1)$, $\cdots$, is $\frac{1}{2}$. *Syn*. Lower limit.

limit point of a set of points. A point such that there is at least one other point of the set in any neighborhood of the given point; a point which is the limit of a sequence of points of the set.

limit of a product, quotient, sum. See above, fundamental theorems on limits.

limit of the ratio of an arc to its chord. Refers to the limit of this ratio when the chord (or arc) approaches zero. If the curve is a *circle*, this limit is *one*, and it is also *one* for rectifiable curves.

limit to the real roots of an equation. See above, inferior limit to the roots of an equation, and below, superior limit to the roots of an equation.

limit of a sequence. See SEQUENCE —limit of a sequence.

limit superior (inferior) of a sequence. Same as MAXIMUM (MINIMUM) LIMIT OF A SEQUENCE.

limits of integration. See INTEGRAL—definite integral.

lower limit to the roots of an equation. Same as INFERIOR LIMIT to the roots of an equation.

maximum (minimum) limit of a sequence. See SEQUENCE—maximum (minimum) limit of a sequence.

superior limit to the roots of an equa-

tion. A number equal to or greater than any root of the equation. *Syn.* Upper bound, or upper limit, to the roots of an equation.

superior limit of a set of numbers. The greatest number in the set, or if there be no greatest, then the least number greater than all numbers in the set. The superior limit of 1, 1/2, $\cdots$, 1/n, $\cdots$, is 1; of 1/2, 2/3, 3/4, $\cdots$, $n/(n+1)$, $\cdots$, it is also 1.

"the" upper (lower) limit of a sequence. See SEQUENCE—"the" upper (lower) limit of a sequence.

upper limit to the roots of an equation. Same as superior limit to the roots.

LIMITED PAYMENT POLICY. A life insurance policy in which the annual premium is to be paid only for a stated number of years.

LIMITING AGE. (*In a mortality table.*) The age which the last survivor of the group upon which the table is based would have attained had he lived to the end of the year during which he died.

limiting point. Same as LIMIT POINT.

limiting value. Same as LIMIT OF A VARIABLE.

LINE, *n.* A path traced out by a point in motion. See below, straight line.

addition of line segments. See ADDITION—addition of directed segments of a line.

angle between two lines. See ANGLE.

bisection point of a line segment. Same as MID-POINT of the line segment.

broken line. A line composed entirely of segments of straight lines, laid end to end.

condition that three lines be concurrent. See CONCURRENT—condition that three lines be concurrent.

condition that three lines all be parallel to some plane. See PARALLEL—necessary and sufficient condition that three lines all be parallel to some plane.

condition that two lines be parallel. See PARALLEL—parallel lines.

condition that two lines be parallel (perpendicular) to a plane. See PAR-

ALLEL—line parallel to a plane, PERPENDICULAR—line perpendicular to a plane.

contour lines. See CONTOUR.

curved line. A line which is neither a broken nor a straight line; a line that continually turns (changes direction).

directed line segment. See DIRECTED.

direction of a line. See DIRECTION—direction of a line.

equation of a straight line in the plane. A relation between the coordinates of a point which holds when, and only when, the point is on the straight line. (1) **slope-intercept form.** The equation (in rectangular Cartesian coordinates) $y = mx + b$, where m is the slope of the line and b its intercept on the y-axis. (2) **intercept form.** The Cartesian equation $x/a + y/b = 1$, where a and b are the x and y intercepts, respectively. (3) **point-slope form.** The equation $y - y_1 = m(x - x_1)$, where m is the slope and (x_1, y_1) is a point on the line. (4) **two point form.** The equation

$$(y - y_1)/(y_2 - y_1) = (x - x_1)/(x_2 - x_1)$$

where (x_1, y_1) and (x_2, y_2) are two points through which the line passes. This form can be written more elegantly by equating to zero the third-order determinant whose first, second, and third rows contain, in order, the sets of elements x, y, 1; x_1, y_1, 1; x_2, y_2, 1. (5) **normal form.** The equation $x \cos \omega + y \sin \omega - p = 0$, where ω is the angle from the x-axis to the perpendicular from the origin to the line and p is the length of the perpendicular from the origin to the line. See ANGLE—angle between lines in a plane, (1). (6) **general form**

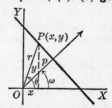

in rectangular Cartesian coordinates. The form which includes all other forms in this system of coordinates as special cases. It is written $Ax + By + C = 0$. (7) **polar form.** The equation $r = p \sec(\theta - \omega)$, where p is the perpendicular distance from the pole to the line, ω is the inclination of this perpendicular to the polar axis and r and θ are the polar coordinates of a variable point on the line; see figure, above.

equation of a straight line in space. (1) The equations of any two planes which intersect in the given line. (2) Equations of planes parallel to the coordinate axes are used as the **symmetric (standard) form** of the equation of a straight line, the equation being written

$$(x - x_1)/l = (y - y_1)/m = (z - z_1)/n,$$

where l, m, and n are *direction numbers* of the line and x_1, y_1, and z_1 are the coordinates of a point on it. (3) The **two point form** of the equations of a line is

$$(x - x_1)/(x_2 - x_1) = (y - y_1)/(y_2 - y_1)$$
$$= (z - z_1)/(z_2 - z_1),$$

where (x_1, y_1, z_1) and (x_2, y_2, z_2) are two points on the line. (4) The **parametric form** is gotten by equating each fraction in the *symmetric form* to a parameter, say t, and solving for x, y, and z. This gives $x = x_1 + lt$, $y = y_1 + mt$, $z = z_1 + nt$. The points determined by giving t any values desired lie on the line. If l, m, n are the direction cosines of the line, t is the distance between the points (x, y, z) and (x_1, y_1, z_1).

foot of a line intersecting a plane. See FOOT.

homologous lines. See HOMOLOGOUS.

ideal line. Same as LINE AT INFINITY. See below.

level lines. See CONTOUR—contour lines.

line of best fit for a set of statistical values. (1) Usually the line determined by the method of least squares. (2) The trend line.

line at infinity. *Algebraically*, the locus of the equation $x_3 = 0$ in the system of *homogeneous coordinates* related to the Cartesian by the relations $x_1/x_3 = x$, $x_2/x_3 = y$. See COORDINATE—homogeneous coordinates. *Geometrically*, the aggregate of all *ideal* points in the plane. *Syn.* Ideal line.

line integral. See INTEGRAL—line integral of a curve.

line parallel to a plane. See PARALLEL—line parallel to a plane.

line perpendicular to a plane. See PERPENDICULAR.

line of regression. (*In statistics.*) (1) Usually the line determined by the method of least squares. If the distances to which least squares are applied are parallel to the y-axis the line is called the *line of regression* of y on x, and if parallel to the x-axis the *line of regression* of x on y. (2) Any line which represents the trend of a set of data.

line segment. A limited part of a straight line.

line values. See VALUE—line value of a trigonometric function.

material line. See MATERIAL.

mid-point of a line. See MID-POINT.

nodal line. See NODAL.

plumb line. (1) The line in which a string hangs, when supporting a weight. (2) The string itself.

polar line. See POLE—pole and polar of a conic.

pole of a straight line. See POLE—pole and polar of a conic.

projection of a line segment on a line or plane. See PROJECTION—projection of a line segment on a line or plane.

straight line. A line such that if any part of it is placed so as to have two points in common with any other part, it will lie along the other part; a straight line is usually called simply a line. *Tech.* An undefined element, which taken with some other element (or elements), such as point, satisfies certain assumptions, such as: two lines determine a point (including the ideal point), and two points determine a line.

trace of a line. See TRACE.

trend line. The line that represents the general drift of a set of data. See above, line of best fit.

vertical line. See VERTICAL.

LINEAL, *adj.* **lineal element.** (*differential equations.*) A short directed line segment through a point, whose slope taken with the coordinates of the point satisfy a given differential equation.

LIN'E-AR, *adj.* (1) In a straight line. (2) Along or pertaining to a curve. (3) Having only one dimension.

coefficient of linear expansion. See COEFFICIENT—coefficient of linear expansion.

consistency of a system of homogeneous linear equations. See HOMOGENEOUS.

consistency of a system of linear equations. See MATRIX—rank of a matrix.

equation of linear regression. (*In statistics*.) $(y - \bar{y})/(x - \bar{x}) = r(\sigma_y/\sigma_x)$, where σ_x and σ_y are the standard deviations of two sets of data (numbers) denoted by x's and y's, respectively, r is the correlation coefficient and $\bar{x}$ and $\bar{y}$ are the means of the x's and y's. See DEVIATION—standard deviation, and COEFFICIENT—correlation coefficient.

general linear transformation. In *one-dimension*, the transformation

$$x' = (ax+b)/(cx+d),$$

or $\rho x_1' = ax_1 + bx_2$, $\rho x_2' = cx_1 + dx_2$, where ρ is an arbitrary constant and x_1, x_2 are *homogeneous coordinates* defined by $x_1/x_2 = x$. In *two dimensions* the general linear transformation is

$$x' = (a_1x+b_1y+c_1)/(d_1x+e_1y+f_1),$$
$$y' = (a_2x+b_2y+c_2)/(d_1x+e_1y+f_1)$$

or in *homogeneous coordinates*

$$\rho x_1' = a_1x_1 + b_1x_2 + c_1x_3,$$
$$\rho x_2' = a_2x_1 + b_2x_2 + c_2x_3,$$
$$\rho x_3' = a_3x_1 + b_3x_2 + c_3x_3.$$

See COORDINATE—homogeneous coordinates. General linear transformations in more than two dimensions are defined similarly. Called **singular** or **non-singular** according as the determinant of the coefficients on the right side is or is not zero.

linear combination of two equations. If the equations are $f(x, y) = 0$ and $F(x, y) = 0$, a linear combination is $kf(x, y) + hF(x, y) = 0$, where k and h are not both zero. The graph of the linear combination of any two equations passes through the points of intersection of their graphs and cuts neither in any other point.

linear combination of two or more quantities. The sum of the quantities, each multiplied by a constant (not all the constants being zero).

linear differential equations. See DIFFERENTIAL—linear differential equations.

linear equation or expression. An algebraic equation or expression which is of the first degree in its variable (or variables); i.e. its highest degree term in the variable (or variables) is of the first degree. The equations, $x + 2 = 0$ and $x + y + 3 = 0$, are linear.

linear equations, or expressions, in a certain variable. An algebraic equation or expression which is of the first degree in that variable. The equation $x + y^2 = 0$ is linear in x but not in y.

linear expansion. Expansion in a straight line; expansion in one direction. The longitudinal expansion of a rod that is being heated is a linear expansion.

linear interpolation. See INTERPOLATION.

linear transformation. A transformation effected by an equality which is a linear algebraic equation in the old variables and in the new variables. The equality itself is usually called the *transformation*, although the concept of *transformation* connotes a change of variables in a function. See above, general linear transformation.

linear velocity. Same as RECTILINEAR VELOCITY. See VELOCITY.

linearly dependent quantities. Quantities such that there exists a linear combination of them which is zero. The quantities $x + 2y$ and $3x + 6y$ are linearly dependent since

$$-3(x+2y) + 3x + 6y \equiv 0.$$

linearly independent quantities. Quantities which are not linearly dependent.

LIST PRICE. The price recorded in wholesale catalogues and other literature. Usually subject to a discount to retail merchants.

LI'TER, (LI'TRE), *n.* One cubic decimeter. Approximately equal to 61.026 cubic inches or 1.056 quarts. See DE-

NOMINATE NUMBERS in the appendix.

LIT'ER-AL, *adj.* **literal constant.** A letter which denotes any one of certain constants (say any real number, or any rational number), as contrasted to a specific constant like 1, 2 or 3. Letters from the first part of the alphabet are usually used (however, see SUBSCRIPT).

literal expression, or equation. An expression or equation in which the constants are represented by letters. $ax^2 + bx + c = 0$ and $ax + by + cz = 0$ are *literal* equations, whereas $3x + 5 = 7$ is a *numerical* equation.

literal notation. The use of letters to denote numbers, either unknown numbers or any of a set of numbers under discussion. For example, algebra uses letters in discussing the fundamental operations of arithmetic in order to make statements regarding all numbers, such as $a + a = 2a$.

LIT'U-US, *n.* [*pl.* **litui.**] A plane curve shaped like a trumpet, from which it gets its name; the locus of a point such that the square of the radius vector varies inversely as the vectorial angle. Its equation in polar coordinates is $r^2 = a/\theta$. The curve is asymptotic to the polar axis and winds around infinitely close to the pole but never touches it. Only positive values of r are used in the figure. Negative values would give an identical branch of the curve in such a position that the two branches would be symmetrical about the pole.

LOAD'ING, *v.* (*In insurance.*) The amount added to the net insurance premiums to cover agents' fees, company expenses, etc.

LOAN VALUE. A term used in connection with an insurance policy. It is an amount, usually somewhat less than the cash surrender value, which the insurance company agrees to loan the policy holder at a stipulated rate as long as the policy is in force.

LOCAL VALUE. Same as PLACE VALUE.

LOCATION THEOREM or PRINCIPLE. If a polynomial has different signs for two values of the variable, it is zero for some value of the variable between these two values; the equation obtained by equating the given polynomial to zero has a root between two values of the unknown for which the polynomial has different signs. Geometrically, if a continuous function of a variable x is at one time on one side of the x-axis, and at another time on the other side (changes sign), it must have crossed the axis between the two positions.

LO'CUS, *n.* [*pl.* **loci.**] Any system of points, lines or curves which satisfies one or more given conditions.

equation of a locus. An equation is called the equation of a locus if it is satisfied by the coordinates of every point on the locus and by no other points.

locus of a point. In *elementary geometry*, the geometrical figure (line, plane, circle, etc.) every point of which satisfies a given condition and which contains no point that does not satisfy this condition; e.g. the locus of a point equidistant from two parallel lines is a line parallel to the given lines and midway between them; in *analytic geometry*, the line, curve, or surface which contains those, and only those, points whose coordinates satisfy certain equations; e.g. a straight line is the *locus* of $2x + y + 1 = 0$.

LOG'A-RITHM, *n.* The logarithm of a number is the power to which it is necessary to raise a given number, called the **base,** to produce the number. The base of a given system of logarithms is the same for all numbers; 2 is the logarithm of 100 to the base 10, written $\log_{10} 100 = 2$; and -2 is the logarithm of .01 to base 10. Logarithms are used to expedite multiplication, division, evolution, and involution. For the processes of using logarithms, see below, *fundamental laws* of logarithms, MANTISSA, CHARACTERISTIC and the logarithm tables in the appendix.

change of base in logarithms. See BASE—change of base in logarithms.

common or Brigg's logarithms. Logarithms having the base 10.

derivative of a logarithm. See DERIVATIVE, and DIFFERENTIATION FORMULAS in the appendix.

fundamental laws of logarithms. (1) The logarithm of the product of two numbers is the sum of the logarithms of the numbers; $\log 4 \times 7 = \log 4 + \log 7 = .60206 + .84510 = 1.44716$ (see TABLE I in the appendix). (2) The logarithm of the quotient of two numbers is equal to the logarithm of the dividend minus the logarithm of the divisor; $\log \frac{4}{7} = \log 4 - \log 7 = 10.60206 - 10 - .84510 = 9.75696 - 10$. (3) The logarithm of a power of a number is equal to the product of the exponent and the logarithm of the number; $\log 7^2 = 2 \log 7 = 1.69020$. (4) The logarithm of a root of a number is equal to the quotient of the logarithm of the number and the index of the root; $\log \sqrt{49} = \log (49)^{1/2} = \frac{1}{2} \log 49 = \frac{1}{2}(1.69020) = .84510$.

logarithm of a complex number. The number w is said to be the *logarithm* of z to base e if $z = e^w$. Writing z in the form

$$z = x + iy = r(\cos \theta + i \sin \theta) = re^{i\theta}$$

it is seen that $\log (x + iy) = i\theta + \log r$, where θ is an argument of z and r is the absolute value of z; i.e. $\log z = \log |z| + i \arg z$. (See COMPLEX—polar form of a complex number and EULER'S FORMULA.) The logarithm of a complex number is a many-valued function since the argument of a complex number is many-valued. Since $e^{i\pi} = \cos \pi + i \sin \pi = -1$, $\log (-1) = i\pi$. For any number, $-n$, $\log (-n) = i\pi + \log n$, thus providing a definition for the logarithm of a negative number. More generally, $\log (-n) = (2k + 1)\pi i + \log n$, where k is any integer. When $\log_e z$ is known, the logarithm of z to any base can be found. See BASE—change of base in logarithms.

logarithm of negative numbers. See above, logarithm of a complex number.

logarithm tables. Tables listing certain numbers and their logarithms. See

TABLES I and II in the appendix.

modulus of common logarithms. See MODULUS.

natural (or Napierian) logarithms. Logarithms having the base e, (2.71828...). See **e.** Sometimes called HYPERBOLIC logarithms.

LOG'A-RITH'MIC, *adj.* **logarithmic coordinates.** See COORDINATE—logarithmic coordinates.

logarithmic coordinate paper. Coordinate paper on which the rulings corresponding (for instance) to the numbers 1, 2, 3, etc., are at distances from the coordinate axes equal to the logarithms of these numbers; i.e. the markings on the graph are not the distances from the axes, but the antilogarithms of the actual distances. This scale is called a **logarithmic scale,** while the ordinary scale, which marks the actual distances, is called a **uniform scale.**

logarithmic curve. The plane locus of the rectangular Cartesian equation $y = \log_a x$. This curve passes through the point whose coordinates are (1, 0) and is asymptotic to the negative y-axis. The ordinates of the curve increase arithmetically while the abscissas increase geometrically; i.e. if the ordinates of three points are 1, 2, 3, respectively, the corresponding abscissas are a, a^2, a^3. When the base a of the logarithmic system is given different values, the general characteristics of the curve are not altered. The figure shows the graph of $y = \log_2 x$.

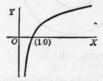

logarithmic differentiation. See DIFFERENTIATION—logarithmic differentiation.

logarithmic equation. See EQUATION—logarithmic equation.

logarithmic plotting (or graphing). A system of graphing such that curves whose equations are of the form $y = kx^n$ are graphed as straight lines. The logarithms of both sides of the equation are taken, giving an equation of the form $\log y = \log k + n \log x$. $\log y$ and $\log x$ are then treated as the variables, and a straight line plotted whose abscissas are $\log x$ and ordinates $\log y$. Points can be found on this straight line whose coordinates are $(\log x, \log y)$, just as the coordinates of points on any line are found. It is then a matter of taking antilogarithms of the coordinates to find x and y, and even this is not necessary if *logarithmic coordinate paper* is used.

logarithmic sine, cosine, tangent, cotangent, secant, or cosecant. The logarithms of the corresponding sine, cosine, etc.

logarithmic solution of triangles. Solutions using logarithms and formulas adapted to the use of logarithms, formulas which essentially involve only multiplication and division.

logarithmic spiral. The plane curve whose vectorial angle is proportional to the logarithm of the radius vector. Its polar equation is $\log r = a\phi$. The angle between the radius vector to a point on the spiral and the tangent at this point is always equal to the modulus of the system of logarithms being used. Also called logistic spiral and equiangular spiral.

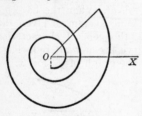

logarithmic tables. Same as LOGARITHM TABLES.

semi-logarithmic coordinate paper. Coordinate paper on which the logarithmic scale is used on one axis and the uniform scale on the other. It is adapted to graphing equations of the type $y = ck^x$. When the logarithms of both sides are taken, the equation takes the form

$$\log y = \log c + x \log k.$$

$\log y$ is now treated as one variable, say u, and the linear equation $u = \log c$

$+ x \log k$ graphed. See above, logarithmic coordinate paper.

LO-GIS'TIC, *adj.* and *n.* (1) Logical. (2) Skilled in or pertaining to computation and calculation. (3) Proportional; pertaining to proportions. (4) The art of calculation. (5) Sexagesimal arithmetic.

logistic spiral. Same as LOGARITHMIC SPIRAL.

LONG, *adj.* **long division.** Division in which the complexity of the divisor requires that the successive steps of the division be written down. A term usually applied to any division when the divisor contains more than one digit (in algebra more than one term). See SHORT—short division.

long radius of a regular polygon. The distance from the polygon's center to any vertex.

LON'GI-TUDE, *n.* The number of degrees in the arc of the equator cut off by the meridian through the place under consideration and the meridian through some established point (Greenwich, England unless otherwise stated). See MERIDIAN—principal meridian.

LOOP, *n.* **loop of a curve.** A section of the curve which completely encloses an area. See CLOSED—closed curve.

LOW'ER, *adj.* **greatest lower bound.** See BOUND.

lower bound of a set of numbers. A number which is less than (or equal to) any number in the set.

lower limit of an integral. See INTEGRAL—definite integral.

LOW'EST, *adj.* **fraction in its lowest terms.** A fraction in which all common factors have been divided out of numerator and denominator; 1/2, 2/3 and $1/(x+1)$ are in their lowest terms, but 2/4, 6/9 and $(x-1)/(x^2-1)$ are not.

lowest common multiple. *Syn.* Least common multiple. See MULTIPLE—least common multiple.

LOX'O-DROME, *n.* Same as **loxodromic spiral.**

LOX-O-DROM'IC, *adj.* **loxodromic spiral.** The path of a ship which cuts the meridians at a constant angle not equal to a right angle; more generally, any curve on a surface of revolution which cuts the meridians at a constant angle. See SURFACE—surface of revolution.

Syn. Rhumb-line, loxodromic line or curve.

LUNE, *n.* A portion of a sphere bounded by two great semi-circles. The angle at which the great circles intersect is the **angle of the lune.**

area of a lune. The product of the ratio of its angle to 360° and the area of the sphere; that is, area = [(angle of lune)/360°] $4\pi r^2$.

M

MACLAURIN'S SERIES (theorem). See TAYLOR'S THEOREM.

trisectrix of Maclaurin. See TRISECTRIX.

MAG'IC, *adj.* **magic square.** A square array of integers such that the sum of the numbers in each row, each column, and each diagonal are all the same, such as:

17	3	13
7	11	15
9	19	5

and

1	15	14	4
12	6	7	9
8	10	11	5
13	3	2	16

MAG-NET'IC, *adj.* **magnetic meridian.** See MERIDIAN—magnetic meridian.

MAG'NI-TUDE, *n.* (1) Greatness, vastness. (2) Size, or the property of having size; length, area, or volume.

geometrical magnitude. See GEOMETRIC—geometric magnitude.

magnitude of a star. Two stars differ by one magnitude if one is $(100)^{1/5}$, or 2.512+, times as bright as the other. The faintest stars seen with the naked eye on a clear moonless night are said to be of the 6th magnitude. The pole star (Polaris) is nearly of the 2nd magnitude.

quartile magnitude or measurement. A magnitude corresponding to a *quartile division* of certain measurements or magnitudes. If 10 students made grades ranging upward from 70% to 100%, the quartile magnitudes would be the grades made by student number three and eight (the median serves as the second quartile). *Syn.* Quartile.

MA'JOR, *adj.* **major arc.** The larger of two arcs; the largest of several arcs. See SECTOR—sector of a circle.

major axis of an ellipse. See ELLIPSE.

major axis of an ellipsoid. See ELLIPSOID.

major and minor segments of a circle. See SEGMENT—segment of a circle.

MAKEHAM'S LAW: The force of mortality (risk of dying) is equal to the sum of a constant and a multiple of a constant raised to a power equal to the age, x, of the life; $M = A + Be^x$. Makeham's law is a closer approximation to statistical findings than Gompertz's law. From the age of 20 to the end of life it very nearly represents the data of most tables.

Makeham's formula for bonds: The price to be paid for a bond n periods before redemption equals $Cv^n + (j/i)F(1 - v^n)$, where C is the redemption price, F the par value, j the divident rate, i the investment rate, and $v = (1+i)^{-1}$.

MAN-TIS'SA, *n.* (1) The decimal part of a logarithm. (2) The decimal part of a logarithm in the system which uses the base 10. The mantissa of a logarithm to base 10 is the same regardless of where the decimal point is located in the number, because shifting the decimal point is equivalent to multiplying or dividing the number by a power of 10, which merely changes the characteristic. See CHARACTERISTIC, and the tables of logarithms in the appendix. Only the mantissas are put in the tables, since the characteristics can be found by a simple rule: This rule is given under CHARACTERISTIC.

mantissa, rule for finding. See TABLE I in the appendix. Using this table when the number whose logarithm is sought has not more than four digits, find the first three in the *column* headed N and the fourth in the row at the top of the table and take the mantissa which is common to the *row* and the *column* headed, respectively, by the first three digits and the fourth. The mantissas for numbers with more digits than those listed in the tables can be found (that is, closely approximated) by interpolation, as follows: think of having a decimal point immediately on the left of the extra digit (digits); subtract the mantissa of the number in the table next less than the given number from the mantissa of the next greater number; multiply this difference by the extra digit (digits) of the number preceded by the decimal; add this result to the lesser mantissa. Analogous procedure holds when using other tables. E.g. to find the mantissa of log 10134, see TABLE I, *p.* 1 of appendix, second row and column headed 3. There we find the mantissa of log 1013 to be .00561. In the next column, we find the mantissa of log 1014 to be .00604. The difference, .00604 − .00561, is .00043; .4 of this difference is .00017, which we add to .00561, getting, for the mantissa of log 10134, .00578. See PROPORTIONAL —proportional parts in a table of logarithms, and CHARACTERISTIC.

MAN′Y, *adj.* **many valued function.** See MULTIPLE—multiple valued function.

MAR′GIN, *n.* (*In finance.*) (1) The difference between the selling price and the cost of goods. (2) A sum of money deposited with a broker by a client to cover any losses that may occur in the broker's dealings for him.

MARIOTT'S LAW. Same as BOYLE and MARIOTT'S LAW. See BOYLE'S LAW.

MAR′KET, *n.* **market value.** The amount a commodity sells for on the open market. *Syn.* Market price.

MASCHERONI'S CONSTANT. See EULER'S CONSTANT.

MASS, *n.* The quantity of matter in a body. It is measured by the standard **pound** of **mass** which is a block of platinum preserved in the Standards Office, London. Mass is usually denoted by *m.* Two masses acted on by the same force are to each other as the inverse ratio of their accelerations; that is, mass varies inversely with acceleration. (Mass increases with the velocity of the body. At any given velocity mass is equal to its value at rest divided by the square root of one minus the square of the quotient of its velocity and that of light, i.e.

$$m = m_0 / \sqrt{1 - v^2/v_1^2}.$$

Hence the mass of a body increases without limit as its velocity approaches that of light, but for velocities not near that of light the effect of velocity on mass can be ignored in practical work.) *Syn.* Inertia.

differential mass. The product of the differential volume by its density. *Syn.* Element of mass. See ELEMENT— element of mass.

mass center. Same as CENTER OF MASS. See CENTROID.

moment of mass. See MOMENT— moment of a mass about a point, line, or plane.

unit mass. The standard unit of mass (see MASS), or some multiple of this unit chosen for convenience.

MA-TE′RI-AL, *adj.* **material point, line, or surface.** A point, line, or surface thought of as having mass. (If one thinks of a lamina with a fixed mass whose thickness approaches zero and density increases proportionally, the limiting situation can be thought of as an area with the fixed mass.)

MATH′E-MAT′I-CAL, *adj.* **mathematical (or complete) induction.** A method of proving a law or theorem by showing that it holds in the first case and showing that if it holds for all the cases preceding a given one, then it also holds for this case. Before the method can be applied it is necessary that the different cases of the law depend upon a parameter which takes on the values, 1, 2, 3, · · · . The essential steps of the proof are as follows: (1) Prove the theorem for the first case. (2) Prove that if the theorem is true for the *n*th case, then it is true for the (*n* +1)th case. (3) Conclude that it must then be true for all cases (there cannot be a case for which it is not true; for if there were, the previous case could not be true, by (2), and so on back to the first case where a contradiction arises. E.g. (1) Since the sun rose today, if it can be shown that if it rises any one day, it will rise the next day, then it follows by mathematical induction that it will always rise. (2) To prove $1 + 2 + 3 + \cdots + n = \frac{1}{2}n(n+1)$. If $n = 1$ the right member becomes

1, which completes step (1). Adding $(n+1)$ to both members gives $1+2+3+\cdots+n+(n+1) = \frac{1}{2}n(n+1)+n+1 = \frac{1}{2}(n+1)(n+2)$, which completes step (2). Therefore the statement must be true for all positive integral values of n.

MATH'E-MAT'ICS, *n.* The logical study of shape, arrangement, and quantity.

applied mathematics. The study and use of mathematical principles as tools in other fields; the application of the principles of mathematics in any other subject or in practical life.

mathematics of finance. The study of the mathematical practices in brokerage, banking, and insurance. *Syn.* Mathematics of investment.

pure mathematics. The study and development of the principles of mathematics as such (for their own sake and possible future usefulness) rather than for their immediate usefulness. *Syn.* Abstract mathematics. See above, applied mathematics.

MA'TRIX, *n.* [*pl.* **matrices.**] A rectangular array of terms called **elements** (written between parentheses or double lines on either side of the array), as:

$$\begin{pmatrix} a_1 & b_1 & c_1 \\ a_2 & b_2 & c_2 \end{pmatrix} \quad \text{or} \quad \left\| \begin{array}{ccc} a_1 & b_1 & c_1 \\ a_2 & b_2 & c_2 \end{array} \right\|.$$

Used to facilitate the study of problems in which the relation between these elements is fundamental, as in the study of the existence of solutions of simultaneous linear equations. Unlike determinants a matrix does not have quantitative value. It is not the symbolic representation of some polynomial, as is a determinant. See below, rank of a matrix.

augmented matrix of a set of simultaneous linear equations. The matrix of the coefficients, with an added column consisting of the constant terms of the equations. The augmented matrix of

$$\begin{array}{l} a_1x+b_1y+c_1z+d_1=0 \\ a_2x+b_2y+c_2z+d_2=0 \end{array} \text{ is } \left\| \begin{array}{cccc} a_1 & b_1 & c_1 & d_1 \\ a_2 & b_2 & c_2 & d_2 \end{array} \right\|.$$

matrix of the coefficients of a set of simultaneous linear equations. The rectangular array left by dropping the variables from the equations when they are written so that the variables are in the same order in all equations and are in such a position that the coefficients of like variables are in the same columns, zero being used as the coefficient if a term is missing. When the number of variables is the same as the number of equations, the matrix of the coefficients is a square array. The matrix of the coefficients of

$$\begin{array}{l} a_1x+b_1y+c_1z+d_1=0 \\ a_2x+b_2y+c_2z+d_2=0 \end{array} \text{ is } \left\| \begin{array}{ccc} a_1 & b_1 & c_1 \\ a_2 & b_2 & c_2 \end{array} \right\|.$$

See below, rank of a matrix.

rank of a matrix. The order of the largest non-zero determinant that can be selected from the matrix by taking out rows and columns. The concept *rank* facilitates, for instance, the statement of the condition for consistency of simultaneous linear equations: *m* linear equations in *n* unknowns are consistent when and only when the *rank* of the matrix of the coefficients is equal to the *rank* of the argumented matrix. In the system of linear equations

$$\begin{array}{l} x+y+z+3=0 \\ 2x+y+z+4=0, \end{array}$$

the matrix of the coefficients is

$$\left\| \begin{array}{ccc} 1 & 1 & 1 \\ 2 & 1 & 1 \end{array} \right\|$$

and the augmented matrix is

$$\left\| \begin{array}{cccc} 1 & 1 & 1 & 3 \\ 2 & 1 & 1 & 4 \end{array} \right\|.$$

The rank of both is two, because the determinant

$$\left| \begin{array}{cc} 1 & 1 \\ 2 & 1 \end{array} \right|$$

is not zero. Hence these equations are satisfied by some set of values of x and y and z. See CONSISTENCY—consistency of equations.

MAX'I-MUM (minimum), *n.* [*pl.* **maxima, minima.**] **maximum (minimum) of an ordinary continuous function of one variable.** A point at which the function (or ordinate of the graph of the function) ceases to increase and begins to decrease (in case of a minimum, ceases to decrease and begins to increase). The highest (lowest) point in a path over a "mountain" (through a "valley"). The function $\sin 2x$ (graph of $y = \sin 2x$, in the illustration) has a maximum for $x = \frac{1}{4}\pi$ radians, in fact maxima for $x = n\pi + \frac{1}{4}\pi$ and minima for $x = n\pi - \frac{1}{4}\pi$, where n is any integer. If the curve (function) has several maximum (minimum) points, each such point is called a relative maximum (minimum), and the largest maximum (smallest minimum) is called the absolute maximum (minimum). The most common practice is to use *maximum* (*minimum*) for *relative maximum* (*relative minimum*). The slope of the graph of a function changes from positive to negative (negative to positive) at a maximum (minimum) point as one passes from left to right, being zero at the point if the derivative is continuous. The elementary condition for testing for maximum (minimum) is that the first derivative be zero at the point and the second derivative be negative (positive) at the point. This rule fails when the second derivative is zero or when the curve has a cusp at the point. For instance, the functions $y = x^3$ and $y = x^4$ both have their first and second derivatives zero at the origin, but the first has a point of inflection there and the second a minimum. For the exceptional cases in which this rule fails, an elementary test can be made by examining the sign of the derivative on either side of the point, or finding the values of the function on either side. A general test for a maximum (minimum) of an analytic function is that the *first derivative* be zero at the point and the lowest order derivative not zero at the point be of even order and negative (positive). A maximum (minimum) is also defined as the greatest (least) value of a function in a given neighborhood, the point at which there is a greater ordinate than at any point on either side of it. A test for maxima (minima) under this definition can be made by examining values of the function very near the point (value) under investigation.

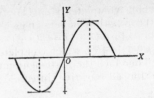

maximum (minimum) of a function of any number of variables. The function $F(x_1, x_2, \cdots, x_n)$ of the n *independent* variables $x_1, x_2, \cdots, x_n$ is said to have a maximum (minimum) at the point $P(x_1, x_2, \cdots, x_n)$ if the difference $F(x_1', x_2', \cdots, x_n') - F(x_1, x_2, \cdots, x_n)$ is negative (positive) for all points in a sufficiently small neighborhood of P. If F and its first partial derivatives are continuous in the neighborhood of a point, a necessary condition for F to have a maximum (minimum) at the point is that all of its first partial derivatives be zero at the point. For the case when the arguments of F are not independent, see LAGRANGE'S METHOD OF MULTIPLIERS.

maximum (minimum) of a function of two variables (or of a surface). The highest point of a hill (the lowest point of a valley); the value of the function at a point in whose neighborhood its values are all less (greater) than at the point. *Tech.* $f(x, y)$ has a maximum (minimum) at the point (a, b) if $f(a+h, b+k) - f(a, b)$ is less than (greater than) zero for all sufficiently small values of h and k different from zero. A necessary condition for a maximum (or minimum) at a point (a, b) in a region in which $f(x, y)$ and its partial derivatives are continuous is that the latter be zero at the point. If these partial derivatives are zero and the expression

$$\left(\frac{\partial^2 f}{\partial x \partial y}\right) - \frac{\partial^2 f}{\partial x^2} \frac{\partial^2 f}{\partial y^2}$$

is greater than zero at the point, there is no maximum (or minimum); if this expression is less than zero at the point, there is a maximum if the derivatives $\partial^2 f/\partial x^2$, $\partial^2 f/\partial y^2$ are both negative (a minimum if both are positive). If the above expression is zero, the test fails. **Relative** and **absolute maximum** of functions of two variables are used in the same sense as in the case of a function of one variable.

maximum limit of a sequence. See SEQUENCE—maximum limit of a sequence.

MEAN, *adj.*, *n.* **arithmetic mean.** See ARITHMETIC, and WEIGHTED MEAN.

double law of the mean. See below, second mean value theorem.

extended mean value theorem. See EXTENDED.

first law of the mean for integrals. See INTEGRAL—properties of definite integrals (5).

generalized mean value theorem. Same as EXTENDED MEAN VALUE THEOREM.

geometric mean between two numbers. Denoted by G. M. A square root of the product of the numbers; the middle term of three successive terms in a *geometric progression*. There are always two such means, but in common usage G. M. is understood to denote the positive root of the product, unless otherwise indicated. The *geometric means* of 2 and 8 are $\pm\sqrt{16}$ or ± 4.

mean axis of an ellipsoid. See ELLIPSOID.

mean curvature of a surface (at a point). The sum of the curvatures of the two normal sections which have respectively the maximum and minimum curvatures at the point. See NORMAL —normal curvature. *Syn.* Mean normal curvature.

mean density. See DENSITY.

mean deviation. Same as AVERAGE DEVIATION. See DEVIATION.

mean (average) ordinate. See below, mean value of a function of one variable.

mean proportional. See PROPORTIONAL—mean proportional.

mean reserve. (*Life insurance.*) The average of the initial and terminal reserve.

mean square ordinate of a curve. The mean square ordinate of the curve

$y = f(x)$ in the interval (a, b) is the mean value of y^2 in the interval, that is

$$\frac{1}{b-a}\int_a^b y^2 dx.$$

See below, mean value of a function of one variable.

mean terms of a proportion. The second and third terms; the consequent in the first ratio and the antecedent in the second. Usually called simply the **means** of the proportion. In the proportion $a/b = c/d$, b and c are the *mean terms*.

mean value of a function, f, over a given range. The integral of f over the range, divided by the magnitude of the range. *Tech.*

$$\frac{1}{s}\int_s f ds,$$

where ds is an element of the range enclosable in an infinitesimal sphere and s is the magnitude of the range. E.g. the mean of xy over the rectangle whose vertices are $(0, 0)$, $(2, 0)$, $(2, 3)$, $(0, 3)$ is

$$\frac{1}{s}\int_s xyds = \frac{1}{6}\int_0^3\int_0^2 xydxdy = \frac{3}{2}.$$

See below, mean value of a function of one variable.

mean value of a function of one variable. The mean value on the interval (a, b) is the quotient of the area bounded by the curve, the ordinates corresponding to a and b, and the axis of the variable, divided by the length of the interval (a, b); the side of the rectangle whose other side is of length $b - a$ and whose area is equal to the above area. *Tech.* the *mean value* of $f(x)$ for

$$a \leq x \leq b \quad \text{is} \quad \frac{1}{b-a}\int_a^b f(x)dx.$$

See INTEGRAL—definite integral. *Syn.* Mean ordinate.

mean value theorem of a function of two variables. For the function $f(x, y)$ on the interval $a \leq x \leq b$, $a' \leq y \leq b'$ the theorem is: If $f(x, y)$ is continuous and has continuous first partial derivatives, there exist numbers x_1 and y_1 such that

$$f(b, b') - f(a, a') =$$
$$(b-a)f_x(x_1, y_1) + (b'-a')f_y(x_1, y_1),$$

where f_x and f_y denote the partial derivatives of $f(x, y)$ with respect to x and y, respectively, and $a < x_1 < b$, $a' < y_1 < b'$. *Syn.* Theorem of the mean for a function of two variables. (This theorem can be extended to any number of variables.)

mean value theorem or law of the mean. Geometrically, this theorem states that an arc of a smooth, single-valued curve has at least one tangent parallel to its secant. When the secant is on the x-axis, this is the same as ROLLE'S THEOREM. *Tech.* If $f(x)$ is single valued and $f'(x)$ is continuous on the interval (a, b), then

$$f(b) - f(a) = (b-a)f'(c),$$

for some c between a and b.

second law of the mean for integrals: (1) If $f(x)$ and $g(x)$ are both integrable on the interval (a, b) and $f(x)$ is always of the same sign, then

$$\int_a^b f(x)g(x)dx = K \int_a^b f(x)dx,$$

where K is between the greatest and the least values of $g(x)$, or possibly equal to one of them. If $g(x)$ is continuous in the interval (a, b), then K may be replaced by $g(k)$, where k is a value of x in the interval (a, b). (2) If in addition to the above conditions $g(x)$ is a *positive monotonically decreasing function*, the theorem can be written in *Bonnet's form*

$$\int_a^b f(x)g(x)dx = g(a) \int_a^p f(x)dx$$

where $a \leq p \leq b$, or if $g(x)$ is only *monotonic*, in the form

$$\int_a^b f(x)g(x)dx = g(a) \int_a^p f(x)dx$$
$$+ g(b) \int_p^b f(x)dx.$$

second mean value theorem of the differential calculus: If the functions $f(x)$ and $g(x)$ have continuous first derivatives on the interval (a, b), then

there exists at least one value of x, say x_1, such that

$$[f(b) - f(a)]/[g(b) - g(a)] = f(x_1)/g(x_1),$$

where $a < x_1 < b$. *Syn.* Double law of the mean, Cauchy's mean value formula. Sometimes called the generalized, or extended, mean value theorem, although these are also used for Taylor's Theorem.

weighted mean. See WEIGHTED MEAN.

MEAS′URE, *n.* Comparison to some unit recognized as a standard.

angular measure. A system of measuring angles. See DEGREE, RADIAN, and SEXAGESIMAL.

board measure. A system of measure in which boards one inch or less in thickness are measured in terms of square feet on the side, the thickness being neglected; those thicker than one inch being measured in terms of the number of square feet one inch thick to which they are equivalent.

circular measure. (1) Same as angular measure. (2) The measure of angles by means of radians. See RADIAN.

common measure. Same as COMMON DIVISOR.

cubic measure. The measurement of volumes in terms of a cube whose edge is a standard linear unit, a *unit cube*. *Syn.* Volume measure.

decimal measure. See DECIMAL—decimal measure.

dry measure. The system of units used in measuring dry commodities, such as grain, fruit, etc. In the United States the system is based on the bushel. See DENOMINATE NUMBERS in the appendix.

land measure. See ACRE and DENOMINATE NUMBERS in the appendix.

linear measure. Measurement along a line, the line being either straight or curved.

liquid measure. The system of units ordinarily used in measuring liquids. See DENOMINATE NUMBERS in the appendix.

measure of central tendency. (*In statistics.*) The *mean*, the *mode*, the *median*, and the *geometric mean* are commonly used.

measure of dispersion. (*In statistics*.) Same as DEVIATION.

measure of a spherical angle. The plane angle formed by the tangents to the sides of the spherical angle at their points of intersection.

square measure. The measure of areas of surfaces in terms of a square whose side is a standard linear unit, a *unit square*. *Syn.* Surface measure.

surveyor's measure. See DENOMINATE NUMBERS in the appendix.

wood measure. See DENOMINATE NUMBERS in the appendix.

MEAS'URE-MENT, *n.* The act of measuring.

median of a group of measurements. See MEDIAN.

ME-CHAN'I-CAL, *adj.* mechanical integration. See INTEGRATION—mechanical integration.

ME-CHAN'ICS, *n.* The mathematical theory of the motions and tendencies to motion of particles and systems under the influence of forces and constraints; the study of motions of masses and of the effect of forces in causing or modifying these motions. Usually divided into *kinematics* and *dynamics*.

analytical mechanics. Mechanics treated by means of differential and integral calculus.

MECHANIC'S RULE. A rule for extracting square roots. The rule is as follows: Make an estimate of the root, divide the number by this estimate, and take for the approximate square root the arithmetic mean (average) of the estimate and the quotient thus obtained. If a more accurate result is desired, repeat the process. *Algebraically*, if a is the estimate, e the error and $(a+e)$ the required number, divide $(a+e)^2$, that is $a^2+2ae+e^2$, by a and take the average between a and the quotient. This gives $a+e+e^2/(2a)$. The error is $e^2/(2a)$, which is very small if e is small: E.g. if one estimates $\sqrt{2}$ to be 1.5, the mechanic's rule gives the root as 1.4167. The error in this is less than .003. The error in a second appli-

cation of the rule is less than $(.003)^2/2$ or .0000045.

ME'DI-AN, *n.* median deviation. See DEVIATION.

median of a group of measurements. The middle measurement; or if there is no middle one, then the one interpolated between the two middle ones. If five students make the grades 60%, 75%, 80%, 95%, and 100%, the median is 80%.

median point. The point of intersection of the medians of a triangle; the centroid of a triangle.

median of a trapezoid. The line joining the mid-points of the non-parallel sides. *Syn.* Mid-line.

median of a triangle. A line joining a vertex to the middle point of the opposite side.

MEM'BER, *n.* member of an equation. The expression on one (or the other) side of the equality sign. The two members of an equation are distinguished as the *left* or *first* and the *right* or *second* member.

MENELAUS' THEOREM. If in the triangle ABC, points P_1, P_2, P_3 are on the sides AB, BC, CA, respectively, then P_1, P_2, P_3 are collinear if and only if

$$\frac{AP_1}{P_1B}\frac{BP_2}{P_2C}\frac{CP_3}{P_3A}=-1.$$

MEN'SU-RA'TION, *n.* The measuring of geometric magnitudes, such as the lengths of lines, areas of surfaces, and volumes of solids.

MERCANTILE RULE. Same as MERCHANT'S RULE.

MERCHANT'S RULE. A rule for computing the balance due on a note after partial payments have been made. The method is to find the amount of each partial payment at the settlement date and subtract the sum of these from the value of the face of the note at the same date. *Syn.* Mercantile rule.

ME-RID'I-AN, *n.* A great circle on the surface of the earth passing through the geographic poles; a geographical north and south line.

celestial meridian. See HOUR—hour angle and hour circle.

first meridian. Same as PRINCIPAL MERIDIAN.

magnetic meridian. The curve in which the earth's surface is cut by a plane perpendicular to the earth's surface and passing through the magnetic poles.

meridians or meridian sections. See SURFACE—surface of revolution.

prime meridian. Same as PRINCIPAL MERIDIAN.

principal meridian. The meridian from which longitude is reckoned; usually the meridian through the transit-circle of the Royal Observatory of Greenwich, England, although observers frequently use the meridian through the capital of their country. *Syn.* First, prime, zone, and zero meridian.

zero meridian. Same as PRINCIPAL MERIDIAN.

zone meridian. Same as PRINCIPAL MERIDIAN.

ME′TER (ME′TRE), *n.* The basic unit of linear measure of the metric system; the distance between two marks on a platinum bar preserved in Paris. It is equal to 39.37 + inches.

METH′OD, *n.* **appraisal method.** See APPRAISAL METHOD.

method of geometric exhaustion. A method used by the Greeks to find such areas as that of the ellipse, a segment of a parabola, etc. Consists of finding an increasing (or decreasing) sequence of areas (expressed in terms of familiar areas of plane geometry), whose terms are always less than (greater than) the desired area and increasing (decreasing); then (in modern terminology) showing that it approaches the desired area as a limit. The idea of exhaustion enters when it is argued that the desired area cannot be different from a certain value, since if it were it would either be less than some term of the increasing sequence or greater than some term of the decreasing sequence.

method of least squares. A method based upon the principle that the best value of a quantity that can be deduced from a set of measurements or observations is that for which the sum of the squares of the deviations of the observed values (from it) is a minimum. In the case of a single set of measurements this principle gives the arithmetic mean of the several measurements as the best value. The *method of least squares* consists in using this principle to determine the arbitrary constants in the equation of a curve which has been assumed to be the type that best fits a given set of data. Suppose $y = mx$ is such a type and that for $x = 1, 2, 3, 4$ the observed values of y are 2, 4, 7, 6. Then the method of least squares would take for m that value which makes

$$(m-2)^2 + (2m-4)^2 + (3m-7)^2 + (4m-6)^2$$

a minimum. This value is 1.8 + and the straight line through the origin whose graph best fits the points (1, 2), (2, 4), (3, 7), (4, 6) is $y = 1.8x$.

METRIC SYSTEM. The system of measurement in which the meter is the fundamental unit. It was first adopted in France and is in general use in most other civilized countries, except the English-speaking countries, and is now almost universally used for scientific measurements. The unit of surface is the *are* (100 square meters) and the theoretical unit of volume is the *stere* (one cubic meter), although the *liter* (one cubic decimeter) is most commonly used. See DENOMINATE NUMBERS in the appendix. The prefixes *deca-, hecto-, kilo-,* and *myria-* are used on the above units to designate 10 times, 100 times, 1000 times and 10,000 times the unit. The prefixes *deci-, centi-,* and *milli-,* are used to designate 1/10, 1/100, 1/1000 parts of the respective unit.

MIDDLE LATITUDE of two places. The mean between the latitudes of the two places; one half the sum of their latitudes if they are on the same side of the equator, one half the difference (taken north or south according to which latitude was the larger) if the places are on different sides of the equator.

middle latitude sailing. See SAIL-
ING.

MID-LINE OF A TRAPEZOID. See
MEDIAN—median of a trapezoid.

MID-PERPENDICULAR, n. The perpendicular bisector of a line segment.

MID-POINT, n. **mid-point of a line
segment.** The point that divides the
line segment into two equal parts; the
point that bisects the line. See BISECT.

MIL, n. A unit of angle measure, equal
to 1/6400 of a complete revolution,
.05625°, and nearly 1/1000 of a radian.
Used by U. S. artillery.

MILE, n. A unit of linear measure equal
to 5280 feet or 320 rods.

geographical mile. Same as NAU-
TICAL MILE. See KNOT.

nautical mile. See KNOT.

MIL'LI-ME'TER, n. One thousandth
part of a meter.

MIL'LION, n. One thousand thousands
(1,000,000).

MIN'I-MUM, n. See MAXIMUM.

minimum of a function of any number of variables. See MAXIMUM—
maximum (minimum) of a function of
any number of variables.

minimum of a function of two variables. See MAXIMUM—maximum
(minimum) of a function of two variables.

MIN'ING, adj. evaluation of mining
property. See PROPERTY.

MI'NOR, adj. minor arc of a circle. See
SECTOR—sector of a circle.

minor axis of an ellipse. The smaller
axis of the ellipse.

minor of an element in a determinant. The determinant, of next lower
order, obtained by striking out the
row and column in which the element
lies. This is sometimes called the
complementary minor. The minor,
taken with a positive or negative sign
according as the *sum* of the orders of
the row and column stricken out of the
original determinant is even or odd, is
called the **signed-minor,** or **cofactor,** of
the element. E.g. the minor of b_1 in the
determinant

$$\begin{vmatrix} a_1 & a_2 & a_3 \\ b_1 & b_2 & b_3 \\ c_1 & c_2 & c_3 \end{vmatrix}$$

is the determinant

$$\begin{vmatrix} a_2 & a_3 \\ c_2 & c_3 \end{vmatrix}$$

and the cofactor of b_1 is

$$-\begin{vmatrix} a_2 & a_3 \\ c_2 & c_3 \end{vmatrix}.$$

MIN'U-END, n. The quantity from
which another quantity is to be subtracted.

MIN'US, adj. A word used between two
quantities to state that the second is
to be subtracted from the first. The
statement 3 minus 2, written $3-2$,
means 2 is to be subtracted from 3.
Minus is also used as a synonym for
negative.

MIN'UTE, n. (1) The sixtieth part of an
hour. (2) The sixtieth part of a degree
(in the sexagesimal system of measuring angles). See SEXAGESIMAL.

MIXED, adj. mixed decimal. See DECI-
MAL.

mixed number, quantity. In *arithmetic*, the sum of an integer and a
fraction, as $2\frac{3}{4}$. In *algebra*, the sum of
a polynomial and a rational algebraic
fraction, as

$$2x+3+\frac{1}{x+1}.$$

MNE-MON'IC, adj. Assisting the memory; relating to the memory.

mnemonics or mnemonic devices.
Any scheme or device to aid in remembering certain facts as: (1) sin $(x+y)$
is equal to the sum of two mixed terms
in sine and cosine, while cos $(x+y)$
is equal to the difference of unmixed
terms; (2) the derivatives of all co-
functions (*trigonometric*) take a negative sign.

MODE, n. (*In statistics.*) The magnitude
of the most frequent item. If more
students (of a given group) make 75%
than any other one grade, then 75%
is the mode.

MOD'ERN, adj. modern analytic geometry. See GEOMETRY—modern analytic geometry.

MOD'U-LUS, n. modulus of common
logarithms. The factor by which *natural logarithms* are multiplied to

change them into *common logarithms.*
It is log$_{10}e$, or 0.434294 +. See BASE—
change of base in logarithms.

modulus of a complex number. The
absolute value of the complex number;
the numerical length of the vector
representing the complex number. The
modulus of $4+3i$ is 5. In general, the
modulus of $a+bi$ is $\sqrt{a^2+b^2}$, or if the
number is in the form $r(\cos \beta + i \sin \beta)$,
the modulus is r.

modulus of a congruence. See CON-
GRUENT—congruent numbers.

MO′MENT, *n.* **element or differential
of moment.** See ELEMENT—element
of moment.

**element or differential of moment
of inertia.** See below, moment of inertia.

moment of area. Same as the MO-
MENT OF MASS of an area having
unit mass per unit area (unit density).

moment of a curve. Same as the
MOMENT OF MASS of a curve
having unit mass per unit length (unit
density).

moment of force about a line. The
product of the projection of the force
on a plane perpendicular to the line
and the perpendicular distance from the
line to the line of action of the force.

moment of a frequency distribution.
(*Statistics.*) The arithmetic mean of a
power of the deviations; the mean of
the first powers is called the *first moment
about the mean;* the mean of the second
powers, the *second moment,* etc.

moment of inertia of a particle about
a point, line, or plane. The product of
the mass and the square of the distance from the particle to the point,
line or plane. The moment of inertia of
a body is the limit of the sum of the
moments of inertia of its particles, that
is, of its **elements of moment of inertia,**
r^2dm. This is the integral of r^2dm over
the entire body, written $\int_s r^2dm$, where
r is the distance from the element of
mass dm to the point, line, or plane
about which the moment of inertia is
being found and $\int_s$ indicates that the
integration is to be taken over the
entire body. Also called *second moment.*
See INTEGRAL—definite integral.

**moment of mass about a point, line,
or plane.** The sum of the products of
each of the particles of the mass and
its distance from the point, line, or
plane. *Tech.* The integral, over the
given mass, of the element of mass
times its perpendicular distance from
the point, line, or plane. See ELE-
MENT—element of moment.

product moment. (*In statistics.*) The
arithmetic average of the products of
the algebraic deviations of the abscissas and the corresponding algebraic
deviations of the ordinates of the points
whose abscissas and ordinates are sets
of statistical data.

second moment. See above, moment
of inertia.

MO-MEN′TUM, *n.* The product of mass
and velocity.

MO-NO′MI-AL, *n.* A single term.

monomial factor of an expression.
A single term that may be divided out
of every member of the expression; x is
a monomial factor of $2x+3xy+x^2$.

MON′O-TONE, *adj.* Same as MONO-
TONIC.

MON′O-TON′IC, *adj.* The property of
either never increasing or never decreasing.

**monotonic (or monotone) decreas-
ing.** Never increasing. Used to describe
a quantity (function, sequence, etc.)
which either decreases or remains the
same, but never increases.

**monotonic (or monotone) increas-
ing.** Never decreasing. Used to describe
a quantity (function, sequence, etc.)
which either increases or remains the
same, but never decreases.

MOR-TAL′I-TY, *n.* **American experi-
ence table of mortality.** See AMERI-
CAN EXPERIENCE TABLE OF
MORTALITY.

force of mortality. See FORCE—
force of mortality.

mortality table. See TABLE—mortality table.

radix of a mortality table. See RA-
DIX.

rate of mortality. See RATE—rate
of mortality.

**select period of a select mortality
table.** See SELECT.

MORT'GAGE, *n.* A conditional conveyance of, or lien upon, property as a security for money lent.

MOST, *adv.* **most probable after lifetime.** (*Insurance*). The time between the year of age in which the life is most likely to end and the life's present age.

most probable lifetime. (*Insurance.*) The time over which one has equal chances of living and dying; the period at the end of which exactly half of the lives of a given age will have ended.

MO'TION, *n.* **constant motion.** See CONSTANT—constant motion.

curvilinear motion. Motion along a curve; motion which is not in a straight line.

curvilinear motion about a center of force. Motion such as that of celestial bodies about the sun; the motion of a particle whose initial velocity was not directed toward the center of force and which is attracted by a force at the given center. If this force is gravitation the path is a conic whose focus (or one of whose foci) is at the center of force.

rigid motion. See RIGID—rigid motion.

simple harmonic motion. See HARMONIC.

uniform circular motion. See UNIFORM.

uniform motion or velocity. Same as CONSTANT MOTION or VELOCITY. See CONSTANT—constant motion, and VELOCITY—uniform velocity.

MUL'TI-FOIL. A plane figure made of congruent arcs of a circle arranged on a regular polygon so that the figure is symmetrical about the center of the polygon and the ends of the arcs are on the polygon. The name is some-

times restricted to the cases in which the polygon has six or more sides. When the polygon is a square, the figure is called a *quatrefoil* (as illus-

trated); when it is a regular hexagon, a *hexafoil*; when a triangle, a *trefoil*.

MUL-TI-NO'MI-AL, *adj.* **multinomial theorem.** A theorem for the expansion of powers of multinomials. It includes the *binomial theorem* as a special case. The formula for the expansion is:

$$(x_1+x_2+\cdots+x_m)^n$$
$$= \sum \frac{n!}{a_1!a_2!\cdots a_m!} x_1^{a_1}x_2^{a_2}\cdots x_m^{a_m}$$

where $a_1, a_2, \cdots, a_m$ are any selection of m numbers from $0, 1, 2, \cdots, n$ such that $a_1+a_2+\cdots+a_m=n$, and $0!=1$.

MUL-TI-NO'MI-AL, *n.* An algebraic expression containing more than one term. Compare POLYNOMIAL.

MUL'TI-PLE, *n.* In *arithmetic*, a number which is the product of a given number and another factor; 12 is a *multiple* of 2, 3, 4, 6, and trivially of 1 and 12. In general, a product, no matter whether it be arithmetic or algebraic, is said to be a *multiple* of any of its factors.

common multiple. A quantity which is a multiple of each of two or more given quantities. The number 6 is a common multiple of 2 and 3; x^2-1 is a common multiple of $x-1$ and $x+1$.

least common multiple, of two or more quantities. Denoted by l.c.m. or L.C.M. The least quantity that is exactly divisible by each of the given quantities; 12 is the l.c.m. of 2, 3, 4, and 6. The l.c.m. of a set of algebraic quantities is the product of all their distinct prime factors, each taken the greatest number of times it occurs in any one of the quantities; the l.c.m. of

$$x^2-1 \quad \text{and} \quad x^2-2x+1$$
is $\qquad (x-1)^2(x+1).$

Tech. The l.c.m. of a set of quantities is a common multiple of the quantities which divides every common multiple of them. Also called *lowest common multiple.*

multiple integral. See INTEGRAL.

multiple point or tangent. See POINT—multiple or k-tuple point.

multiple root of an equation. In an algebraic equation, $f(x)=0$, a root a

such that $(x-a)$ is contained in $f(x)$ two or more times. If $(x-a)^n$ is the highest power of $(x-a)$ which is a factor of $f(x)$, a is called a *double* or *triple* root when n is 2 or 3, respectively, and an *n-tuple* root in general. A multiple root is a root of $f(x)=0$ and $f'(x)=0$, where $f'(x)$ is the derivative of $f(x)$. In general, a root is of order n, or an n-tuple root, if and only if it is a common root of $f(x)=0$, $f'(x)=0$, $f''(x)=0$, $\cdots$, to $f^{[n-1]}(x)=0$. Analogously, when $f(x)$ is not a polynomial, a root is said to be of order n if the nth derivative is the lowest order derivative of which it is not a root; the **order of multiplicity** of the root is then said to be n. *Syn.* Repeated root.

multiple valued function. A function having more than one value for some values of the argument (independent variable). $y^2=x$ defines a *double valued* function of x, since for each value of x there correspond two values of y, namely $\pm x^{1/2}$; $y=\sin^{-1}x$ has infinitely many values of y for each value of x, for if $y_1=\sin^{-1}x$ then $n\pi+(-1)^ny_1=\sin^{-1}x$, where n is any integer. *Syn.* Many valued function.

MUL'TI-PLI-CAND', n. The number to be multiplied by another number, called the **multiplier.**

MUL'TI-PLI-CA'TION, n. abridged multiplication. The process of multiplying and dropping, after each multiplication by a digit of the multiplier, those digits which do not affect the degree of accuracy desired. If in the product 235×7.1624 two decimal place accuracy is desired (which requires the retention of only the third place throughout the multiplication), the abridged multiplication would be performed as follows:

235×7.1624

$= 5 \times 7.1624 + 30 \times 7.1624 + 200 \times 7.1624$

$= 35.812 + 214.872 + 1432.480$

$= 1683.164 = 1683.16.$

algebraic multiplication. The process of multiplying signed (positive and negative) numbers. For the process of multiplying positive integers, see *multiplication of two integers.* The rule for algebraic multiplication is: Multiply the numerical values of the numbers (quantities) as in arithmetic and take the result positive if both numbers are positive or both negative and take it negative if the numbers have different signs. The rule of signs is: *Like signs give plus, unlike give minus.* E.g. $2 \times (-3) = -6$, $-2 \times 3 = -6$, $-2 \times (-3) = 6$.

multiplication of complex numbers. The procedure for forming their product as the product of algebraic binomials is as follows:

$$(a+bi)(c+di) = ac + (ad+bc)i + bdi^2$$
$$= ac - bd + (ad+bc)i,$$

since $i^2 = -1$. If the complex numbers are in the form $r_1(\cos A + i \sin A)$ and $r_2(\cos B + i \sin B)$, their product is $r_1 r_2 [\cos (A+B) + i \sin (A+B)]$, i.e. to multiply two complex numbers multiply their moduli and add their amplitudes.

multiplication of decimals. Some process equivalent to multiplying as if the decimal numbers were whole numbers and then pointing off as many decimal places in this product as there are in both multiplicand and multiplier together. The meaning and application of this rule are shown by the example:

$$2.3 \times .02 = \frac{23}{10} \times \frac{2}{100} = \frac{46}{1000} = .046.$$

multiplication of a determinant by a constant. Multiplication of each term in the expanded form by the constant. This is the same as multiplying each element of any one row (or any one column) by the constant. See DETERMINANT.

multiplication by a fraction. Dividing the multiplicand into a certain number of parts and taking a specified number of them. To multiply 1/2 by 2/3 one divides 1/2 (which is the same as 3/6) by three, obtaining 1/6, then takes two times 1/6 getting 2/6 (which simplifies into 1/3). The same result is obtained by the rule: Multiply numerators for the numerator of the product and denominators for the denominator of the product.

multiplication of mixed numbers. Some process equivalent to reducing them to fractions, multiplying the fractions, and simplifying. E.g.

$$2\tfrac{1}{2}\times3\tfrac{1}{4}=\frac{5}{2}\times\frac{13}{4}=\frac{65}{8}=8\tfrac{1}{8}.$$

multiplication of the roots of an equation. The process of deriving an equation whose roots are each the same multiple of a corresponding root of the given equation. This is effected by the substitution (transformation) $x=x'/k$. The roots of the equation in x' are each k times one of the roots of the equation in x.

multiplication of two determinants of the same order. Finding the product of their values. The product can be written as another determinant of the same order, in which an element in the ith row and jth column is the sum of the products of the elements in the ith row of the first determinant by the corresponding elements of the jth column of the second determinant (or vice versa). For a 2nd order determinant

$$\begin{vmatrix} a & b \\ d \end{vmatrix}\cdot\begin{vmatrix} A & B \\ C & D \end{vmatrix}=\begin{vmatrix} aA+bC & aB+bD \\ cA+dC & cB+dD \end{vmatrix}$$

multiplication of two integers. The process of taking one of them additively as many times as there are units in the other; e.g. $2\cdot3$ is $2+2+2$ or $3+3$.

multiplication of two polynomials. See DISTRIBUTIVE—distributive law of algebra.

multiplication of two vectors. There are two types of multiplication for vectors. (1) **Scalar multiplication.** The product of the numerical values of the vectors and the cosine of the angle between them (the angle from the first to the second). This is frequently called the **dot product,** denoted by $A\cdot B$. The scalar product is a scalar, not a vector. (2) **Vector multiplication.** The vector product is the *vector* whose numerical value is the product of the numerical values of the given vectors by the sine of the angle between them (the angle from the first to the second),

and which is perpendicular to the plane of the given vectors and directed so that the three vectors form a *right-handed trihedral* (see RIGHT). The product is also called the **cross product.** It is indicated: $A\times B=C$. (If the right forearm is placed along A with the fingers of the half closed right hand pointing in the direction A would be rotated to coincide with B, the erect thumb will point in the direction of C.) Scalar multiplication is commutative, but vector multiplication is not, for $B\times A=-A\times B$. They are both associative and distributive. The scalar product of $(2i+3j+5k)$ and $(3i-4j+6k)$ is $(2\cdot3-3\cdot4+5\cdot6)$ or 24; while the vector product is $(38i+3j-17k)$ if the vectors are multiplied in the given order, and the negative of this if they are multiplied in the reverse order.

MUL′TI-PLIC′I-TY, *n.* multiplicity of a root of an equation. See MULTIPLE —multiple root of an equation.

MUL′TI-PLI′ER, *n.* The number which is to multiply another number, called the **multiplicand.**

Lagrange's method of multipliers. See LAGRANGE'S METHOD OF MULTIPLIERS.

MUL′TI-PLY, *v.* To perform the process of *multiplication*.

MULTIPLY CONNECTED REGION. See SIMPLY—simply connected region.

MU′TU-AL, *adj.* mutual fund method. (*Insurance.*) A method of computing the present value (single premium) for a *whole life annuity immediate.* See COMMUTATION—commutation tables.

mutual insurance company. A cooperative association of policyholders who divide the profits of the company among themselves. The policies, which usually provide for such division, are called *participating policies.*

mutual savings bank. A bank whose capital is that of the depositors who own the bank.

MU′TU-AL-LY, *adv.* mutually equiangular polygons. Polygons whose corresponding angles are equal.

mutually equilateral polygons. Polygons whose corresponding sides are equal.

mutually exclusive events. See EVENT.

N

NA'DIR, *n.* The point in the celestial sphere diametrically opposite to the zenith; the point where a plumb line at the observer's position on the earth, extended downward, would pierce the celestial sphere.

NAPIERIAN (or NAPERIAN) LOG-ARITHMS. A name commonly used for *natural logarithms*, but Napier did not originate them. *Syn.* Natural logarithms.

NAPIER'S ANALOGIES. Formulas for use in solving a spherical triangle. They are as follows (*a*, *b*, *c* representing the sides of a spherical triangle and A, B, C the angles opposite *a*, *b*, *c*, respectively):

$$\frac{\sin\frac{1}{2}(A-B)}{\sin\frac{1}{2}(A+B)} = \frac{\tan\frac{1}{2}(a-b)}{\tan\frac{1}{2}c}$$

$$\frac{\cos\frac{1}{2}(A-B)}{\cos\frac{1}{2}(A+B)} = \frac{\tan\frac{1}{2}(a+b)}{\tan\frac{1}{2}c}$$

$$\frac{\sin\frac{1}{2}(a-b)}{\sin\frac{1}{2}(a+b)} = \frac{\tan\frac{1}{2}(A-B)}{\cot\frac{1}{2}C}$$

$$\frac{\cos\frac{1}{2}(a-b)}{\cos\frac{1}{2}(a+b)} = \frac{\tan\frac{1}{2}(A+B)}{\cot\frac{1}{2}C}$$

NAPIER'S RULES of circular parts. Two ingenious rules by which one can write out the ten formulas needed in the solution of right spherical triangles. Omitting the right angle, one can think of the complements of the other two angles, the complement of the hypotenuse, and the other two sides as arranged on a circle in the same order as on the triangle. Any one of these is a middle point in the sense that there are two on either side of it. The two points nearest to a given point are called *adjacent parts*, and the two farthest are called *opposite parts*. Napier's rules are then stated as follows: I. The sine of any part is equal to the product of the tangents of the adjacent parts. II. The sine of any part is equal to the product of the cosines of the opposite parts.

NAPPE, *n.* **nappe of a cone.** One of the two parts of a conical surface into which the surface is divided by the vertex. Better called *nappe* of a *conical surface*.

NAT'U-RAL, *adj.* **natural logarithms.** Logarithms using the base *e* (2.71828183+). See *e*, and NAPIER-IAN LOGARITHMS.

natural numbers. The numbers 1, 2, 3, 4, etc. The same as *positive integers*.

natural premium. The net single premium for a one year term insurance policy at a given age.

natural scale. That section of the number scale containing positive numbers only.

NAUGHT, *n.* Same as ZERO.

NAU'TI-CAL, *adj.* **nautical mile.** See KNOT.

NEC'ES-SAR'Y, *adj.* **necessary condition.** See CONDITION—necessary condition.

necessary condition for convergence of an infinite series: that the terms approach zero as one goes farther out in the series; that the *n*th term approaches zero as *n* becomes infinite. This is not a sufficient condition for convergence; e.g. the series

$$1+\frac{1}{2}+\frac{1}{3}+\cdots+\frac{1}{n}+\cdots$$

is divergent, although $1/n$ approaches zero as n becomes infinite.

necessary and sufficient conditions for convergence of a series. See CAUCHY.

NEG'A-TIVE, *adj.* **negative angle.** See ANGLE.

negative correlation. See CORRELATION.

negative direction. The direction opposite the direction that has been chosen as positive.

negative exponent. See EXPONENT—negative exponent.

negative number. See POSITIVE—positive number.

negative sign. The mark, −, denoting a negative number. See POSITIVE—positive number.

NE-GO'TI-A-BLE, *adj.* **negotiable paper.** An evidence of debt which may be transferred by indorsement or delivery, so that the transferee or holder may sue on it in his own name with like effect as if it had been made to him originally; such as bills of exchange promissory notes, drafts, and checks payable to the order of a payee or to bearer.

NEIGH'BOR-HOOD, *n.* **neighborhood of a point.** The set of points consisting of all the points whose numerical distance from the given point is less than a given number. A neighborhood of a point on a line, plane, or surface is usually taken as the set of points within a stated distance of the point (i.e. an *interval* on the line, the interior of a circle in the plane, or an area on the surface).

NET, *adj.* **net level premiums.** Equal annual premiums.

net proceeds. The amount remaining of the sum received from the sale of goods after all expenses except the original cost have been deducted.

net profit. Same as PROFIT.

net tonnage. See TONNAGE.

NEWTON. Gregory-Newton interpolation formula. See GREGORY-NEWTON FORMULA.

Newton's laws of motion. (1) Every body continues in its state of rest, or of motion with a constant velocity in a straight line, unless acted upon by some external force. (2) Change of momentum is proportional to the force and to the time during which it acts, and is in the same direction as the force. (3) To every action there is an equal and opposite reaction.

Newton's method of approximation. A method of step by step approximation to the roots of an equation in one unknown. It is based on the fact that the tangent of an ordinary curve very nearly coincides with a small arc of the curve, i.e. that the sub-tangent is approximately the same as the distance from the curve's x-intercept to the foot of the ordinate of the point whose abscissa is the last approximation to the root. Suppose the equation is $f(x) = 0$, and a_1 is an approximation to one of the roots. The next approximation, a_2, is the abscissa of the point of intersection of the x-axis and the tangent to the curve $y = f(x)$ at the point whose abscissa is a_1, i.e., $a_2 = a_1 - f(a_1)/f'(a_1)$, where $f'(a_1)$ is the derivative of $f(x)$ evaluated for $x = a_1$. This is equivalent to using the first two terms (dropping all higher degree terms) in Taylor's expansion of $f(x)$ about the point whose abscissa is a_1 and assuming that $f(a_2) = 0$.

trident of Newton. See TRIDENT.

NICOMEDES, conchoid of Nicomedes. Same as CONCHOID.

NIM, *n.* **game of nim.** A game in which two players draw articles from three piles, each player in turn taking as many as he pleases from any one pile, the player who draws the last article winning. To win, a player must, with each draw, make the sum of the corresponding digits of the numbers of articles, written in the binary scale, either 2 or 0. If the numbers of articles are 17, 6, 5, they are written 10001, 110, 101 in the binary scale, which we write with digits having the same place value in the same column as follows:

10001
  110

101. To win, the next player, A, must take fourteen articles from the large pile leaving the columns,

  11
110

101. The other player, B, has no choice but to make the sum, in at least one column, odd. A then makes it even and they finally come to the situation where it is B's draw and the numbers are 1 and 1, so that A wins.

NINE-POINT CIRCLE. See CIRCLE—nine-point circle.

N-LEAFED ROSE. The graph of $r = a \sin n\theta$, or $r = a \cos n\theta$, where n is a positive integer. It consists of rose petal-shaped loops with the origin a point common to all of them. When n is odd there are n of the loops, when n is even there are $2n$ of them. See FOUR-LEAFED ROSE.

NOD'AL, *adj.* **nodal line.** A line in a configuration which remains fixed while the configuration is being rotated or deformed in a certain manner; a line in an elastic plate which remains fixed while the plate vibrates. See EULER'S ANGLES.

NODE, *n.* **node of a curve.** (1) A *double point*, which is a *crunode* or *acnode*. (2) A double point at which the two tangents are distinct; in this sense the same as crunode.

NOM'I-NAL, *adj.* **nominal rate of interest.** See INTEREST—nominal rate of interest.

NOM'O-GRAM, *n.* A graph consisting of lines (usually parallel) graduated for different variables in such a way that a straight edge cutting the three lines gives the related values of the three variables. E.g. when considering automobile tires, one line might be graduated with the price, another with the cost per mile, and the other the mileage life of the tire, in such a way that a straight edge through a certain price point and mileage life point would cross the other line at the cost per mile. *Syn.* Alignment chart.

NON, *prefix.* Negating prefix.

finite non-removable discontinuity. See DISCONTINUITY.

non-Euclidean geometry. A geometry whose marked characteristic is its rejection of Euclid's parallel postulate; any geometry not based on the postulates of Euclid.

non-interest bearing note. See NOTE.

non-linear. Of higher degree than the first.

non-negotiable paper. A contract to pay in which the payee cannot be legally changed. See NEGOTIABLE.

non-participating insurance company. See STOCK—stock insurance company.

non-singular affine transformation. See AFFINE TRANSFORMATION —non-singular affine transformation.

non-singular linear transformation. A linear transformation whose determinant is not zero. See LINEAR— general linear transformation.

non-terminating. Having infinitely many (an unlimited number of) terms or steps. An infinite sequence is non-terminating, since there is no last term.

non-trivial solutions. See TRIVIAL.

non-uniform continuity or convergence. Not uniform, only ordinary continuity or convergence.

non-uniform velocity. Velocity which is not constant; velocity that changes with time.

NON'A-GON, *n.* A polygon having nine sides.

regular nonagon. A nonagon whose sides and interior angles are all equal.

NORM, *n.* (1) Mean; average. (2) Customary degree or condition. (3) Established pattern or form.

NOR'MAL, *adj.* or *n.* (1) Perpendicular. (2) According to rule or pattern; usual.

bi-normal. See OSCULATING— osculating plane.

mean normal curvature of a surface at a point. See MEAN—mean curvature of a surface.

normal acceleration. See ACCELERATION—total acceleration for motion in a plane.

normal curvature of a surface at a point. The curvature of a *normal section* of the surface at the point. At an ordinary point the normal curvature varies when the plane cutting the section revolves about the normal at the point.

normal derivative. The *directional derivative* of a function in the direction of the normal at the point where the derivative is taken; the rate of change of a function in the direction of the normal to a curve. See DIRECTIONAL DERIVATIVE.

normal distribution curve. See FREQUENCY—normal frequency curve.

normal form of the equation of a plane. See PLANE—equation of a plane.

normal form of the equation of a straight line. See LINE—equation of a straight line in the plane.

normal frequency curve. See FREQUENCY—normal frequency curve.

normal to a line. A perpendicular to the line. In a *plane*, a line whose slope is the negative reciprocal of the slope of the given line. In *space*, a line with direction numbers l, m, n such that $Ll + Mm + Nn = 0$, where L, M, N, are the direction numbers of the given line.

normal line to a plane. See PLANE —normal line to a plane.

normal line to a plane curve at a point. A perpendicular to the tangent line at the point. Its equation is

$$(y - y_1) = [-1/f'(x_1)](x - x_1),$$

where $f'(x_1)$ is the slope of the curve at the point (x_1, y_1) in which the normal cuts the curve. See DERIVATIVE—derivative of a function of one variable.

normal line to a surface at a point. The line perpendicular to the tangent plane at the point. See TANGENT—tangent plane to a surface.

normal order. See ORDER—normal order.

normal plane to a space curve at a point. The plane perpendicular to the tangent line at the point; the plane determined by the *bi-normal* and the *principal normal*.

normal section of a surface. A plane section made by a plane containing a normal to the surface.

polar normal. See POLAR—polar tangent.

principal normal. See OSCULATING—osculating plane.

reduction to normal form of the equation of a straight line or plane. See REDUCTION—reduction to normal form.

NORTH, *adj.* **north declination.** See DECLINATION—declination of a celestial point.

NO-TA'TION, *n.* Symbols denoting quantities, operations, etc.

continuation notation. See CONTINUATION NOTATION.

factorial notation. The notation used in writing factorials. See FACTORIAL.

functional notation. See FUNCTIONAL.

Plücker's abridged notation. See ABRIDGED.

NOTE, *n.* A signed promise to pay a specified sum of money at a given time, or in partial payments at specified times.

bank note. A note given by a bank and used for currency. Usually has the shape and general appearance of government paper money.

demand note. A note that must be paid when the payee demands payment.

interest bearing note. A note containing the words "with interest at — per cent," meaning that interest must be paid when the note is paid or at other times agreed upon by the payee and payer.

negotiable note. See NEGOTIABLE —negotiable paper.

non-interest bearing note. (1) A note on which no interest is paid. (2) A note on which the interest has been paid in advance.

note receivable. *A promissory note*, payment of which is to be made *to* the person under consideration, as contrasted to *note payable* which is to be paid *by* this person. Terms used in bookkeeping and accounting.

proceeds of a note. See PROCEEDS —proceeds of a note.

promissory note. A note, usually given by an individual, promising to pay a given sum of money at a specified time (or on demand).

term of a note. See TERM—term of a note.

time note. A note that is due at the end of a certain time specified in the note.

NOUGHT, *n.* Same as ZERO; more commonly spelled naught.

NULL, *adj.* (1) Nonexistent; of no value or significance. (2) Zero.

null circle. See CIRCLE—null circle.

null ellipse. The point which is the graph of an equation of the form

$$x^2/a^2 + y^2/b^2 = 0$$

or $\quad (x-h)^2/a^2 + (y-k)^2/b^2 = 0.$

See CONIC—degenerate conic.

NUM'BER, *n.* In *arithmetic*, a symbol denoting how many times a thing is taken. *Tech*. That property of a set of individuals which is independent of the natures of the individuals; that property common to all sets of individuals which can be put into one-to-one correspondence. The set of individuals is called a **number class.** A set consisting of part of the individuals in the class is called a **sub-class.** The concept of number is extended to include fractions, mixed numbers, irrational numbers, transcendental numbers and finally complex numbers. In advanced courses the term *number* would suggest any one of these types, although *number* is still used quite commonly to denote integers, in such phrases as *The Theory of Numbers.*

absolute number. See ABSOLUTE.

abstract number. See ABSTRACT —abstract number.

algebraic number. (1) Any ordinary positive or negative number; any real directed number. (2) Any number which is a root of a rational integral (polynomial) equation with rational coefficients.

amicable numbers. See AMICABLE.

arithmetic numbers. Real positive numbers; positive integers, fractions, or radicals such as occur in arithmetic; numbers themselves rather than letters denoting numbers.

Bernoulli's numbers. See BERNOULLI.

bounded set of numbers. See BOUNDED—bounded set of numbers.

cardinal number. See CARDINAL.

concrete number. See CONCRETE.

defective number. A number (integer) the sum of all of whose divisors except itself is less than the number. See below, perfect number.

denominate number. A number whose unit represents a unit of measure.

denomination of a number. The kind of unit to which the number refers, as pounds, feet, gallons, tenths, hundreds, thousands, etc.

dense set of numbers. A set of numbers such that every number of the set is a *limit point* of the set. The set of all rational numbers, of all real numbers, and of all complex numbers are all dense.

imaginary number. See IMAGINARY.

irrational number. See IRRATIONAL.

mixed number. See MIXED.

negative number. See POSITIVE— positive number.

number e. See e.

number field. Same as DOMAIN.

number interval. See INTERVAL.

number scale. See SCALE—number scale.

number sieve, photoelectric number sieve. A mechanical device for factoring large numbers.

number theory. See THEORY— number theory.

ordinal number. See ORDINAL.

perfect number. An integer which is equal to the sum of all of its factors except itself. 28 is a perfect number since $28 = 1 + 2 + 4 + 7 + 14$.

positive number. See POSITIVE.

real algebraic number. See REAL —real algebraic number.

real number. Rational numbers, and irrational numbers that do not involve an even root of a negative number.

reciprocal of a number. See RECIPROCAL.

redundant number. A number (integer) the sum of all of whose divisors, except itself, is greater than the number. See above, perfect number.

square numbers. The numbers 1, 4, 9, 16, 25, $\cdots$, n^2, $\cdots$.

triangular numbers. The numbers 1, 3, 6, 10, $\cdots$. They are called triangular numbers because they are the number of dots employed in making successive triangular arrays of dots. The process is started with one dot, successive rows of dots being placed beneath the first dot, each row having one more dot than the preceding one. The number of dots in the nth array is $(1 + 2 + 3 + \cdots + n) = \frac{1}{2}n(n+1)$. See ARITHMETIC—arithmetic series.

NU'MER-ALS, *n.* Symbols used to denote numbers, as Arabic numerals or Roman numerals.

Arabic numerals. The symbols 0, 1, 2, 3, 4, 5, 6, 7, 8, 9.

Roman numerals. See ROMAN.

NU'MER-A'TION, *n.* The process of writing or stating numbers in order of their size; the process of numbering.

NU'MER-A'TOR, *n.* The term above the line in a fraction; the term which is to be divided by the other term, called the *denominator.*

NU-MER'I-CAL, *adj.* Consisting of numbers, rather than letters; of the nature of numbers.

numerical determinant. A determinant whose elements are all numerical, rather than literal. See DETERMINANT.

numerical equation. An equation in which the coefficients and constants are numbers rather than letters. The equation $2x+3=5$ is a numerical equation, whereas $ax+b=c$ is a *literal* equation.

numerical value. (1) Same as ABSOLUTE VALUE. (2) Value given as a number, rather than by letters.

O

OB'LATE, *adj.* oblate ellipsoid of revolution. See ELLIPSOID—ellipsoid of revolution.

oblate spheroid. Same as OBLATE ELLIPSOID OF REVOLUTION.

OB'LI-GA'TION, *n.* A debt or other liability.

commuting obligations. See COMMUTING.

OB-LIQUE', *adj.* oblique angle. An angle which is acute, obtuse, or reflex; any angle not a right angle.

oblique circular cone. See CONE.

oblique coordinates. Coordinates which refer to oblique Cartesian coordinate axes (or planes). See COORDINATE—oblique coordinates.

oblique lines in a plane. Lines forming an oblique angle; lines that are neither parallel nor perpendicular.

oblique triangle. A triangle which does not contain a right angle.

oblique spherical triangle. A spherical triangle which does not contain a right angle.

OB'SER-VA'TION, *n.* observation equation. (*In statistics.*) An equation relating to the coefficients of an equation

which is assumed to represent certain data. It is obtained by substituting values of the variables (taken from the data) in the assumed literal equation.

OB'SO-LES'CENCE, *n.* obsolescence of an asset, machinery or other equipment. The state of becoming obsolete, ceasing to be useful because of new inventions and improvements which make the old unable to show a profit.

OB-TUSE', *adj.* obtuse angle. An angle greater than a right angle and smaller than a straight angle.

OC'TA-GON, *n.* A polygon having eight sides.

regular octagon. An octagon whose angles and sides are all equal.

OC'TA-HE'DRON, *n.* A polyhedron having eight faces.

regular octahedron. An octahedron whose faces are all congruent equilateral triangles. See POLYHEDRON—regular polyhedron.

OC'TANT, *n.* See COORDINATE—coordinate planes.

OC-TIL'LION, *n.* (1) In the U.S. and France, the number represented by one followed by 27 zeros. (2) In England, the number represented by one followed by 48 zeros.

ODD, *adj.* odd function. See FUNCTION—odd function.

odd number. An integer that is not evenly divisible by 2; any number of the form $2n+1$, where n is an integer. 1, 3, 5, 7 are odd numbers.

ODDS, *n.* (1) *In betting,* the ratio of the wager of one party to that of the other, as to lay or give *odds,* say 2 to 1. (2) The probability or degree of probability in favor of some event on which bets are laid. (3) An equalizing allowance given to a weaker side or player by a stronger, as a piece at chess or points at tennis.

long odds. Large odds. Ten to one would be long odds.

OFFICE, *n.* office premium. See PREMIUM—office premium.

OFF'SET', *n.* (*Surveying.*) A shift from a *given direction* perpendicular to that direction in order to pass an obstruction and yet obtain the total distance through the obstruction in the given direction. The distance across a pond in a given direction can be obtained by adding all the line segments in this direction which appear in a set of off-sets (steps) going around the pond.

O-GIVE′, *n.* Same as CUMULATIVE FREQUENCY CURVE.

OHM, *n.* (*Electricity.*) A unit of electrical resistance; the resistance offered to the flow of a constant current by a column of mercury of 1 square millimeter cross-section with length 106.3 centi-meters, and temperature that of melt-ing ice.

OHM'S LAW. (*Electricity.*) Current is proportional to electromotive force divided by resistance.

ONE, *adj.* The cardinal number denot-ing a single unit.

    one-dimensional strains. The trans-formation $x' = x$, $y' = Ky$, or $x' = Kx$, $y' = y$. These transformations elongate or compress a configuration in the directions parallel to the axes, accord-ing as $K > 1$ or $K < 1$. The constant K is called the *coefficient of the strain*. *Syn.* Simple elongations and compres-sions, one dimensional elongations and compressions.

    one parameter family of curves or surfaces. See FAMILY.

    one-to-one correspondence. See CORRESPONDENCE.

    one-valued, *adj.* Same as SINGLE-VALUED.

O′PEN, *adj.* **open interval.** See INTER-VAL—closed number interval.

OP′ER-A′TION, *n.* The process of carry-ing out rules of procedure like addition, subtraction, differentiation, taking log-arithms, making substitutions or trans-formations.

    four fundamental operations of arith-metic. See FUNDAMENTAL.

    operations with series. Addition, multiplication, division, etc. of series. See SERIES.

OP′ER-A′TOR, *n.* **differential operator.** See DIFFERENTIAL—differential operator in differential equations.

OP′PO-SITE, *adj.* **opposite sides** in a rectangle, quadrilateral, or any poly-gon having an even number of sides.

Two sides having the same number of sides between them whichever way one travels around the polygon from one of the sides to the other.

    opposite vertices (angles) of a poly-gon. Two vertices (angles) having an equal number of vertices (or sides) between them whichever way one counts around the polygon.

OP′TION, *n.* **option term insurance.** Term life insurance which permits the insured to reinsure (usually done at the end of the period) without another medical examination.

OP′TION-AL, *adj.* Same as CALLABLE. See BOND—callable bonds.

OR′DER, *n.* **derivatives of higher order.** See DERIVATIVE—derivatives of higher order.

    differences of first, second, third order. See DIFFERENCES.

    exact differential equation of the first order. See DIFFERENTIAL—exact differential equation.

    linear differential equations. See DIFFERENTIAL—linear differential equations.

    normal order. An established ar-rangement of numbers, letters, or ob-jects which is called *normal* relative to all other arrangements. If a, b, c is defined as the normal order for these letters, then b, a, c is an *inversion*. See INVERSION—inversion in a sequence of objects.

    order of an algebraic curve or sur-face. The degree of its equation; the greatest number of points in which any straight line not in the surface can cut it.

    order of contact of two curves. A measure of how close the curves lie together in the neighborhood of a point at which they have a common tangent. *Tech.* The order of contact of two curves $y = f(x)$ and $y = g(x)$ is one less than the order of the infinitesimal difference of the distances from the two curves to their common tangent (measured along the same perpendicu-lar) relative to the distance from the foot of this perpendicular to their point of contact with the tangent; the order of contact of two curves is n when the nth order differential coefficient, from their equations, and all lower orders are equal at the point of contact. See INFINITESIMAL—order of an infinitesimal.

order of the fundamental operations of arithmetic. When several of the fundamental operations occur in succession, multiplications and divisions are performed before additions and subtractions, and in the order in which they occur.

$$3+6\div2\times4-7=3+3\times4-$$
$$=3+12-7=8.$$

order of an infinitesimal. See INFINITESIMAL.

order of infinity. See INFINITY—order of infinities.

order of a radical. Same as the INDEX OF THE RADICAL.

order relation between real numbers. A relation which makes it possible to tell whether one or two distinct real numbers precedes or follows the other one.

order of units. The place of a digit in a number. Units in unit's place are units of the *first order*, in ten's place, of the *second order*, etc.

OR′DERED, *adj.* **ordered sets.** Sets such that: (1) One can always say which of two distinct elements *precedes* and which *follows* the other; (2) these concepts are such that if a first element precedes (or follows) a second and the second precedes (or follows) a third, then the first precedes (or follows) the third. E.g. the positive integers, arranged in the order of their size, are an ordered set.

OR′DIN-AL, *adj.* **ordinal numbers.** Numbers that denote direction as well as the cardinal number property; the positive and negative real numbers.

OR′DI-NAR′Y, *adj.* **ordinary annuity.** See ANNUITY.

ordinary interest. See INTEREST.

ordinary life insurance. See INSURANCE.

ordinary point on a curve. See POINT—ordinary point on a curve.

OR′DI-NATE, *n.* The coordinate (of a point) in Cartesian coordinates, which is the distance from the axis of abscissas (x-axis) to the point, measured along a line parallel to the axis of ordinates (y-axis).

average (mean) ordinate. See AVERAGE—average or mean ordinate of a curve.

double ordinate. A line segment between two points on a curve and parallel to the axis of ordinates (in Cartesian coordinates), used with reference to curves that are symmetrical with respect to the axis of abscissas, such as the parabola $y^2 = 2px$ or the ellipse $x^2/a^2 + y^2/b^2 = 1$.

graphing by composition of ordinates. See GRAPHING.

OR′I-GIN, *n.* **origin of Cartesian coordinates in the plane.** The point of intersection of the axes. See CARTESIAN —Cartesian coordinates in the plane.

origin of a coordinate trihedral. The point of intersection of the **planes.** See COORDINATE—coordinate planes.

origin of a ray. See RAY.

OR′THO-CEN′TER, *n.* **orthocenter of a triangle.** The point of intersection of the three altitudes of the triangle.

OR-THOG′O-NAL, *adj.* Right-angled; pertaining to or depending upon the use of right angles.

orthogonal projection. A projection in which the projecting rays are perpendicular to the plane of the configuration obtained by the projection.

orthogonal substitution or transformation. A substitution which transforms from one set of rectangular coordinates to another.

orthogonal trajectory of a family of curves. A curve which cuts all the curves of the family at right angles. Any line through the origin is an *orthogonal trajectory* of the family of circles which has the origin as a common center, and any one of these circles is an orthogonal trajectory of the family of lines passing through the origin. The equation of the orthogonal trajectories of a family of curves may be obtained from the differential equation of the family by replacing dy/dx in that equation by its negative reciprocal, $-dx/dy$, and solving the resulting differential equation.

triply orthogonal system of surfaces. Three families of surfaces which are such that one member of each family passes through each point in space and each surface is orthogonal to every member of the other two families. In the figure the three triply orthogonal systems of surfaces $x^2+y^2=r_0^2$, $y=x\tan\theta_0$ and $z=z_0$ intersect at right angles, for instance at the point P.

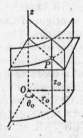

OS′CIL-LAT′ING, *adj.* **oscillating series.** See DIVERGENT—divergent series.

OS′CIL-LA′TION, *n.* **forced oscillations.** Oscillations imparted to a body by an intermittent or oscillatory force, giving the motion of the body a different amplitude from what it would have without such a force.

free oscillation. Oscillations which are not forced oscillations. A pendulum which has *free oscillation* very nearly describes simple harmonic motion if the oscillation is small.

oscillation of a function in a given interval. The difference between the greatest and least values of the function in that interval.

OS′CU-LAT′ING, *adj.* **osculating circle of a curve** at a given point. The circle which has three coincident points in common with the curve; the circle which has contact of at least the second order with the curve. See ORDER— order of contact of two curves.

osculating plane of a curve (at a point). The limiting plane of the planes through the tangent line at the given point and another point as the latter point approaches the former along the curve; the plane in the limiting position of the plane through the point and two others on the curve as the latter move up to the former. The perpendiculars to the tangent to the curve at the given point, which lie in the osculating plane and the plane perpendicular to it, are called, respectively, the **principal normal** and **binormal.**

OS′CU-LA′TION, *n.* **point of osculation.** Same as DOUBLE CUSP, and TACNODE. See TACNODE.

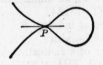

O′VAL, *adj.* and *n.* A curve shaped like a section of a football or an egg; any curve which is closed and always concave toward the center.

oval of Cassini. See CASSINI.

OVERHEAD EXPENSES. (*In finance.*) All expenses except labor and material.

P

P-FORM OF AN EQUATION. An equation of the form $x^n+p_1x^{n-1}+\cdots+p_n=0$, where the ps are, usually, restricted to integers.

PAID, *adj.* **paid-up (free) insurance policy.** A policy free from all premiums, usually by virtue of heavy early premiums over a set period.

PAN′TO-GRAPH, *n.* A mechanical device for copying figures and at the same time changing the scale by which they are drawn, i.e. for drawing figures similar to given figures. It consists of four graduated bars forming an ad-

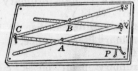

justable parallelogram with the sides extended (see figure). The point P is fixed and while the point Q traces out the figure, the point S traces out the copy (or vice versa). A, B, and C are free to move.

PAPPUS, two theorems of Pappus. I. The area of a surface of revolution formed by revolving a curve about a line in its plane not cutting the curve is equal to the product of the length of the generating curve and the circumference of the circle described by the centroid of the curve. II. The volume of a solid of revolution formed by revolving a plane area about a line in its plane not cutting the area is equal to the product of the generating area and the circumference of the circle described by the centroid of the area.

PAR, *n.* (*Finance.*) (1) Value stated in a contract to pay, such as a bond or note. Also called **par value.** *At par, below par,* and *above par* refer to an amount equal to, less than, or greater than the face value (the amount stated in the contract). (2) The established value of the monetary unit of one country expressed in the monetary unit of another; called in full *par of exchange, mint par,* or *commercial par.*

PA-RAB'O-LA, *n.* The plane section of a conical surface by a plane parallel to an element; the locus of a point which moves so as to remain equidistant from a fixed point and a fixed line. Its standard equation in rectangular Cartesian coordinates is $y^2 = 2px$ (also written $y^2 = 4mx$), where the fixed point is on the positive x-axis, at a distance $\frac{1}{2}p$ (or m) from the origin, and the given line is parallel to the y-axis at a distance $\frac{1}{2}p$ to the left of the origin. The given point is called the **focus** of the parabola and the given line is called the **directrix.** The axis of symmetry (the x-axis in the standard form given

above) is called the **axis** of the parabola. The point where the axis cuts the parabola is called the **vertex** and the chord through the focus and perpendicular to the axis is called the **latus rectum.** The path of a projectile is a parabola, except for the modification of the curve due to the air resistance.

cubical parabola. See CUBICAL.

diameter of a parabola. The locus of the mid-points of a set of parallel chords. Any line parallel to the axis of the parabola is a diameter with reference to some set of chords. See DIAMETER—diameter of a conic.

parametric equations of a parabola. See PARAMETRIC—parametric equations of a curve. Important parametric equations of the parabola are those used, for instance, in determining the trajectory of a projectile. If v_0 is the initial velocity and β the angle the projectile makes with the horizontal plane when it starts, the equations of its path are,

$$x = v_0 t \cos \beta, \quad y = v_0 t \sin \beta - \tfrac{1}{2} g t^2,$$

where the parameter t represents the time that has elapsed since the flight of the object started and g is the acceleration of gravity. These equations represent a parabola. If $\beta = 45°$ (the angle at which a projectile must be thrown to travel farthest, neglecting air resistance), the equations reduce to $x = \frac{1}{2}\sqrt{2}v_0 t$, $y = \frac{1}{2}\sqrt{2}v_0 t - 16t^2$, from which $y = x - 32x^2/v_0^2$.

reflection property of the parabola. See REFLECTION—reflection property of the parabola.

semi-cubical parabola. See SEMI—semi-cubical parabola.

PAR'A-BOL'IC, *adj.* Of, relating to, resembling, or generated by a parabola.

parabolic cable. A cable suspended at both ends and supporting equal weights at equal distances apart horizontally. If the curve is an exact parabola the weights must be uniformly and *continuously* distributed along the horizontal and the weight of the cable negligible. See CATENARY. A supporting cable of a suspension bridge hangs in a parabolic curve except for the slight modification of the curve due to the weight of the cable and the fact that the load is attached at intervals, not continuously.

parabolic curve. See CURVE—parabolic curve.

parabolic cylinder. A cylinder whose right section is a parabola. The equation of the cylinder in the figure is $x^2 = 2py$, where $\frac{1}{2}p$ is the distance from the z-axis of the focus of a cross-section.

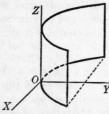

parabolic point on a surface. A point whose Dupin indicatrix is a pair of parallel straight lines. See INDICATRIX.

parabolic segment. A segment of a parabola which is subtended by a chord perpendicular to the axis of the parabola. Its area is $\frac{2}{3}cd$, where c (called the **base**) is the length of the chord and d (called the **altitude**) is the distance from the vertex to the chord.

parabolic spiral. The spiral in which the square of the radius vector is proportional to the vectorial angle. Its equation in polar coordinates is $r^2 = a\theta$. Also called Fermat's spiral.

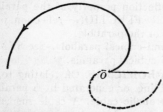

PA-RAB'O-LOID, *n.* A term applied to the *elliptic* and *hyperbolic paraboloids*.

elliptic paraboloid. A surface whose sections parallel to one of the coordinate planes are ellipses and, parallel to the other coordinate planes, parabolas. When the surface is in the position illustrated, with its axis along the z-axis its equation is $x^2/a^2 + y^2/b^2 = cz$.

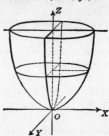

hyperbolic paraboloid. A surface whose sections parallel to one coordinate plane are hyperbolas, and parallel to the other coordinate planes, parabolas. In the position illustrated, its equation is

$$x^2/a^2 - y^2/b^2 = 2cz.$$

This is a ruled surface, the two families of rulings being:

$$x/a - y/b = 1/p, \quad x/a + y/b = 2pcz,$$

and $x/a + y/b = 1/p, \quad x/a - y/b = 2pcz$, where p is an arbitrary parameter. These rulings are called RECTILINEAR GENERATORS, since either set may be used to generate the surface.

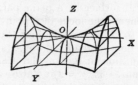

PAR'A-DOX, *n.* An argument in which it appears that an obvious untruth has been proved. Mathematical paradoxes are constructed by the use of ingeniously concealed erroneous steps.

Zeno's paradox of Achilles and the tortoise. See ZENO'S PARADOX.

PAR'AL-LAC'TIC, *adj.* **parallactic angle of a star.** The angle between the arcs of great circles joining the star and the zenith, and the star and the pole. See HOUR—hour angle and hour circle.

PAR-AL-LAX', *n.* **geodesic parallax of a star.** The plane angle subtended at the star by the radius of the earth.

PAR'AL-LEL, *adj.* Equidistant apart. See below, parallel curves, lines, planes.

Euclid's postulate of parallels. If

two lines are cut by a transversal and the sum of the interior angles on one side of the transversal is less than a straight angle, the two lines will meet if produced and will meet on that side of the transversal. This is logically equivalent to: only one line can be drawn parallel to a given line through a given point not on this line.

line parallel to a plane. A line and plane which do not meet however far produced. The **condition that a line be parallel to a plane** is that it be perpendicular to the normal to the plane. See PERPENDICULAR—perpendicular lines.

necessary and sufficient condition that three lines all be parallel to some plane. The vanishing of the third order determinant whose rows are the direction numbers of the three lines, taken in a fixed order.

parallel circle. See SURFACE—surface of revolution.

parallel curves. See CURVE—parallel curves (in a plane).

parallel lines. Lines which lie in a plane and do not meet however far they are produced. The **analytic condition that two lines in a plane be parallel** is that the coefficients of the corresponding variables in their rectangular Cartesian equations be proportional, that their slopes be equal, or that the determinant of the coefficients of the variables in their equations be zero. The **condition that two lines in space be parallel** is that they have the same direction cosines (or direction cosines of opposite signs) or that their direction numbers be proportional.

parallel planes. Two planes which do not meet however far produced. The **analytic condition that two planes be parallel** is that the direction numbers of their normals be proportional or that the coefficients of like variables in the Cartesian equations of the planes be proportional.

parallel sailing. See SAILING.

PAR′AL-LEL′E-PI′PED, *n.* A prism whose bases are parallelograms; a polyhedron all of whose faces are parallelograms. The faces other than the

bases are called **lateral faces,** their area the **lateral area** of the prism, and their intersections the **lateral edges.** Volume = base ×altitude. Lateral area =(perimeter of a base) ×(altitude of a face).

diagonal of a parallelepiped. See DIAGONAL—diagonal of a parallelepiped.

oblique parallelepiped. A parallelepiped whose lateral edges are oblique to its bases.

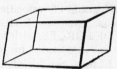

rectangular parallelepiped. A right parallelepiped whose bases are rectangles. If its edges are a, b, c, its volume is $a \cdot b \cdot c$ and the area of its lateral surface is $2(ab+bc+ac)$.

right parallelepiped. A parallelepiped whose bases are perpendicular to its lateral faces. It is a special type of right prism.

PAR′AL-LEL′O-GRAM, *n.* A quadrilateral with its opposite sides parallel. The two lines, AC and BL, which pass through opposite vertices are called the **diagonals.**

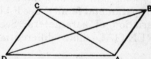

altitude of a parallelogram. See ALTITUDE—altitude of a parallelogram.

area of a parallelogram. The product of its altitude by its base, i.e. the product of any side (taken as a base) by the perpendicular distance from that side to the opposite side.

parallelogram of forces. A parallelogram in which adjacent sides represent given forces (the sides, parallel to these, representing the same forces), both in magnitude and direction, while the hypotenuse, properly directed, represents the resultant of the two forces. In the figure, if the vectors A and B represent forces, then the diagonal C is the vector sum, or resultant, of A and B. The figure also shows that vector addition is commutative, i.e.

$$A+B=B+A.$$

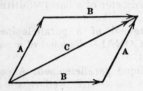

parallelogram of velocities or accelerations. Same as PARALLELOGRAM OF FORCES, with *velocities* or *accelerations* substituted for *forces*.

PAR'AL-LELS, *n.* See SURFACE—surface of revolution.

parallels of latitude. Circles on the earth's surface whose planes are parallel to the plane of the equator.

PA-RAM'E-TER, *n.* A quantity which is given values at the immediate discretion of the operator, distinguished from the variables by the fact that the latter always take on all values not excluded by restrictions which are placed upon them by the form of the function, or equation, in which they appear; also sometimes used in speaking of any letter, variable, or constant which denotes some number or numbers.

one parameter family. See FAMILY.

variation of parameters. See DIFFERENTIAL—linear differential equations.

PAR-A-MET'RIC, *adj.* **differentiation of parametric equations.** Finding the derivative from parametric equations. If the parametric equations are $y=h(t)$, $x=g(t)$, the derivative is given by

$$\frac{dy}{dx}=\frac{dy}{dt}\Big/\frac{dx}{dt}$$

provided dx/dt is not zero (in case dx/dt is zero there may either be no derivative or it may be possible to use some other parametric equation to find it). E.g. if $x=\sin t$ and $y=\cos^2 t$,

$$\frac{dx}{dt}=\cos t$$

$$\frac{dy}{dt}=-2\sin t\cos t,$$

and $$\frac{dy}{dx}=\frac{dy}{dt}\div\frac{dx}{dt}=-2\sin t.$$

parametric equations of a circle. See CIRCLE—parametric equations of a circle.

parametric equations of a curve. Equations in which the coordinates (two in the plane and three in space) are each expressed in terms of a quantity called the parameter. The curve may be plotted point by point by giving this parameter values and thus determining the coordinates. In practice parametric equations are used mostly in rectangular coordinate systems. Any equation can be written in an unlimited number of parametric forms, since the parameter can be replaced by an unlimited number of functions of the parameter. However the term *parametric equations* usually refers to a specific parameter intrinsically related to the curve, as in the parametric equations of the circle: $x=r\cos\theta$, $y=r\sin\theta$, where θ is the central angle. See PARABOLA, ELLIPSE, LINE—equation of a straight line in space, for specific parametric equations.

parametric equations of a surface. Three equations (usually in Cartesian coordinates) giving x, y, z each as a function of two other variables, parameters. Elimination of the two parameters between the three equations results in the Cartesian equation of the surface. The points determined when one parameter is fixed and the other varies form a curve on the surface called a **parametric curve.** The parameters are called **curvilinear coordinates,** since a point on the surface is uniquely determined by the intersection of two parametric curves.

PA-REN'THE-SIS, *n.* The symbol ( ). It encloses sums or products to show that they are to be taken collectively; e.g. $2(3+5-4)=2\times4=8$. See AGGREGATION, and DISTRIBUTIVE—distributive law.

PAR'TIAL, *adj.* **partial derivative** of a function of two or more variables. The ordinary derivative of the function with respect to one of the variables, considering the others as constants. If the variables are x and y, the partial derivatives of $f(x,y)$ are written $\partial f(x,y)/\partial x$ and $\partial f(x,y)/\partial y$, or $D_x f(x,y)$ and $D_y f(x, y)$, or $f_x(x, y)$ and $f_y(x, y)$. The partial derivative of $x^2 + y$ with respect to x is $2x$, with respect to y it is 1. Geometrically, the partial derivative of a function of two variables, $f(x, y)$, with respect to one of the variables, is the slope of the tangent to the curve which is the intersection of the surface $z = f(x, y)$ and the plane whose equation is the other variable set equal to the constant which is its value at the point where the derivative is being evaluated. In the figure, the partial derivative with respect to x, evaluated at the point P, is the slope of the line PT which is tangent to the curve AB.

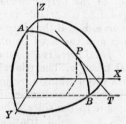

partial derivatives of the second and higher orders. Partial derivatives of partial derivatives. If the repeated partials are taken with respect to the same variable, the process is the same as fixing the other variables and taking the ordinary higher derivatives of a function of one variable. However, after having taken a partial derivative with respect to one variable it may be desirable to take the partial derivative of the resulting function with respect to another variable. One may desire the partial derivative with respect to y, of the partial derivative of a function $f(x, y)$ with respect to x; in which case the question arises as to when $f_{xy}(x, y) = f_{yx}(x, y)$. Such is the case when f_{xy} and f_{yx} are continuous at and in the neighborhood of the point at which the partials are taken. This result can be extended to any order par-

tial derivatives by successive applications of the second order case.

partial differential. See DIFFERENTIAL—partial differential.

partial differential equations. See DIFFERENTIAL—partial differential equations.

partial fractions. A set of fractions whose algebraic sum is a given fraction. The term *method of partial fractions* is applied to the study of methods of finding these fractions. Partial fractions are used to aid in integrating certain rational fractions. Undetermined coefficients are generally used to find partial fractions. E.g. it is known that $1/(x^2-1) = A/(x-1) + B/(x+1)$ for some values of A and B, from which $A = \frac{1}{2}$, $B = -\frac{1}{2}$, are obtained by clearing of fractions and equating coefficients of like powers of x.

partial product. The product of the multiplicand and one digit of the multiplier, when the latter contains more than one digit.

partial quotient. See FRACTION—continued fraction.

partial remainders. The (detached) coefficients of the quotient in synthetic division. See SYNTHETIC—synthetic division.

PAR-TIC'I-PAT'ING, *adj.* **participating insurance policy.** A policy which entitles the holder to participate in the profits of the insurance company, the profits usually being paid in the form of a bonus at the time of payment of the policy, or at periods when the company invoices its insurance contracts. *Syn.* Insurance policy with profits.

PAR'TIC-LE, *n.* (1) A very small portion of matter. (2) A portion of space (or matter) which can be inclosed in a sphere whose radius is arbitrarily small, an infinitesimal. (3) A point with mass; matter considered as being concentrated at a point.

PAR-TIC'U-LAR, *adj.* **particular integral** of a differential equation. Any solution that does not involve arbitrary constants (constants of integration); a solution obtainable from the general solution by giving special values to the constants of integration. *Syn.* Particu-

lar solution, partial solution. See DIF-
FERENTIAL—linear differential equations.

particular solution of a differential
equation. Same as PARTICULAR
INTEGRAL.

PARTS, *n.* **integration by parts.** See IN-
TEGRATION—integration by parts.

PASCAL, **limacon of pascal.** See LIM-
ACON.

Pascal's Theorem. If any simple
hexagon is inscribed in a conic, the
three pairs of opposite sides intersect
in collinear points.

Pascal's triangle. A triangular array
of numbers composed of the coefficients of the expansion of $(a+b)^n$, for
$n = 0, 1, 2, 3$, etc. Ones are written on
a vertical leg and on the hypotenuse
of an isosceles right triangle. Each
other element filling up the triangle is
the sum of the element directly above
it and the element above and to the
left. The numbers in the $(n+1)$th row
are then the coefficients in the binomial
expansion of $(x+y)^n$. The array giving the binomial coefficients of orders
0, 1, 2, 3, 4, and 5 is:

```
1
1   1
1   2   1
1   3   3   1
1   4   6   4   1
1   5  10  10   5   1
```

principle of Pascal. The pressure in
a fluid is transmitted undiminished in
all directions. E.g. if a pipe projects
vertically above a closed tank and the
tank and pipe are filled with water, the
total pressure on every unit of the inside surface of the tank is equal to that
due to the water in the tank *plus a constant due to the water in the pipe.* That
constant is equal to the weight of a
column of water the height of the pipe
and with unit cross-section, regardless
of the diameter of the pipe.

PATH, *n.* **path curves.** A name used for
curves whose equations are in parametric form, a point being said to trace
out the curve when the parameter
varies.

path of a projectile. See PARAB-
OLA—parametric equations of a parabola.

PAY'EE', *n.* The person to whom a sum
of money is to be paid. Most frequently
used in connection with notes and
other written promises to pay.

PAY'MENT, *n.* A sum of money used to
discharge a financial obligation, either
in part or in its entirety.

defaulted payments. See DE-
FAULTED PAYMENTS.

equal-payment method. See IN-
STALLMENT—installment payments.

installment payments. See IN-
STALLMENT—installment payments.

PEARSON'S COEFFICIENT. See CO-
EFFICIENT—correlation coefficient.

PEAUCELLIER'S CELL. See INVER-
SOR, and INVERSION—inversion of
a point with respect to a circle.

PED'AL, *adj.* **pedal curve.** The locus of
the foot of the perpendicular from a
fixed point to a variable tangent to a
given curve. E.g. if the given curve is a
parabola and the fixed point the vertex, the *pedal curve* is a cissoid.

pedal triangle. The triangle formed
within a given triangle by joining the
feet of the perpendiculars from any
given point to the sides. The triangle
DEF is the pedal triangle formed
within the triangle ABC by joining
the feet of the altitudes. The figure
illustrates the fact that the altitudes
of the given triangle bisect the angles
of this pedal triangle.

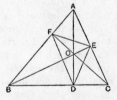

PEN'CIL, *n.* **pencil of circles.** All the
circles which lie in a given plane and
pass through two fixed points. The
equations of all members of the pencil
can be obtained from the equations of
any two circles passing through the two
points by multiplying each equation by
an arbitrary parameter and adding the
results. The pencil of circles through

the intersections of $x^2+y^2-4=0$ and $x^2+2x+y^2-4=0$ is given by

$$h(x^2+y^2-4)+k(x^2+2x+y^2-4)=0,$$

where h and k are arbitrary parameters not simultaneously zero. Frequently one of these parameters is taken as unity, but this excludes one of the circles from the pencil. In the figure, $S=0$ is the equation of one circle and $S'=0$ is the equation of the other. The equation $S-S'=0$ is the equation of the *radical axis* of any two members of the pencil.

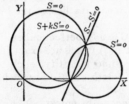

pencil of lines through a point. All the lines passing through the given point and lying in a given plane. The point is called the **vertex** of the pencil. The equations of the lines in the pencil can be obtained from the equations of any two lines of the pencil by multiplying each equation by an arbitrary parameter and adding the results. The pencil through the intersection of $2x+3y=0$ and $x+y-1=0$ is denoted by $h(2x+3y)+k(x+y-1)=0$ where h and k are not simultaneously zero. This equation contains only one essential parameter, because either h or k can be divided out since both are not zero. One parameter is frequently taken as unity, but that excludes one of the lines from the pencil; if $k=1$, for instance, there is no value of h which will reduce the equation of the pencil to $2x+3y=0$.

pencil of parallel lines. All the lines having a given direction; all the lines parallel to a given line. In projective geometry, a pencil of parallel lines (pencil of parallels) is included in the classification of *pencils of lines*; the vertex of the pencil, when the lines are parallel, being an *ideal point*. The notion of ideal point thus unifies the concepts of *pencil of lines* and *pencil of parallels*. The equations of the lines of a parallel pencil can be obtained by holding m (the slope) constant and varying b (the y-intercept) in the slope-intercept form $y=mx+b$ of the equation of a line, except when the pencil is perpendicular to the x-axis, in which case the equation $x=c$ suffices. Also, see above, pencil of lines through a point.

pencil of plane algebraic curves. All curves whose equations are given by assigning particular values to h and k in $hf_1(x,\ y)+kf_2(x,\ y)=0$, where $f_1=0$ and $f_2=0$ are of the same order (degree). If n is this order, the family passes through the n^2 points common to $f_1=0$ and $f_2=0$. A pencil of conics consists of all conics passing through four fixed points, and a pencil of cubics consists of all the cubics passing through nine fixed points. A pencil of curves is often defined as above with either h or k taken equal to unity. See above, pencil of lines through a point.

pencil of planes. All the planes passing through a given line. The line is called the **axis** of the pencil (the line AB in the figure). The equation of the pencil can be obtained by multiplying the equations of two of the planes by arbitrary parameters and adding the results. For any given values of the parameters, this is the equation of a plane passing through the line. In elementary work, one of the parameters is usually taken as unity (see above, pencil of lines through a point).

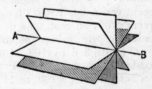

pencil of spheres. All the spheres which pass through a given circle. The equations of all the members of the pencil can be gotten by multiplying each of the equations of two spheres belonging to the pencil by an arbitrary parameter and adding the results; for particular values of these parameters this is the equation of a sphere of the pencil.

PEN'DU-LUM, *n.* **Foucault's pendulum.** A pendulum with a very long wire and a heavy bob, designed to exhibit the revolution of the earth about its axis. It is supported so as not to be restricted to remain in the same plane relative to the earth.

simple pendulum. A particle suspended by a weightless rod or cord; a body suspended by a cord whose weight is neglected, the body being treated as if it were concentrated at its center of gravity.

PEN'TA-DEC'A-GON, *n.* A polygon having fifteen sides.

regular pentadecagon. A pentadecagon having all of its sides and interior angles equal. Each interior angle is equal to 156°.

PEN'TA-GON, *n.* A polygon having five sides.

regular pentagon. A pentagon whose sides and interior angles are all equal. Each interior angle is equal to 108°.

PEN-TAG'O-NAL, *adj.* **pentagonal pyramid.** A pyramid whose base is a pentagon.

PEN'TA-GRAM (of Pythagoras). The five-pointed star formed by drawing all the diagonals of a regular pentagon and deleting the sides.

PE-NUM'BRA, *n.* See UMBRA.

PERCENT or PER CENT, *n.* Hundredths; denoted by %; 6% of a quantity is 6/100 of it.

condition percent. See CONDITION —condition percent of equipment.

percent error. See ERROR.

percent profit on cost. The quotient of the selling price minus the cost, by the cost, multiplied by 100. If an article costs 9 cents and sells for 10 cents, the *percent gain* is $\frac{1}{9} \times 100$, or 11.11%.

percent profit on selling price. The quotient of the selling price minus the cost, by the selling price, multiplied by 100, or $100(s-c)/s$. The percent gain on the cost price is always greater than the percent gain on the selling price. If an article costs 9 cents and sells for 10 cents, the percent gain on selling price is $1/10 \times 100$, or 10%. Compare **percent profit on cost.**

percent of a quantity. See PERCENT.

rate percent. Rate in hundredths; same as YIELD.

PER-CENT'AGE, *n.* (1) The part of arithmetic dealing with percent. (2) The result found by taking a certain percent of the base. (3) Parts per hundred. One would say "a percentage (or percent) of the students are excellent," but he would say "money is worth 6 percent" (never 6 percentage).

PER-CEN'TILE, *n.* (*In statistics.*) A given percentile is the value which divides the range of a set of data into two parts such that a given percentage of the measures lies to the left of this value.

PER'FECT, *adj.* **perfect cubes.** Numbers (quantities) which are exact third powers of some quantity, such as 8, 27, and $a^3 + 3a^2b + 3ab^2 + b^3$ which is equal to $(a+b)^3$.

perfect nth power. A number or quantity which is the exact nth power of some quantity. See above, perfect cubes.

perfect number. See NUMBER— perfect number.

perfect square. A quantity which is the exact square of another quantity. 4 is a perfect square, as is also $a^2 + 2ab + b^2$, $= (a+b)^2$.

perfect trinomial square. See SQUARE—perfect trinomial square.

PER'I-GON, *n.* An angle equal to the sum of two straight angles; an angle containing 360° or 2π radians.

PER-IM'E-TER, *n.* The length of a closed curve, as the perimeter of a circle, the perimeter of an ellipse, or the sum of the sides of a polygon.

PE'RI-OD, *n.* **conversion period.** The time between two successive conversions of interest. *Syn.* Interest period.

period in arithmetic. (1) The number of digits set off by a comma when writing a number. It is customary to set off periods of three digits, as 1,253,689. These periods are called units period, thousands period, millions period, etc. (2) When using certain methods for extracting roots, periods are set off equal to the index of the root to be extracted. (3) Period of a repeating decimal. The number of digits that repeat. See DECIMAL—repeating decimal.

period of a function. The length of the shortest equal sub-intervals into which the range of the independent variable can be divided and obtain exactly the same graph of the function in each sub-interval. *Tech.* If $f(x+p) = f(x)$ for all x, and p is the smallest number greater than zero for which such a relation holds, then p is the period of the function. Sin x has the period 2π (radians), because

$$\sin(x+2\pi) = \sin x.$$

period of simple harmonic motion. See HARMONIC—simple harmonic motion.

select period of a mortality table. See SELECT—select period of a select mortality table.

PE'RI-OD'IC, *adj.* **frequency of a periodic function.** See FREQUENCY—frequency of a periodic function.

periodic continued fractions. See FRACTION—continued fraction.

periodic curves. Curves whose ordinates repeat at equal distances on the axis of abscissas; the graph of a periodic function. The loci of $y = \sin x$ and $y = \cos x$ are periodic curves, repeating themselves in every successive interval of length 2π.

periodic function or expression. A function or expression possessing periods. See PERIOD—period of a function.

periodic motion. Motion which repeats itself, occurs in cycles. See HARMONIC—simple harmonic motion.

PE'RI-O-DIC'I-TY, *adj.* **periodicity of a function (or curve).** The property of having periods or being periodic.

PE-RIPH'ER-Y, *n.* The boundary line or *circumference* of any figure; the surface of a solid.

PER'MA-NENT-LY, *adj.* **permanently convergent series.** See CONVERGENT—permanently convergent series.

PER-MIS'SI-BLE, *adj.* **permissible values of a variable.** The values for which a function under consideration is defined and which lie on the interval on which the function is being considered. Zero is not a *permissible* value for x in the function log x, and 4 is not a permissible value for x if log x is being considered on the interval (1, 2). *Permissible* is also used of *any* values for which a function is defined.

PER'MU-TA'TION, *n.* An ordered arrangement or sequence of all or part of a set of things. All possible permutations of the letters a, b, and c are: a, b, c, $ab, ac, ba, bc, ca, cb, abc, acb, bac, bca$, cab, and cba.

circular permutation of n different things n at a time. An arrangement of the n things around a circle. The total number of such permutations is equal to the number of permutations of n things n at a time, divided by n because each arrangement will be exactly like $n-1$ others except for a shift of the places around the circle.

cyclic permutation. The advancing of each member of a set of ordered objects one position, the last member taking the position of the first. If the objects are thought of as arranged in order around a circle, a cyclic permutation is effected by rotating the circle. cab is a cyclic permutation of abc.

even and odd permutations. See INVERSION—inversion in a sequence of objects.

number of permutations of n things taken all at a time when some members of the set are alike. The number of permutations of n different things taken all at a time divided by the product of the factorials of the numbers representing the number of repetitions of the various things. The letters a, a, a, b, b, c can be arranged in $6!/(3!2!)$ or 60 different ways (permutations). See below, permutations of n things taken all at a time.

permutations of n things taken all at a time. An ordered arrangement of all the members of the set. If n is the number of members of the set, the total possible number of such permutations is $n!$, for any one of the set can be put in the first place, any one of the remaining $n-1$ things in the second place, etc., until n places are filled.

permutations of n things taken r at a time. A permutation containing only r members of the set. Denoted by $_nP_r$. The total number of such permutations is

$$n(n-1)(n-2)\cdots(n-r+1)$$

or $n!/(n-r)!$, for any one can be put first, any one of the remaining $n-1$ second, etc. until r places have been filled.

permutations of n things taken r at a time with repetitions. An arrangement obtained by putting any member of the set in the first position, any member of the set, including a repetition of the one just used, in the second, and continuing this until there are r positions filled. The total number of such permutations is $n\cdot n\cdot n\cdot\cdots$ to r factors, i.e. n^r. The ways in which a, b, c can be arranged two at a time are aa, ab, ac, ba, bb, bc, ca, cb, cc.

PER'PEN-DIC'U-LAR, *n.* or *adj.* **common perpendicular** to two or more lines. A line perpendicular to each of them. In a plane, the only lines that can have a common perpendicular are parallel lines, and they have any number. In space any two lines have any number of common perpendiculars (only one of which intersects both lines unless the lines are parallel).

foot of a perpendicular. See FOOT.

line perpendicular to a plane. A line perpendicular to every line through its foot in the plane. It is sufficient that it be perpendicular to two non-parallel lines in the plane. The **condition** (in *analytic geometry*) **that a line be perpendicular to a plane** is that it have the same direction numbers as the normal to the plane; or, what amounts to the same thing, that its direction numbers be proportional to the coefficients of the corresponding variables in the equation of the plane.

perpendicular lines. Two straight lines which intersect so as to form a pair of equal adjacent angles. Each line is said to be *perpendicular* to the other. The **condition** (in *analytic geometry*) **that two lines be perpendicu-**

lar is (1) *In a plane,* that the slope of one of the lines be the negative reciprocal of the slope of the other. (2) *In space,* that the sum of the products of the corresponding direction numbers (or direction cosines) of the two lines be zero.

perpendicular planes. Two planes such that a line in one, which is perpendicular to their line of intersection, is perpendicular to the other; planes forming a *right dihedral angle.* The **condition** (in *analytic geometry*) **that two planes be perpendicular** is that their normals be perpendicular, or that the sum of the products of the coefficients of like variables in their two equations be zero.

PER-PET'U-AL, *adj.* **perpetual bonds.** Bonds which are not redeemable, and pay dividends forever, perpetually.

PER'PE-TU'I-TY, *n.* (*Math. of finance.*) An annuity that continues forever. See CAPITALIZED COST.

PHASE, *n.* **phase of simple harmonic motion.** The angle $(\phi+kt)$ in the equation of simple harmonic motion, $x=a\cos(\phi+kt)$. See HARMONIC—simple harmonic motion.

initial phase. The phase when $t=0$, namely ϕ in $x=a\cos(\phi+kt)$.

PHOTO-ELECTRIC NUMBER SIEVE. See NUMBER—number sieve.

PI, *n.* The name of the Greek letter π, Π, which corresponds to the Roman P. The symbol π denotes the ratio of the circumference of a circle to its diameter; $\pi=3.14159+$. Π denotes an infinite product. See INFINITE—infinite product.

PI'CA, *n.* (*In printing.*) A measure of type body, equal to 12 points in U. S. scale. See POINT—point in printing.

PIC'TO-GRAM, *n.* Any figure showing numerical relations, as *bar graphs, broken line graphs.* See GRAPHING—statistical graphing.

PIERC'ING, *adj.* **piercing point of a line in space.** See POINT—piercing point of a line in space.

PITCH, *n.* **pitch of a roof.** The quotient of the **rise** (height from the level of plates to the ridge) by the **span** (length of the plates); one half of the *slope* of the roof.

PLACE, *n.* decimal place. See DECIMAL.

place value. The value given to a digit by virtue of the place it occupies in the number relative to the units place. In 423.7, 3 denotes merely 3 units, 2 denotes 20 units, 4 denotes 400 units and 7 denotes 7/10 of a unit; 3 is in unit's place, 2 in ten's place, 4 in hundred's place, etc. *Syn.* Local value.

PLAN, *n.* amortization plan. See AMORTIZE.

Dayton Ohio plan of building and loan association. See DAYTON OHIO PLAN.

guaranteed stock plan of building and loan association. See GUARANTEED—guaranteed stock plan.

long-end interest plan. See INSTALLMENT—installment payments.

preliminary term plan. See PRELIMINARY—preliminary term plan.

serial plan of building and loan association. See SERIAL.

short-end interest plan. See INSTALLMENT—installment payments.

terminating plan of building and loan association. See TERMINATING.

PLANE, *adj.* or *n.* A surface such that a straight line joining any two of its points lies entirely in the surface. *Syn.* Plane surface.

complex plane. See COMPLEX.

condition that three planes pass through a line (or are parallel). See CONDITION—condition that three planes pass through a line.

coordinate planes. See COORDINATE—coordinate planes.

diametral plane. See DIAMETRAL.

equation of a plane. In Cartesian coordinates, an equation of the first degree. The equation $Ax+By+Cz+D=0$ is called the **general form** of the equation of a plane. Several types of the general form are: (1) **Intercept form:** The equation $x/a+y/b+z/c=1$, where a, b and c are the x, y, z intercepts, respectively. (2) **Three-point**

form: The equation of the plane expressed in terms of three points on the plane. The simplest form is obtained by equating to zero the determinant whose rows are x, y, z, 1; x_1, y_1, z_1, 1; x_2, y_2, z_2, 1 and x_3, y_3, z_3, 1, where the subscript letters are the coordinates of the three given points. (3) **Normal form:** The equation

$$lx+my+nz-p=0,$$

where l, m, and n are the direction cosines of the normal to the plane, directed from the origin to the plane, and p is the length of the normal from the origin to the plane. For the reduction of any equation to the normal form, see REDUCTION. If l, m, n and the coordinates of a point in the plane, say x_1, y_1, z_1, are given then $p=lx_1+my_1+nz_1$ and the equation of the plane can be written

$$l(x-x_1)+m(y-y_1)+n(z-z_1)=0.$$

foot of a line intersecting a plane. The point of intersection of the line and plane.

line parallel to a plane. See PARALLEL.

line perpendicular to a plane. See PERPENDICULAR.

normal line to a plane. A line perpendicular to the plane.

normal plane to a space curve at a point. The plane perpendicular to the tangent line at the point; the plane determined by the *bi-normal* and the *principal normal.*

parallel planes. See PARALLEL.

pencil of planes. See PENCIL.

perpendicular planes. See PERPENDICULAR.

plane angle of a dihedral angle. The angle formed by two intersecting lines, one of which lies in each face and both of which are perpendicular to the edge of the dihedral angle; the plane angle between the intersections of the faces of the dihedral angle with a third plane which is perpendicular to the edge of the dihedral angle. Such a plane angle is said to **measure** its dihedral angle. When the plane angle is *acute, right, ob-*

tuse, etc., its *dihedral* angle is said to be *acute, right, obtuse,* etc.

plane figure. A figure lying entirely in a plane.

plane geometry. See GEOMETRY.

plane sailing. See SAILING.

plane section. The intersection of a plane and a surface or a solid.

projection plane. The plane upon which a figure is projected; the plane section of the projection rays of a projection. See PROJECTION.

sheaf of planes. See SHEAF.

shrinking of the plane. See SIMILITUDE—transformation of similitude, and ONE—one-dimensional strains.

PLA-NIM'E-TER, *n.* A mechanical device for measuring plane areas. Merely requires moving a pointer on the *planimeter* around the bounding curve. A common type is the *polar planimeter.*

PLATE, *n.* **plate of building.** A horizontal timber (beam) that supports the lower end of the rafters.

PLOT, *v.* **plot a point.** To locate the point geometrically, either in the plane or space, when its coordinates are given in some coordinate system. In Cartesian coordinates, to plot a point is to locate it on cross-section paper or by drawing lines on plain paper parallel to indicated axes of coordinates and at a distance from them equal to the proper coordinate of the point. See COORDINATE.

point by point plotting (graphing) of a curve. Finding an ordered set of points which lie on a curve and drawing through these points a curve which is assumed to resemble the required curve.

PLÜCKER'S ABRIDGED NOTATION. See ABRIDGED.

PLUMB, *n.* A weight suspended by a cord.

plumb line. See LINE—plumb line.

PLUS, *adj.* or *n.* Denoted by +. (1) Indicates addition, as 2+3 (3 added to 2). (2) Property of being positive. (3) A little more or in addition to, as 2.35 +.

plus sign. The sign +. See PLUS.

POINT, *n.* (1) An element of geometry which has position but no extension.

(2) An element which satisfies the axioms of geometry. (3) An element defined by a set of coordinates.

condition that three points be collinear. See CONDITION.

conjugate points relative to a conic. See CONJUGATE—conjugate points relative to a conic.

decimal point. See DECIMAL.

double point. A point on a curve at which the curve crosses itself or is tangent to itself. A point on a curve at which there are at least two tangents real and distinct, coincident, or imaginary. (The equations of the tangents at a double point on an algebraic curve can be gotten by equating to zero the quadratic terms in the equation of the curve referred to a rectangular Cartesian coordinate system whose origin is at the double point, the linear terms being zero in this case. This quadratic may be a perfect square, in which case the two tangents are coincident.)

homologous point. See HOMOLOGOUS.

isolated point, acnode, or conjugate point. A point in whose neighborhood there is no other point on the curve. Such a point exists on an algebraic curve when the lowest degree homogeneous polynomial in the equation of the curve, referred to a system of Cartesian coordinates having its origin at the given point, vanishes for no values of x and y in a neighborhood of zero, except for both x and y equal to zero. The curve $x^2+y^2=x^3$ has an isolated point at the origin, since the equation $x^2+y^2=0$ is satisfied only by the point $(0, 0)$. The lowest degree homogeneous polynomial which can satisfy the above conditions is a quadratic; hence isolated points are at least double points.

material point. See MATERIAL.

mid-point. See MID-POINT—midpoint of a line segment.

multiple or *k*-tuple point. A point on a curve at which the curve crosses or touches itself at least k times. A point on a curve where there are k tangents, distinct or coincident. The equations of the tangents at a k-tuple point on an algebraic curve can be gotten by equating to zero the lowest degree terms (in this case the terms of the kth degree) in the equation of the curve referred to a Cartesian coordinate system whose origin is at the multiple point. If a curve has several (k) coincident tangents at a point, it is said to have a **multiple (k-tuple) tangent** at the point.

ordinary point on a curve. A point at which the curve possesses a single tangent, runs smoothly, does not have an isolated point, and does not cross itself or make a sharp turn. A point that is not an ordinary point is called a **singular point.** *Tech.* An ordinary point is a point at which either the ordinate can be expressed as an analytic function of the abscissa in a neighborhood of the point or the abscissa as such a function of the ordinate. *Syn.* Simple point.

piercing point of a line in space. Any one of the points where the line passes through one of the coordinate planes.

plotting points. See PLOT.

point of contact. See TANGENCY—point of tangency.

point of discontinuity. A point at which a curve (or function) is not continuous. See CONTINUOUS.

point of division. The point which divides the line segment joining two given points in a given ratio. If the two given points have the coordinates (x_1, y_1) and (x_2, y_2) and it is desired to find a point such that the distance from the first point to the new point, divided by the distance from the new point to the second point, is equal to r_1/r_2, the formulas giving the coordinates x and y of the desired point are

$$x = \frac{r_2 x_1 + r_1 x_2}{r_1 + r_2}, \qquad y = \frac{r_2 y_1 + r_1 y_2}{r_1 + r_2}.$$

When r_1/r_2 is positive, the point of division lies between the two given points, and the division is said to be **internal;** the new point is said to divide the line segment **internally** in the ratio r_1/r_2. When this ratio is negative, the point of division must lie on the line segment extended, and it is then said to divide the line segment **externally** in the ratio r_1/r_2. When $r_1 = r_2$, the new point bisects the line segment and the

above formulas reduce to

$$x = \frac{x_1 + x_2}{2}, \qquad y = \frac{y_1 + y_2}{2}.$$

point of division of a line in space. The situation is the same here as in the plane (see point of division) except that the points now have three coordinates. The formulas for x and y are the same, and the formula for z is

$$z = \frac{r_2 z_1 + r_1 z_2}{r_1 + r_2}.$$

point ellipse. See ELLIPSE.

point of inflection. See INFLECTION.

point, or null, circle. See CIRCLE—null circle.

point of osculation. A point at which two branches of a curve have a common tangent and lie on opposite sides of it. E.g. $y^2 = (x-1)^4$ has a point of osculation at $x = 1$, the curve consisting of the two parabolas $y = (x-1)^2$ and $y = -(x-1)^2$, both tangent to the x-axis at the point $(1, 0)$ and extending upward and downward, respectively. See OSCULATION.

point by point plotting (graphing) of a function. See PLOT—point by point plotting (graphing) of a function.

point in printing. The unit used in measuring bodies of type, leads, etc. It is equal to .0138 inches or .0351 centimeters, in the U. S. system.

point-slope form of the equation of a straight line. See LINE—equation of a straight line in the plane.

point of tangency. See TANGENCY.

power of a point. See POWER—power of a point.

salient point. See SALIENT.

simple point. Same as ORDINARY POINT.

singular point. See SINGULAR.

stationary point. Same as CUSP.

umbilical point on a surface. See UMBILICAL.

PO′LAR, *adj.* **polar coordinates in the plane.** The system of coordinates in which a point is located by its distance from a fixed point and the angle that the line from this point to the given point makes with a fixed line, called the **polar axis.** The fixed point, O in the figure, is called the **pole**; the distance, $OP = r$, from the pole to the given point, the **radius vector**; the angle, θ, the **polar angle** or **vectorial angle.** The polar coordinates of the point P are written (r, θ). The polar angle is sometimes called the **amplitude, anomaly** or **azimuth** of the point. From the figure it can be seen that the relations between Cartesian and polar coordinates are $x = r \cos \theta$, $y = r \sin \theta$. If r is positive (as in the figure), the amplitude, θ, of the point P is any angle (positive or negative) having OX as initial side and OP as terminal side. If r is negative, θ is any angle having OX as initial side and the extension of PO through O as terminal side. The point whose coordinates are $(1, 130°)$ or $(-1, -50°)$ is in the 2nd quadrant; the point whose coordinates are $(-1, 130°)$ or $(1, -50°)$ is in the 4th quadrant. See ANGLE.

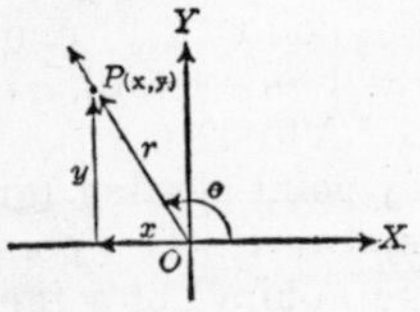

polar coordinates in space. Same as SPHERICAL COORDINATES.

polar distance of a circle on a sphere. See DISTANCE—polar distance of a circle on a sphere.

polar equation of conics. See CONIC —general equation of any conic.

polar equation of a line. See LINE —equation of a straight line in the plane.

polar form of a complex number. See COMPLEX.

polar line or plane. See POLE—pole and polar of a conic, and pole and polar of a quadric surface.

polar planimeter. See PLANIME-TER.

polar reciprocal curves. See RE-CIPROCAL—polar reciprocal curves.

polar tangent. The segment of the tangent line to a curve cut off by the point of tangency and a line through the pole perpendicular to the radius

vector. The projection of the polar tangent on this perpendicular is the **polar sub-tangent.** The segment of the normal between the point on the curve and this perpendicular is the **polar normal.** The projection of the polar normal on this perpendicular is the **polar sub-normal.**

polar triangle of a spherical triangle. The spherical triangle whose vertices are poles of the sides of the given triangle, the poles being the ones nearest to the vertices opposite the sides of which they are poles. See POLE—pole of an arc of a circle on a sphere.

reciprocal polar figures. See RE-CIPROCAL.

POLE, *n.* **pole of the celestial sphere.** One of the two points where the earth's axis, produced, pierces the celestial sphere. They are called the *north,* and *south, celestial poles,* See HOUR— hour angle and hour circle.

pole of an arc of a circle on a sphere. A pole of the circle containing the arc. See below, pole of a circle on a sphere.

pole of a circle on a sphere. A point of intersection of the sphere and the line through the center of the circle and perpendicular to the plane of the circle. The North and South poles are the poles of the equator.

pole and polar of a circle. See below, pole and polar of a conic, noting that a circle is a conic.

pole and polar of a conic. A point and the line which is the locus of the harmonic conjugates of this point with respect to the two points in which a secant through the given point cuts the conic; a point and the line which is the locus of points conjugate (see CONJUGATE—conjugate points relative to a conic) to the given point. The point is said to be the **pole** of the line and the line the **polar** of the point. Analytically, the polar of a point is the locus of the equation obtained by replacing the coordinates of the point of contact in the equation of a general tangent to the conic by the coordinates of the given point. See CONIC—tangent to a general conic. E.g. If a circle has the equation $x^2 + y^2 = a^2$, the equation of the *polar* of the point (x_1, y_1) is $x_1x + y_1y = a^2$. When a point lies so that two tangents can be drawn from it to the conic, the *polar* of the point is the secant through the points of contact of the tangents. The *polar line* of P_1 (in the figure), relative to the ellipse, is the line P_2P_3.

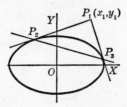

pole and polar of a quadric surface. A point (called the **pole** of the plane) and a plane (called the **polar** of the point) which is the locus of the harmonic conjugates of the point with respect to the two points in which a variable secant through the pole cuts the quadric. Analytically, the polar plane of a given point is the plane whose equation is that obtained by replacing the coordinates of the point of tangency in the general equation of a tangent plane by the coordinates of the given point. See TANGENT— tangent plane to a quadric surface. If, for instance, the quadric is an ellipsoid whose equation is $x^2/a^2 + y^2/b^2 + z^2/c^2 = 1$, the polar of the point (x_1, y_1, z_1) is the plane $x_1x/a^2 + y_1y/b^2 + z_1z/c^2 = 1$.

pole and polar of a sphere. See above, pole and polar of a quadric surface. A sphere is a quadric surface, an ellipsoid with its axes all equal.

pole of a system of coordinates. See POLAR—polar coordinates in the plane.

POL′I-CY, *n.* **annuity policy.** See AN- NUITY.

continuous installment policy. An endowment policy with the condition attached that if the insured survives the term of the contract an annuity will be paid for a certain period and so long thereafter as the insured lives.

debenture policy. See DEBEN- TURE.

discounted bonus policy. See DIS- COUNTED.

increasing premium policy. See IN- CREASING—increasing premium pol- icy.

installment policy. See INSTALL- MENT—installment policies.

insurance policy. A contract under which an insurance company agrees to pay the beneficiary a certain sum of money in case of death, fire, sickness, accident or whatever contingency the policy provides against.

limited payment policy. See LIMIT- ED PAYMENT POLICY.

loan value of a policy. See LOAN VALUE.

n-payment endowment policy. An endowment life insurance policy whose premiums are paid annually for n years.

n-year payment life policy. A life in- surance policy whose premiums are all paid in n years. Same as N-PAY- MENT LIFE POLICY.

n-year term policy. A life insurance policy which is paid only if the insured dies within the n years.

paid-up policy. See PAID—paid-up policy.

participating policy. See PARTIC- IPATING.

policy date. The date on which the policy is written, i.e. comes into force.

policy life. See CONTINGENT— contingent insurance.

policy year. (*Life insurance.*) Any year after the policy date.

reserve of an insurance policy. See RESERVE.

true premium policy. See TRUE.

value of a policy. See VALUE— value of an insurance policy.

POL′Y-GON, *n.* A closed plane figure bounded by straight lines; a plane figure consisting of a set of points (called **vertices**) no three of which lie in a straight line, and the line segments (called **sides**) that join these points, each point being joined to two and only two other points. A polygon of 3 sides is a **triangle**; of 4 sides, a **quadrilateral**; of 5 sides, a **pentagon**; of 6 sides, a **hexagon**; of 7 sides, a **heptagon**; of 8 sides, an **octagon**; of 9 sides, a **nonagon**; of 10 sides, a **decagon**; of 12 sides, a **dodecagon**; of n sides, an n-gon.

angles (interior) of a convex polygon. The angles made by adjacent sides of the polygon and lying within the polygon.

area of a regular polygon. If a is the apothem of the polygon, s the length of a side, and n the number of sides, then the area is $\frac{1}{2}ans$ or $\frac{1}{2}ap$, where p is the perimeter.

concave polygon. A polygon such that a part of it lies on each side of at least one of its sides produced; a polygon such that there is a straight line which cuts it in four or more points; a polygon that is not convex. See figure below, under convex polygon.

convex polygon. A polygon which lies entirely on one side of any one of its sides extended; a polygon such that no side extended cuts any other side or vertex; a polygon which can be cut by a line in at most two points; a polygon which is not concave.

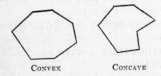

CONVEX   CONCAVE

diagonal of a polygon. A line segment joining any two non-adjacent vertices of the polygon.

equiangular polygon. A convex polygon with all its interior angles equal. See EQUIANGULAR.

equilateral polygon. See EQUILATERAL.

frequency polygon. See FREQUENCY—frequency distribution.

inscribed polygon of a circle. See INSCRIBED.

interior of a polygon. The plane area bounded by the sides of the polygon. A convex polygon always has an interior. In the case of a concave polygon, if no side cuts any other side, except at a vertex, the polygon bounds a definite area of the plane, which is called the interior of the polygon; but in general, a concave polygon does not have a unique interior.

perimeter of a regular polygon. If a is the apothem and n the number of sides, its perimeter is

$$2an \tan \frac{180°}{n}.$$

projection of a polygon on a line or plane. See PROJECTION—projection of a polygon on a line or plane.

regular polygon. A polygon whose sides are all equal, and whose interior angles are all equal.

similar polygons. Polygons having their corresponding angles equal and their corresponding sides proportional. See SIMILAR.

spherical polygon. A portion of a sphere bounded by arcs of great circles.

POL′Y-HE′DRAL, *adj.* **corresponding polyhedral angle in a spherical pyramid.** See CORRESPONDING—corresponding polyhedral angle in a spherical pyramid.

polyhedral angle. See ANGLE—polyhedral angle.

section of a polyhedral angle. The polygon formed by cutting all the edges (and faces) of the angle by a plane.

POL′Y-HE′DRON, *n.* A solid bounded by plane polygons. The bounding polygons are called the **faces;** the intersections of the faces, the **edges,** and the points where three or more edges intersect the **vertices.** A polyhedron of four faces is a **tetrahedron;** one of six faces, a **hexahedron;** one of eight faces, an **octahedron;** one of twelve faces, a **dodecahedron,** and one of twenty faces, an **icosahedron.**

concave polyhedron. A polyhedron such that a part of it lies on each side of at least one plane which contains one of its faces; a polyhedron some of whose plane sections are concave polygons.

convex polyhedron. A polyhedron which lies entirely on one side of any plane containing one of its faces; a polyhedron any plane section of which is a convex polygon.

diagonal of a polyhedron. See DIAGONAL—diagonal of a polyhedron.

Euler's theorem on polyhedrons. See EULER'S THEOREM.

polyhedron circumscribed about a sphere. See SPHERE—inscribed sphere of a polyhedron.

polyhedron inscribed in a sphere.

See SPHERE—circumscribed sphere of a polyhedron.

regular polyhedron. A polyhedron whose faces are congruent regular polygons and whose polyhedral angles are congruent. There are only five regular polyhedrons; the regular tetrahedron, hexahedron (or cube), octahedron, dodecahedron, and icosahedron. These are shown in the figure.

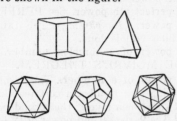

similar polyhedrons. Polyhedrons which can be made to correspond in such a way that corresponding faces are similar each to each and similarly placed and such that their corresponding polyhedral angles are congruent.

POL'Y-NO'MI-AL, *n.* (1) A sum of two or more rational integral terms in one or more variables, the coefficients usually being taken as real; e.g. $2x^3+3x^2+x+1$. (2) A sum of two or more terms. *Syn.* Multinomial.

continuation of sign in a polynomial. See CONTINUATION OF SIGN.

degree of a polynomial. See DEGREE.

Legendre's polynomials. See LEGENDRE.

polynomial equation. An equation which consists of a polynomial set equal to zero. *Syn.* Algebraic equation. The *general polynomial equation* is written in the form

$$a_0x^n+a_1x^{n-1}+\cdots+a_{n-1}x+a_n=0.$$

polynomial expression. Same as POLYNOMIAL.

polynomial in one variable. A polynomial which has only one variable; a sum of terms consisting of constant multiples of positive, integral powers of the variable. (Usually meant when the term *polynomial* is used.) The expression $2x^3+3x^2+x+1$ is a polynomial in one variable.

POS'I-TIVE, *adj.* **positive angle.** See ANGLE.

positive correlation. See CORRELATION.

positive derivative. See DERIVATIVE—sign of a derivative at a point, significance of.

positive number. *Positive* and *negative numbers* are used to denote numbers of units taken in opposite directions or opposite senses. If a positive number denotes miles east, a negative number denotes miles west. *Tech.* If a is a positive number, then b is the negative number containing a units if $a+b=0$; positive a is written $+a$, or simply a, while b, the negative of a, is written $-a$.

positive sign. Same as PLUS SIGN. See PLUS.

POS'TU-LATE, *n.* See AXIOM.

Euclid's postulates. (1) A straight line may be drawn between any two points. (2) Any terminated straight line may be produced indefinitely. (3) About any point as center a circle with any radius may be described. (4) All right angles are equal. (5) (The parallel postulate.) If two straight lines lying in a plane are met by another line, making the sum of the internal angles on one side less than two right angles, then those straight lines will meet, if sufficiently produced, on the side on which the sum of the angles is less than two right angles. (There is not complete agreement on how many of Euclid's assumptions were designated as postulates, but these five are generally so recognized.)

PO-TEN'TIAL, *n.* In *dynamics*, the sum of the products of all the pairs of particles of two systems (one from each system), each product divided by the distance between the pair—in the limit, a double integral; the work that would be done by a system of attracting and repelling masses in moving from situations infinitely remote from one another to their actual position. In *electrostatics*, at any point near or within an electrified body, the quantity of work necessary to bring a unit of positive electricity from an infinite distance to that point, the given distribution of electricity remaining unaltered. In *magnetostatics*, at any point in a magnetic field, the quantity of work expended in bringing a positive unit magnetic pole from a fixed given distance to that point. In general, potential is a scalar quantity distributed through space in such a way that a given vector quantity distributed through space equals (both in magnitude and direction) the most rapid change of value of the scalar (the potential) with space; i.e. the vector at any given point is equal to

$$\nabla \Phi = i\,\frac{\partial \Phi}{\partial x} + j\,\frac{\partial \Phi}{\partial y} + k\,\frac{\partial \Phi}{\partial z}$$

where Φ is the potential and i, j, and k are unit vectors in the directions of the x-axis, y-axis, and z-axis, respectively.

POUND, *n.* A unit of weight; the weight of one mass pound. See MASS and WEIGHT. Since weight varies slightly at different points on the earth, for extremely accurate work one pound of force is taken as the weight of a mass pound at sea level and 45° north latitude.

    pound of mass. See MASS.

POUND'AL, *n.* A unit of force. See FORCE—unit of force.

POW'ER, *n.* **Abel's theorem on power series.** See ABEL'S THEOREM.

    derivative of a power of a variable. See DIFFERENTIATION FORMULAS in the appendix.

    difference of like powers of two quantities. See DIFFERENCE.

    differentiation of a power series. See DIFFERENTIATION—differentiation of a power series.

    fitting by a power law. (*Statistical graphing.*) Determining the constants, a and n, in the equation $y = ax^n$ by means of a set of statistics which are known (or assumed) to approximately satisfy this type of equation. This problem is reduced to the problem of fitting a linear equation to the data, by taking the logarithm of both sides of this equation, which changes it to

$$\log y = n \log x + \log a, \quad \text{or} \quad u = nv + c,$$

where $\log y = u$, $\log x = v$, and $\log a = c$.

    horsepower. See HORSEPOWER.

    integration of a power series. See INTEGRATION—integration of a power series.

    operations with power series. Addition, multiplication, division, etc., of the power series. See SERIES.

    perfect nth power. See PERFECT.

    power. (*In physics.*) The rate at which work is done.

    power of a complex number. See DE MOIVRE'S THEOREM.

    power of a number. The result of taking that number a certain number of times as a factor; the second power of 3 is 9, the second power of $(x+1)$ is $(x+1)(x+1)$, written $(x+1)^2$. *Power* is sometimes used in the same sense as *exponent*.

    power of a point with reference to a circle. The quantity obtained by substituting the coordinates of the point in the equation of the circle when written with the right-hand side equal to zero and the coefficients of the square terms equal to unity; the algebraic product of the distances from the point to the points where any line through the given point cuts the circle (this product is the same for all such lines); the square of the length of a tangent from the point to the circle when the point is external to the circle.

    power of a point with reference to a sphere. The power of the point with reference to any circle formed by a plane passing through the point and the center of the sphere; the value obtained by substituting the coordinates of the point in the equation of the sphere when written with the right-hand side equal to zero and the coefficients of the square terms equal to unity; the algebraic product of the distances from the point to the points where any line through the given point cuts the sphere; the square of the length of a tangent from the point to the sphere if the point is external to the sphere.

    power series. See SERIES.

sum of like powers of two quantities. See SUM—sums of like powers of two quantities.

PRE-CI'SION, *n.* **index of precision.** See INDEX—index of precision.

PREFERRED STOCK. Stock which pays a set dividend or rate of interest, after the interest on all the company's bonds have been paid, and before dividends are paid on common stock. If the company fails, the order of redemption is the same as the above order of payments.

PRE-LIM'I-NAR'Y, *adj.* **preliminary term plan.** A plan for paying premiums of an insurance policy. The annual premium during a certain term is based on the insured's age at the beginning of that term, and after the end of that term it is based on the age at the end of the term.

PRE'MI-UM, *n.* (1) The amount paid for insurance. (2) The amount paid for the loan of money, in addition to normal interest. (3) The difference between the selling price and par value of stocks, bonds, notes, and shares, when the selling price is larger. Compare DISCOUNT. (4) One kind of currency is at a *premium* when it sells for more than its face value in terms of another; when one dollar in gold sells for $1.10 in paper money, gold is at a *premium* of 10 cents per dollar.

amortization of a premium on a bond. See AMORTIZATION—amortization of a premium on a bond.

gross premium. (*Insurance.*) The premium paid to the insurance company; net premium, plus allowances for office expenses, medical examinations, agent's fees, etc., minus deductions due to income. *Syn.* Office premium.

increasing premium policy. See INCREASING—increasing premium policy.

installment premiums. Annual premiums payable in installments during the year.

insurance with return of premiums. See INSURANCE—insurance with return of premiums.

natural premium. See NATURAL.

net annual premiums. Equal annual payments made at the beginning of each policy year to pay the cost of a policy figured under the following assumptions: all policyholders will die at a rate given by a standard (accepted) mortality table; the insurance company's funds will draw interest at a certain given rate; every benefit will be paid at the close of the policy year in which it became due, and there will be no charge for carrying on the company's business.

net level premiums. Fixed (equal) annual premiums, over a period of years, which are equivalent to the natural premiums over the same period. In the early years, the premiums are greater than the natural premium; in the later years, they are less.

net single premium. The amount required to pay, on the policy date, the equivalent of all net annual premiums; the present value, on the policy date, of all the net annual premiums.

office premium. The gross premium. The premium ordinarily paid by the insured.

premium bonds. Bonds which sell at a premium.

single premium. See SINGLE—single premium on an insurance policy.

true premium. See TRUE—true premium policy.

PRES'ENT, *adj.* **present value or worth.** See VALUE—present value.

PRES'SURE, *n.* (*In physics.*) A force, per unit area, exerted over the surface of a body. See below, fluid pressure.

center of pressure. See CENTER—center of pressure.

differential of pressure. See below, fluid pressure.

fluid pressure. The force exerted per unit area by a fluid. The fluid pressure on a unit horizontal area (plate) at a depth h is equal to the product of the density of the fluid and h. The total pressure on a horizontal area at depth h is khA, where A is the area and k the density of the fluid. The total pressure on a non-horizontal area is found by dividing the area into infinitesimal (differential) areas (horizontal strips, if the area is in a vertical plane) and summing the pressure on these strips (the **differentials of pressure** or **elements of pressure**) by integration. See ELEMENT—element of plane area. (The height of the fluid can be measured from any point in the element of area and the pressure on the element computed the same as if the element were in a horizontal plane at that depth. See DUHAMEL'S THEOREM.)

PREVAILING INTEREST RATE for any given investment. The rate which is generally accepted for that particular type of investment at the time under consideration. *Syn.* Income rate, current rate, yield rate.

PRICE, *n.* The quoted sum for which merchandise or contracts (bonds, mortgages, stock, etc.) are offered for sale.

"and interest price" of a bond. The purchase price minus the accrued dividend. Same as quoted price.

calling price on a bond. See CALLING.

flat price. See FLAT.

list price. See LIST PRICE.

net price. The price after all discounts and other reductions have been made.

profit on cost. See PERCENT—percent profit on cost.

profit on selling price. See PERCENT—percent profit on selling price.

purchase price of a bond. The flat price minus the accrued dividend.

quoted price of a bond. Same as "and interest price."

redemption price of a bond. See REDEMPTION—redemption price.

selling price. The price at which something is actually sold.

PRI′MA-RY, *adj.* **primary infinitesimal and infinite quantity.** See STANDARD—standard or primary infinitesimal and infinite quantity.

PRIME, *adj.* or *n.* **prime direction.** An initial directed line; a fixed line with reference to which directions (angles) are defined; usually the positive x-axis or the *polar axis*.

prime factors of a quantity. All the prime quantities (numbers, polynomials) that will exactly divide the given quantity. E.g. (1) the numbers 2, 3 and 5 are the prime factors of 30; (2) the quantities x, $(x+1)$ and $(x-1)$ are the prime factors of $x^5 - 2x^3 + x$. See below, prime number, and prime polynomial.

prime meridian. See MERIDIAN—principal meridian.

prime number. An integer which has no integral factors except unity and itself: as 2, 3, 5, 7, or 11. *etc.*

prime polynomial. A polynomial which has no factors except itself and unity. The polynomials $x-1$ and $x^2 + x + 1$ are prime. *Tech.* A polynomial which is *irreducible*. See IRREDUCIBLE—polynomials irreducible in a given field.

prime (or accent) as a symbol. The symbol ($'$) placed to the right and above a letter. (1) Used to denote the first derivative of a function; y' and $f'(x)$, called *y-prime* and *f-prime*, denote the first derivatives of y and $f(x)$. Similarly y'' and $f''(x)$, called *y double prime* and *f double prime*, denote second derivatives. In general, $y^{[n]}$ and $f^{[n]}(x)$ denote the nth derivatives. (2) Sometimes used on letters to denote constants, x' denoting a particular value of x, (x', y') denoting the particular point whose coordinates are x' and y', in distinction to the variable point (x, y). (3) Used to denote different variables with the same letters, as x, x', x'' etc. (4) Used to denote feet and inches, as $2'3''$, read two feet and three inches. (5) Used to denote minutes and seconds in circular measurement of angles, as $3° 10' 20''$, read three degrees, ten minutes and twenty seconds.

relatively prime quantities. Quantities which have no factor in common except unity. They are also said to be *prime to each other*.

PRIM′I-TIVE, *adj.* (1) A geometrical or analytic form from which another is derived; a quantity whose derivative is a function under consideration. (See DERIVATIVE.) (2) A function which satisfies a differential equation. (3) A curve of which another is the polar or reciprocal, etc.

primitive curve. A curve from which another curve is derived; a curve of which another is the polar, reciprocal, etc.; the graph of the primitive of a differential equation (a member of the family of curves which are graphs of the solutions of the differential equation). See INTEGRAL—integral curves.

primitive of a differential equation. A solution of the differential equation. If the primitive has the requisite number of arbitrary constants (i.e. if it is the general solution) it is said to be a **complete primitive.**

primitive nth root of unity. A solution of the equation $x^n = 1$, which is a solution of no lower degree equation of this type; an nth root of unity which is not a root of unity of a lower order than n. Primitive roots are always imaginary except in the cases $n = 1$ and $n = 2$. The primitive square root of unity is -1; the primitive cube roots are

$$\frac{-1 \pm \sqrt{-3}}{2};$$

the primitive fourth roots are $\pm \sqrt{-1}$.

PRIN'CI-PAL, *adj.* or *n.* Most important or most significant.

principal. (*In finance.*) Money put at interest, or otherwise invested.

principal angle. Same as PRINCIPAL VALUE of an inverse trigonometric function.

principal diagonal of a determinant. See DETERMINANT.

principal diagonal of a parallelepiped. See DIAGONAL—diagonal of a parallelepiped.

principal meridian. See MERIDIAN —principal meridian.

principal normal. See OSCULATING—osculating plane.

principal part of an increment of a function. The part of the increment that is left after dropping certain higher order infinitesimals; the infinitesimal of lowest order in the increment. Explicitly, the term $f'(x)\Delta x$ in the increment of $f(x)$, where

$$\Delta f(x) = f'(x)\Delta x + \epsilon \Delta x.$$

See INCREMENT.

principal parts of a triangle. The sides and interior angles. The other parts, such as the bisectors of the angles, the altitudes, the circumscribed and inscribed circles, are called **secondary parts.**

principal radii of curvature at a point on a surface. The two radii of curvature of the normal sections whose curvatures are respectively the maximum and minimum of the curvatures of all normal sections at the point. These two sections are orthogonal at the point.

principal root of a number. The positive real root in the case of roots of positive numbers; the negative real root in the case of odd roots of negative numbers. (Every number has two square roots, three cube roots, and in general n nth roots.)

principal trigonometric functions. The sine, cosine, and tangent.

principal value. See VALUE—principal value of an inverse trigonometric function.

PRIN'CI-PLE, *n.* A general truth or law, either assumed or proved.

principle of continuity. See AXIOM —axiom of continuity.

principle of duality of projective geometry. The principle that if one of two dual theorems is true the other is also. In a *plane*: point and line are called **dual elements;** the drawing of a line through a point and the marking of a point on a line are known as **dual operations,** as are also the drawing of two lines through a point and the marking of two points on a line, or the bringing of two lines to intersect in a point and the joining of two points by a line; figures which can be obtained from one another by replacing each element by the dual element and each operation by the dual operation are called **dual figures,** as three lines passing through a point and three points lying on a line (three *concurrent* lines and three *collinear* points). Theorems which can be obtained from one another by replacing each element in one by the dual element and each operation by the dual operation are called **dual theorems.** In *space*: the point and plane are dual elements (called **space duals**) the definitions of dual operations, figures, and theorems being analogous to those in the plane. Some writers state dual theorems in such terms that they are interchanged merely by interchanging the words point and line (or point and plane) as, for instance, two points determine a line—two lines determine a point, or two points on a line—two lines on a point. E.g. the two following statements are plane duals: (a) one and only one line is determined by a point and the point common to two lines; (b) one and only one point is determined by a line and the line common to two points.

principle of duality in a spherical triangle. In any formula involving the sides and the supplements of the angles opposite the sides, another true formula may be obtained by interchanging each of the sides with the supplement of the angle opposite it. The new formula is called the dual formula.

principle of proportional parts. See PROPORTIONAL.

PRINGSHEIM'S THEOREM on double series. See SERIES—double series.

PRISM, *n.* A polyhedron with two congruent and parallel faces, called the **bases,** and whose other faces, called **lateral faces,** are parallelograms formed by joining corresponding vertices of the bases. Its **lateral area** is the total area of its lateral faces (equal to an edge times the perimeter of a right section), and its volume is equal to the product of its base and its altitude. A prism with a triangle as base is called a **triangular prism;** one with a quadrilateral as base is called a **quadrangular prism;** etc. The figure shows three types of prisms.

altitude of a prism. The distance between the bases.

circumscribed prism of a cylinder. A prism whose bases are coplanar with the bases of the cylinder and whose lateral faces are tangent to the cylindrical surface. The cylinder is said to be *inscribed in* the prism.

diagonal of a prism. See DIAGONAL—diagonal of a polyhedron.

inscribed prism of a cylinder. A prism whose bases are coplanar with the bases of the cylinder and whose lateral edges are elements of the cylinder. The cylinder is said to be *circumscribed about* the prism.

lateral edge of a prism. The intersection of two of its lateral faces.

regular prism. A right prism whose bases are regular polygons.

right prism. A prism whose bases are perpendicular to the lateral edges.

right section of a prism. A plane section perpendicular to the lateral faces of the prism.

truncated prism. See TRUNCATED —truncated prism.

PRIS-MAT'IC, *adj.* **prismatic surface.** A surface generated by a moving straight line which always intersects a broken line lying in a given plane and is always parallel to a given line not in the plane. When the broken line is closed, the surface is called a **closed prismatic surface.**

PRIS'MA-TOID, *n.* A polyhedron whose vertices all lie in one or the other of two parallel planes. The faces which lie in the parallel planes are the **bases** of the prismatoid and the perpendicular distance between the bases is the **altitude.** See PRISMOIDAL—prismoidal formula.

prismatoid formula. Same as the PRISMOIDAL FORMULA.

PRIS'MOID, *n.* A prismatoid whose bases are polygons having the same number of sides, the other faces being trapezoids or parallelograms.

prismoid formula. Same as the PRISMOIDAL FORMULA.

PRIS-MOI'DAL, *adj.* **prismoidal formula.** The volume of a prismatoid is equal to one-sixth of the altitude times the sum of the areas of the bases and four times the area of a plane section midway between the bases; $V = \frac{1}{6}h(B_1 + 4B_2 + B_3)$. This formula also gives the volume of any solid having two parallel plane bases, whose cross-sectional area (by a plane parallel to the bases) is given by a linear, quadratic, or cubic function of the distance of the cross-section from one of the bases (an elliptic cylinder, and quadratic cone, satisfy these conditions). The prismoidal formula is sometimes given as $V = \frac{1}{4}h(B_1 + 3S)$, where S is the area of a section parallel to the base and $\frac{2}{3}$ the distance from B_1 to B_2. This is equivalent to the preceding form. See SIMPSON'S RULE.

PROB'A-BIL'I-TY, *n.* compound survivorship probability. See COMPOUND —compound survivorship probability.

contingent probability. See CONTINGENT–contingent probability.

empirical or *a posteriori* probability. If in a number of trials an event has occurred *n* times and failed *m* times, the *probability* of its occurring in the next trial is $n/(n+m)$. It is assumed, in determining *empirical probability*, that there is no known information relative to the probability of the occurrence of the event other than the past trials. The probability of a man living through any one year, based upon past observations as recorded in a mortality table, is *empirical probability*.

mathematical or *a priori* probability. If an event can occur in *n* ways and fail to occur in *m* ways, and if these $m+n$ ways are each equally likely, then the *mathematical probability* that the event will occur in any one trial is $n/(n+m)$. If one ball is to be drawn from a bag containing two white balls and three red balls, the *mathematical probability* of drawing a white ball is $\frac{2}{5}$, the *mathematical probability* of the event failing, that is of drawing a red ball, is $\frac{3}{5}$.

probability curve. A curve of the type shown in the figure; the locus of any curve of the type $y = ke^{-h^2(x-A)^2}$ where A, h and k are constants. *Syn.* Error curve, normal distribution curve, normal frequency curve. See FREQUENCY—normal frequency curve.

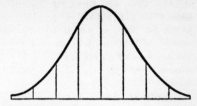

PROB'A-BLE, *adj.* Likely to be true or to happen.

most probable after lifetime. See MOST—most probable after lifetime.

most probable lifetime. See MOST —most probable lifetime.

probable deviation. A special name given to the *quartile deviation* when the distribution is normal.

PROB'LEM, *n.* A question proposed for solution; a matter for examination; a proposition requiring an operation to be performed or a construction to be made, as to bisect a line or find the cube root of 2.

accumulation problem. See ACCUMULATION.

Dido's problem. See DIDO'S PROBLEM.

discount problem under compound interest. See DISCOUNT.

four-color problem. See FOUR-COLOR PROBLEM.

problem of Apollonius. To construct a circle tangent to three given circles.

PRO'CEEDS, *n.* (1) The sum of money obtained from a business transaction or enterprise. The proceeds of a farm for a year is the sum of all the money taken in during the year; the proceeds of a sale of goods is the money received in return for the goods. (2) The difference between the face of a note, or other contract to pay, and the discount.

net proceeds. The amount of money left after deducting all discounts and expenses from the proceeds of a transaction.

proceeds of a note. The difference between the face value and the bank discount; the balance after interest, in advance, has been deducted from the face of the note.

PRO-DUCE', *v.* produce a line. To continue the line. *Syn.* Prolong, extend.

PROD'UCT, *n.* The result of multiplying several quantities together. Also used of multiplications which are only indicated. Both 6 and $2 \cdot 3$ are spoken of as the product of 2 and 3.

continued product. See CONTINUED.

infinite product. See INFINITE—infinite product.

limit of a product. See LIMIT—fundamental theorems on limits.

partial product. See PARTIAL—partial product.

product of the elements of a group. See GROUP.

product formulas. See FORMULA—product formulas.

product moment. See MOMENT—product moment.

product of the sum and difference of two quantities. Such products as $(x+y)(x-y)$ used in factoring, since this product is equal to $x^2 - y^2$.

scalar and vector products. See MULTIPLICATION—multiplication of two vectors.

PROFILE MAP. A vertical section of a surface, showing the relative altitudes of the points which lie in the section.

PROF'IT, *n.* The difference between the price received and the sum of the original cost and the selling expenses, when the price received is the larger. The selling expenses include storage, depreciation, labor, and sometimes accumulations in a reserve fund. *Syn.* Net profit.

gross profit. The difference between the selling price and the original cost; cost not including selling expenses, storage or other overhead expenses.

net profit. Same as PROFIT.

percent profit on cost. See PERCENT.

percent profit on selling price. See PERCENT.

PRO-GRES'SION, *n.* arithmetic progression. A sequence of terms each of which is equal to the preceding plus a fixed constant. See ARITHMETIC—arithmetic progression.

geometric progression. A sequence of terms such that the ratio of each term to the immediately preceding one is the same throughout the sequence. The general form is usually written: $a,\ ar,\ ar^2,\ \cdots,\ ar^{n-1}$, where a is the **first term,** r the **common ratio** (or simply **ratio**) and ar^{n-1} the last or nth term. The sum of such terms is sometimes called a *geometric progression*, although *geometric series* is more common. See SERIES—geometric series.

harmonic progression. See HARMONIC.

PRO-JEC'TILE, *n.* path of a projectile. See PARABOLA—parametric equations of a parabola.

PRO-JECT'ING, *adj.* projecting cylinder. A cylinder whose elements pass through a given curve and are perpendicular to one of the coordinate planes. There are three such cylinders for any given curve, unless the curve lies in a plane perpendicular to a coordinate plane, and their equations in rectangular Cartesian coordinates can each be obtained by eliminating the proper one of the variables x, y, and z between the two equations which define the curve. The space curve, a circle, which is the intersection of the sphere $x^2+y^2+z^2=1$ and the plane $x+y+z=0$ has the three projecting cylinders whose equations are: $x^2+y^2+xy=\frac{1}{2}$, $x^2+z^2+xz=\frac{1}{2}$, and $y^2+z^2+yz=\frac{1}{2}$. These are elliptic cylinders.

projecting plane of a line in space. A plane containing the line and perpendicular to one of the coordinate planes. There are three projecting planes for every line in space, unless the line is perpendicular to a coordinate axis. The equation of each projecting plane contains only two variables, the missing variable being the one whose axis is parallel to the plane. These equations can be gotten as the three equations given by the double equality of the symmetric space equation of the straight line. See LINE—equation of a straight line in space.

PRO-JEC'TION, *n.* central projection. A projection of one plane configuration (A, B, C, D, in figure) on another plane (called the **plane of projection**) in which the projected configuration (A', B', C', D') is formed by the intersections, with the second plane, of all lines passing through a fixed point (not in either plane) and the various points in the configuration. The image on a photographic film is a projection of the image being photographed, if the lense is considered as a point. The point is called the **center of projection** and the lines, or rays, are called the **projectors.** When the center of projection is a point at infinity (when the rays are parallel) the projection is called a **parallel projection.** See also OR-THOGONAL—orthogonal projection.

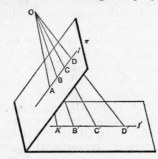

center of projection. See above, central projection.

orthogonal projection. See OR-THOGONAL—orthogonal projection.

plane of projection. The plane upon which a figure is projected.

projection of an area on a plane. The area in the plane which is bounded by the projection on the plane of the curve bounding the given area.

projection of a curve on a plane. The locus of the projections on the plane of the points of the curve. See below, projection of a point on a line or plane.

projection of a directed broken line, in a plane, on a straight line. The algebraic sum of the projections of the directed line segments making up the broken line. See below, projection of a vector on a line or plane.

projection of a directed line segment on a line or plane. Same as projection of a vector since a directed line segment is a vector.

projection of a force on a plane. The force represented by the projection, on that plane, of the vector representing the force.

projection of a line segment on a line or plane. The line segment joining the projections of the extremities of the given line segment.

projection of a point on a line or plane. The foot of the perpendicular from the point to the line or plane.

projection of a polygon on a line or plane. The projection of the broken line forming the polygon. Its projection on a line is zero if the sides are directed in the same sense around the polygon.

projection of a vector on a line or plane. The vector joining the projections on the line or plane of the initial and terminal points of the given vector, and taken in the same sense as the vector.

PRO-JEC'TIVE, *adj.* **projective geometry.** The study of those properties of geometric configurations which are invariant under projection.

PRO-JEC'TORS, *n.* See PROJECTION —central projection.

PRO'LATE, *adj.* **prolate cycloid.** A *trochoid* which has loops.

prolate ellipsoid of revolution. See ELLIPSOID—ellipsoid of revolution.

PRO-LONG', *v.* **prolong a line.** To continue the line. *Syn.* Produce.

PROM'IS-SO'RY, *adj.* **maker of a promissory note.** The person who signs the note; the one who first guarantees its payment. See INDORSE.

promissory note. A written promise to pay a certain sum on a certain future date, the sum usually drawing interest until paid.

PROOF, *n.* The logical argument which establishes the truth of a theorem or statement. The process of showing that what is to be proved is consistent with what has already been accepted as true by representative (qualified) mathematicians.

analytic proof. See ANALYTIC.

deductive proof. See DEDUCTIVE.

indirect proof. See INDIRECT.

inductive proof. See INDUCTIVE METHODS, and MATHEMATICAL —mathematical induction.

reductio ad absurdum proof. See

REDUCTIO AD ABSURDUM PROOF.

synthetic proof. See SYNTHETIC.

PROP'ER, *adj.* **proper fraction.** See FRACTION.

proper subset. See SET—subset.

PROP'ER-TY, *n.* **evaluation of mining property.** Evaluating it as a depreciating asset. A redemption fund is usually built up to equal the cost of the mine when the ore is all gone.

PRO-POR'TION, *n.* The statement of equality of two ratios; an equation whose members are ratios. Four numbers, a, b, c, d, are in proportion when the ratio of the first pair equals the ratio of the second pair. This is denoted by $a:b=c:d$, or better by $a/b=c/d$; a notation fast becoming obsolete is $a:b::c:d$. The letters a and d are called the **extremes**, b and c the **means**, of the proportion.

continued proportion. An ordered set of three or more quantities such that the ratio between any two successive ones is the same. This is equivalent to saying that any one of the quantities except the first and last is the *geometric mean* between the previous and succeeding ones, or that the quantities form a *geometric progression*. 1, 2, 4, 8, 16 form a continued proportion, written

$$1:2:4:8:16 \quad \text{or} \quad 1/2=2/4=4/8=8/16.$$

proportion by addition. Refers to the fact that if four numbers are in proportion, the sum of the first two is to the second as the sum of the last two is to the last; if $a/b=c/d$ then $(a+b)/b=(c+d)/d$. The second proportion is said to be derived from the first by addition.

proportion by addition and subtraction. Refers to the fact that if four numbers are in proportion, say

$a/b=c/d$, then $(a+b)/(a-b)=(c+d)/(c-d)$.

The second proportion is said to be derived from the first by **addition and subtraction.**

proportion by alternation. Refers to the fact that if four numbers are in proportion, then the first is to the third as the second is to the fourth; if $a/b=c/d$, then $a/c=b/d$. The second proportion is said to be derived from the first by **alternation.**

proportion by inversion. Refers to the fact that if four numbers are in proportion, the second is to the first as the fourth is to the third; if $a/b=c/d$, then $b/a=d/c$. The second proportion is said to be derived from the first by **inversion.**

proportion by subtraction. Refers to the fact that if four numbers form a proportion, the difference of the first two is to the second as the difference of the last two is to the fourth, the difference being taken in the same sense; if $a/b=c/d$, then $(a-b)/b=(c-d)/d$. The second proportion is said to be derived from the first by **subtraction.**

PRO-POR'TION-AL, *adj.* **directly proportional quantities.** Same as PROPORTIONAL QUANTITIES.

inversely proportional quantities. Two quantities whose product is constant; two quantities such that one is *proportional* to the reciprocal of the other.

principle of proportional parts. The assumption that a function of a variable varies linearly with the independent variable for small values of the difference between the values of the variable (in other words, short arcs of the graph of the function are very nearly straight line segments). This principle is used mostly in interpolation. See below, proportional parts.

proportional parts. Parts which are in the same proportion as a given set of numbers. The parts of 12 proportional to 1, 2, and 3 are 2, 4, and 6.

proportional parts in a table of logarithms. The numbers to be added to the next smaller mantissa to produce a desired mantissa (see MANTISSA). See TABLE I in the appendix; the proportional parts are the products of the differences between successive mantissas (written above them) and the numbers .1, .2, $\cdots$, .9 (written in the table without decimal points). These *proportional parts tables* are multiplication (and division) tables to aid in interpolating for logarithms of numbers not in the tables (and for numbers whose logarithms are not in the tables).

proportional quantities. Two variable quantities having fixed (constant) ratio.

proportional sets of numbers. (1) Two sets of numbers such that the ratios of corresponding numbers are equal. (2) Two sets of numbers for which there exist two numbers m and n, not both zero, such that m times any number of the first set is equal to n times the corresponding number of the second set. The two sets of numbers are also said to be **linearly dependent,** although the concept of linear dependence is not limited to two sets. The sets 1, 2, 3, 7, and 4, 8, 12, 28 are proportional. The numbers $m = 4$ and $n = 1$ suffice for these sets. This definition is more general than that involved in ordinary arithmetic proportion, for the sets 1, 5, 0, 9, 0 and 0, 0, 0, 0, 0 are in proportion, where m is zero and n is any number not zero. The elementary definition, (1), fails here because of the impossibility of dividing by zero.

PRO-POR'TION-AL, *n.* One of the terms in a proportion.

fourth proportional. If

$$\frac{a}{b} = \frac{c}{x},$$

then x is the *fourth proportional* to a, b, and c.

mean proportional between two numbers. A mean when the means are equal; 4 is the mean proportional between 2 and 8, for $2/4 = 4/8$. See PROPORTION. Same as GEOMETRIC MEAN.

third proportional. The second extreme in a proportion (see PROPORTION) when the means are equal. If

$$\frac{a}{b} = \frac{b}{x},$$

x is the *third proportional* to a and b.

PRO-POR'TION-AL'I-TY, *n.* The state of being in proportion.

factor of proportionality. See FACTOR—factor of proportionality.

PROP'O-SI'TION, *n.* (1) a theorem or problem. (2) A theorem or problem with its proof or solution.

PROSPECTIVE METHOD of computing reserves. (*Insurance.*) The method of computing reserves which is based upon the fact that after the date of the policy the present value of future premiums is less than at the policy date (when it was the same as the present value of the policy benefits), while the present value of the insurance benefits has increased, since the date of payment is nearer. This difference between the increased value of the benefits and the decreased value of future net premiums must be represented by money in the company's reserve fund.

PRO-TRAC'TOR, *n.* A semi-circular plate graduated, usually in degrees, from one extremity of the diameter to the other and used to measure angles.

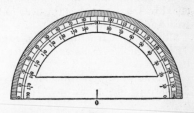

PROVE, *v.* To establish by evidence or demonstration; show the truth of; find a proof for. See PROOF.

PTOLEMY'S THEOREM. A necessary and sufficient condition that a convex quadrilateral be inscribable in a circle is that the sum of the products of the two pairs of opposite sides be equal to the product of the diagonals.

PUR'CHASE, *n.* purchase price of a bond on a dividend date. The present value of the redemption price (usually face value) plus the present value of an annuity whose payments are equal to the dividends on the bond.

purchase price of a bond between interest dates. See BOND.

PURE, *adj.* pure endowment insurance. A sum payable at the end of a given period if and only if the insured survives that period.

pure geometry. See SYNTHETIC—synthetic geometry.

pure imaginary number. See IM-AGINARY—pure imaginary number.

pure mathematics. See MATHE-MATICS.

pure projective geometry. Projective geometry employing only geometric methods and only bringing up properties other than projective in a subordinate way. See GEOMETRY—modern analytic geometry.

pure surd. See SURD—pure surd.

PYR'A-MID, *n.* A polyhedron with one face a polygon and the other faces triangles with a common vertex. The polygon is called the **base** of the pyramid and the triangles are called the **lateral faces.** The common vertex of the lateral faces is called the **vertex** of the pyramid and the intersections of pairs of lateral faces are called **lateral edges.** The **lateral area** is the total area of the lateral faces and the volume is equal to $\frac{1}{3}bh$, where b is the area of the base and h is the altitude.

altitude of a frustum of a pyramid. The perpendicular distance between its bases.

altitude of a pyramid. The perpendicular distance from the *vertex* to the *base.*

frustum of a pyramid. The section of a pyramid between the base and a plane parallel to the base. The volume of a frustum of a pyramid is equal to $\frac{1}{3}h(A+B+\sqrt{AB})$, where A and B are the areas of the bases and h is the altitude. If the pyramid is regular, the lateral area of a frustum is $\frac{1}{2}S(P_1+P_2)$ where S is the slant height (altitude of a face) and P_1 and P_2 are the perimeters of the bases.

regular pyramid. A pyramid whose base is a regular polygon and whose lateral faces make equal angles with the base; a pyramid with a regular polygon for base and with the foot of its altitude at the center of the base. Its lateral surface is $\frac{1}{2}SP$, where S is

the **slant height** (common altitude of its faces) and P the perimeter of the base.

spherical pyramid. A figure formed by a spherical polygon and planes passing through the sides of the polygon and the center of the sphere. Its volume is

$$\frac{\pi r^3 E}{540}$$

where r is the radius of the sphere and E the *spherical excess* of the base of the pyramid.

truncated pyramid. The part of a pyramid between the base and a plane oblique to the base. The **bases** are the base of the pyramid and the intersection of the plane and the pyramid.

PY-RAM'I-DAL, *adj.* **pyramidal surface.** A surface generated by a line passing through a fixed point and moving along the sides of a polygon whose plane does not contain the fixed point.

PY-THAG'O-RE'AN, *adj.* **Pythagorean identities.** (*Trigonometry.*) The relations: $\sin^2 x + \cos^2 x = 1$; $1 + \tan^2 x = \sec^2 x$; $1 + \cot^2 x = \csc^2 x$. See TRIGONOMETRIC—relations between the trigonometric functions.

Pythagorean relation between direction cosines: The sum of the squares of the direction cosines of a line is equal to unity.

Pythagorean theorem: The sum of the squares of the lengths of the legs of a right-angle triangle is equal to the square of the hypotenuse. The right triangle whose legs are 3 and 4, and hypotenuse 5, has been used for ages to square corners. Geometrically this theorem states that the area of $ABGF$ (in the figure) is equal to the sum of the areas of $ACDE$ and $BCKH$.

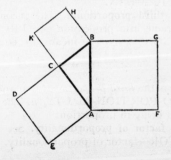

pentagram of Pythagoras. See PEN-
TAGRAM.

Q

QUAD'RAN'GLE, *n.* **simple quadrangle.**
Four points no three of which are collinear and the four lines connecting
them in a given order.

complete quadrangle. Four points no
three of which are collinear and the six
lines determined by the points in pairs;
complete as distinguished from *simple*
quadrangle.

QUAD-RAN'GU-LAR, *adj.* **quadrangular prism.** A prism whose bases are
quadrilaterals.

QUAD-RANT, *n.* **laws of quadrants.** See
LAW—laws of quadrants.

quadrant angles. Angles are designated as first, second, third, or fourth
quadrant angles when the initial side
coincides with the positive abscissa
axis in a system of rectangular coordinates and the terminal side lies in the
first, second, third, or fourth quadrants, respectively. The angles in the
first figure are in the first and second
quadrants; those in the second are in
the third and fourth quadrants.

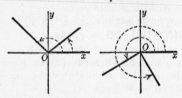

quadrant of a circle. (1) One half of
a semi-circle; one fourth of a circumference. (2) The plane area bounded by
two perpendicular radii and the arc
they subtend.

**quadrant of a great circle on a
sphere.** One-fourth of the great circle;
the arc of the great circle subtended by
a right angle at the center of the sphere.

**quadrant in a system of plane rect-
angular coordinates.** One of the four
compartments into which the plane is
divided by the axes of reference in a
Cartesian system of coordinates. They
are called first, second, third, and
fourth quadrants as counted counter-
clockwise beginning with the quadrant

in which both coordinates are positive.
See CARTESIAN—Cartesian coordinates in the plane.

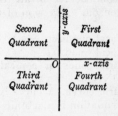

QUAD-RAN'TAL, *adj.* **quadrantal angles.** The angles 0°, 90°, 180°, 270° or
in radians 0, $\pi/2$, π, $3\pi/2$, and all angles having the same terminal sides
as any one of these, as: 2π, $5\pi/2$, 3π,
$7\pi/2$, · · · .

quadrantal spherical triangle. See
SPHERICAL.

QUAD-RAT'IC, *adj.* Of the second degree, or second order.

quadratic equation. An equation of
the second degree. The general form,
sometimes called an **affected quadratic,**
is $ax^2+bx+c=0$.

quadratic form. A homogeneous
polynomial of the second degree in
two or more variables.

quadratic formula. A formula for
computing the roots of a quadratic
equation. If the equation is in the
form $ax^2+bx+c=0$, the formula is:

$$x=\frac{-b\pm\sqrt{b^2-4ac}}{2a}.$$

See DISCRIMINANT—discriminant
of a quadratic equation in one variable.

QUAD-RAT'IC, *n.* **pure quadratic.** A
quadratic of the form $ax^2+c=0$.

**reduced form (p-form) of the quad-
ratic.** The form $x^2+px+q=0$.

QUAD'RA-TURE, *n.* The act of squaring
an area; the process of finding a square
equal in area to a given surface.

quadrature of a circle. Finding (con-
structing) a square which has the same
area as a given circle; usually called
squaring the circle. It is impossible to
do this with ruler and compass alone,
since a line segment of length π cannot
be so constructed from one of unit
length.

QUAD'RE-FOIL, *n.* See MULTIFOIL.

QUAD'RIC, *adj., n.* (1) Of the second degree; quadratic. (2) An expression of the second degree in all its terms; a homogeneous expression of the second degree.

    confocal quadrics. See CONFOCAL —confocal quadrics.

    quadric cones or conical surfaces. See CONICAL.

    quadric curve. A curve whose Cartesian equation is algebraic and of the second degree.

    quadric quantic. See QUANTIC.

    quadric surface. A surface whose Cartesian equation is algebraic and of the second degree.

QUAD'RI-LAT'ER-AL, *n.* A polygon having four sides. See PARALLELOGRAM, RECTANGLE, RHOMBUS, TRAPEZOID.

    complete quadrilateral. A figure consisting of four lines and their six points of intersection.

    quadrilateral inscribable in a circle. See PTOLEMY'S THEOREM.

    regular quadrilateral. A quadrilateral whose sides and interior angles are all equal; a square.

    simple quadrilateral. A figure consisting of four sides and their four successive intersections in pairs. Simple as distinguished from a *complete* quadrilateral.

QUAD-RIL'LION, *n.* (1) In the U. S. and France, the number represented by one followed by 15 zeros. (2) In England, the number represented by one followed by 24 zeros.

QUAN'TIC, *n.* A rational integral homogeneous function of two or more variables; a homogeneous algebraic polynomial in two or more variables. Quantics are classified as *quadric, cubic, quartic,* etc., according as they are of the second, third, fourth, etc., degrees. They are also classified as *binary, ternary, quarternary,* etc., according as they contain two, three, four, etc., variables.

QUAN'TI-TY, *n.* Any arithmetic, algebraic, or analytic expression which is concerned with value rather than relations between such expressions.

QUAR'TER, *n.* One fourth part.

QUAR'TIC, *adj.* Of the fourth degree; of the fourth order.

    quartic curve. An algebraic curve of the fourth degree or order.

    quartic equation. An algebraic equation of the fourth degree.

    quartic symmetry. Symmetry like that of a regular octagon.

    solution of the quartic. See FERRARI'S solution of the general quartic.

QUAR'TILE, *n.* (*Statistics.*) One of three items which divide a set of data into four parts in such a way that each part contains the same number of items. The second quartile is also the median.

    quartile deviation. See DEVIATION—quartile deviation.

    quartile magnitude. See MAGNITUDE—quartile magnitude.

QUA-TER'NA-RY, *adj.* Consisting of four; containing four.

    quaternary quantic. See QUANTIC.

QUIN'TIC, *adj., n.* (1) Of the fifth degree; (2) An algebraic function of the fifth degree.

    quintic curve. An algebraic curve whose equation is of the fifth degree.

    quintic equation. An algebraic equation of the fifth degree.

    quintic quantic. See QUANTIC.

QUIN-TIL'LION, *n.* (1) In the U. S. and France, the number represented by one followed by 18 zeros. (2) In England, the number represented by one followed by 30 zeros.

QUOTED, *adj.* quoted price of a bond. See PRICE—"and interest price" of a bond.

QUO'TIENT, *n.* The quantity resulting from the division of one quantity by another. The division may have been actually performed or merely indicated; e.g. 2 is the quotient of 6 divided by 3, as is also 6/3. In case the division is not exact one speaks of the *quotient* and the *remainder,* or simply the *quotient* (meaning the integer obtained plus the indicated division of the remainder), e.g. $7 \div 2$ gives the quotient 3 and the remainder 1, or the *quotient* $3\frac{1}{2}$.

    derivative of a quotient. See DIF-

FERENTIATION FORMULAS in the appendix.

difference quotient. See DIFFERENCE.

limit of a quotient of two variables. See LIMIT—fundamental theorems on limits.

R

RAABE'S (or DUHAMEL'S) RATIO TEST. A test for the convergence or divergence of an infinite series: If the series is $u_1+u_2+u_3+\cdots+u_n+\cdots$, and $u_{n+1}/u_n=1/(1+a_n)$; then the series converges if after a certain term the product na_n is always greater than a fixed number which is greater than unity, and it diverges if after a certain term the same product is always less than unity.

RA'DI-AL-LY, *adv.* **radially related figures.** Figures which are central projections of each other; figures such that a line drawn from some fixed point to a point of one of them passes through a point of the other, such that the ratio of the distances from the fixed point to the two points is always the same (two similar figures can always be so placed). The fixed point is called the **homothetic center,** the **center of similitude,** or **ray center.** The ratio of the two line segments is called the **ray ratio, ratio of similitude** or **homothetic ratio.** Two radially related figures are similar. They are also called **homothetic figures.**

RA'DI-AN, *n.* A central angle subtended in a circle by an arc whose length is equal to the radius of the circle. Thus the **radian measure** of an angle is the ratio of the arc it subtends to the radius of the circle in which it is the central angle (a constant ratio for all such cir-

cles); also called circular measure, π measure (rare), natural measure (rare). 2π radians $=360°$, π *radians* $=180°$ or

1 *radian* $=(180/\pi)°$; $\tfrac{1}{4}\pi$ *radians* $=45°$, $\tfrac{1}{3}\pi$ *radians* $=60°$, $\tfrac{1}{2}\pi$ *radians* $=90°$. See SEXAGESIMAL, and MIL.

RA'DI-ATE, *v.* **radiate from a point.** To be a *ray* with the point as origin.

RAD'I-CAL, *adj.* **radical axis of two circles.** The locus of the equation resulting from eliminating the square term between the equations of the circles. When the circles intersect, the radical axis passes through their two points of intersection. *Tech.* The locus of the point whose *powers* with respect to the two circles are equal. See POWER—power of a point with reference to a circle.

radical axis of three spheres. The line of intersection of the three radical planes taken with respect to the three possible pairs of spheres. The line is finite if and only if the centers of the spheres do not lie on a straight line.

radical center of four spheres. The point of intersection of the six radical planes formed with respect to the six possible pairs of spheres made up from the given four. The point is finite if and only if the centers of the four spheres are not co-planar.

radical center of three circles. The point in which the three radical axes of the circles, taken in pairs, intersect. This point is finite if and only if the centers of the circles do not lie on a line.

radical plane of two spheres. The locus of the equation resulting from eliminating the square terms between the equations of the two spheres. When the spheres intersect the radical plane is the plane of their circle of intersection.

radical sign. The sign $\sqrt{\ }$ (a modified form of the letter *r*, the initial of the Latin *radix*, meaning root), placed before a quantity to denote that its root is to be extracted. To distinguish the particular root, a number (the **index**) is written over the sign: thus, $\sqrt[2]{\ }$, $\sqrt[3]{\ }$, $\sqrt[n]{\ }$, etc., denote respectively the square root, cube root, nth root, etc. In the case of the square root, the index is omitted, $\sqrt{\ }$ instead of $\sqrt[2]{\ }$ being written. The *radical sign* is frequently said to include a bar above the radicand as well as the above sign. This combination is written $\sqrt{}$.

RAD'I-CAL, *n.* (1) The indicated root of a quantity, as $\sqrt{2}$, $\sqrt{x}$. (2) The sign indicating a root to be taken, a *radical sign.*

　　simplification of radicals. See SIMPLIFICATION—simplification of radcals.

RAD-I-CAND', *n.* The quantity under a radical sign; as 2 in $\sqrt{2}$, or $a+b$ in $\sqrt{a+b}$.

RA'DI-US, *n.* [*pl.* radii.] **radius of a circle.** The distance from the center to the circumference.

　　long radius of a regular polygon. The distance from the center to a vertex; the radius of the circumscribed circle.

　　radius of curvature. See CURVATURE.

　　radius of gyration. The distance from a fixed line (point, or plane) to a point in, or near, a body where all of the mass of the body could be concentrated without altering the *moment of inertia* of the body about the line (point, or plane); the square root of the quotient of the moment of inertia by the mass.

　　radius vector. [*pl.* radii vectores; radius vectors.] See POLAR—polar coordinates, SPHERICAL—spherical coordinates.

　　short radius of a regular polygon. The perpendicular distance from the center to a side; the radius of the inscribed circle. *Syn.* Apothem.

RA'DIX, *n.* [*pl.* radices.] (1) A root. (2) Any number which is made the fundamental number or base of any system of numbers; thus, 10 is the radix of the decimal system of numeration. (3) A name sometimes given to the base of a system of logarithms. In the common system of logarithms the radix is 10; in the natural system it is $2.7182818284\cdots$, denoted by e.

　　radix fractions. Fractions of the form $a/r+b/r^2+c/r^3+d/r^4\cdots$, where the letters a, b, $\cdots$ are all integers less than r (which is also an integer). This is a generalization of decimals, for when r is 10 it reduces to a decimal fraction.

　　radix of a mortality table. The number of lives at the age with which the table starts.

RANGE, *n.* (*In statistics.*) The most general measure of dispersion; the difference between the greatest and the least of a set of quantities.

　　range of a variable. The set of values the variable may take. See FUNCTION—function of one variable.

RANK, *n.* **rank of a matrix.** See MATRIX.

RATE, *v.* or *n.* (1) Reckoning by comparative values or relations. (2) Relative amount, quantity, or degree; as, the *rate* of interest is 6 percent (i.e. $6 for every $100 for every year); the *rate* per mile of railroad charges; a rapid *rate* of growth.

　　bond rate. Same as DIVIDEND RATE.

　　central death rate. See CENTRAL.

　　corresponding rates. See CORRESPONDING—corresponding rates.

　　current rate. Same as PREVAILING INTEREST RATE.

　　death rate. See below, rate of mortality.

　　effective bond rate. The *prevailing*, or *current*, interest rate.

　　equivalent rates. Same as CORRESPONDING RATES.

　　income rate. Same as PREVAILING INTEREST RATE. See INTEREST.

　　interest rate. See INTEREST.

　　investor's (purchaser's) rate. The rate percent which the investor expects to make on his investment. Unless otherwise stated it is assumed to be the prevailing interest rate.

　　prevailing interest rate. See INTEREST.

　　rate of change of a function at a point. The limit of the ratio of an infinitesimal increment of the function at the point to that of the independent variable; the limit of the average rate of change over an interval including the point as the length of the interval approaches zero. This is sometimes called the **instantaneous rate of change** since the rates of change at neighboring points are in general different. The rate of change of a function at a point is the slope of the tangent to the graph of the function, the **derivative at the point.**

rate of mortality, or death rate. The probability that a person will die within one year after attaining a certain age; d_x/l_x, where d_x is the number dying during the year x and l_x is the number attaining the age x in the group on which the mortality table is based.

rate percent yield. See YIELD.

time rate of change. The rate of change relative to time; the speed or velocity. See SPEED and VELOCITY.

yield rate. Same as PREVAILING INTEREST RATE. See INTEREST.

RA'TIO, *n.* The quotient of two numbers (or quantities); the relative sizes of two numbers (or quantities).

cross ratio. If A, B, C, D are four distinct collinear points, the cross ratio (AB, CD) is defined as the quotient of the ratio in which C divides AB by the ratio in which D divides AB; if the abscissas (or ordinates) of the four points are x_1, x_2, x_3, x_4, the cross ratio is

$$\frac{(x_3-x_1)(x_4-x_2)}{(x_3-x_2)(x_4-x_1)}.$$

If no ordering of the four points will give a harmonic ratio (see below, harmonic ratio) there are, in general, six distinct values of the cross ratio, depending upon how the points are ordered.

cross ratio of four lines. If L_1, L_2, L_3, L_4 are four distinct concurrent lines with slopes equal to m_1, m_2, m_3, m_4, respectively, the cross ratio of the four lines is

$$\frac{(m_3-m_1)(m_4-m_2)}{(m_3-m_2)(m_4-m_1)}.$$

division ratio or ratio of division. See POINT—point of division.

generalized ratio test for convergence, or divergence, of an infinite series: If after some term in a given series the absolute value of the ratio of any term to the preceding is less than a fixed number less than unity, the series converges; if it is greater than unity, the series diverges. This is also called **d'Alembert's test.** Compare below, ratio test.

harmonic ratio. If the cross ratio of four points (or four lines) is equal to -1, it is called a **harmonic ratio** and the last two points are said to divide the first two **harmonically.**

internal and external ratio. See POINT—point of division.

inverse ratio of two quantities. The ratio of their reciprocals; the reciprocal of their ratio. The *inverse ratio* of 2 to 3 is $(\frac{1}{2})/(\frac{1}{3})=3/2$.

Raabe's ratio test. See RAABE'S RATIO TEST.

ratio of similitude. The ratio of the lengths of corresponding lines of similar figures; the *ray ratio* (see RADIALLY—radially related figures). Also called *homothetic ratio.*

ratio test for convergence, or divergence, of an infinite series: A series converges or diverges according as the absolute value of the limit, as n becomes infinite, of the ratio of the nth to the $(n-1)$th term is less than or greater than one. If it is equal to one, the test fails. E.g. (1) For the series
$$1+1/2!+1/3!+\cdots+1/n!+\cdots,$$
the ratio of the nth to the $(n-1)$th term is

$$(1/n!)/[1/(n-1)!]=1/n, \text{ and } \lim_{n\to\infty}(1/n)=0.$$

Hence the series converges. (2) For the harmonic series,

$$1+1/2+1/3+\cdots+1/n+\cdots$$

the ratio is

$$(1/n)/[1/(n-1) =(n-1)/n$$
$$\lim_{n\to\infty}(n-1)/n=1$$
and

hence the test fails. However, this series diverges, as can be shown by grouping the terms so that each group equals or exceeds $\frac{1}{2}$, namely

$$1+\tfrac{1}{2}+(\tfrac{1}{3}+\tfrac{1}{4})+(\tfrac{1}{5}+\tfrac{1}{6}+\tfrac{1}{7}+\tfrac{1}{8})+\cdots.$$

Also called **Cauchy's ratio test.**

ray ratio. See RADIALLY—radially related figures.

reciprocal ratio. Same as INVERSE RATIO.

RA'TION-AL, *adj.* **integration of a rational fraction.** The process of integration which consists of breaking the fraction into partial fractions (unless the fraction is itself readily integrable) and integrating these separately. See PARTIAL—partial fractions.

rational expression. An algebraic expression which involves no variable in an irreducible radical or under a fractional exponent. The expressions $2x^2+1$, and $2x+1/x$, are *rational*, but $\sqrt{x+1}$ and $x^{3/2}+1$ are not.

rational fraction. See FRACTION—rational fraction.

rational function. An algebraic function in which the variable (or variables) do not appear in an irreducible radical or with fractional exponents (the coefficients need not be rational). $2x^2+x\sqrt{y}+\sqrt{3}$ is rational in x (but neither in y nor in x and y together).

rational integral function. A function containing only rational and integral terms in the variable (or variables). A function may be rational and integral in one or more of the variables while it is not in others; e.g. $w+x^2+2xy^{1/2}+1/z$ is rational and integral in x and in w and x together, but not rational in y and not integral in z. See TERM—rational, integral term. *Syn.* Polynomial.

rational number. A number that can be expressed as an integer or as a quotient of integers.

RA′TION·AL·I·ZA′TION, *n.* The process of rationalizing.

rationalization of integrals. Making a substitution (changing variables) so that the radicals in the integrand disappear; the integral

$$\int \frac{x^{1/2}}{1+x^{3/4}}\,dx \text{ is } rationalized \text{ into } \int \frac{4z^5}{1+z^3}\,dz$$

by the substitution $x = z^4$ $(dx = 4z^3 dz)$.

RA′TION·AL·IZE, *v.* To remove radicals without altering the value of an expression, or the roots of an equation.

rationalize an algebraic equation. To remove the radicals which contain the variable (not always possible). A procedure that sometimes suffices is to isolate the radical in one member of the equation (or if there be more than one radical, to arrange them to the best advantage) and raise both sides to a

power equal to the index of the radical (or one of the radicals), repeating this process if necessary. (Extraneous roots may be introduced by this procedure.) E.g. (1) $\sqrt{x-1} = x-2$ rationalizes into $x-1 = x^2-4x+4$ or $x^2-5x+5=0$; (2) $\sqrt{x-1}+2 = \sqrt{x+1}$ is written $\sqrt{x-1}-\sqrt{x+1} = -2$; squaring gives $x-1 -2\sqrt{x^2-1}+x+1 = 4$ or $\sqrt{x^2-1} = x-2$, whence $x^2-1 = x^2-4x+4$ or $4x-5 = 0$.

rationalize the denominator of a fraction. To multiply numerator and denominator by a factor that will remove the radical in the denominator. E.g. if the fraction is $\dfrac{1}{\sqrt{a}+\sqrt{b}}$ the rationalizing factor is $\sqrt{a}-\sqrt{b}$ and we obtain $\dfrac{\sqrt{a}-\sqrt{b}}{a-b}$ if the fraction is $\dfrac{1}{\sqrt[3]{c^2}}$, the rationalizing factor is $\sqrt[3]{c}$ and we obtain $\dfrac{\sqrt[3]{c}}{c}$.

RAY, *n.* A straight line extending from a point. The point is called the **origin** of the ray.

ray center. Same as CENTER OF PROJECTION. See PROJECTION—central projection, and RADIALLY—radially related figures.

ray ratio. See RADIALLY—radially related figures.

REAL, *adj.* **real algebraic number.** (1) An ordinary positive or negative number. Usually called *algebraic number*. (2) An *algebraic number* which is real; see NUMBER—algebraic number, (2).

real continuum. See CONTINUUM.

real number. Ordinary rational and irrational numbers; numbers that do not contain an even root of a negative number, as contrasted to imaginary numbers.

real number system. All rational and irrational numbers.

real part of a complex number. The term which does not contain the imaginary factor, i, $= \sqrt{-1}$. If the number is $z = x+iy$ (where x and y are real) the real part is x, sometimes denoted by $R(z)$.

real plane. A plane in which all

points are assigned real numbers for coordinates, as contrasted to the *complex plane.*

real variable. A variable which takes only real numbers for its values.

real zero of a polynomial. A real value of the variable for which the polynomial is zero; a value of the variable for which the graph of the polynomial crosses the axis of abscissas.

REALS, *n.* **axis of reals.** A straight line upon which the real numbers are plotted; the horizontal axis in an Argand diagram. See COORDINATE—complex coordinates, and ARGAND DIAGRAM.

REAM, *n.* A measure of paper; twenty quires. See DENOMINATE NUMBERS in the appendix.

RE-CEIPT', *n.* (*Finance.*) (1) The act of receiving payment in money or goods. (2) A statement acknowledging money or goods having been received.

RE-CEIPTS', *n.* Money or other assets taken in, as contrasted to expenditures.

RE-CEIV'A-BLE, *adj.* See NOTE—note receivable.

RE-CIP'RO-CAL, *adj.* or *n.* **polar reciprocal curves:** If two curves are so related that the polar, with respect to a given conic, of every point on one of them is tangent to the other, then the polars of the points on the latter are tangent to the former, and the two curves are called **polar reciprocals** with respect to the given conic.

reciprocal curve of a curve. The curve obtained by replacing each ordinate of a given curve by its reciprocal; the graph of the equation gotten from the given equation (in Cartesian coordinates) by replacing y by $1/y$. The graphs of $y = 1/x$ and $y = x$ are reciprocals of each other; so are the graphs of $y = \sin x$ and $y = \operatorname{cosec} x$.

reciprocal equation. An equation in one variable whose set of roots remains unchanged if the roots are replaced by their reciprocals; an algebraic equation which is unchanged if the unknown is replaced by its reciprocal. E.g. when x is replaced by $1/x$, $x + 1 = 0$ becomes $1 + x = 0$, and $x^4 - ax^3 + bx^2 - ax + 1 = 0$ becomes $1 - ax + bx^2 - ax^3 + x^4 = 0$.

reciprocal of a fraction. The fraction formed by interchanging the numerator and denominator in the given fraction; unity (1) divided by the fraction.

reciprocal of a number (or any quantity). Unity divided by that number (or quantity); one over the number (or quantity). The reciprocal of 2 is $\frac{1}{2}$, the reciprocal of x is $1/x$.

reciprocal polar figures in the plane. Two plane figures made up of lines and their points of intersection, and such that all points in either one of them are poles of lines in the other. See POLE—pole and polar of a conic, and below, reciprocal polar triangles.

reciprocal polar triangles. Two plane triangles such that the vertices of either one of them are the poles of the sides of the other with respect to some conic. See POLE—pole and polar of a conic.

reciprocal proportion. See INVERSE—inverse or reciprocal proportion.

reciprocal quantities. Two quantities whose product is unity: as 2 and $\frac{1}{2}$ or $(x + 1)$ and $1/(x + 1)$.

reciprocal ratio. See INVERSE—inverse or reciprocal ratio.

reciprocal spiral. See HYPERBOLIC—hyperbolic spiral.

reciprocal substitution. The substitution of a new variable for the reciprocal of the old; a substitution such as $y = 1/x$.

reciprocal theorems. (1) In *plane geometry*, theorems such that the interchanging of two geometric elements such as angles and sides, points and lines, etc. transfers each of the theorems into the other. Two such theorems are not always simultaneously true or false. (2) In *projective geometry*, same as DUAL THEOREMS.

REC'TAN'GLE, *n.* A parallelogram with one angle a right angle; a quadrilateral whose angles are all right angles.

altitude of a rectangle. See ALTITUDE—altitude of a parallelogram.

area of a rectangle. The product of two adjacent sides. If a rectangle has two sides of length 2 and 3, respectively, its area is 6. See AREA.

diagonal of a rectangle. A line joining opposite vertices. If the sides are of length a and b, the length of the diagonal is $\sqrt{a^2+b^2}$.

perimeter of a rectangle. The sum of the lengths of its sides; twice the sum of the lengths of two adjacent sides.

REC-TAN′GU-LAR, *adj.* Like a rectangle; mutually perpendicular.

rectangular axes. See CARTESIAN.

rectangular Cartesian coordinates. See CARTESIAN, and COORDINATE—coordinate planes.

rectangular coordinates of a point. Same as RECTANGULAR CARTESIAN COORDINATES of the point.

rectangular form of a complex number. The form $x+yi$, as distinguished from the polar or trigonometric form $r(\cos\theta+i\sin\theta)$.

rectangular graphs. Same as BAR GRAPHS. See GRAPH.

rectangular hyperbola. See HYPERBOLA—rectangular hyperbola.

rectangular solid. A solid all of whose faces are rectangles; a right prism whose bases are rectangles; a rectangular parallelepiped.

REC′TI-FI′A-BLE, *adj.* rectifiable curve. A curve whose length can be found by calculus methods. See ARC—length of arc of a curve.

REC′TI-LIN′E-AR, *adj.* (1) Consisting of lines. (2) Bounded by lines.

rectilinear generators. See RULED —ruled surface, HYPERBOLOID— hyperboloid of one sheet, and PARABOLOID—hyperbolic paraboloid.

rectilinear motion. Motion along a straight line. See VELOCITY—rectilinear velocity.

RE-CUR′RING, *adj.* recurring continued fraction. See FRACTION—continued fraction.

recurring decimal. Same as REPEATING DECIMAL.

RE-DEEM′, *v.* To repurchase, to release by making payments. To redeem a note, bond, or mortage means to pay the sum it calls for. To redeem property means to get ownership by paying off lapsed liability for which it was security.

RE-DEMP′TION, *n.* The act of redeeming.

redemption price of a bond or other promise to pay. The face value, unless otherwise stipulated.

RE-DUCED′, *adj.* reduced cubic equation. A cubic equation of the form $y^3+py+q=0$; the form that the general cubic, $x^3+ax^2+bx+c=0$, takes when the x^2 term is removed. (This term is removed by substituting $y-\frac{1}{3}a$ for x.)

reduced form of the quadratic equation. The form $x^2+px+q=0$. It is distinguished from the general form in that it has one for the coefficient of x^2, which generally simplifies the process of completing the square. *Syn.* p-form of the quadratic.

REDUCTIO AD ABSURDUM PROOF. The method of proof which shows that it is impossible for that which is to be proved to be false because if it is false some accepted facts are contradicted; in other words the method which supposes that the contrary to the fact to be proved is true and then shows that this supposition leads to an absurdity. E.g. accepting the axiom that only one line can be drawn through a given point parallel to a given line, prove that if two lines are parallel to a third line they are parallel to each other. Assume that the two lines are not parallel, that is, intersect in a point; we then have two lines through a point parallel to a third line, which contradicts the axiom. *Syn.* Indirect proof.

RE-DUC′TION, *n.* (1) A diminution or decreasing, as a reduction of 10% in the price. (2) The act of changing to a different form, by collecting terms, powering equations, simplifying fractions, making substitutions, etc.

reduction ascending. Changing a denominate number into one of higher order, as feet and inches into yards.

reduction of a common fraction to a decimal. Annexation of a decimal point and zeros to the numerator and dividing (usually approximately) by the denominator. E.g.

$$\frac{1}{4}=\frac{1.00}{4}=.25; \quad \frac{2}{3}=\frac{2.000}{3}=.667-.$$

reduction descending. Changing a denominate number into one of lower order, as yards and feet into inches.

reduction of an expression or equation. See REDUCTION, (2).

reduction formulas in integration. Formulas expressing an integral as the sum of certain functions and a simpler integral. Such formulas are most commonly derived by *integration by parts.*

reduction formulas of trigonometry. Formulas stating the values of the trigonometric functions of angles greater than 90° in terms of functions of angles less than 90°. The formulas for the sine, cosine, and tangent are:

$$\sin\ (90°\pm A)=\cos A,$$
$$\sin\ (180°\pm A)=\mp\sin A,$$
$$\sin\ (270°\pm A)=-\cos A,$$
$$\cos\ (90°\pm A)=\mp\sin A,$$
$$\cos\ (180°\pm A)=-\cos A,$$
$$\cos\ (270°\pm A)=\pm\sin A,$$
$$\tan\ (90°\pm A)=\mp\cot A,$$
$$\tan\ (180°\pm A)=\pm\tan A,$$
$$\tan\ (270°\pm A)=\mp\cot A,$$

where, in each formula, either the upper signs, or the lower, are to be used throughout.

reduction of a fraction to its lowest terms. The process of dividing all common factors out of numerator and denominator.

reduction to the normal form of an equation of a plane in rectangular coordinates. Dividing all the coefficients by the square root of the sum of the squares of the coefficients of the variables, the radical having its sign opposite that of the constant term (compare below, *reduction to normal form* of an equation of a straight line). See PLANE—equation of a plane.

reduction to normal form of an equation of a straight line in rectangular coordinates. The multiplication of the equation by a constant that will put it into the normal form, $x \cos \omega + y \sin \omega - p = 0$ (see LINE—equation of a straight line). The proper multiplier is the reciprocal of the square root of the sum of the squares of the coefficients of x and y with the sign of the radical taken opposite the sign of the constant term in the given equation when all terms are on one side of the equality sign. To reduce $3x - 4y + 5 = 0$ to the normal form, multiply the equation by $-\frac{1}{5}$, getting $-\frac{3}{5}x + \frac{4}{5}y - 1 = 0$. (It is sometimes required that the angle in the normal form be less than 180°, in which case the sign of the coefficient of y is taken as positive, or the coefficient of x positive if y doesn't appear.)

reduction of the roots of an equation. Same as DIMINUTION of the roots of an equation.

RE-DUN'DANT, *adj.* **redundant equation.** See EQUATION—redundant equation.

redundant number. See NUMBER —redundant number.

REENTRANT ANGLE. See ANGLE.

REF'ER-ENCE, *n.* **axis of reference.** One of the axes of a Cartesian coordinate system, or the polar axis in a polar coordinate system; in general, any line used to aid in determining the location of points, either in the plane or in space.

frame of reference. See FRAME.

REFINEMENT OF RESULTS. The statement of angles accurate to an agreed fraction of a degree, of numbers to an agreed number of decimal places, etc.

RE-FLEC'TION, *n.* (*Physics.*) The change of direction which a ray of light, radiant heat, or sound experiences when it strikes upon a surface and is thrown back into the same medium from which it approached. Reflection follows two laws: (1) the reflected and incident rays are in a plane normal to the surface; (2) the angle of incidence is equal to the angle of reflection (the **angle of incidence** is the angle the incident ray makes with the normal at the point of incidence; the **angle of reflection** is the angle which the reflected ray makes with this normal).

reflection in an axis. The transformation: $x' = x$, $y' = -y$, or $x' = -x$, $y' = y$. Each given point is replaced by a point symmetric to the given point with respect to the axis in which the reflection is made, the x-axis and y-axis, respectively, in the above transformations.

reflection in any line. Replacing each point in the reflected configuration by a point symmetric to the given point with respect to the line.

reflection in the origin. Replacing each point by a point symmetric to the given point with respect to the origin; a rotation through 180°; the result of successive reflections in each axis of a rectangular system of coordinates. See above, reflection in an axis.

reflection property of the ellipse. The property that a ray of light from one focus is reflected by the ellipse through the other focus; that the normal to the ellipse at a given point bisects the angle between the focal radii at that point. Owing to this property, a light at one focus of an ellipse appears to be at the other focus also.

reflection property of a hyperbola. The property that a reflected ray of light from one focus appears to have come from the other focus; that the angle between a normal to a hyperbola at a point and one focal radius is bisected by the other focal radius.

reflection property of the parabola. The property of the parabola that a ray of light from the focus is reflected parallel to the axis; that the normal to a parabola at the point of tangency bisects the angle between the focal radius of that point and the line parallel to the axis and passing through that point.

RE′FLEX, *adj.* **reflex angle.** An angle greater than 180° and less than 360°.

RE-FLEX′IVE, *adj.* **anti-reflexive relation.** A relation which is *not* reflexive. The relation of being greater than is *anti-reflexive*, since it is not true for any x that $x > x$.

non-reflexive relation. A relation

which may or may not be reflexive. The relation of *being the reciprocal of* is *non-reflexive*, since x may or may not be the reciprocal of x, according as x is equal to unity or is not equal to unity.

reflexive relation. A relation of which it is true that, for any x, x bears the given relation to itself. The relation of equality in arithmetic is *reflexive*, since $x = x$, for all x.

RE-FRAC′TION, *n.* (*Physics.*) A change of direction of rays (as of light, heat or sound) which are obliquely incident upon and pass through a surface bounding two media in which the ray has different velocities (as light going from air to water). It is found that for isotropic media: (1) When passing into a denser medium, the ray is refracted toward a perpendicular to the surface, and when passing into a less dense medium, it is bent away from the perpendicular; (2) the incident and refracted rays are in the same plane; (3) the sines of the angle of incidence and the angle of refraction bear a constant ratio to each other for any two given media (the **angles of incidence** and **refraction** are the angles which the incident and refracted ray make, respectively, with the perpendicular to the surface). If the first medium is air, this ratio is called the **index of refraction** or the **refractive index** of the second medium. The law stated in (3) is known as **Snell's law.**

RE′GION, *n*, simply and multiply connected regions. See SIMPLY—simply connected region.

RE-GRES′SION, *n*, equation of linear regression. See LINEAR.

line of regression. See LINE—line of regression.

REGULA FALSI (rule of false position). The method of calculating an unknown (as a root of a number) by making an estimate (or estimates) and working from it and properties of the unknown to secure the value of the latter. If one estimate is used, it is called **simple position;** if two, **double position.** Double position is used in approximating irrational roots of an equation and in approximating logarithms of numbers which contain more significant digits than are listed in the tables being used. The method assumes that small arcs are approximately coincident with the chords which join their extremities. This makes the changes in the abscissas proportional to the changes in the corresponding ordinates; e.g. if y, $=f(x)$, has the value -4 when x is 2 and the value 8 when x is 3, then the chord joining the points whose coordinates are (2, -4) and (3, 8) crosses the x-axis at a point whose abscissa x is such that $\frac{1}{4}(x-2)=\frac{1}{8}(3-x)$, which gives $x=2\frac{1}{3}$ as an approximate value of a root of $f(x)=0$. *Newton's method* for approximating roots is an example of *simple position* (see NEWTON).

REG'U-LAR, *adj.* **regular polygon.** A polygon with its sides all equal and its interior angles all equal. See TWO —two-fold, three-fold, and n-fold symmetry.

regular curve. A curve all of whose points are ordinary points. See POINT —ordinary point on a curve.

regular polyhedron. See POLY-HEDRON—regular polyhedron.

regular sequence. A *convergent sequence*. See SEQUENCE—convergence of a sequence.

REJECTING FIGURES. Discarding figures when *rounding off* a number. See ROUNDING OFF NUMBERS.

RE-LAT'ED, *adj.* **related angle.** The acute angle (angle in the first quadrant) for which the trigonometric functions have the same absolute values as for a given angle in another quadrant, with reference to which the acute angle is called the *related angle;* 30° is the related angle of 150° and of 210°.

related expressions or functions. Same as DEPENDENT FUNCTIONS, but less commonly used. See DEPENDENT.

RE-LA'TION, *n.* Equality, inequality, ratio, proportion, etc.; any dependence of one quantity upon another. See FUNCTION.

anti-reflexive, non-reflexive, and reflexive relation. See REFLEXIVE.

asymmetric, non-symmetric, and symmetric relations. See SYMMETRIC, and ASYMMETRIC RELATION.

fundamental relations of trigonometry. See TRIGONOMETRIC—relations between the trigonometric functions.

intransitive, non-transitive, and transitive relations. See TRANSITIVE.

relation between the roots and coefficients of a quadratic equation. The sum of the roots is equal to the negative of the coefficient of the first degree term and the product is equal to the constant term, when the coefficient of the square term is 1. In $ax^2+bx+c=0$, the sum of the roots is $-b/a$ and the product is c/a.

relation between the roots and coefficients of an algebraic equation. If the equation is of the nth degree and the coefficient of the nth degree term is unity, the sum of the roots is the negative of the coefficient of x^{n-1}, the sum of the products of the roots taken two at a time in every possible way is the coefficient of x^{n-2}, the sum of the products of the roots taken three at a time is the negative of the coefficient of x^{n-3}, etc.; finally the product of all the roots is the constant term with a positive or negative sign according as n is even or odd. If $r_1, r_2, \cdots, r_n$ are the roots of

$$x^n+a_1x^{n-1}+a_2x^{n-2}+\cdots+a_n=0,$$

then $r_1+r_2+\cdots+r_n=-a_1,$

$$r_1r_2+r_1r_3+\cdots+r_1r_n+r_2r_3+\cdots+r_{n-1}r_n=a_2,$$

. . . .

and finally $r_1r_2r_3\cdots r_n=(-1)^na_n$.

relation between the zeros and the factors of an algebraic polynomial. If r is a zero of the polynomial, then $(x-r)$ is a factor, and conversely. The polynomial x^2-4x+3 has the zeros 1 and 3, hence factors into $(x-1)(x-3)$. See FACTOR—factor theorem.

REL'A-TIVE, *adj.* **relative frequency.** See FREQUENCY—relative frequency.

relative maximum and minimum. See MAXIMUM.

relative velocity. See VELOCITY—relative velocity.

RE-MAIN'DER, *n.* (1) In *arithmetic,* the part of the dividend left when it does not contain the divisor an exact (integral) number of times (17 divided by 5 equals 3, with a *remainder* of 2); the minuend minus the subtrahend in subtraction (also called the *difference*). (2) In *algebra,* a polynomial (or monomial) of lower degree than the divisor and equal to the dividend minus the product of the quotient and divisor (when the divisor is of the first degree the *remainder* is a constant). See below, remainder theorem.

remainder of an infinite series after the nth term. (1) The difference between the sum, S, of the series and the sum, S_n, of n terms, i.e. $R_n = S - S_n$, when the series is known to converge. (2) The difference between the sum of the first n terms of the series and the quantity (or function) whose expansion is sought; see TAYLOR'S THEOREM, and FOURIER SERIES. The series converges and represents the quantity or function for all values of the independent variable for which the remainder converges to zero.

remainder, after the nth term, in Taylor's series. The difference between the function and the sum of n terms of the series given for the function by Taylor's Theorem. See TAYLOR'S THEOREM.

remainder theorem. When a polynomial in x is divided by $x - h$, the remainder is equal to the number obtained by substituting h for x in the polynomial. More concisely, $f(x) = (x-h)q(x) + f(h)$, where $q(x)$ is the quotient and $f(h)$ the remainder, which is easily verified by substituting h for x. E.g. $(x^2 + 2x + 3) \div (x-1)$ leaves a remainder of $1^2 + 2 \times 1 + 3$, or 6.

RE-MOV'A-BLE, *adj.* removable discontinuity. See DISCONTINUITY.

RE-MOV'AL, *n.* removal of a term of an equation. Transforming the equation into a form having this term missing. See ROTATION—rotation of

rectangular axes, TRANSLATION—translation of axes, and REDUCED—reduced cubic.

RENT, *n.* (1) A sum of money paid at regular intervals in return for the use of property or non-perishable goods. (2) The periodic payments of an annuity.

rent period. The period between successive payments of rent.

RENTES, *n.* French perpetuity bonds.

RE-PEAT'ED, *adj.* repeated root. See MULTIPLE—multiple root.

probability of the occurrence of an event in a number of repeated trials. (1) The probability that an event will happen *exactly r times* in n trials, for which p is the probability of its happening and q of its failing in any given trial, is given by the formula $n! p^r q^{n-r} / [r!(n-r)!]$, which is the $(n-r+1)$th term in the expansion of $(p+q)^n$. The probability of throwing exactly two aces in five throws of a die is

$$5!(\tfrac{1}{6})^2(\tfrac{5}{6})^3/(2!3!) = .16+$$

(2) The probability that an event will happen *at least r times* in n throws is the probability that it will happen every time plus the probability that it will happen exactly $n-1$ times, $n-2$ times, etc., to exactly r times. This probability is given by the sum of the first $n-r+1$ terms of the expansion of $(p+q)^n$.

REPEATING DECIMAL. See DECIMAL—repeating decimal.

RE-PLACE'MENT, *n.* replacement cost of equipment. (1) The cost of new equipment minus the scrap value. (2) The purchase price minus scrap value.

RE-SERVE' *n.* (*In life insurance.*) The accumulated balance of the premiums minus the cost of the insurance.

deficiency, or premium deficiency, reserve. A reserve equal to the difference between the present value of future net premiums and future gross premiums. Required in most states when gross premium is less than net premium.

initial reserve. The reserve at the beginning of a policy year just after the premium has been received.

mean reserve. The average of the initial and terminal reserves for the year under consideration.

net premium reserve. When the net premium is the same throughout the life of the policy, the early premiums are larger and the late smaller than the natural premiums. The net premium reserve is the accumulation of the early surplus.

prospective method of computing reserves. See PROSPECTIVE.

retrospective method of computing reserves. See RETROSPECTIVE.

terminal reserve of an insurance policy. The reserve at the end of any policy year, before the next premium has been paid.

RE-SID'U-AL, *adj.* **residual error.** The differences between the true value (best known value) of a quantity and the observed values. If y represents the true value of a function and y_1, y_2, y_3 are observed values, the residuals are $y - y_1$, $y - y_2$, $y - y_3$. These are often called simply **residuals.** *Syn.* Deviation.

RE-SIST'ANCE, *n.* **electrical resistance.** That property of a conductor which causes the passage of an electric current through it to be accompanied by the transformation of electric energy into heat.

RE-SOL'VENT, *adj.* **resolvent cubic.** See FERRARI'S solution of the general quartic.

RE-SULT', *n.* The end sought in a computation or proof.

refinement of results. See REFINEMENT OF RESULTS.

RE-SULT'ANT, *n.* **resultant of a set of** $n+1$ **equations in** n **variables.** The relation between the coefficients, which is obtained by eliminating the n variables. *Syn.* Eliminant. See ELIMINATION—elimination of n variables from $n+1$ equations.

resultant of two or more forces (velocities, accelerations, etc.). That force (velocity, acceleration, etc.), whose effect is equivalent to the several forces (velocities, accelerations, etc.); see PARALLELOGRAM—parallelogram of forces. The resultant is

the closing side, with direction reversed, of the open vector polygon whose sides represent the forces and are taken with the initial end of each vector on the terminal end of another.

RET'RO-SPEC'TIVE, *adj.* **retrospective method of computing reserves in insurance.** The method starting with consideration of the fact that in the early years of the life of a policy the net level premium is more than sufficient to pay the annual cost of the insurance, while in the later years they are insufficient. See PROSPECTIVE METHOD.

RE-TURNS', *n.* (*Finance.*) Profits, dividends, interest, and sometimes principal or part of principal, paid to an investor.

RE-VERSE', *adj.* Backwards. A series of steps in a computation are taken in *reverse order* when the last is taken first, the next to last second, etc.; a finite sequence of terms are in *reverse order* when the last is made first, etc.

RE-VER'SION, *adj.* **reversion of a series.** The process of expressing x as a series in y, having given y expressed as a series in x.

RE-VER'SION-AR'Y, *adj.* **contingent reversionary life interest.** See CONTINGENT.

reversionary annuity. An annuity to be paid during the life of one person, beginning with the death of another.

reversionary, compound reversionary, and uniform reversionary bonus. See BONUS.

reversionary life interest. See LIFE —reversionary life interest.

REV'O-LU'TION, *n.* **axis of revolution.** See SOLID—solid of revolution.

cone of revolution. A right circular cone. See CONE—cone of revolution.

cylinder of revolution. A right circular cylinder. See CYLINDER—right circular cylinder.

element (differential) of volume of a solid of revolution. See ELEMENT—element of volume of a solid of revolution.

ellipsoid of revolution. See ELLIPSOID.

solid of revolution. See SOLID— solid of revolution.

surface of revolution. See SUR-FACE—surface of revolution.

RE-VOLVE′, *v.* To rotate about an axis or point. One would speak of revolving a figure in the plane about the origin, through an angle of a given size, or of *revolving* a curve in space about the *x*-axis with the understanding that the revolution is through an angle of 360° unless otherwise stipulated. See SUR-FACE—surface of revolution.

RHOM′BOID, *n.* A parallelogram with adjacent sides not equal.

RHOM′BUS, *n.* A parallelogram with adjacent sides equal (all of its sides are then necessarily equal). Some authors require that a rhombus not be a square, but the preference seems to be to call the square a special case of the rhombus.

RHUMB LINE. The path of a ship sailing so as to cut the meridians at a constant angle; a spiral on the earth's surface, winding around a pole and cutting the meridians at a constant angle. *Syn.* Loxodromic spiral.

RIDGE, *n.* **ridge of a roof.** The line along which the upper ends of the rafters meet; the highest part of the roof.

RIGHT, *adj.* **condition that a directed tri-rectangular trihedral be right-handed.** See TRIHEDRAL—condition that a directed trihedral be tri-rectangular.

diagonal of a right prism. A line joining two vertices, but not lying in a face. There are four of these.

right angle. See ANGLE—right angle.

right dihedral angle. See PLANE— plane angle of a dihedral angle.

right-handed coordinate system. See COORDINATE—right-handed coordinate system.

right-handed trihedral. A directed trihedral with an order given to the lines, which is such that if the thumb of the right hand extends along and in the positive direction of the first line, the fingers fold in the direction in which the second line could be rotated about the first line to coincide with the third, the angle of rotation being 90° if the coordinate system is rectangular, and in any case less than 180°.

right line. A straight line.

right section of a cylinder. See CYLINDER—right circular cylinder.

right spherical triangle. See SPHER-ICAL—right spherical triangle.

right triangle. See TRIANGLE— right triangle.

solution of a right triangle. See SO-LUTION—solution of a plane right triangle.

RIG′ID, *adj.* **rigid motion.** Moving a configuration into another position, but making no change in its shape or size; a rotational transformation followed by a translation, or the two taken in reverse order or simultaneously. Superposition of figures in plane geometry is a *rigid motion*.

RING, *n.* **ring surface, torus ring.** Same as ANCHOR RING. See ANCHOR.

RISE, *n.* **rise between two points.** The difference in elevation of the two points. See RUN.

rise of a roof. (1) The vertical distance from the plates to the ridge of the roof. (2) The vertical distance from the lowest to the highest point of the roof.

ROLLE'S THEOREM: If a curve crosses the *x*-axis at two points and has a unique tangent at all points between these two *x*-intercepts, it has a tangent parallel to the *x*-axis at at least one point between the two intercepts. *Tech.* If $f(x)$ is a single-valued function and vanishes for $x = a$ and $x = b$ and has derivatives at all points on (a, b), then $f'(x)$ vanishes at some point between and distinct from a and b. (It may also vanish at a or b or both.) E.g. the sine curve crosses the *x*-axis at the origin and at $x = \pi$, and has a tangent parallel to the *x*-axis at $x = \frac{1}{2}\pi$ (radians).

RO'MAN, *adj.* **Roman numerals.** A system of writing integers, used by the Romans, in which I denotes 1; V, 5; X, 10; L, 50; C, 100; D, 500; M, 1000. All integers are then written using the following rules: (1) When a letter is repeated or immediately followed by a letter of lesser value, the values are added. (2) When a letter is immediately followed by a letter of greater value, the smaller is subtracted from the larger. The integers from 1 to 10 are written: I, II, III, IIII or IV, V, VI, VII, VIII, IX, X. The tens are written: X, XX, XXX, XL, L, LX, LXX, LXXX, XC, C. Hundreds are written: C, CC, CCC, CD, D, DC, DCC, DCCC, CM, M.

ROOT, *n.* **approximate root of an equation or of a number.** A root accurate only to a certain number of decimal places.

changing the signs of the roots of an equation. Finding the equation whose roots are the negatives of the roots of the given equation. This can be accomplished by replacing the unknown by its negative.

condition that the roots of a quadratic equation be equal. See DISCRIMINANT—discriminant of a quadratic equation in one variable.

diminution of roots. See DIMINUTION.

equal roots of an equation. See MULTIPLE—multiple root of an equation.

infinite root of an algebraic equation. A root of an algebraic equation which is infinite because one (or more) of the coefficients approaches zero. If in the equation $ax + 2 = 0$, a approaches 0, the root $x = -2/a$ becomes infinite.

isolating a root. See ISOLATING.

limits to the real roots of an equation. See LIMIT—inferior limit to the roots of an equation, and superior limit to the roots of an equation.

location of roots. See LOCATION THEOREM.

nth root of a number. A number which when taken as a factor n times (raised to the nth power) produces the given number. There are n nth roots of any number. If n is odd and the number real, there is one real root; e.g. the cube roots of 27 are 3 and $\frac{3}{2}(-1 \pm \sqrt{-3})$. If n is even and the number positive, there are two real roots, numerically equal but opposite in sign; e.g. the 4th roots of 4 are $\pm\sqrt{2}$ and $\pm\sqrt{-2}$. See RADICAL.

root of a complex number. If the number is written in the form

$$r[\cos \theta + i \sin \theta]$$

or the equivalent form

$$r[\cos (2k\pi + \theta) + i \sin (2k\pi + \theta)],$$

its nth roots are the numbers

$$\sqrt[n]{r}\left[\cos \frac{(2k\pi + \theta)}{n} + i \sin \frac{(2k\pi + \theta)}{n}\right],$$

where k takes on the values 0, 1, 2, $\cdots$, $(n-1)$ and $\sqrt[n]{r}$ is an nth root of the real positive number r. See DEMOIVRE'S THEOREM.

root of an equation. A number which when substituted for the unknown in the equation reduces it to an identity; a root of the equation $x^2 + 3x - 10 = 0$ is 2, since $2^2 + 3 \cdot 2 - 10 = 0$. A root of an equation is said to *satisfy the equation* or to be a *solution* of the equation, but *solution* more often refers to the process of finding the root.

root mean square deviation. See DEVIATION—standard deviation.

roots of a quadratic equation. See COMPLETING THE SQUARE, and QUADRATIC—quadratic formula.

simple root. See SIMPLE—simple root.

square root of a number. A number which when multiplied by itself produces the given number. There are always two of these, the sign before the radical indicating whether the positive, negative, or both is meant; $\sqrt{4} = 2$, $-\sqrt{4} = -2$ and $\pm\sqrt{4} = \pm 2$. See MECHANIC'S RULE.

triple root. See TRIPLE—triple root.

ROSE-LEAFED CURVES. See THREE—three-leafed rose, FOUR-LEAFED ROSE, and N-LEAFED ROSE.

RO-TA'TION, *n.* **rotation about a line.**
Movement about the line of such a
kind that every point in the figure
moves in a circular path about the
line in a plane perpendicular to the
line.

rotation about a point. Movement
in a circular path (in a plane) about
the point.

**rotation of the coordinate trihedral
or rotation of axes in space.** Moving
the coordinate trihedral in any manner
which leaves the origin fixed and keeps
the axes in the same relative position.
The coordinates of a point are transformed from those referred to one system of rectangular axes to coordinates
referred to another system of axes
having the same origin but different
directions and making certain given
angles with the original axes. If the
direction angles, with respect to the
old axes, of the new x-axis (the x'-axis)
are A_1, B_1, C_1; of the y'-axis are A_2,
B_2, C_2; and of the z'-axis, A_3, B_3, C_3,
then the formulas for rotation of axes
in space are:

$$x = x' \cos A_1 + y' \cos A_2 + z' \cos A_3,$$
$$y = x' \cos B_1 + y' \cos B_2 + z' \cos B_3,$$
$$z = x' \cos C_1 + y' \cos C_2 + z' \cos C_3.$$

**rotation of rectangular axes in the
plane.** Rotation of the axes about the
origin in such a manner that the new
set of axes has the same origin, but its
axes make a given angle with the axes
of the old system. Such a transformation of axes is a matter of convenience
in studying curves and does not alter
them intrinsically (it is a rigid motion,
preserving the size and shape of all
figures). For instance, by a proper rotation of the coordinate axes they can be
made parallel to the axes of any ellipse
or hyperbola, or one of them parallel
to the axis of a parabola, thus in all
cases making the term in their equations which contains xy disappear.
The **formulas for rotation (rotation
formulas)** which give the relations
between the coordinates (x', y') of a
point with reference to a set of axes
obtained by rotating a set of rectangu-

lar axes through the angle θ (in the
plane), and the coordinates (x, y) relative to the old axes, are:

$$x = x' \cos \theta - y' \sin \theta,$$
$$y = x' \sin \theta + y' \cos \theta,$$

where θ is the angle ROQ.

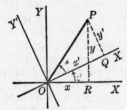

ROUND ANGLE. An angle of 360°; a
perigon.

ROUNDING OFF NUMBERS. Dropping decimals after a certain given
decimal place. When the first digit
dropped is less than 5, the preceding
digit is not changed; when the first
digit dropped is greater than 5, or 5
and some succeeding digit is not zero,
the preceding digit is increased by 1;
when the first digit dropped is 5, and
all succeeding digits are zero, the commonly accepted rule is to make the
preceding digit even, i.e. add 1 to it
if it is odd, and leave it alone if it is
already even. E.g. 2.324, 2.316, and
2.315 would take the form 2.32, if
rounded off to two places.

ROW, *n.* An arrangement of terms in a
horizontal line. Used with determinants and matrices to distinguish
horizontal arrays of elements from
vertical arrays, which are called **columns.**

row of a determinant. See DETER-
MINANT.

RULE, *n.* (1) A prescribed operation or
method of procedure; a formula (usually in words, although *rule* is often
used synonymously with *formula*). (2)
A graduated straight edge; *Syn.* Ruler.

Descartes' rule of signs. See DES-
CARTES' RULE OF SIGNS.

empirical rule. See EMPIRICAL.

l'Hospital's rule. See L'HOSPI-
TAL'S RULE.

mechanic's rule. See MECHANIC'S
RULE.

merchant's rule or mercantile rule. See MERCHANT'S RULE.

rule of three. The rule that the product of the means of a proportion equals the product of the *extremes* (see PROPORTION). This rule enables one to find any one of the numbers of a proportion if the other three are given. If $3/x = 2/5$, $2x = 15$ and $x = 7\frac{1}{2}$.

rules of equality. See AXIOM—axioms of equality.

rules for use of logarithms. See LOGARITHM—fundamental laws of logarithms.

slide rule. See SLIDE RULE.

RULED, *adj.* **ruled paper.** Same as CROSS-SECTION PAPER.

ruled surface. A surface that can be generated by a moving straight line. The generating straight line is called the **rectilinear generator.** See HYPERBOLOID—hyperboloid of one sheet, and PARABOLOID—hyperbolic paraboloid.

rulings on a ruled surface. See RULINGS.

RUL'ER, *n.* A straight edge graduated in linear units. If English units are used, the *ruler* is usually a foot long, graduated to fractions of an inch. *Syn.* Rule.

RUL'INGS, *n.* **rulings of a ruled surface.** The various positions of a straight line which generates the surface. See RULED—ruled surface.

rulings of a cone or cylinder. The positions of the generating straight lines; the *elements* of the cone or cylinder.

rulings of a hyperbolic paraboloid. See PARABOLOID—hyperbolic paraboloid.

rulings of a hyperboloid of one sheet. See HYPERBOLOID—hyperboloid of one sheet.

RUN, *n.* A term sometimes used in speaking of the difference between the abscissas of two points. The *run* from the point whose coordinates are (2, 3) to the one whose coordinates are (5, 7) is $5-2$, or 3. The distance between the ordinates is sometimes called the **rise.** Thus the *run* squared plus the *rise* squared is equal to the square of the distance between the two points.

S

SAIL'ING, *n.* **middle latitude sailing.** Approximating the difference in longitude (DL_0) of two places from their latitudes (L_1 and L_2) and departure (p) by the formula $p \sec \frac{1}{2}(L_1 + L_2) = (DL_0)$ measured in minutes.

parallel sailing. Sailing on a parallel of latitude; using the above formula, putting $L_1 = L_2$.

plane sailing. Sailing on a rhumb line. The constant angle which the rhumb line makes with the meridians is called the **ship's course.** Requires solving a plane right triangle.

triangle of plane sailing. See TRIANGLE—triangle of plane sailing.

SA'LI-ENT, *adj.* **salient point on a curve.** A point at which two branches of a curve meet and stop and have different tangents. The curve
$$y = x/(1 + e^{1/x})$$
has a *salient point* at the origin.

SAL'VAGE, *n.* **salvage value.** Same as SCRAP VALUE.

SAT'IS-FY, *v.* (1) To fulfill the conditions of, such as to *satisfy* a theorem, a set of assumptions, or a set of hypotheses. (2) A set of values of the variables which will reduce an equation (or equations) to an identity are said to *satisfy* the equation (or equations); $x = 1$ *satisfies* $4x + 1 = 5$; $x = 2$, $y = 3$ *satisfy* the simultaneous equations
$$x + 2y - 8 = 0$$
$$x - 2y + 4 = 0.$$

SCA'LAR, *adj.* **scalar product.** See MULTIPLICATION—multiplication of two vectors.

scalar quantity. (1) The ratio between two quantities of the same kind, a real number. (2) A real number, as distinguished from a vector. (3) Any complex number, real or imaginary. (4) A tensor of order zero. See TENSOR.

SCALE, *n.* A system of marks in a given order and at known intervals. Used on rulers, thermometers, etc. as aids in measuring various quantities.

binary scale. Numbers written with the base two, instead of ten. Numbers in which the second digit to the left indicates the twos, the third fours, etc., 1101 with base 2 means $2^3+2^2+0\times2+1$ or 13 written with base ten. See BASE—base of a system of numbers.

diagonal scale. See DIAGONAL—diagonal scale.

drawing to scale. Making a copy of a drawing with all distances in the same ratio to the corresponding distances in the original; making a copy of a drawing of something with all distances multiplied by a constant factor, usually a fraction. E.g. an architect drawing the plan of a house lets feet in the house be denoted by inches, or fractions of an inch, in his drawing.

logarithmic scale. See LOGARITH-MIC—logarithmic coordinate paper.

natural scale. The section of the number scale which contains positive numbers only.

number scale (complete number scale). The scale formed by marking a point 0 on a line, dividing the line into equal parts, and labeling the points of division to the right of 0 with the integers 1, 2, 3, $\cdots$ and those to the left with the negative integers, -1, -2, -3, $\cdots$.

scale of imaginaries. The number scale modified by multiplying each of its numbers by i, $(=\sqrt{-1})$. In plotting complex numbers the scale of imaginaries is laid off on a line perpendicular to the line which contains the real number scale. See ARGAND DIAGRAM.

uniform scale. A scale in which equal numerical values correspond to equal distances.

SCA-LENE′, *adj.* **scalene plane triangle.** A triangle no two of whose sides are equal. See TRIANGLE.

scalene spherical triangle. A spherical triangle no two of whose sides are equal.

SCHED′ULE, *n.* **amortization schedule.** See AMORTIZATION—amortization schedule.

SCRAP, *n.* **scrap value of equipment.** Its sale value when it is no longer useful. *Syn.* Salvage value.

SE′CANT, *n.* (1) A line of unlimited length cutting a given curve. (2) One of the trigonometric functions; see TRIGONOMETRIC—trigonometric functions.

secant curve. The graph of $y=\sec x$. Between $-\tfrac{1}{2}\pi$ and $\tfrac{1}{2}\pi$, it is concave up. It is asymptotic to the lines $x=-\tfrac{1}{2}\pi$ and $x=\tfrac{1}{2}\pi$, and has its y-intercept equal to unity. Similar loops appear in other intervals of length π radians, being alternately concave upward and downward.

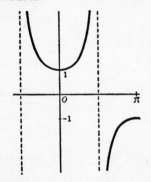

SEC′OND, *adj.* or *n.* **second of angle.** One sixtieth of a minute and one thirty-six hundredth part of a degree. Denoted by a double accent, as 10″, read ten seconds. See SEXAGES-IMAL—sexagesimal measure of an angle.

second derivative. The derivative of the first derivative. See DERIVA-TIVE—derivatives of higher order.

second law of the mean for integrals. See MEAN.

second mean value theorem of the differential calculus. See MEAN—second mean value theorem.

second moment. Same as MO-MENT OF INERTIA.

second of time. One sixtieth of a minute.

SEC′OND-AR′Y, *adj.* **secondary diagonal of a determinant.** See DETER-MINANT.

secondary parts of a triangle. Parts other than the sides and interior angles, such as the altitude, exterior angles and medians. See PRINCIPAL—principal parts of a triangle.

SEC′TION, *n.* **harmonic section of a line.** Four points of the line, harmonically related. See HARMONIC—harmonic division of a line.

meridian section. See SURFACE—surface of revolution.

method of sections. A method for graphing a surface. Consists of drawing sections of the surface (usually those made by the coordinate planes and planes parallel to them) and inferring the shape of the surface from these sections.

normal section of a surface. A plane section made by a plane containing a normal to the surface.

plane section. The plane geometric configuration obtained by cutting any configuration by a plane.

right section of a prism, cylinder, etc. See PRISM, CYLINDER, etc.

section of a polyhedral angle. The polygon formed by cutting all the edges of the angle by a plane not passing through the vertex.

SEC′TOR, *n.* **sector of a circle.** A portion of a circle bounded by two radii of the circle, and one of the arcs which they intercept. The smaller arc is called the **minor arc,** and the larger the **major arc.** The area of a sector is $\frac{1}{2}r^2\phi$, where r is the radius of the circle and ϕ the angle in radian measure subtended at the center of the circle by the arc of the sector.

spherical sector. A solid generated by rotating a sector of a circle about a diameter. Some writers require that this diameter not lie in the sector, while some require that it contain one of the radii bounding the circular sector. Most writers do not restrict the diameter at all, including both of the above cases as spherical sectors. The figure shows a sector of a circle and the spherical sector resulting from rotating it about a diameter (the dotted line). The volume of a spheri-

cal sector is equal to the product of the radius of the sphere and one third the area of the zone which forms the **base** of the sector; or $\frac{2}{3}\pi r^2 h$, where r is the radius of the sphere and h the altitude of the zone (see ZONE).

SEC′U-LAR, *adj.* **secular trend.** See TREND.

SE-CU′RI-TY, *n.* (*Finance.*) Property, or written promises to pay, such as notes and mortgages, used to guarantee payment of a debt. See COLLATERAL.

SEG′MENT, *n.* A part cut off from any figure by a line or plane (or planes). Used most commonly when speaking of a limited piece of a line or of an arc of a curve. See below, segment of a curve, and segment of a line.

addition of line segments. See ADDITION—addition of directed segments of a line.

directed line segment. See DIRECTED.

mid-point or bisecting point of a line segment. See MID-POINT.

segment of a circle. The area between a chord and an arc subtended by the chord. Any chord bounds two segments, which are different in area except when the chord is a diameter. The larger and smaller segments are called the **major** and **minor segments,** respectively. The area of a segment of a circle is $\frac{1}{2}r^2(\beta - \sin \beta)$, where r is the radius of the circle and β the angle in radians subtended at the center of the circle by the arc. See figure under SECTOR.

segment of a curve. (1) The part of the curve between two points on it. (2) The area bounded by a chord and the arc of the curve subtended by the chord.

segment of a line or **line segment.** The part of a straight line between two points.

spherical segment. The solid bounded by a sphere and two parallel planes intersecting, or tangent to, the sphere, or by a *zone* and the planes (or plane) of its bases (or base). If one plane is tangent to the sphere, the segment is a *spherical segment of one base*, otherwise it is a *spherical segment of two bases*. The **bases** are the intersections of the parallel planes with the solid bounded by the sphere; the **altitude** is the perpendicular distance between these planes. The volume of a spherical segment is equal to

$$\tfrac{1}{6}\pi h(3r_1{}^2+3r_2{}^2+h^2)$$

where h is the altitude and r_1 and r_2 are the radii of the bases. The formula for the volume of a segment of one base is gotten by making one of these r's, say r_2, zero.

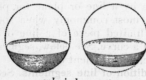

spherical segment
of one base   *of two bases.*

SE-LECT′, *adj.* **select mortality tables.** Mortality tables based on lives of people who have had medical examinations, or are chosen from special groups, or otherwise selected so as to constitute a better risk than the general run of persons.

    select period of a select mortality table. The period during which the selection has effect upon the table. The effect of selection wears off with the passing of years.

SELLING PRICE. See PRICE.

    percent profit on selling price. See PERCENT.

SEM′I, *pref.* Meaning half; partly; somewhat less than; happening or published twice in an interval or period.

    semi-annual. Twice a year.

    semi-circle. One half of a circle; either of the parts of a circle which are cut off by a diameter.

    semi-circumference. One half of a circumference.

    semi-conjugate axis of a hyperbola. See HYPERBOLA.

semi-cubical parabola. The plane locus of the equation $y^2=kx^3$. It has a cusp of the first kind at the origin, the x-axis being the double tangent. It is the locus of the intersection of a variable chord, perpendicular to the axis of an ordinary parabola, with a line drawn through the vertex of the parabola and perpendicular to the tangent at the end of the chord.

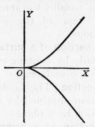

    semi-major and semi-minor axes. See ELLIPSE, and ELLIPSOID.

    semi-mean axis. See ELLIPSOID.

    semi-transverse axis of a hyperbola. See HYPERBOLA.

SENSE OF AN INEQUALITY. The direction (*greater than* or *less than*) in which the inequality points. Used in the phrases *same sense,* and *opposite sense.* The inequalities $a<b$ and $c<d$, or $b>a$ and $d>c$, are said to have the same *sense;* the inequalities $a<b$ and $d>c$ are said to have opposite *senses.*

SEP′A-RA′TION, *n.* **separation of ordered numbers, separation of the first kind.** A *separation* in which each member of one class is less than every member of the other class and in which the separating number belongs to one or the other of the classes. The number 3 may be thought of as separating all rational numbers into those less than or equal to 3 and those greater than 3.

    separation of the second kind. A *separation* in which each member of one class is less than every member of the other and there is no last number in the class of lesser numbers and no first in the class of larger numbers. See DEDEKIND CUT.

    separation of a system of numbers. The division of the system into two classes with or without regard to order.

    separation of variables. See DIF-

FERENTIAL—differential equation with variables separable.

SEP'A-RA-TRIX, *n.* Something that separates; a comma that divides a number into periods as in 234,569; a space that divides a number into periods as in 234 569. A decimal point is sometimes called a *separatrix.*

SEP-TIL'LION, *n.* (1) In the U. S. and France, the number represented by one followed by 24 zeros. (2) In England, the number represented by one followed by 42 zeros.

SE'QUENCE, *n.* An ordered set of quantities. The sets

$$1, \frac{1}{2}, \frac{1}{3}, \cdots, \frac{1}{n},$$

and $x, 2x^2, 3x^3, \cdots, nx^n$, are sequences. If after every term of a sequence there is another term, the sequence is called an *infinite sequence* and written,

$$a_1, a_2, a_3, \cdots, a_n, \cdots \quad \text{or} \quad (a_n).$$

a lower limit (or bound) to a sequence. A number which is equal to or less than any number in the sequence.

an upper limit (or bound) to a sequence. A number which is equal to or greater than any number in the sequence.

bounded sequence. A sequence such that there exists a constant that is larger than the absolute value of every one of its terms.

Cauchy's necessary and sufficient condition for convergence of an infinite sequence. An infinite sequence converges if and only if the numerical difference between every two of its terms is as small as desired, provided both terms are sufficiently far out in the sequence. *Tech.* The infinite sequence $s_1, s_2, s_3, \cdots, s_n, \cdots$ converges if and only if for every $\epsilon > 0$ there exists an N such that

$$|s_{n+h} - s_n| < \epsilon$$

for all $n > N$ and all $h > 0$. Same as CAUCHY'S NECESSARY AND SUFFICIENT CONDITION FOR CONVERGENCE of a series when s_n

is looked upon as the sum to n terms of the series

$$s_1 + (s_2 - s_1) + (s_3 - s_2) + \cdots + (s_n - s_{n-1}) + \cdots.$$

convergence of a sequence. The property possessed by a sequence whenever its nth term approaches a limit. E.g. the sequence

$$1, \frac{1}{2}, \frac{2}{3}, \cdots, \frac{n-1}{n}, \cdots$$

is convergent (possesses the property of convergence) because its nth term

$$\frac{n-1}{n}$$

approaches the limit 1. See below, limit of a sequence.

greatest (least) of the limits of a sequence. Same as MAXIMUM (MINIMUM) limit of a sequence.

limit of a sequence. A number such that the numerical value of the difference between it and the nth term of the sequence becomes and remains less than any arbitrarily small quantity. *Tech.* A sequence (s_n) has the limit s if for every $\epsilon > 0$ there exists an N such that $|s - s_n| < \epsilon$ for all n greater than N. See above, convergence of a sequence.

limited sequence. Same as BOUNDED SEQUENCE.

maximum (minimum) limit of a sequence. The largest (least) limit number of the numbers comprising the terms (see LIMIT—limit point of a set of points); the limit of the *upper (lower) bounds* of the subsequences:

$$a_1, a_2, a_3, \cdots, a_n, \cdots$$
$$a_2, a_3, a_4, \cdots, a_n, \cdots$$
$$a_3, a_4, a_5, \cdots, a_n, \cdots$$
$$\cdots \cdots \cdots \cdots$$

The maximum and minimum limits are not always the upper and lower bounds of a sequence. One or both of the maximum and minimum limits may be infinite if the sequence is not bounded. The maximum and minimum limits of the sequence.

$$2, -3/2, 4/3, \cdots (-1)^{n-1}(1+1/n), \cdots$$

are 1 and -1, while the upper and

lower bounds are 2 and $-3/2$. The *maximum* and *minimum limits* of any sequence, (a_n), are denoted respectively by

$$\overline{\lim_{n \to \infty}} a_n \quad \text{and} \quad \underline{\lim_{n \to \infty}} a_n.$$

Either limit is denoted by

$$\lim_{n \to \infty} a_n.$$

When these two limits are the same the sequence has a *limit*, written

$$\lim_{n \to \infty} a_n.$$

See above, limit of a sequence.

monotonic (or monotone) sequence. See MONOTONIC.

regular sequence. See REGULAR.

sequence of areas. A succession of related areas; for instance, the areas of the regular polygons inscribed in a circle, each of which has twice as many sides as the previous one.

sequence of Sturm's functions. See STURM'S FUNCTIONS.

"the" lower bound of a sequence having a lower bound. The smallest term, or if there is no smallest then a number l, such that there are terms of the sequence between l and $l+\epsilon$ for every $\epsilon > 0$, but no terms less than l. See LIMIT—inferior limit of a set of numbers.

"the" upper bound of a sequence having an upper bound. The largest term in the sequence if there is a largest, otherwise a number, L, say, such that there are terms between $L-\epsilon$ and L for every $\epsilon > 0$ but no terms greater than L. See LIMIT—superior limit of a set of numbers.

SE'RI-AL, *adj.* **serial issue of bonds.** An issue of serial bonds. See BOND—serial bonds.

serial plan of building and loan association. A plan under which shares are issued at different times, to accommodate new members. Monthly dues are paid and profits distributed to all share holders. This plan naturally resolves into the INDIVIDUAL ACCOUNT PLAN. See BUILDING AND LOAN ASSOCIATION.

SE'RIES, *n.* The indicated sum of a finite or ordered infinite set of terms. If the number of terms is infinite, the series is said to be an **infinite series.** Such a series can be written in the form $a_1 + a_2 + a_3 + \cdots + a_n + \cdots$, or Σa_n, where a_n is called the **general term** or the *n*th **term.** *Infinite series* is usually shortened to *series*, as in *convergent series, Taylor's series*, etc.

Abel's theorem on power series. See ABEL'S THEOREM.

addition of infinite series of constant terms. The addition of corresponding terms of the two series. If two convergent series of constant terms,

$$a_1 + a_2 + a_3 + \cdots + a_n + \cdots$$

and $\quad b_1 + b_2 + b_3 + \cdots + b_n + \cdots,$

have the sums S and S', then the series,

$$(a_1 + b_1) + (a_2 + b_2) + (a_3 + b_3) + \cdots$$
$$+ (a_n + b_n) + \cdots$$

converges and has the sum $S + S'$.

addition of power series, or series with variable terms. The term by term addition of the series. If the series

$$u_1 + u_2 + u_3 + \cdots + u_n + \cdots$$

and the series

$$v_1 + v_2 + v_3 + \cdots + v_n + \cdots$$

whose terms are functions of x converge in certain intervals, the term by term sum of these series, namely

$$(u_1 + v_1) + (u_2 + v_2) + (u_3 + v_3) \cdots$$
$$+ (u_n + v_n) + \cdots$$

converges in any interval common to the two intervals.

alternating series. A series whose terms are alternately positive and negative, as $1 - \frac{1}{2} + \frac{1}{3} - \frac{1}{4} + \cdots$.

arithmetic series. The sum of the terms of an arithmetic progression. The sum to n terms is denoted by S_n and $S_n = \frac{1}{2}n(a + l)$ or $\frac{1}{2}n[2a + (n-1)d]$. See ARITHMETIC—arithmetic progression.

ascending or increasing series. A series in which the numerical value of each term is greater than that of the preceding (compare with *monotonic* *increasing*). Such a series is always divergent.

binomial series. The binomial expansion with infinitely many terms; the expansion of a binomial raised to a power that is not a positive integer or zero. The expansion of $(a+x)^n$ by the binomial theorem results in a convergent series for all values of n, provided the absolute value of x is less than the absolute value of a.

Cauchy's necessary and sufficient condition for convergence of a series. See CAUCHY.

conditionally convergent series. See CONVERGENT.

convergence of an infinite series. See CONVERGENCE—convergence of an infinite series.

decreasing or descending series. A series in which the numerical value of each term is less than that of the preceding (compare with *monotonic decreasing*).

differentiation of an infinite series. The term by term differentiation of the series. This is permissible, i.e. the resulting series represents the derivative of the function represented by the given series in the same interval, if the resulting series is uniformly convergent in this interval. This condition is always satisfied by a **power series** in any interval within its interval of convergence; e.g. the series

$$x-\frac{x^2}{2}+\frac{x^3}{3}-\cdots\pm\frac{x^n}{n}\mp\cdots$$

converges for $-1<x\leqq1$ and represents $\log(1+x)$ in this interval; the derived series

$$1-x+x^2-\cdots\pm x^{n-1}\mp\cdots$$

converges uniformly for $-a<x<a$ if $a<1$, and represents

$$\frac{1}{1+x}$$

in any such interval.

discount series. See DISCOUNT—discount series.

divergent series. See DIVERGENT.

division of two power series. The division of the two series as if they were polynomials arranged in ascending powers of the variable. Their quotient converges and represents the quotient of the sums of the series for all values of the variable within a region of convergence common to both their regions and numerically less than the numerically least value for which the series in the denominator is zero.

double series. Consider an array of the form

$$u_{1,1} \quad u_{1,2} \quad u_{1,3} \cdots$$
$$u_{2,1} \quad u_{2,2} \quad u_{2,3} \cdots$$
$$u_{3,1} \quad u_{3,2} \quad u_{3,3} \cdots$$
$$\cdots\cdots\cdots$$

Let the sum of the terms inside the rectangle formed by the first m rows of the first n columns of this array be denoted by $S_{m,n}$. If $S_{m,n}$ approaches a number S as m and n become infinite together, then S is called the sum of the series. *Tech.* A double series converges if there is a number S (the *sum*) such that for any $\epsilon(>0)$ it is possible to find integers M and N such that $|S_{m+n}-S|<\epsilon$ whenever $m>M$ and $n>N$. If infinite series are formed from the terms in each row (or column) then the infinite series consisting of the sums of these series is called the **sum by rows** (or the **sum by columns**) of the double series. If S exists (as defined above) and the sum by rows and the sum by columns exist, then these three sums are equal. This is known as **Pringsheim's Theorem.**

entire series. See ENTIRE.

exponential series. See EXPONENTIAL—exponential series.

factorial series. The series

$$1+1/2!+1/3!+1/4!+\cdots+1/n!+\cdots.$$

finite series. The sum of a finite number of terms which follow some law. E.g. the arithmetic series to n terms.

Fourier series. See FOURIER SERIES.

geometric series. A series whose terms form a geometric progression. The general form of a geometric series is

$$a+ar+ar^2+ar^3+\cdots+ar^{n-1}+\cdots.$$

Its sum to n terms is

$$S_n = \frac{a(1-r^n)}{1-r}.$$

When r is numerically less than one, the series converges since

$$\lim_{n\to\infty} r^n = 0,$$

and its sum is $a/(1-r)$. E.g. the sum of

$$1+1/2+1/2^2+\cdots+1/2^{n-1}$$

is $[1-(1/2)^n]/(1-1/2) = 2[1-(1/2)^n]$. The limit of this sum (the sum of the infinite series $1+1/2+1/2^2+\cdots+1/2^{n-1}+\cdots$) is 2.

harmonic series. A series whose terms are in *harmonic progression;* a series the reciprocal of whose terms form an *arithmetic series*. See HARMONIC—harmonic progression.

hypergeometric series. See HYPERGEOMETRIC.

infinite series of complex terms. An infinite series of the form

$$(a_1+b_1i)+(a_2+b_2i)+\cdots+(a_n+b_ni)+\cdots.$$

This series converges if the sum of the real terms and the coefficients of the i's separately converge, and diverges if either of these diverges; i.e. it converges if and only if each of the series $a_1+a_2+a_3+\cdots$, and $b_1+b_2+b_3+\cdots$ converges. If the sum of the absolute values of the terms converges, the series is said to converge absolutely.

integration of an infinite series. The term by term integration (definite integration) of an infinite series. Any series of continuous functions which converges uniformly on an interval may be integrated term by term and the result will converge and equal the integral of the function represented by the original series, provided the limits of integration are finite and lie within the interval of uniform convergence. Any **power series** satisfies this condition in any interval within its interval of convergence; hence a power series may be integrated term by term provided the limits of integration lie within the interval of convergence.

logarithmic series. The expansion in Taylor's Series of $\log(1+x)$, namely,

$$x-x^2/2+x^3/3-x^4/4+\cdots$$
$$+(-1)^{n+1}x^n/n\cdots.$$

From this series is derived the relation

$$\log(n+1) = \log n+2[(2n+1)^{-1}+\tfrac{1}{3}(2n+1)^{-3}$$
$$+\tfrac{1}{5}(2n+1)^{-5}+\cdots],$$

which is convenient for approximating logarithms of numbers because it converges rapidly.

Maclaurin's series. See TAYLOR'S THEOREM.

multiplication of infinite series. The multiplication of the series as if they were polynomials, multiplying each term of one series by all the terms of the other, that is, forming the double series, the first row of which is the first term of one of the series times the successive terms of the other, the second row the second term of the one times the terms of the other, etc. (see above, double series). The double series converges to the product of the sums of the individual series provided they both converge and one of them converges absolutely. However absolute convergence is not a necessary condition here. A **power series** converges absoutely within its interval of convergence; hence two power series can always be multiplied, and the result will be valid within their common interval of convergence.

negative series. A series having only negative terms.

oscillating series. See DIVERGENT.

positive series. A series having only positive terms.

power series. A series whose terms contain ascending positive integral powers of a variable, or of a polynomial in a variable; a series of the form

$$a_0+a_1x+a_2x^2+\cdots+a_nx^n+\cdots,$$

where the a's are constants and x is a variable; or a series of the form

$$a_0+a_1(x-h)+a_2(x-h)^2+\cdots$$
$$+a_n(x-h)^n+\cdots.$$

See TAYLOR'S THEOREM.

reciprocal series. A series whose terms are each reciprocals of the corresponding terms of another series, of which it is said to be the *reciprocal series.*

remainder of an infinite series. See REMAINDER—remainder of an infinite series.

reversion of a series. See REVERSION.

summation of an infinite series. See SUMMATION.

Taylor's series. See TAYLOR'S THEOREM.

telescopic series. The series

$$\frac{1}{k(k+1)}+\frac{1}{(k+1)(k+2)}+\cdots$$
$$+\frac{1}{(k+n-1)(k+n)}+\cdots,$$

where k is not a negative integer. It is called *telescopic* because it can be written in the form

$$\left[\frac{1}{k}-\frac{1}{k+1}\right]+\left[\frac{1}{k+1}-\frac{1}{k+2}\right]+\cdots$$
$$+\left[\frac{1}{k+n-1}-\frac{1}{k+n}\right]+\cdots$$

which sums to $\frac{1}{k}$.

the p series. The series

$$1+1/2^p+1/3^p+\cdots+1/n^p+\cdots.$$

It is of importance in applying the *comparison test,* since it converges for all values of p greater than one and diverges for p equal to or less than one. When p equals 1, it is the *harmonic series.*

time series. See TIME—time series.

trigonometric series. See TRIGONOMETRIC—trigonometric series.

uniform convergence of a series. See CONVERGENCE—uniform convergence.

SER′PEN-TINE, *adj.* **serpentine curve.** The curve defined by the equation $x^2y+b^2y-a^2x=0$. It is symmetric about the origin, passes through the origin, and has the x-axis as an asymptote.

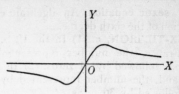

SERVICE TABLE. A table showing (for various convenient ages) the number of lives in the service of a company, the total *decrement,* and the *decrements* due to specific causes.

SET, *n.* A number of particular things, as the *set* of numbers between 3 and 5, the *set* of points on a segment of a line, or within a circle, etc.

bounded set of numbers. A set such that the absolute value of each of its members is less than some constant. All proper fractions constitute a bounded set, for they are all less than 1.

infinite set. See INFINITE—infinite set.

ordered set. See ORDERED.

set of numbers. Numbers classed together because they have some common property, as the even numbers, or the numbers between 1 and 2.

subset. A set contained within a set; sets whose members are members of another set. A subset is said to be a **proper subset** of another set if it is a subset of the set and does not contain all the members of it.

SEX′A-GES′I-MAL, *adj.* Pertaining to the number sixty.

sexagesimal measure of an angle. The system in which one complete revolution is divided into 360 parts, written 360° and called **degrees;** one degree into 60 parts, written 60′ and called **minutes;** and one minute into 60 parts, written 60″ and called **seconds.**

sexagesimal system of numbers. A number system using sixty for a base instead of ten. See BASE—base of a system of numbers.

SEX′TIC, *adj.* Of the sixth degree; of the sixth order, when speaking of curves or surfaces.

sextic curve. An algebraic curve of the sixth order.

sextic equation. An algebraic equation of the sixth degree.

SEX-TIL'LION, *n.* (1) In the U. S. and France, the number represented by one followed by 21 zeros. (2) In England, the number represented by one followed by 36 zeros.

SHEAF, *n.* **sheaf of planes.** All the planes that pass through a given point. The point is called the **center** of the sheaf. The equations of all the planes in the sheaf can be found by multiplying the equations of three planes not having a line in common and passing through the point by different parameters (arbitrary constants), adding these equations, and letting the parameters take all possible values. See PENCIL— pencil of planes. *Syn.* Bundle of planes.

SHEAR'ING, *adj.* **shearing force.** One of two equal forces acting in opposite directions and not in the same line, causing, when acting upon a solid, a distortion known as a *shearing strain.*

shearing motion. The motion that takes place when a body gives way due to a shearing stress.

shearing stress. A stress that tends to slide one part of a body upon another.

simple shear transformation. See TRANSFORMATION—simple shear transformation.

SHEET, *n.* **hyperboloid of one (or two) sheets.** See HYPERBOLOID.

sheet of a surface. A part of the surface such that one can travel from any point on it to any other point on it without leaving the surface. See HYPERBOLOID—hyperboloid of two sheets.

SHORT, *adj.* **short arc of a circle.** The shorter of the two arcs subtended by a chord of the circle.

short division. (1) Division in which the divisor is such that the process can be carried out mentally. The present day tendency is to discriminate between long and short division solely upon the basis of the complexity of the problem. When the steps in the division must be written down, it is called **long division;** otherwise it is **short division.** (2) Division in which the divisor is one of the integers from 1 to 10 inclusive (sometimes 1 to 12).

short radius of a regular polygon. See RADIUS.

SHRINKING OF THE PLANE. See SIMILITUDE—transformation of similitude, and ONE—one-dimensional strain.

SIDE, *n.* **side of an angle.** See ANGLE.

side opposite an angle in a triangle or polygon. The side separated from the vertex of the angle by the same number of sides no matter which way they are counted around the triangle, or polygon.

side of a polygon. Any one of the line segments forming the polygon.

SI-DE'RE-AL, *adj.* Pertaining to the stars.

sidereal clock. A clock that keeps sidereal time.

sidereal time. Time as measured by the apparent diurnal motion of the stars. It is equal to the hour angle of the vernal equinox (see HOUR). The sidereal day, the fundamental unit of sidereal time, is assumed to begin and to end with two successive passages over the meridian of the vernal equinox. There is one more sidereal day than mean solar days in a sidereal year.

sidereal year. The time during which the earth makes one complete revolution around the sun with respect to the stars. Its length is 365 days, 6 hours, 9 minutes, 9.5 seconds.

SIEVE, *n.* **number sieve.** See NUMBER —number sieve.

SIG'MA, *n.* The name of the Greek letter Σ, σ, equivalent to the English S, s. See SUMMATION—summation sign.

SIGN, *n.* **algebraic sign.** A positive or negative sign.

continuation of sign in a polynomial. See CONTINUATION OF SIGN.

Descartes' rule of signs. See DESCARTES' RULE OF SIGNS.

law of signs in addition and subtraction: Two successive like signs give a positive result, and two unlike signs give a negative result.

$$2-(-1)=3,$$
while $\quad 2-(+1)=2-1=1$
and $\quad 2+(-1)=1.$

law of signs in division. The quotient of two factors with like signs is positive, with unlike signs negative.

$$(-4)/(-2) = 2,$$

and

$$(-4)/2 = 4/(-2) = -2.$$

law of signs in multiplication. See MULTIPLICATION—algebraic multiplication.

summation sign. See SUMMATION.

SIGNED NUMBERS. Positive and negative numbers. *Syn.* Directed numbers.

SIG-NIF'I-CANT, *adj.* significant digit or figure. See DIGIT.

SIM'I-LAR, *adj.* **similar ellipses (or hyperbolas).** Ellipses (or hyperbolas) which have the same eccentricity; ellipses (or hyperbolas) whose semi-axes are in the same ratio. If the axes of one are a, b and of the other a', b', then $a/b = a'/b'$.

similar figures in plane geometry. (1) Figures having all corresponding angles equal and all corresponding line segments (sides) proportional. (2) Figures having all corresponding angles and corresponding constructed angles equal, where *constructed angles* refers to angles formed by drawing corresponding lines.

similar fractions. See FRACTION —similar fractions.

similar polygons. Two polygons having the angles of one equal to the corresponding angles of the other and the corresponding sides proportional; two polygons whose vertices are respectively the points of two *similar sets of points*. See below, similar sets of points.

similar sets of points. Points so situated on a pencil of lines (two points on each line) that all the ratios of the distances from the vertex of the pencil to the two points (one in each of the two sets) on a given line are equal. The set of points (one on each line) whose distances from the vertex are the antecedents of the ratios, and the set of points whose distances are the conse-

quents, are called *similar sets* of points, or *similar systems* of points. Two such sets of points are also said to be **homothetic** and any figures formed by joining corresponding pairs of points in each set are said to be **homothetic.** See SIMILITUDE— transformation of similitude.

similar solids. See SOLID.

similar surfaces. Surfaces which can be made to correspond point to point in such a way that the distance between any two points on one surface is always the same multiple of the distance between the two corresponding points on the other. The areas of similar surfaces are to each other as the squares of corresponding distances.

similar terms in one (or more) unknowns. Terms which contain the same power (or powers) of the unknowns. The terms $3x$ and $5x$, ax and bx, axy and bxy, are similar terms.

similar triangles. Triangles with corresponding angles equal. Corresponding sides are then proportional.

SIM'I-LAR'LY, *adv.* **similarly placed conics.** Conics of the same type (both ellipses, both hyperbolas, or both parabolas) which have their corresponding axes parallel.

SIM'I-LAR'I-TY, *n.* The property of being similar.

general similarity transformation. A transformation (composed possibly of a translation, a rotation, and a homothetic transformation), which transforms figures into similar figures.

SI-MIL'I-TUDE, *n.* **center of similitude.** See RADIALLY—radially related figures.

ratio of similitude. See RATIO— ratio of similitude.

transformation of similitude. The transformation $x' = kx$, $y' = ky$, in rectangular coordinates. It multiplies the distance between every two points by the same constant k, called the ratio of similitude. If k is less than one the transformation is said to shrink the plane. In the figure, the circumference of the larger circle is k times the circumference of the smaller, and the point P' is k times as far from the origin as the point *P*. This transformation is also called the **homothetic transformation**. See RADIALLY—radially related figures.

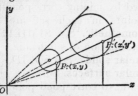

SIM′PLE, *adj.* **simple cusp.** See CUSP —cusp of the first kind.

simple elongations and compressions. Same as ONE-DIMENSIONAL STRAINS. See ONE.

simple equation. Same as LINEAR EQUATION.

simple event. See EVENT—simple event.

simple fraction. See FRACTION.

simple harmonic motion. See HARMONIC.

simple hexagon. See HEXAGON— simple hexagon.

simple integral. A single integral, as distinguished from multiple and iterated integrals.

simple interest. See INTEREST.

simple pendulum. See PENDULUM.

simple point on a curve. Same as ORDINARY POINT. See POINT.

simple root. A root of an equation that is not a repeated root. If the equation is algebraic, $f(x) = 0$, a simple root is a root r such that $f(x)$ is divisible by only the first power of $(x-r)$. See MULTIPLE—multiple root of an equation.

simple shear transformation. See TRANSFORMATION—simple shear transformation.

simple strains. See STRAIN— simple strains.

SIM′PLI-FI-CA′TION, *n.* The process of reducing an expression or a statement to a briefer form, or one easier to work with.

simplification of a complex fraction. See FRACTION—complex fraction.

simplification of an equation by rotation of axes. See ROTATION— rotation of rectangular axes.

simplification of a fraction. Reducing it to its lowest terms. See REDUCTION—reduction of a fraction to its lowest terms.

simplification of radicals. The process of reducing (changing) the radicals to simplified forms. See SIMPLIFIED—simplified form of a radical.

SIM′PLI-FIED, *adj.* **simplified (or simplest) form of a radical term.** The form in which there is no fraction under the radical and no factor under the radical which possesses the root indicated by the index. $\sqrt{2}$ and $2\sqrt{3}$ are in simplest form, but $\sqrt{2/3}$ and $\sqrt{12}$ are not.

simplified form of an expression, a quantity or an equation. (1) The briefest, least complex form. (2) The form best adapted to the next step to be taken in the process of seeking a certain result. Probably the most indefinite term used seriously in mathematics. Its meaning depends upon the operation as well as the expression at hand and its setting. E.g. if one desired to factor $x^4 + 2x^2 + 1 - x^2$, to collect the x^2 terms would be foolish, since it would conceal the factors.

simplified fraction. A simple fraction whose numerator and denominator have no common factor.

SIM′PLI-FY, *v.* To reduce to a simplified form.

SIM′PLY, *adv.* **simply connected region.** A region such that any closed curve within it can be shrunk continuously to a point without leaving the region; a region (area) such that no closed curve lying entirely within the region can enclose a boundary point of the region. A region which is not simply connected is said to be **multiply connected.** If the greatest number of closed paths which can be found in the region (such that no two can be continuously deformed into each other) is n, the region is said to be **doubly connected, triply connected,** etc., according as n is equal to 2, 3, etc. The region between two unequal concentric circles in a plane is *multiply* (*doubly*) *connected;* but if two points in their circumferences are joined by a straight line, the open region bounded by this line and the two circles is *simply connected*.

SIMPSON'S RULE. A rule for approximating the area bounded by a curve (whose equation is given in rectangular coordinates) the x-axis, and the ordinates corresponding to two abscissas, say a and b. It assumes that small arcs of the curve are very nearly coincident with the arc of the parabola through the mid-point and terminal points of the arc. In algebraic terms, it makes use of Taylor's series, dropping all terms after the quadratic term. The formula is:

$$A = \frac{(b-a)}{6n}\,[y_a+4y_1+2y_2+4y_3$$
$$+2y_4+\cdots+4y_{2n-1}+y_b],$$

where $2n$ equal sub-intervals have been laid off on the x-axis by

$$a,\ x_1,\ x_2,\cdots,\ x_{2n-1},\ b$$

an $\quad y_a,\ y_1,\ y_2,\cdots,\ y_{2n-1},\ y_b$

are the respective ordinates of these points. The numerical difference between the number given by this formula and the actual area is known to be less than

$$\frac{M(b-a)^5}{180\,(2n)^4},$$

where M is the greatest numerical value of the 4th derivative of the function whose graph is the given curve. This rule can be used to approximate the value of any definite integral. If the curve is not of higher order than 3, this formula in the form

$$\frac{b-a}{6}\,[y_a+4y_1+y_b],$$

where $n=1$, gives the exact area and is called the **prismoidal formula** (for areas).

SI'MUL-TA'NE-OUS, *adj.* **number of simultaneous solutions of two polynomial equations in two variables.** The product of their degrees, provided they have no common factor, infinite values (see homogeneous coordinates) being allowed, and equal solutions being counted to the degree of their multi-

plicity. E.g. (1) the equations $y=2x^2$ and $y=x$ have the two common solutions $(0, 0)$ and $(\frac{1}{2}, \frac{1}{2})$; (2) the equations $y-2x^2=0$ and $y^2-x=0$ have two real and two imaginary common solutions.

simultaneous equations. (1) Equations which are all satisfied by the same values of the variables. E.g. $x+y=2$ and $3x+2y=5$, treated as simultaneous equations, are satisfied by $x=1$, $y=1$, these values being the coordinates of the point of intersection of the straight lines which are the graphs of the two equations. (2) Systems of equations which may or may not have common solutions but are to be treated together to investigate for common solutions are called *simultaneous equations* by some writers. See CONSISTENCY.

simultaneous inequalities. Two or more inequalities, both of which are true for some common set of values of the variables. The simultaneous inequalities $x^2+y^2<1$, $y>0$ are satisfied simultaneously by the points above the x-axis and inside the unit circle about the origin.

simultaneous linear equations. Simultaneous equations which are linear (of the first degree) in the variables.

solution of simultaneous equations. Finding sets of values of the variables that satisfy all the equations. For various methods of solution, see ELIMINATION, and CRAMER'S RULE.

SINE, *n.* **exponential values of sin x and cos x.** See EXPONENTIAL—exponential values of sin x and cos x.

law of sines: The sides of a plane triangle are proportional to the sines of the opposite angles. If the angles are A, B, C, and the sides opposite these angles are a, b, c this law is:

$$\frac{a}{\sin A}=\frac{b}{\sin B}=\frac{c}{\sin C}.$$

natural sine of an angle. Same as the sine of the angle. *Natural sine* is used in distinction from the *logarithmic sine.*

sine of an angle. See TRIGONOMETRIC—trigonometric functions of an acute angle.

sine curve. The graph of $y = \sin x$. The curve passes through the origin and all points on the x-axis whose abscissas are multiples of π (radians), is concave toward the x-axis, and the greatest distance from the x-axis to the curve is unity.

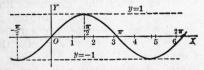

sine of half an angle. See FORMULA—half-angle formulas.

sine of twice an angle. See FORMULA—double-angle formulas.

sine series. See FOURIER SERIES—Fourier's half-range series.

SIN'GLE, *adj*. **net single premium.** (*In insurance*.) The present value, at the policy date, of all benefits assured to the policyholder.

single life annuity. See LIFE—life annuity.

single premium on an insurance policy. The amount which, if paid on the policy date, would meet all premiums on the policy.

single valued function of one or more variables. A function which has one and only one value corresponding to each value (or values) of its variable (or variables). E.g. the function $x^2 + 1$ is a *single valued function*. See MULTIPLE—multiple valued function.

SIN'GU-LAR, *adj*. **singular affine transformation.** See AFFINE TRANSFORMATION.

singular point on a curve. A point on a curve, $f(x, y) = 0$, which is not an ordinary point (see POINT—ordinary point). Points where $f_x(x, y)$ and $f_y(x, y)$ (the partial derivatives of f with respect to x and y) are both zero are singular points. These are points where an algebraic curve has multiple tangents, two or more distinct tangents, or no real tangent. Cusps, crunodes, and isolated points are *singular points*.

singular solution of a differential equation. See SOLUTION—singular solution of a differential equation.

SINKING FUND. See FUND—sinking fund.

SI'NUS-OID, *n*. The *sine curve*. See SINE.

SIX PERCENT METHOD. A method of computing simple interest by computing it first for 6%, then for the given rate, if it is different. At 6%, the interest on $1 for one year is $.06, for one month $.005, and for one day $\frac{1}{30}$(.005). When the rate is other than 6%, one computes the interest for 6% as above and then takes the proper part of the result; for instance if the rate is 5%, the interest is $\frac{5}{6}$ of the result obtained for 6%.

SIXTY DAY METHOD. A method for computing simple interest at 6%. The rate for 60 days is (60/360)6/100 or 1%, so the interest for 60 days is 1/100 of the principal and for 6 days 1/1000 of the principal. The time over which interest is to be computed is expressed in terms of 6 days and 60 days and fractional parts thereof. Also used when the rate is other than 6%. See SIX PERCENT METHOD.

SKEW, *adj*. **distance between two skew lines.** See DISTANCE.

skew lines. Non-intersecting, non-parallel lines in space.

skew quadrilateral. The figure formed by joining four non-coplanar points by line segments, each point being joined to two and only two other points.

skew-symmetric determinant. A determinant having its conjugate elements numerically equal but opposite in sign. If the element in the first row and second column is 5, the element in the first column and second row would be −5. A skew-symmetric determinant of odd order is always equal to zero.

skew-symmetric tensor. See TENSOR.

SLANT, *adj*. **slant height of a cone of revolution.** The length of an element of the cone.

slant height of a frustum of a regular pyramid. The common altitude of its faces.

slant height of a frustum of a right circular cone. The segment of an element of the cone intercepted by the bases of the frustum; the length of the straight line segment lying in the surface and joining points in the circumferences of the bases.

slant height of a regular pyramid. The common altitude of its lateral faces.

SLIDE RULE. A mechanical device to aid in calculating by the use of logarithms. It consists essentially of two rules, one sliding in a groove in the other, containing logarithmic scales by means of which products and quotients are calculated by adding and subtracting logarithms. Detailed explanations of the construction and use of any particular slide rule can be secured from its manufacturer.

SLOPE, *n.* **point-slope form of the equation of a straight line.** See LINE—equation of a straight line in the plane.

slope of a curve at a point. The slope of the tangent line at that point; the derivative, dy/dx, evaluated at the point. See DERIVATIVE.

slope-intercept form of the equation of a straight line. See LINE—equation of a straight line in the plane.

slope of a straight line. The tangent of the angle that the line makes with the positive x-axis; the tangent of the smallest positive angle through which the positive axis of abscissas can be revolved in order to be parallel to the given line; the rate of change of the ordinate with respect to the abscissa, that is,

$$\frac{y_2-y_1}{x_2-x_1},$$

where (x_1, y_1) and (x_2, y_2) are points on the line. In *calculus* the slope at (x_1, y_1) is the derivative of the ordinate with respect to the abscissa,

$$\lim_{x_2\to x_1}\frac{y_2-y_1}{x_2-x_1} \text{ or } \left(\frac{dy}{dx}\right)_{x=x_1}$$

(which is the same for all points on the line). The slope of $y=x$ is 1; of $y=2x$, 2; of $y=3x+1$, 3. See DERIVATIVE—derivative of a function of one variable.

SMALL, *adj.* **small arcs, angles, or line segments.** Arcs, lines, or line segments,

which are small enough to satisfy certain conditions, such as making the difference between two ordinates of a curve less than a stipulated amount, or the quotient of the sine of an angle by the angle (in radians) differ from 1 by less than a given amount.

small circle. See CIRCLE—small circle.

SNELL'S LAW. See REFRACTION.

SOLAR TIME. See TIME—apparent solar time, and mean solar time.

SOL'ID, *adj.* and *n.* See GEOMETRIC —geometric solid.

frustum of a solid. See FRUSTUM.

similar solids. Solids bounded by similar surfaces; solids whose points can be made to correspond in such a way that the distances between all pairs of points of the one are a constant multiple of the distances between corresponding points of the other. Volumes of similar solids are proportional to the cubes of the distances between corresponding points. All spheres are similar solids, so are all cubes.

solid angle. The solid angle at any point P (see figure) subtended by a surface S is equal to the area A of the portion of the surface of a sphere of unit radius, with center at P, which is cut out by a conical surface with vertex at P and the perimeter of S as a generatrix. The unit solid angle is called the **steradian.** The total solid angle about a point is equal to 4π steradians.

solid geometry. See GEOMETRY —solid geometry.

solid of revolution. A solid generated by revolving a plane area about a line (the **axis of revolution**). If the line is the x-axis and the area is that bounded by the x-axis, the ordinates corresponding to $x=a$ and $x=b$, and the curve $y=f(x)$, the volume can be thought of as the limit of the sum of a set of cylinders with radius $f(x)$ and altitude dx. This limit is

$$\int_a^b \pi f^2(x)dx.$$

See INTEGRAL—definite integral.

volume of a solid. The number of times it will contain a unit cube.

SO-LU'TION, *n.* The process of finding a required result by the use of certain given data, previously known facts or methods, and newly observed relations. The *result* is also spoken of as the *solution*. E.g. a root of an equation is sometimes called a *solution* of the equation it satisfies, although a *solution* of the equation usually refers to the process of finding a root, or the roots.

algebraic solution. A solution whose steps involve no operations other than addition, subtraction, multiplication, division, taking of roots, and raising to powers, and only a finite number of these.

ambiguous case in the solution of triangles. See AMBIGUOUS.

analytic solutions. See ANALYTIC.

Cardan's solution of the cubic. A solution of the general cubic in which the square term is removed by a substitution (see REDUCED—reduced cubic) and the reduced cubic is put in quadratic form by means of substitutions. This solution is satisfactory in all cases except the **irreducible case** (see IRREDUCIBLE). Ferro discovered this solution, but Cardan first published it.

general solution of a differential equation. A solution in which the number of essential arbitrary constants is equal to the order of the differential equation.

geometric solution. See GEOMETRIC.

geometric solution of an equation. The process of finding the roots of an equation by graphing the function and estimating where its graph crosses the x-axis. See GRAPHICAL—graphical solution of an equation.

graphical solution of inequalities. See GRAPHICAL—graphical solution of inequalities.

partial solution of a differential equation. See PARTICULAR—particular integral.

particular solution of a differential equation. See PARTICULAR—particular integral.

singular solution of a differential equation of first order. A solution not obtainable by assigning particular values to the parameters in the general solution; the equation of an envelope of the family of curves represented by the general solution. (This envelope satisfies the differential equation because at every one of its points its slope and the coordinates of the point are the same as those of some member of the family of curves representing the general solution.)

solution of an algebraic equation. See EQUATION—solution of an algebraic equation of the nth degree, and ROOT—root of an equation.

solution of a differential equation. Any function which reduces the differential equation to an identity when substituted for the dependent variable. $y = x^2 + cx$ is a solution of

$$x\frac{dy}{dx} - x^2 - y = 0, \quad \text{for} \quad \frac{dy}{dx} = 2x + c$$

and substituting

$$2x + c \text{ for } \frac{dy}{dx}, \text{ and } x^2 + cx \text{ or } y$$

in the differential equation, reduces it to the identity $0 = 0$ (c is a **constant parameter,** the above being true for any value of c, and $y = x^2 + cx$ is the **general solution**).

solution of an equation by inspection. Guessing at a root and testing it by substitution in the equation.

solution of the general cubic. See above, Cardan's solution of the cubic.

solution of the general quartic. See FERRARI'S.

solution of an oblique plane triangle. Finding the remaining angles and sides when sufficient of these have been given. A sufficient number is two sides and an angle, three sides, two angles and a side—except that when two sides and the angle opposite one of them is given there may be two solutions. See SINE—law of sines, COSINE—cosine law, TANGENT—tangent law, FORMULA—half-angle formulas, AMBIGUOUS—ambiguous case in the solution of plane triangles, and HERO'S FORMULA.

solution of an oblique spherical triangle. Finding the other parts when three parts are given. For formulas (laws) providing solutions in all cases when solutions exist, see LAW—law of sines in a spherical triangle, LAW —law of cosines in a spherical triangle, HALF—half-angle and half-side formulas of spherical trigonometry, NAPIER'S ANALOGIES, and GAUSS' FORMULA.

solution of a plane right triangle. Finding the other parts when two legs, a leg and the hypotenuse, or an acute angle and a leg or the hypotenuse are given. The unknown parts are found by use of trigonometric tables and the definitions of the trigonometric functions (see TRIGONOMETRIC); if a, b, c represent the legs and hypotenuse respectively and A, B are the angles opposite sides a and b, then: $a = b \tan A = c \sin A$, $b = c \cos A$, $A = \tan^{-1} a/b$, $B = 90° - A$.

solution of a right spherical triangle. Finding the unknown sides or angles when two parts other than the right angle are given. See *Napier's rules;* these supply all the formulas needed.

solution of simultaneous equations. See SIMULTANEOUS, CONSISTENCY, and CRAMER'S RULE.

solution of a trigonometric equation. Finding a root of the equation, usually possible by reducing the equation to one containing only one trigonometric function and solving this equation.

SOUTH DECLINATION. See DECLINATION—declination of a celestial point.

SPACE, *n.* A three dimensional region. See DIMENSION.

coordinate in space. See COORDINATE—coordinate planes, CYLINDRICAL—cylindrical coordinates,

and SPHERICAL—spherical coordinates.

equations of a circle in space. See CIRCLE.

space curves. Curves that may or may not be plane curves; the intersection of any two distinct surfaces. Space curves do not lie in a plane (are twisted) except when their *tortion* is zero.

SPAN, *n.* **span of a roof.** The length of the plates of the building; the width of the building.

SPE′CIES, *n.* **species of angles (sides) of a spherical triangle.** Two angles, two sides, or an angle and a side are said to be of the *same species* if they are both acute or both obtuse, and of *different species* if one is acute and one obtuse.

law of species (*Spherical trigonometry.*) One half the sum of any two sides of a spherical triangle and one half the sum of the opposite angles are of the same species.

SPE-CIF′IC, *adj.* **specific gravity.** The ratio of the weight of a given volume of any substance to the weight of the same volume of a standard substance. The substance taken as the standard for solids and liquids is water at 4°C, the temperature at which water has the greatest density.

specific heat. (1) The number of calories required to raise the temperature of one gram of a substance one degree Centigrade or the number of B.T.U.'s required to raise 1 pound of the substance 1°F. Sometimes called *thermal capacity.* (2) The ratio of the quantity of heat necessary to change the temperature of a given mass 1° to the amount necessary to change an equal mass of water 1°.

SPEED, *n.* **angular speed (in a plane).** The number of angle units, degrees or radians, through which the radius vector to the point passes per unit of time. If this is not constant, the angular speed (the **instantaneous angular speed**) is the limit of the average speed over an interval of time, as that interval approaches zero. *Tech.* If the vectorial angle is a function of time the angular speed is the absolute value of the derivative of this function with respect to time.

average speed. See AVERAGE.

constant speed. See CONSTANT—constant speed.

speed of a particle. Distance passed over per unit of time. Speed is concerned only with the length of the path passed over per unit of time, and not with its direction (see VELOCITY). If the distance passed over per unit of time is not constant, then the speed (the **instantaneous speed**) is defined as the limit of the **average speed** over an interval of time, as that interval approaches zero. For instance, if the distance passed over is equal to the cube of the time, the speed at a time t_0 is the limit of $(t_1{}^3 - t_0{}^3)/(t_1 - t_0)$ as t_1 approaches t_0, which is $3t_0{}^2$. *Tech.* If the distance travelled is a function of the time, speed is the absolute value of the derivative of this function with respect to the time.

SPHERE, *n.* (1) The locus of points at a given distance from a fixed point. (2) A portion of space all points of whose boundary are equidistant from a fixed point. The fixed point is called the **center,** the given distance the **radius.**

area of the surface of a sphere. Four *pi* times the square of the radius, written $4\pi r^2$; four times the area of a great circle of the sphere.

celestial sphere. The spherical surface in which the stars appear to move.

chord of a sphere. The segment cut out of a secant by the surface of the sphere; a line segment joining two points on the sphere.

circumscribed sphere of a polyhedron. A sphere passing through all the vertices of the polyhedron. The polyhedron is said to be *inscribed in* the sphere.

diameter of a sphere. The segment intercepted by the sphere on a line passing through the center; twice the radius of the sphere.

equation of a sphere: In rectangular coordinates,

$$x^2 + y^2 + z^2 = r^2$$

when the center is at the origin and

the sphere is of radius r, and

$$(x-a)^2 + (y-b)^2 + (z-c)^2 = r^2$$

when the center is at the point whose coordinates are (a, b, c). In spherical coordinates, $\rho = r$ when the center is at the origin. See DISTANCE—distance between two points.

family of spheres. See FAMILY—one parameter family of surfaces.

inscribed sphere of a polyhedron. A sphere which is tangent to all the faces of the polyhedron. The polyhedron is said to be *circumscribed about* the sphere.

secant of a sphere. Any line cutting the sphere.

volume of a sphere. Four-thirds *pi* times the cube of the radius, written

$$\tfrac{4}{3}\pi r^3.$$

SPHER'I-CAL, *adj.* **ambiguous case in the solution of a spherical triangle.** The case in which a side and the opposite angle are given. See AMBIGUOUS—ambiguous case in the solution of plane triangles.

area of a spherical triangle. *Pi* times the product of the square of the radius of the sphere and the triangle's spherical excess, divided by 180; i.e. $\pi r^2 E/180$. See below, spherical excess.

cosine law of spherical triangles. See LAW—law of cosines in a spherical triangle.

isosceles spherical triangle. A spherical triangle having two equal sides.

Napier's rules for the solution of a right spherical triangle. See NAPIER'S RULES.

oblique spherical triangle. A spherical triangle which does not contain a right angle.

quadrantal spherical triangle. A spherical triangle having one side equal to 90° (a quadrant).

right spherical triangle. A spherical triangle having at least one right angle. (It may have two, or three.)

scalene spherical triangle. See SCALENE.

sine law of spherical triangles. See LAW—law of sines in a spherical triangle.

spherical angle. See ANGLE—spherical angle.

spherical cone. See CONE—spherical cone.

spherical coordinates. A system of coordinates in space. The position of any point P (see the figure) is assigned by its **radius vector** $OP = r$ (i.e. the distance of P from a fixed origin or **pole** O), and two angles: the **colatitude** θ, which is the angle NOP made by OP with a fixed axis ON, the **polar axis**; and the longitude ϕ, which is the angle AOP' made by the plane of θ with a fixed plane NOA through the polar axis, called the **initial meridian plane.** A given radius vector r confines the point P to the sphere of radius r about the pole O. The angles θ and ϕ serve to determine the position of P on this sphere. The angle θ is always taken between 0 and π radians, while ϕ can have any value (r being taken as negative if ϕ is measured to $P'O$ extended). The relations between the spherical and Cartesian coordinates are:

$$x = r \sin\theta \cos\phi,$$
$$y = r \sin\theta \sin\phi$$
$$z = r \cos\theta.$$

Sometimes ρ is used in place of r, and θ and ϕ are often interchanged. *Syn.* Geographical coordinates, polar coordinates in space.

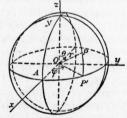

spherical degree. The area of the *birectangular spherical triangle* whose

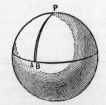

third angle is one degree. The area of the triangle APB in the figure is one spherical degree.

spherical excess. Of a **spherical triangle:** The difference between the sum of the angles of a spherical triangle and 180° (the sum of the angles of a spherical triangle is greater than 180° and less than 540°). Of a **spherical polygon** of n sides: the difference between the sum of the angles of the spherical polygon and $(n-2)180°$ (the sum of the angles of a plane polygon of n sides).

spherical indicatrix. See INDICATRIX.

spherical polygon. A portion of a spherical surface bounded by three or more arcs of great circles. Its area is

$$\frac{\pi r^2 E}{180},$$

where r is the radius of the sphere and E is the spherical excess of the polygon.

spherical pyramid. See PYRAMID.

spherical sector. See SECTOR—spherical sector.

spherical segment. See SEGMENT—spherical segment.

spherical triangle. A spherical polygon with three sides; a portion of a sphere bounded by three arcs of great circles. In the spherical triangle ABC (in figure), the sides of the triangle are $a = $ angle BOC, $b = $ angle AOC, and $c = $ angle AOB. The angles of the triangle are $A = $ angle $B'A'P$, B and $C = $ angle $B'C'P$. See above, area of a spherical triangle.

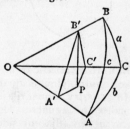

spherical trigonometry. The study of spherical triangles—finding unknown sides, angles and areas by the use of trigonometric functions of the plane angles which measure angles and sides of the triangles.

spherical wedge. A solid the shape of a slice (from stem to blossom) of a spherical melon; the solid bounded by a lune of a sphere and the two planes of its great circles. Its volume is

$$\frac{\pi r^3 A}{270},$$

where r is the radius of the sphere and A is the dihedral angle (in degrees) between the plane faces of the wedge.

SPHE'ROID, n. Same as ELLIPSOID OF REVOLUTION.

oblate spheroid. Same as OBLATE ELLIPSOID OF REVOLUTION.

SPI'NODE, n. Same as CUSP.

SPI'RAL, n. See HYPERBOLIC—hyperbolic spiral, LOGARITHMIC—logarithmic spiral, PARABOLIC—parabolic spiral.

equiangular spiral. Same as LOG-ARITHMIC SPIRAL.

spiral of Archimedes. The plane curve which is the locus of a point that moves with uniform speed, starting at the pole, along the radius vector while the radius vector moves with uniform angular speed. Its polar equation is $r = a\theta$. The figure shows the portion of the curve for which r is positive. See POLAR—polar coordinates in the plane.

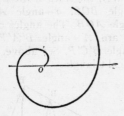

SQUARE, n. In *arithmetic* or *algebra*, the result of multiplying a quantity by itself. In *geometry*, a quadrilateral with equal sides and equal angles; a rectangle with two adjacent sides equal. The area of a square is equal to the square of the length of a side.

difference of two squares. See DIFFERENCE—difference of two squares.

magic squares. See MAGIC.

method of least squares. See METHOD—method of least squares.

perfect trinomial square. The square of a binomial; an expression of the form $a^2 + 2ab + b^2$, which is equal to $(a+b)^2$.

square numbers. Numbers which are the squares of integers: as 1, 4, 9, 16, 25, 36, 49, etc.

square root. See ROOT—square root of a number.

square units of area. The number of times a square, whose side is the given unit, is contained in the given area.

SQUARING THE CIRCLE. See QUADRATURE—quadrature of a circle.

STAND'ARD, *adj.* or n. **standard deviation.** See DEVIATION.

standard form of an equation. A form that has been universally accepted by mathematicians as such, in the interest of simplicity and uniformity. E.g. the *standard form* of a rational integral (polynomial) equation of the nth degree in x is

$$a_0 x^n + a_1 x^{n-1} + \cdots + a_n = 0:$$

the *standard form* of the equation of an ellipse is

$$\frac{x^2}{a^2} + \frac{y^2}{b^2} = 1.$$

standard or primary infinitesimal and infinite quantities. The infinitesimal or infinite quantity relative to which *orders* are defined. If x is the *standard* or *primary infinitesimal*, then x^2 is an infinitesimal of higher (second) order with respect to x. Similarly if x is infinite, then x^2 is an infinite quantity of higher (second) order with respect to the *standard* or *primary infinite quantity* x. See INFINITESIMAL—order of an infinitesimal, and INFINITY—order of infinities.

standard time. See TIME—standard time.

STAT'IC, *adj.* **static moment.** Same as MOMENT OF MASS.

STAT'ICS, n. The branch of dynamics which deals with bodies in equilibrium, situations in which the several forces are so related as to balance or neutralize each other so far as giving the body motion as a whole is concerned.

STATIONARY POINT. Same as CUSP.

STA-TIS′TI-CAL, *adj.* **statistical graphs.** See GRAPHING—statistical graphing.

statistical record. A record of many events of the same type, such as: the number of deaths per year at specified age; the price of steel at given intervals over a long period; the weight of a large number of people of a given height.

STA-TIS′TICS, *n.* The study of methods of obtaining statistical records and drawing conclusions from them.

vital statistics. See VITAL STATISTICS.

STEPS, *n.* **successive steps.** See SUCCESSIVE.

STERE, *n.* One cubic meter, or 35.3156 cubic feet. Used mostly in measuring wood. See METRIC SYSTEM.

STIRLING′S FORMULA. (1) $n!$ approaches $(n/e)^n \sqrt{2\pi n}$ as n increases, written $n! \sim (n/e)^n \sqrt{2\pi n}$; (2) Maclaurin's series, discovered by Stirling, but published first by Maclaurin.

STOCK, *n.* See CAPITAL.

common stock. Stock which receives as dividends its proportionate share of the proceeds after all other demands have been met.

preferred stock. Stock upon which a fixed rate of interest (dividend) is paid, after the dividends on bonds have been paid and before any dividends are paid on common stock.

stock certificate. A written statement that the owner of the certificate has a certain amount of capital in the corporation which issued the certificate.

stock company. A company composed of the purchasers of certain stock.

stock insurance company. A stock company whose business is insurance. The policies they sell are non-participating. The profits go to the stockholders. However some stock companies, because of the competition of mutual companies, write participating policies. *Syn.* Non-participating insurance company.

STOKE′S THEOREM. The integral of $Pdx + Qdy + Rdz$ around a space curve

on a surface, taken in the direction such that the enclosed surface is always on the observer's left as he moves counterclockwise around the curve, is equal to the integral, over the enclosed surface, of

$$(D_y R - D_z Q) dy dz$$
$$+ (D_z P - D_x R) dz dx$$
$$+ (D_x Q - D_y P) dx dy,$$

where D_x, D_y, D_z denote partial derivatives with respect to x, y, and z, respectively.

STRAIGHT, *adj.* Continuing in the same direction; not swerving or turning; in a *straight line*. See LINE.

straight angle. See ANGLE—straight angle.

straight line. See LINE—straight line.

STRAIN, *n.* **coefficient of strain.** See ONE—one dimensional strains.

homogeneous strains. The concept in dynamics represented approximately by the *homogeneous affine transformation;* the forces acting internally in an elastic body when it is deformed.

simple strains. A general name given to *simple elongations* and *compressions*, and *simple shears*.

STRESS, *n.* **internal stress.** The resistance of a physical body to external forces; the unit internal resistance set up by external forces.

shearing stress. See SHEARING.

STRETCHING AND SHRINKING TRANSFORMATIONS. See SIMILITUDE—transformation of similitude.

STROPH′OID, *n.* The plane locus of a point on a variable line passing through a fixed point when the distance from the describing point to the intersection of the line with the *y*-axis is equal to

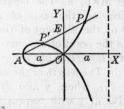

the *y*-intercept. If the coordinates of the fixed point are taken as $(-a, 0)$, the equation of the curve is $y^2 = x^2(x+a) \div (x-a)$. In the figure, $P'E = EP = OE$, A is the point through which the line always passes, and the dotted line is the asymptote of the curve.

STURM'S FUNCTIONS. A sequence of functions derived from a given polynomial, $f(x)$; explicitly, the sequence of functions $f_0(x)$, $f_1(x)$, $\cdots$, $f_n(x)$, where $f_0(x) \equiv f(x)$, $f_1(x) \equiv f'(x)$, and $f_2(x)$, $f_3(x)$, etc., are the negatives of the remainders occurring in the process of finding the highest common factor of $f(x)$ and $f'(x)$ by Euclid's algorithm. This sequence is called a **sequence of Sturm's functions.**

STURM'S THEOREM. A theorem determining the number of real roots of an algebraic equation which lie between any two arbitrarily chosen values of the unknown. The theorem states that the number of real roots of $f(x) = 0$ between two values a and b of the unknown, x, is equal to the difference between the number of variations of sign in the sequence of *Sturm's functions* (derived from $f(x)$) when $x = a$ and when $x = b$, vanishing terms not being counted and multiple roots being counted to the degree of their multiplicity. See VARIATION—variation of sign in an ordered set of numbers.

SUB'CLASS', *n.* Same as SUBSET. See SET.

SUB-FAC-TO'RI-AL, *n.* **subfactorial of an integer.** If n is the integer, *subfactorial* n is $n![1/2! - 1/3! + 1/4! - \cdots (-1)^n/n!]$. This is equal to $n!E$, where E is the sum of the first $n+1$ terms in the Maclaurin expansion of e^x with $x = -1$. E.g. *subfactorial* 4 is equal to $4!(1/2! - 1/3! + 1/4!) = 24(1/2 - 1/6 + 1/24) = 9$.

SUB'GROUP', *n.* See GROUP.

SUB-NOR'MAL, *n.* The length of the projection on the axis of abscissas (x-axis) of the segment of the normal between the point of the curve and the point of intersection of the normal with the x-axis. The length of the subnormal is $y(dy/dx)$, where y and dy/dx (the derivative of y with respect to x) are evaluated at the given point on the curve. See TANGENT—length of a tangent.

polar subnormal. See POLAR—polar tangent.

SUB'RE'GION, *n.* A region within a region.

SUB'SCRIPT, *n.* A small number or letter written below and to the right or left of a letter as a mark of distinction, or as part of an operative symbol; used on a variable to denote a constant value of that variable or to distinguish between variables. The symbols a_1, a_2, etc., denote different constants; $D_x f$ denotes the derivative of f with respect to x; $(x_0, y_0), (x_1, y_1)$, etc., denote coordinates of fixed points; $f(x_1, x_2, \cdots, x_n)$ denotes a function of n variables, $x_1, x_2, \cdots, x_n$; $_nC_r$ denotes the number of possible combinations of n things r at a time.

double subscript. See DOUBLE.

SUB-SE'QUENCE. A sequence within a sequence; $1/2, 1/4, \cdots, 1/(2n), \cdots$, is a subsequence of $1, 1/2, 1/3, 1/4, \cdots, 1/n, \cdots$.

SUB'SE-QUENT, *adj.* **subsequent terms.** Terms following a given term (or set of terms) in some arrangement of terms such as a sequence or a series.

SUBSET. See SET.

SUB'STI-TU'TION, *n.* **elimination by substitution.** See ELIMINATION.

integration by substitution. See INTEGRATION.

inverse substitution. The substitution which exactly undoes the effect of a given substitution. For examples, see TRANSFORMATION—inverse transformation.

substitution of one quantity for another. Replacing the one quantity by the other. Substitutions are made in order to simplify equations, simplify integrands (in the calculus), and to change (transform) geometric configurations into other forms or to different positions. See TRANSFORMATION.

trigonometric substitution. See TRIGONOMETRIC.

SUB'TAN'GENT, *n.* The projection on the axis of abscissas (x-axis) of the segment of the tangent joining the point of tangency on the curve and the point of intersection of the tangent with the x-axis; the segment of the axis of abscissas between the foot of the ordinate at the point on the curve and the x-intercept of the tangent. The length of the subtangent is $y(dx/dy)$, where y and dx/dy are evaluated at the point on the curve. See DERIVATIVE, and TANGENT—length of a tangent.

SUB-TEND', v. To be opposite to, or measure off: as a side of a triangle subtends the opposite angle, and an arc of a circle subtends the central angle of the arc. The angle is also said to be *subtended by* the side of the triangle or arc of the circle.

SUB-TRAC'TION, n. The process of finding a quantity which when added to one of two given quantities will give the other. These quantities are called, respectively, the **subtrahend** and **minuend,** and the quantity found is called the **difference** or **remainder.** E.g. 2 subtracted from 5 is written $5-2=3$; 5 is the *minuend,* 2 the *subtrahend,* and 3 the *difference* or *remainder.*

algebraic subtraction. The subtracting of algebraic numbers; the process of changing the sign of the subtrahend and adding it to the minuend. E.g. 5 minus 7 is equal to 5 plus negative 7, written $5-7=5+(-7)$, which is -2. See ADDITION—addition of algebraic quantities.

subtraction formulas. See FORMULA—subtraction formulas of trigonometry.

SUB'TRA-HEND', n. A quantity to be subtracted from another.

SUC-CES'SIVE, *adj.* **successive terms or steps.** Terms or steps following one after the other.

successive trials. (*Probability.*) Successive trials (occurrences of a given event) in which one is interested in the number of times the favorable occurrence of the event is likely to take place in a certain number of trials. The probability of an event happening exactly r times in n trials is $_nC_r p^r q^{n-r}$, where p and q are the probabilities of the event happening and failing, respectively, in a single trial and $_nC_r$ is the number of combinations of n things taken r at a time (see COMBINATION). Using this formula, the probability of a six coming up exactly once in three throws of a die is $3(1/6)(5/6)^2 = 25/72$; the probability of its coming up twice is $3(1/6)^2(5/6) = 5/72$; and the probability of its coming up three times is $(1/6)^3 = 1/216$.

SUF-FI'CIENT, *adj.* **sufficient condition.** See CONDITION.

SUM, n. **algebraic sum.** The combination of terms either by addition or subtraction in the sense that adding a negative number is equivalent to subtracting a positive one. The expression $x-y+z$ is an *algebraic sum* in the sense that it is the same as $x+(-y)+z$.

arithmetic sum of two quantities. The quantity obtained by adding the two quantities. Five is the sum of two and three, written $2+3=5$.

limit of a sum. See LIMIT—fundamental theorems on limits.

sums of like powers of two quantities. Sums such as a^2+b^2 and a^3+b^3. They are of interest in factoring, because when the power is odd the sum is divisible by the sum of the quantities. See DIFFERENCE—difference of like powers of two quantities.

SUM-MA'TION, n. **integration as a summation process.** See INTEGRAL—definite integral.

summation convention. The convention of writing a summation of the form

$$\sum_{i=1}^{n} a_i x^i \text{ simply as } a_i x^i$$

or $a_1 x^1 + a_2 x^2 + \cdots + a_n x^n$ as $a_i x^i$; the indicating of a summation by the convention that any term in which the same index (subscript or superscript) appears twice shall stand for the sum of all terms obtainable by giving the index all possible values. A superscript, as k in x^k, does not denote a power in this convention, but is merely an index to distinguish between n variables, $x^1, x^2, \cdots, x^n$. A repeated index, such as i in $a_i x^i$, is called a **dummy index,** since the value of the expression does not depend on the symbol used for this index. An index which is not repeated, such as i in $a_{ij}x^j$, is called a **free index**.

summation of an infinite series. The process of finding the limit of the sum of the first n terms, as n increases. This is not a sum in the ordinary sense of arithmetic, because the terms of an infinite series can never all be added term by term. The sum of the series

$$1/2+1/4+1/8+\cdots+1/2^n+\cdots$$

is 1, because that is the limit approached by the sum of n of these terms, namely $(2^n-1)/2^n$, as n becomes infinite. See SERIES—geometric series.

summation sign. Sigma, the Greek letter corresponding to the English S, written Σ. When the process of summing includes the first to the nth terms of a set of numbers a_1, a_2, a_3, $\cdots$, a_n, $\cdots$, the sum is written

$$\sum_{i=1}^{n} a_i, \text{ or } \sum_{1}^{n} a_i.$$

When the summation includes infinitely many terms, it is written

$$\sum_{n=1}^{\infty} a_n, \quad \sum_{1}^{\infty} a_i, \text{ or simply } \sum a_i.$$

SU-PE'RI-OR, *adj.* **superior limit.** See LIMIT.

SU'PER-POSE', *v.* To place one configuration upon another in such a way that corresponding parts coincide. To superpose two triangles which have their corresponding sides equal is to place one upon the other so that corresponding sides coincide.

SU'PER-POS'A-BLE, *adj.* **superposable configurations.** Two configurations which can be superposed. *Syn.* Congruent.

SU'PER-PO-SI'TION, *n.* **axiom of superposition.** See AXIOM.

SU'PER-SCRIPT, *n.* A number written above and to the right of a letter, usually denoting a power or a derivative, but sometimes used in the same sense as subscript. See ACCENT, PRIME —prime as a symbol, and EXPONENT.

SUP'PLE-MENT'AL, *adj.* **supplemental chords of a circle.** The chords joining a point on the circumference to the two extremities of a diameter.

SUP'PLE-MEN'TA-RY, *adj.* **supplementary angles.** Two angles whose sum is 180°; two angles whose sum is a straight angle. The angles are said to be *supplements* of each other.

SURD, *n.* An indicated root of a number, which can only be approximated. It is called *quadratic, cubic, quartic, quintic,* etc., according as the index of the radical is two, three, four, five, etc.

binomial quadratic surd. A binomial surd which contains no higher root than the square root. See below, binomial surd.

binomial surd. A binomial, at least one of whose terms is a surd, such as $2+\sqrt{3}$ or $\sqrt[3]{2}-\sqrt{3}$.

conjugate binomial surds. Two binomial surds whose product is rational, as $a+\sqrt{b}$ and $a-\sqrt{b}$, whose product is a^2-b.

entire surd. A surd that contains no rational factor. E.g. $\sqrt{3}$ or $\sqrt{2}+\sqrt{3}$.

mixed surd. A surd that contains a rational factor. E.g. $2\sqrt{3}$.

pure surd. A surd every term of which is a surd, as

$$\sqrt{2}+\sqrt{3}, \text{ or } \sqrt{2}+\sqrt{5}+\sqrt{6}.$$

trinomial surd. A trinomial at least two of whose terms are surds which cannot be combined without evaluating them; $2+\sqrt{2}+\sqrt{3}$ and $3+\sqrt{5}+\sqrt[3]{2}$ are trinomial surds.

SUR'FACE, *n.* That which bounds (or encloses) a solid, or suffices to do so when taken with at most three planes; the graph of a function of two variables when the value of the function is plotted on a perpendicular to the plane of the variables, e.g. a hemisphere, with radius 1, center at the origin, and lying above the xy-plane, is the graph of $z=\sqrt{1-(x^2+y^2)}$; the graph of an equation in three variables (in space). *Tech.* The locus of a point which moves with two degrees of freedom, i.e. whose coordinates x, y, z are expressible as functions of two parameters (the elimination of these parameters gives, of course, an equation in x, y, z).

curved surface. A surface no part of which is a plane surface.

cylindrical surface. See CYLINDRICAL—cylindrical surface.

equation of a surface. See SURFACE, EQUATION—equation of a surface, and PARAMETRIC—parametric equations of a surface.

generator of a surface. See GENERATRIX.

imaginary surface. See IMAGINARY—imaginary curve (surface).

irrational algebraic surface. See IRRATIONAL.

lateral area of a cone, cylinder, etc. See the specific configuration.

material surface. See MATERIAL.

mean normal curvature of a surface. See MEAN—mean curvature of a surface.

normal curvature of a surface. See NORMAL—normal curvature of a surface.

normal line to a surface. See NORMAL—normal line to a surface.

plane surface. A plane.

quadric surface. A surface of the second order. See QUADRIC—quadric surface.

ruled surface. See RULED—ruled surface.

rulings on a ruled surface. See RULINGS.

similar surfaces. See SIMILAR—similar surfaces.

surface area. The limit of the sum of the area of the polygons formed by the intersections of tangent planes at neighboring points distributed over the entire surface, as the area of the largest of these polygons approaches zero. Each of these plane tangential areas is obtainable by projecting some area lying in one of the coordinate planes onto the tangent plane. Hence if these areas are taken so that they are projections of rectangles, say, in the xy-plane with their sides parallel to the axes and if β is the angle between the tangent plane and the xy-plane, the surface is equal to the integral of $(\sec \beta)\ dx\ dy$ (the **element of area** or

differential of area) over the area in the xy-plane which is bounded by the projection on that plane of the boundary of the given surface. If the equation of the surface is in the form $z = f(x, y)$, then

$$\sec \beta = \sqrt{(1 + D_x{}^2 z + D_y{}^2 z)},$$

where $D_x z$ and $D_y z$ denote the partial derivatives of z with respect to x and y. It is assumed here that $\sec \beta$ is finite, i.e. none of the tangent planes are perpendicular to the plane on which the surface is being projected.

surface integral. The integral of some function, $f(x, y, z)$, over a surface. It is usually written

$$\int_s f(x, y, z)ds.$$

If the surface is divided into a number of smaller non-overlapping areas and the sum of the products of each of these areas by a value of $f(x, y, z)$ at a point in that area is formed, then the integral over the surface is the limit of this sum as the number of subdivisions becomes infinite in such a way that the upper bound of all distances between two points in the same subdivision approaches zero. If the equation of the surface is $z = g(x, y)$ then the surface integral can be written

$$\int_a^b \int_{x_1}^{x_2} \sec \beta f[x, y, g(x, y)]dxdy,$$

the integration being taken over the projection of the surface on the xy-plane. Similar forms can be gotten for the projections on the xz and yz planes. See above, surface area, for the value of $\sec \beta$ and an example of a surface integral.

surface of revolution. A surface which can be generated by revolving a plane curve about an axis in its plane. Sections of a surface of revolution perpendicular to this axis are circles, called **parallel circles** or simply **parallels;** sections containing the axis are called **meridian sections,** or simply **meridians.** The earth is a surface of revolution which can be generated by revolving a meridian about the line through the north and south poles. A surface of revolution can also be gen-

erated by a circle moving always perpendicular to a fixed line with its
center on the fixed line and expanding
or contracting so as to continually
pass through a curve which lies in a
plane with the straight line. The **element of area** of a surface of revolution
can be taken as $2\pi r ds$, where r is the
distance from the axis of revolution of
any point in the element of arc, ds, of
the curve which is rotated to form the
surface. If the curve $y = f(x)$ is revolved
about the x-axis (as in the figure),
$2\pi r ds = 2\pi f(x) ds$ and the area of the
surface of revolution, between the
values a and b of x, is

$$\int_a^b 2\pi f(x)\sqrt{1+(dy/dx)^2}\,dx.$$

From the figure, it can be seen that
$2\pi r \Delta s$ is the area gotten by rotating
the arc $BC = \Delta s$ about the x-axis, and
hence $2\pi r ds$ is an approximation to
this area (see ELEMENT—element of
arc of a curve).

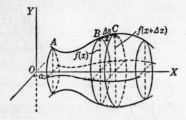

traces of a surface. See TRACE—
traces of a surface.

umbilical point on a surface. See
UMBILICAL.

SUR-REN′DER, *adj.* **surrender charge.**
(*Insurance.*) The deduction that is
made from the terminal reserve to determine the cash surrender value (not
over $2\frac{1}{2}\%$ of the terminal reserve is
allowed by law in most states).

**surrender value of an insurance
policy.** The amount the insurance
company is willing to pay the insured
for the return (cancellation) of the
policy; the difference between the
terminal reserve and the surrender
charge.

SUR′TAX′, *n.* Tax, additional to the
normal tax, levied on incomes above
a certain level.

SURVEYOR'S MEASURE. See DE-
NOMINATE NUMBERS in the appendix.

SUR-VI′VOR-SHIP, *n.* **compound survivorship probability.** See COM-
POUND — compound survivorship
probability.

SYLVESTER'S DIALYTIC METHOD.
A method of eliminating a variable
from two algebraic equations. It consists essentially of multiplying each of
the equations by the variable, thus
getting two more equations and only
one higher power of the variable, doing
the same with the two new equations,
etc., until the number of equations is
one greater than the number of powers
of the variable, then eliminating the
various powers of the variable between
these equations as if the powers were
different unknowns. (See ELIMINA-
TION—elimination of n variables
from $n + 1$ equations.) *Sylvester's method*
is equivalent to the procedure illustrated by the following example, which
does not require determinants: It is
desired to eliminate x from

(1) $x^2 + ax + b = 0$

and

(2) $x^3 + cx^2 + dx + e = 0.$

Multiply equation (1) by x and subtract the result from equation (2). This
results in an equation of the second
degree. Eliminate x^2 between this equation and equation (1), and so on.
Finally one reaches two linear equations, subtraction of which eliminates
the variable entirely.

SYM′BOL, *n.* A letter or mark of any
sort representing quantities, relations,
or operations. See the appendix for a
list of mathematical symbols.

algebraic symbols. Symbols representing numbers, and algebraic combinations and operations with these
numbers.

SYM-MET′RIC,   SYM-MET′RI-CAL,
adj. Possessing symmetry.

cyclo-symmetric function. A function which remains unchanged under a
cyclic change of the variables. See AB-
SOLUTE—absolute symmetry.

non-symmetric relation. A relation which may or may not be symmetric, depending on the particular case under consideration. The relation of *love* is *non-symmetric*, since if *a* loves *b*, *b* may, or may not, love *a*.

skew-symmetric determinant. See SKEW.

symmetric determinant. A determinant having all its *conjugate elements* equal, a determinant which is symmetric about the principal diagonal.

symmetric form of the equations of a line in space. See LINE—equation of a straight line in space.

symmetric function. A function of two or more variables which remains unchanged under every interchange of two of the variables. $(xy+xz+yz)$ is a symmetric function of *x*, *y*, and *z*. *Syn.* Absolutely symmetric function. See ABSOLUTE.

symmetric pair of equations. A pair of equations which remains unchanged as a pair, although the equations may be interchanged, when the variables are interchanged. The equations $x^2+2x+3y-4=0$ and $y^2+2y+3x-4=0$ are a symmetric pair.

symmetric relation. A relation which has the property that if *a* is related to *b*, then *b* is related in like manner to *a*. The equals relation of arithmetic is symmetric, since if $a=b$, then $b=a$.

symmetric spherical triangles. Spherical triangles whose corresponding sides and corresponding angles are equal, but appear in opposite order when viewed from the center of the sphere. The triangles are not superposable.

symmetric tensor. See TENSOR.

symmetric trihedral angles. See TRIHEDRAL.

SYM′ME-TRY, *adj.* and *n.* **absolute symmetry of a function.** See ABSOLUTE.

axial symmetry. Symmetry with respect to a line. See below, symmetry of a geometrical configuration. *Syn.* Line symmetry.

axis of symmetry. See below, symmetry of a geometric configuration.

center of symmetry. See below, symmetry of a geometric configuration.

central symmetry. Symmetry with respect to a point. See below, symmetry of a geometric configuration.

cyclo-symmetry. See SYMMETRIC —cyclo-symmetric function.

symmetry of a geometric configuration. A geometric configuration (curve, surface, etc.) is said to have symmetry (be *symmetric*) with respect to a point, a line, or a plane, when for every point on the configuration there is another point of the configuration such that the pair is symmetric with respect to the point, line or plane. The point is called the **center of symmetry;** the line, the **axis of symmetry,** and the plane, the **plane of symmetry.** See below, symmetry of two points, and tests for symmetry.

symmetry of two points. (1) Two points are said to possess symmetry (be *symmetric*) with respect to a third point (called the **center of symmetry**) if the third point bisects the line joining the points. (2) Two points are said to possess symmetry with respect to a line or plane (called the **axis or plane of symmetry**) if the line, or plane, is the perpendicular bisector of the line segment joining the two points. The pairs of points whose coordinates are (x, y) and $(-x, -y)$ or $(-x, y)$ and $(x, -y)$, are symmetric with respect to the origin; the points (x, y) and $(x, -y)$, or $(-x, y)$ and $(-x, -y)$, are symmetric with respect to the *x*-axis; the points (x, y) and $(-x, y)$ or $(x, -y)$ and $(-x, -y)$, are symmetric with respect to the *y*-axis.

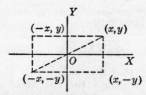

tests for symmetry of a plane curve. (1) In Cartesian coordinates, if its equation is unaltered when the variables are replaced by their negatives, it is symmetric with respect to the origin; if its equation is unaltered when y is replaced by $-y$, it is symmetric with respect to the x-axis (in this case the equation contains only even powers of y, if it is rational in y); if its equation is unaltered when x is replaced by $-x$, it is symmetric with respect to the y-axis (in this case the equation contains only even powers of x, if it is rational in x). If it is symmetric with respect to both axes, it is symmetric with respect to the origin, but the converse is not true. (2) In polar coordinates, (r, θ), a curve is symmetric with respect to the origin if its equation is unchanged when r is replaced by $-r$ ($r^2 = \theta$ is symmetrical with respect to the origin); it is symmetric about the polar axis if its equation is unchanged when θ is replaced by $-\theta$ ($r = \cos\theta$ is symmetrical with respect to the polar axis); and it is symmetrical about the line $\theta = \frac{1}{2}\pi$ if its equation is unchanged when θ is replaced by $180° - \theta$ ($r = \sin\theta$ is symmetrical about $\theta = \frac{1}{2}\pi$). The conditions for polar coordinates are sufficient, but not necessary.

two-fold, three-fold, n-fold symmetry. See TWO—two-fold, three-fold, n-fold symmetry.

SYN-THET'IC, *adj.* **synthetic division.** Division of a polynomial in one variable, say x, by x minus a constant (positive or negative), making use of detached coefficients and a simplified arrangement of the work. Consider the division of $2x^2 - 5x + 2$ by $x - 2$. Using ordinary long division, the process would be written

$$
\begin{array}{r|l}
2x^2-5x+2 & \underline{x-2} \\
\underline{2x^2-4x} & 2x-1 \\
-x+2 & \\
\underline{-x+2} & \\
\end{array}
$$

Noting that the coefficient in the quotient is always the coefficient of the first term in the dividend; that it is useless to write down the $-x$; and that by changing the sign of -2 in the quotient one could add instead of subtract, the process can be put in the *synthetic division* form

$$
\begin{array}{r|l}
2-5+2 & \underline{2} \\
\underline{4-2} & \\
2-1+0 & \\
\end{array}
$$

The detached coefficients of the quotient, 2 and -1, are called the **partial remainders.**

synthetic geometry. The study of geometry by synthetic and geometric methods. See below, synthetic method of proof. Synthetic geometry usually refers to projective geometry. *Syn.* Pure geometry.

synthetic method of proof. A method of proof involving a combining of propositions into a whole or system; involving reasoning by advancing to a conclusion from principles established or assumed and propositions already proved; the opposite of *analysis. Syn.* Deductive method of proof.

synthetic substitution. Same as SYNTHETIC DIVISION. The latter is more commonly used.

SYS'TEM, *n.* (1) A set of quantities having some common property, such as the *system* of even integers, the *system* of lines passing through the origin, etc. (2) A set of principles concerned with a central objective, as, a *coordinate system*, a *system* of notation, etc.

coordinate system. See COORDINATE.

decimal system. See DECIMAL—decimal system.

dense system of numbers. See DENSE.

duodecimal system. See DUODECIMAL.

logarithmic system. Logarithms using a certain base, as the *Brigg's system* (which uses 10 for a base), or the *natural system* (which uses $e = 2.71828 \cdots$).

metric system. See METRIC SYSTEM.

number system. A system of numbers distinguished from other numbers by some particular characteristic, as the number system with base 10, called the decimal system, or the binary system.

system of circles. Sometimes used

TABLE 249 TANGENT

for family of circles. See CIRCLE—family of circles.

system of equations. A set of two or more equations, which are to be treated simultaneously, generally to be solved for values of the variables which satisfy all of them, if there are such values.

system of linear equations. See SIMULTANEOUS — simultaneous equations.

T

TA′BLE, *n.* A systematic listing of results already worked out, which reduces the labor of computors and investigators or forms a basis for future predictions. See below, logarithm table, mortality table, etc.

accuracy of tables. See ACCURACY—accuracy of a table.

American experience table of mortality. See AMERICAN.

bond table. See BOND—bond table.

commutation table. See COMMU-TATION.

conversion table. (*Insurance.*) See CONVERSION—conversion tables.

integrable tables. See the table of integrals in the appendix.

logarithm tables. See LOGARITHM and the appendix.

mortality table. A table showing the number of deaths that are likely to occur during a given year among a group of persons of the same age (the table being based upon past statistics). See the appendix.

radix of a mortality table. See RADIX.

select mortality table. See SELECT.

service table. See SERVICE.

table of derivatives. See DIFFERENTIATION FORMULAS in the appendix.

ultimate life table. See ULTIMATE.

TAB′U-LAR, *adj.* **tabular differences.** The differences between successive values of a function, as recorded in a table. See below, tabular differences of a table of logarithms, and tabular differences of a trigonometric table.

tabular differences of a table of logarithms. The differences between successive mantissas, usually recorded in a column of their own.

tabular differences of a trigonometric table. The differences between successive recorded values of a trigonometric function.

TAC′NODE, *n.* A point on a curve at which two branches have a common tangent, but do not stop like they do at a cusp. The curve $y^2 = x^4(1 - x^2)$ has a *tacnode* at the origin, the double tangent there being the *x*-axis. A *tacnode* is also called a *double cusp*, and a *point of osculation*. See OSCULATION.

TAN-CHORD ANGLE. The angle between a tangent to a circle and a chord through the point of contact of the tangent with the circle.

TAN′GEN-CY, *n.* point of tangency. The point in which a line tangent to a curve meets the curve, and the point in which a line or a plane tangent to a surface meets the surface. *Syn.* Point of contact. See TANGENT—tangent to a curve.

TAN′GENT, *adj.* or *n.* **externally tangent.** Closed curves which lie on opposite sides of the line tangent to both of them at the same point are said to be externally tangent. Two circles such that the distance between their centers is equal to the sum of their radii are externally tangent.

general equation of a tangent to a conic. See CONIC—tangent to a general conic.

internally tangent. Closed curves which lie on the same side of a line tangent to both of them at the same point are said to be *internally tangent*. Two circles such that the distance between their centers is equal to the difference between their radii are internally tangent.

length of a tangent. The distance from the point of contact to the intersection of the tangent line with the *x*-axis. In the figure, the length of the

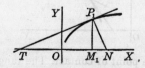

tangent at P_1 is TP_1; the length of the **normal** at P_1 is NP_1; the **subtangent** at P_1 is TM_1; and the **subnormal** at P_1 is NM_1.

polar tangent. See POLAR—polar tangent.

tangent of an angle. See TRIGONO-METRIC—trigonometric functions.

tangent to a circle. A straight line in the plane of the circle which meets the circumference in only one point. *Tech.* the limiting position of a secant when one of its two intersections with the circle moves into coincidence with the other.

tangent cone. See CONE—tangent cone of a sphere, of a quadric surface.

tangent curve. The graph of $y = \tan x$. The curve has a point of inflection at the origin; is asymptotic to the lines $x = -\frac{1}{2}\pi$ and $x = \frac{1}{2}\pi$; is convex toward the x-axis (except at the points of inflection) and duplicates itself in each successive interval of length π. See TRIGONOMETRIC — trigonometric functions.

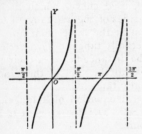

tangent to a curve, $y = f(x)$. The limiting position of a secant (P_1P_2 in the figure) when two of its points of intersection with the curve (P_1 and P_2) have moved into coincidence (at P_1). The point P_1 at which these two points coincide is called the **point of tangency,**

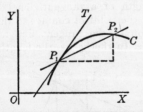

or the **point of contact.** The tangent is the line P_1T. The equation of the tan-

gent at a point on a curve is obtained by substituting the coordinates of the point and the slope of the curve at the point in the point-slope form of the equation of a line. The derivative y', evaluated at the point, is the slope of the tangent.

tangent formulas of spherical trigonometry. Same as HALF-ANGLE and HALF-SIDE FORMULAS. See HALF.

tangent law, or law of tangents. A relation between two sides and the tangents of the sum and difference of the opposite angles of a plane triangle, which is adapted to calculations by logarithms. If A and B are two angles of a triangle, and a and b the sides opposite A and B, respectively, then the law is:

$$\frac{a-b}{a+b} = \frac{\tan \frac{1}{2}(A-B)}{\tan \frac{1}{2}(A+B)}.$$

tangent line to a sphere. A line tangent to a great circle on the sphere; a line which touches the sphere in only one distinct point.

tangent plane to a cone (or cylinder). A plane containing one and only one element of the cone (or cylinder).

tangent plane to a quadric surface. If the equation of the quadric surface is $ax^2 + by^2 + cz^2 + 2dxy + 2exz + 2fyz + 2gx + 2hy + 2kz + l = 0$, then the equation of the tangent plane at the point (x_1, y_1, z_1) can be gotten by replacing x^2 by xx_1, y^2 by yy_1, etc., $2xy$ by $(xy_1 + x_1y)$, etc., $2x$ by $(x + x_1)$, etc.

tangent plane to a sphere. A plane which touches the sphere at one point only; a plane perpendicular to a radius at its extremity in the surface.

tangent plane to a surface. The limiting plane of those planes through a given point and two other points when the latter two approach the given point along curves not in the same plane. It is also the plane containing all the straight lines tangent to the surface at the given point. The direction numbers of the normal line of the plane tangent to the surface whose equation is $f(x, y, z) = 0$, at the point (x_0, y_0, z_0), are the partial derivatives of $f(x, y, z)$

with respect to x, y, and z, respectively, evaluated at the point. Hence the equation of the tangent plane is

$$D_x f(x_0, y_0, z_0)(x-x_0)+D_y f(x_0, y_0, z_0)(y-y_0)$$
$$+D_z f(x_0, y_0, z_0)(z-z_0)=0,$$

where D_x, D_y and D_z denote partial derivatives with respect to x, y, and z. Sec PLANE—equation of a plane, and PARTIAL—partial derivative.

TAN-GEN'TIAL, *adj.* **tangential acceleration.** See ACCELERATION—total acceleration for motion in a plane.

TAR'IFF, *n.* Duties, considered collectively. Sometimes used in the same sense as *duty*.

TAX, *n.* A charge levied for the support of the government.

  direct tax. Tax levied upon the person who actually pays it: such as tax levied on real estate, personal property, etc.

  indirect tax. A tax actually paid by a person other than the one upon whom it is levied, like taxes on industry which are paid by the consumer in the form of increased prices.

  poll tax. Tax levied on the individual, usually on voters only.

TAYLOR'S FORMULA. Same as TAYLOR'S THEOREM.

TAYLOR'S SERIES. See TAYLOR'S THEOREM.

TAYLOR'S THEOREM. A theorem which defines a polynomial whose graph runs very close to that of a given function throughout a certain interval, and a **remainder** which supplies a numerical limit to the difference between the ordinates of the two curves; the approximate representation of a given function on a certain interval (in the neighborhood of a certain point) by a polynomial. *Tech.* for a function of one variable, say $f(x)$, *Taylor's Theorem* can be written:

$$(x)=f(a)+f'(a)(x-a)+f''(a)(x-a)^2/2!$$
$$+f'''(a)(x-a)^3/3!+\cdots$$
$$+f^{[n-1]}(a)(x-a)^{n-1}/(n-1)!+R_n,$$

where R_n is the **remainder** or the remainder after n terms. The remainder has been put in several different forms,

the usefulness of the particular form depending upon the particular type of function being expanded. Two of these forms in common use are: (1) **Lagrange's form,**

$$\frac{h^n}{n!}f^{[n]}(a+\theta h);$$

(2) **Cauchy's form,**

$$\frac{h^n(1-\theta)^{n-1}}{(n-1)!}f^{[n]}(a+\theta h).$$

In both of these, θ is some number between 0 and 1, and $h=x-a$. If n be allowed to increase without limit in the polynomial obtained by *Taylor's Theorem*, the result is called a **Taylor's Series.** The sum of such a series represents the expanded function if and only if the limit of R_n as n becomes infinite is zero. If $a=0$ in a *Taylor's series* in one variable, the series is called a **Maclaurin's series.** The binomial expansion of $(x+a)^n$ is a Maclaurin's series, R_{n+1} being zero when n is an integer. In fact if any function can be expressed as a power series, such as $c_0+c_1(x-a)+c_2(x-a)^2+\cdots+c_n(x-a)^n+\cdots$, that series is a *Taylor's series.* Obviously a function can not be expanded in a *Taylor's series* which represents the function in the above sense unless it possesses infinitely many derivatives on the interval under consideration. **For a function of two variables,** say $f(x, y)$, *Taylor's Theorem* states:

$$(x, y)=f(a, b)$$
$$+\left[(x-a)\frac{\partial}{\partial x}+(y-b)\frac{\partial}{\partial y}\right]f(a, b)+\cdots$$
$$+\left[(x-a)\frac{\partial}{\partial x}+(y-b)\frac{\partial}{\partial y}\right]^{n-1}\frac{f(a, b)}{(n-1)!}+R_n,$$

where $f(a, b)$ following the brackets means that the partials within the brackets are to operate upon $f(x, y)$ at the point (a, b), and the brackets indicate that the expansion of the quantity within is to be a binomial expansion except that

$$\left(\frac{\partial}{\partial x}\right)^h\left(\frac{\partial}{\partial y}\right)^k$$

is to be replaced by

$$\frac{\partial^{h+k}}{\partial x^h \partial y^k}, \quad \text{and} \quad \left(\frac{\partial}{\partial x}\right)^0 \quad \text{and} \quad \left(\frac{\partial}{\partial y}\right)^0$$

are to be taken as unity. R_n is equal to or less than the numerically greatest value of all the partial derivatives, multiplied by $(|x-a|+|y-b|)^n$. Explicitly,

$$R_n = \left[(x-a)\frac{\partial}{\partial z}+(y-b)\frac{\partial}{\partial y}\right]^n \frac{f(x_n, y_n)}{n!},$$

for certain x_n and y_n such that $a<x_n<x$ and $b<y_n<y$. If an unlimited (infinite) number of terms of the form used above are taken (it being necessary that all the partial derivatives of $f(x, y)$ exist) the result is a **Taylor's series in two variables.** The series represents the function from which it was derived if and only if the remainder approaches zero as the number of terms becomes infinite. Similarly, *Taylor's theorem* and series can be extended to any number of variables. Taylor's theorem is also called TAYLOR'S FORMULA, and sometimes the EXTENDED or GENERALIZED mean value theorem, although the latter two are sometimes used for the second mean value theorem.

TEM'PO-RAR'Y, *adj.* **deferred temporary (or term) insurance.** See DEFERRED—deferred temporary insurance.

temporary annuity. An annuity, extending over a given period of years provided the recipient continues to live throughout that period, otherwise terminating at his death.

temporary annuity due. A *temporary annuity* in which the payments are made at the beginning of each period.

temporary contingent insurance. A contingent insurance contract good over a given number of years.

temporary life insurance. Same as TERM LIFE INSURANCE. See LIFE—life insurance.

temporary reversionary annuity. An annuity to be paid to one person for a given number of years beginning immediately after the death of another.

TEN'S PLACE. See PLACE—place value.

TEN'SION, *n.* Any force which tends to extend a body lengthwise, in contrast to a **compression** which is a force that tends to shorten or compress it. A weight hanging on a cord causes a *tension* in the cord, while a weight resting on a stool causes a *compression* in the legs of the stool.

TEN'SOR, *n.* An abstract object having a definitely specified system of components in every coordinate system under consideration and which can be considered to be defined by the totality of its components in the various coordinate systems. Under transformations of coordinates the components of the tensor undergo a transformation which is linear in these components and a homogeneous form in the first partial derivatives of the coordinate transformation. Explicitly let

$$A^{pq\cdots t}_{jk\cdots m}$$

be one of a set of functions of the variables x^i $(i=1, 2, \cdots n)$, where each index can take on the values $1, 2, \cdots n$ and the number of superscripts is r, the number of subscripts s. Then these n^{r+s} quantities are the x-components of a **tensor of order** $r+s$, provided its components in any other system

$$x'^i (i=1, 2, \cdots n$$

are given by

$$A'^{pq\cdots t}_{jk\cdots m}=$$

$$A^{ab\cdots d}_{ef\cdots h}\frac{\partial x'^p}{\partial x^a}\cdots\frac{\partial x'^t}{\partial x^d}\frac{\partial x^e}{\partial x'^i}\cdots\frac{\partial x^h}{\partial x'^m}$$

where the summation convention is to be applied to the indices $a, b, \cdots d$ and $e, f, \cdots h$. (See SUMMATION—summation convention.) Such a tensor is said to be *contravariant of order r* and *covariant of order s*. The superscripts are called **contravariant indices,** the subscripts **covariant indices.** See *contravariant tensor* and *covariant tensor* (below) for examples of tensors.

contravariant tensor. A tensor which has only contravariant indices. If there are r indices, it is said to be a **contra-**

variant tensor of order r. If the variables are x^1, x^2, x^3, the differentials dx^1, dx^2, and dx^3 are the components of a contravariant tensor of order one (i.e. a *contravariant vector*), since

$$dx'^i = \frac{\partial x'^i}{\partial x^j} dx^j = \frac{\partial x'^i}{\partial x^1} dx^1$$
$$+ \frac{\partial x'^i}{\partial x^2} dx^2 + \frac{\partial x'^i}{\partial x^3} dx^3,$$

for $i = 1$, 2, or 3.

covariant tensor. A tensor which has only covariant indices. If there are s indices, it is said to be a **covariant tensor of order** s. The *gradient* of a function is a covariant tensor of order one (i.e. a *covariant vector*). If the function is $f(x^1, x^2, x^3)$, the components of the tensor are

$$\frac{\partial f}{\partial x^i} \quad (i = 1, 2, 3),$$

and we have

$$\frac{\partial f}{\partial x'^i} = \frac{\partial f}{\partial x^j} \frac{\partial x^j}{\partial x'^i} = \frac{\partial f}{\partial x^1} \frac{\partial x^1}{\partial x'^i}$$
$$+ \frac{\partial f}{\partial x^2} \frac{\partial x^2}{\partial x'^i} + \frac{\partial f}{\partial x^3} \frac{\partial x^3}{\partial x'^i}.$$

skew-symmetric tensor. When the interchange of two contravariant (or covariant) indices changes only the sign of each component, the tensor is said to be *skew-symmetric with respect to these indices*. A tensor is **skew-symmetric** if it is skew-symmetric with respect to every two contravariant and every two covariant indices.

symmetric tensor. When the relative position of two or more contravariant (or covariant) indices in the components of a tensor is immaterial, the tensor is said to be *symmetric with respect to these indices*. A tensor is **symmetric** if it is symmetric with respect to every two contravariant and every two covariant indices.

tensor field. The system of tensors at each point, $P(x^1, x^2, \cdots, x^n)$, where the components are defined.

TERM, *n.* **absolute term.** See ABSOLUTE.

algebraic term. A term containing only algebraic symbols.

constant term. See CONSTANT.

deferred term insurance. See DEFERRED—deferred temporary insurance.

degree of a term. See DEGREE—degree of a term.

dissimilar terms. See DISSIMILAR TERMS.

exponential term. A term containing the variable only in exponents. Sometimes terms are called exponential when they contain both exponential and algebraic factors.

general term. A term containing parameters in such a way that the parameters can be given specific values so that the term itself reduces to any special term of some set under consideration. See BINOMIAL—binomial theorem. The general term in the general algebraic equation of the nth degree $a_0 x^n + a_1 x^{n-1} + \cdots + a_n = 0$ would be written $a_i x^{n-i}$, $(i = 0, \cdots n)$.

higher terms. See HIGHER—higher degree terms.

homologous terms. See HOMOLOGOUS—homologous elements.

like terms. Terms that contain the same unknowns, each unknown of the same kind being raised to the same power. $2x^2 yz$ and $5x^2 yz$ are *like terms*.

logarithmic term. A term containing the variable or variables affected by logarithms, such as $\log x$, $\log (x+1)$. Sometimes terms are called logarithmic when they contain algebraic factors also, as $x^2 \log x$.

preliminary term plan. See PRELIMINARY.

rational, integral term. An algebraic term in which the variable (or variables) do not appear under any radical sign, in any denominator, or with fractional or negative exponents. The terms $2xy$ and $2x^2 y^2$ are rational and integral in x and y.

similar terms. See SIMILAR—similar terms.

successive terms. See SUCCESSIVE.

term. (*Finance*). A period of time.

term of an annuity certain. The time between the beginning of the first rent period and the end of the last.

term of discount. The time from the day when a bank discount is made on a note to and including the day on which the note matures. This is not always equal to the term of the note, since a bank frequently discounts a note that has been running for some time.

term of an equation or an inequality. A *member* of the equation, or inequality; the entire quantity on one (or the other) side of the sign of equality, or inequality.

term of a fraction. The numerator or denominator.

term life insurance. See LIFE—life insurance.

term (time) of a note. The period between the date when the note was drawn and its date of maturity.

term of a polynomial. Any quantity combined as a whole with other quantities by addition. In the polynomial $x^2 - 5x - 2$, the terms are x^2, $-5x$, and -2; in $x^2 + (x+2) - 5$, the terms are x^2, $(x+2)$, and -5.

terms of a proportion. Any one of the *extremes* or *means*. See PROPORTION.

transcendental term. A term which is not algebraic, such as $\sin x$, $\log x$ or e^x.

trigonometric term. A term containing only trigonometric functions and constants. Sometimes a term is called trigonometric when it contains algebraic factors, also.

TER′MI-NAL, *adj.* **terminal form of commutation columns.** See COMMUTATION—commutation tables.

terminal reserve. The reserve on a life insurance policy at the end of any policy year and before the next premium has been paid.

terminal side of an angle. See ANGLE.

TER′MI-NAT′ING, *adj.* **terminating continued fraction.** See FRACTION—continued fraction.

terminating plan of building and loan association. The plan under which the members pay dues for a certain number of years to facilitate their building homes, the highest bidder getting the use of the money, since there is not enough to go around. New

members coming in have to pay back-dues and back-earnings. This is the earliest plan of building and loan association and is not usually practiced now.

TER-RES′TRI-AL, *adj.* **terrestrial triangle.** A spherical triangle on the earth's surface (considered as a sphere) having for its vertices the north pole and two points whose distance apart is being found.

TEST, *n.* **tests for convergence of an infinite series.** Rules which are used to determine whether or not a series converges. The rules may indicate convergence, divergence, or in certain cases fail to give any information. See RATIO, COMPARISON, CAUCHY, ALTERNATING, and RAABE'S RATIO TEST.

tests for symmetry of a plane curve. See SYMMETRY.

TET′RA-HE′DRAL, *adj.* **tetrahedral angle.** A polyhedral angle having four faces.

TET′RA-HE′DRON, *n.* A four-faced polyhedron. *Syn.* Triangular pyramid.

regular tetrahedron. A tetrahedron having all of its faces equilateral triangles. See POLYHEDRON—regular polyhedron.

THE′O-REM, *n.* (1) A general conclusion proposed to be proved upon the basis of certain given hypotheses (assumptions). (2) A general conclusion which has been proved.

Abel's theorem on power series. See ABEL'S THEOREM.

binomial theorem. See BINOMIAL —binomial theorem.

Euler's theorem. See EULER'S THEOREM.

fundamental theorem of algebra. See FUNDAMENTAL—fundamental theorem of algebra.

fundamental theorem of the integral calculus. See FUNDAMENTAL—fundamental theorem of the integral calculus.

implicit function theorem. See IMPLICIT.

Leibniz' theorem. See LEIBNIZ' THEOREM.

L'Huiler's theorem. See L'HUILER'S THEOREM.

mean value theorems. See MEAN.

THE'O-RY, *n.* The principles concerned with a certain concept, and the facts postulated and proved about it.

function theory. The theory of functions of a real variable, the theory of functions of a complex variable, etc.

group theory or theory of groups. See GROUP.

number theory or theory of numbers (elementary). The study of integers and relations between them.

theory of equations. The study of methods of solving and the possibility of solving algebraic equations, and of the relation between roots and between roots and coefficients of equations.

THOU'SAND, *n.* Ten hundreds (1,000).

THREE, *adj.* **rule of three.** See RULE.

three dimensional geometry. The study of figures in three (as well as two) dimensions. See GEOMETRY—solid geometry, and DIMENSION.

three-leafed rose. The graph of the equation $r = a \sin 3\theta$, or $r = a \cos 3\theta$. The curve consists of three loops (rose-like petals) with their vertices at the pole. The locus of the first equation has the first petal tangent to the positive polar axis, and symmetric about the line $\theta = 30°$; the second petal symmetric about the line $\theta = 150°$, and the third symmetric about the line $\theta = 270°$, each loop thus being tangent to the sides of an angle of 60°. The length of the line of symmetry of each petal, from the pole to the intersection of the curve, is a. The locus of the second equation is the same as that of the first rotated 30° about the origin. See FOUR-LEAFED ROSE, and N-LEAFED ROSE.

three point form of the equation of a plane. See PLANE—equation of a plane.

three point problem: Given three points, A, B, C, the distances AB and BC being known, and a fourth point S, with the angles ASB and BSC known, to find the distance SB. This is the problem of finding the distance from a ship S to a point B on the shore.

TIME, *n.* Continuous existence as indicated by some sequence of events, such as the hours indicated by a clock or the rotation of the earth about its axis; the experience of duration or succession.

apparent solar time. The time indicated by the sun dial, which divides each day into 24 hours; the hour-angle of the apparent or true sun (see HOUR) plus 12 hours. The hours are not exactly the same length, owing to the inclination of the Earth's axis to the plane of the ecliptic (the plane of the Earth's orbit) and to the eccentricity (elliptic shape) of the Earth's orbit.

apparent time. Same as APPARENT SOLAR TIME.

equated time. See EQUATED.

mean solar time. The average time required for the sun to pass over the meridian of a place twice; the time that would be shown by a sun dial if the sun were always on the celestial equator (in the plane of the earth's equator) and moving at a uniform rate. Sometimes called *astronomical time*.

sidereal time. See SIDEREAL.

standard time. A uniform system of measuring time, originated for railroad use in the United States and Canada and now in common use. The American continent is divided into four belts, each extending through approximately 15 degrees of longitude, designated as *Eastern, Central, Mountain*, and *Pacific*. The time in each belt is the mean solar time of its central meridian. For instance 7 a.m. *Central Time* is 8 a.m. *Eastern Time*, 6 a. m. *Mountain Time*, and 5 a.m. *Pacific Time. Tech.* standard time is the mean solar time of a standard meridian, a meridian whose longitude differs by a certain multiple of 15° from the longitude at Greenwich, 15° being equivalent to one hour.

time discount. See DISCOUNT—time discount.

time note. See NOTE—time note.

time rate. See RATE—time rate of change.

time series. Data taken at time intervals, such as the temperature or the rainfall taken at a certain time each day for a succession of days.

TON, *n.* See DENOMINATE NUMBERS in the appendix.

TONNAGE OF VESSELS. The number of hundreds of cubic foot space in the vessel, less certain deductions such as crew and space for ship machinery. The cubic space in feet available for freight and passengers, divided by 100, is the **net tonnage.**

TON-TINE′, *adj.* **tontine annuity.** An annuity purchased by a group with the *benefit of survivorship* (that is, the share of each member who dies is divided among the others, the last survivor getting the entire annuity during the balance of his life).

tontine fund. A fund accumulated by investments of withheld annuity payments.

tontine insurance. Insurance in which all benefits except those due to death, including such as dividends and cash surrender values, are allowed to accumulate until the end of a certain period and then are divided among those who have carried this insurance throughout the period.

TOR′SION, *n.* The rate of turning of a curve in the plane determined by the tangent line and the binormal; the limit of the ratio of the angle between two binormals and the arc joining their points of intersection with the curve, as these points move up to the given point. The torsion of a plane curve is zero, that of a cylindrical spiral is constant. *Syn.* Second curvature.

TORUS RING. Same as ANCHOR RING.

TO′TAL, *adj.* **total curvature.** See CURVATURE—total curvature.

total depreciation. (*Finance.*) The difference between the original cost of a composite plant, such as a factory, and its value at the time under consideration.

total differential. See INCREMENT—total increment.

TO′TIENT, *n.* **totient of an integer.** Same as the INDICATOR of the integer; the number of *totitives* of the integer. See INDICATOR.

TOT′I-TIVE, *n.* **totitive of an integer.** An integer not greater than the given integer and relatively prime to it (having no factor in common with it except unity). Each integer less than a given prime is a totitive of the prime; 1, 3, 5 and 7 are the totitives of 8.

TRACE, *n.* **trace of a line in space.** (1) A point at which it pierces a coordinate plane. (2) Its projection in a coordinate plane; the intersection of a *projecting plane* of the line with the corresponding coordinate plane. When trace is used in the latter sense, the point of definition (1) is called the *piercing point*.

traces of a surface. The curves in which it cuts the coordinate planes.

TRAC′ING, *n.* **curve tracing.** See CURVE—curve tracing.

TRAC′TRIX, *n.* The involute of a catenary; a curve the lengths of whose *tangents* are all equal; the path of one end (*P* in the figure) of a rod *PQ* of fixed length *a* attached to a point *Q* which moves along the *x*-axis from 0 to ± ∞, the initial position of the rod being *OA*. Its equation is

$$x = a \ \text{og} \ \frac{(a \pm \sqrt{a^2 - y^2})}{y} \mp \sqrt{a^2 - y^2}.$$

TRA-JEC′TO-RY, *n.* (1) The path of a moving particle or a celestial body. (2) A curve which cuts all curves of a given family at the same angle. (3) A curve or surface which fits some given law such as passing through a given set of points.

orthogonal trajectory. A trajectory which cuts all the members of a given family at right angles.

trajectory of a family of curves or surfaces. A curve which cuts all members of the family at the same angle.

TRAN′SCEN-DEN′TAL, *adj.* **transcendental curves.** Graphs of *transcendental functions*.

transcendental functions. Functions which can not be expressed algebraically in terms of the variable (or variables) and constants. Contains terms involving trigonometric functions, logarithms, exponentials, etc.

TRANS'FOR-MA'TION, *n.* **affine transformation.** See AFFINE.

division transformation. Same as LONG DIVISION, but rarely used.

equiangular transformation. Same as ISOGONAL TRANSFORMATION.

factoring of a transformation. See FACTORIZATION—factorization of a transformation.

general linear transformation. See LINEAR—general linear transformation.

homogeneous transformation. A transformation whose equations are algebraic and contain only terms of the same degree. Rotation of axes, reflection in the axes, stretching and shrinking are homogeneous transformations.

homothetic transformation. See SIMILITUDE—transformation of similitude.

identical transformation. A transformation which makes no change in a configuration (or function); a transformation such as $x' = x$, $y' = y$. It is trivial in itself but is important as the product of a transformation and its inverse. *Syn.* Identity transformation. See GROUP.

inverse transformation. The transformation which exactly undoes the effect of a given transformation. The transformation $x' = 1/x$ is its own inverse, because two reciprocations of a quantity return it to its original value. The transformations $x' = \sin x$ and $x = \arcsin x'$ are inverses of each other, for if in a function of x', say $2x'^2 + 3x' + 1$, $\sin x$ is substituted for x', there results $2 \sin^2 x + 3 \sin x + 1$. If now x is replaced by arc sin x', the result reduces to the original function of x'.

isogonal transformation. See ISOGONAL—isogonal transformation.

linear transformation. See LINEAR—general linear transformation.

product of two transformations. The transformation resulting from the successive application of the two given transformations. Such a product may

not be commutative, that is, the product may depend upon the order in which the transformations are applied. E.g. the transformation $x = x' + a$ and $x = (x')^2$ are not commutative, since replacing x by $x' + a$ and the new x (x' with the prime dropped) by $(x')^2$ gives $x = (x')^2 + a$ as the product transformation, while reversing the order gives $x = (x' + a)^2$.

rational transformation. The replacement of the variables of an equation, or function, by other variables which are each rational functions of the first. The transformations $x' = x + 2$, $y' = y + 3$ and $x' = x^2$, $y' = y^2$ are rational transformations.

simple shear transformation. A transformation representing a shearing motion; a transformation of the form $x' = x$, $y' = lx + y$, or $x' = ly + x$, $y' = y$.

transformation between Cartesian and polar coordinates. The changing of the coordinates of a point from those in a system of Cartesian coordinates to those in a system of polar coordinates, or vice versa. See POLAR—polar coordinates in the plane.

transformation between Cartesian and spherical coordinates. See SPHERICAL—spherical coordinates.

transformation of coordinates. Changing the coordinates of a point to another set which refer to a new system of coordinates, either of the same type or of another type. See transformation between Cartesian and polar coordinates.

transformation of an equation. Changing it by making some substitution for the variable or variables. The equation $x^4 + 3x^2 - 1 = 0$ is transformed into the quadratic form $y^2 + 3y - 1 = 0$ by the substitution $y = x^2$.

transformation group. A set of transformations which form a group. *Syn.* Group of transformations. See GROUP, and above, product of two transformations, and inverse transformation.

transformation to parallel axes. See TRANSLATION.

transformation of similitude. See SIMILITUDE.

transformation theorems for equations. Theorems relating to the changing of the roots of an equation. Some of the familiar changes of algebra are *change of signs* of the roots, *reduction* or *increase* in size of the roots, *multiplication of the roots by constants*, and *reciprocation of the roots*.

TRANS'IT, *n.* (*Surveying*.) An instrument for measuring angles. Consists essentially of a small telescope which rotates horizontally and vertically, the angles through which it rotates being indicated on graduated scales.

TRAN'SI-TIVE, *adj.* **transitive relation.** A relation which has the property that if A bears the relation to B and B bears the same relation to C, then A bears the relation to C. Equality in arithmetic is transitive, since if $A = B$ and $B = C$, then $A = C$. A relation which is not transitive is said to be **intransitive.** The relation of *being the father of* is *intransitive*, since if A is the father of B, and B is the father of C, then A is not the father of C. A relation which is sometimes transitive and sometimes intransitive is said to be **non-transitive.** The relation of *being a friend of* is *non-transitive*, since if A is a friend of B, and B is a friend of C, then A may or may not be a friend of C.

TRANS-LA'TION, *n.* **translation formulas.** Formulas expressing a translation of rectangular axes analytically (see below, translation of rectangular axes). In the *plane*, these formulas are:

$$x = x' + h, \quad y = y' + k,$$

where h and k are the coordinates of the origin of the x', y' system with

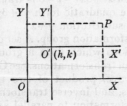

reference to the x, y system. i.e. when $x' = y' = 0$, $x = h$ and $y = k$. In *space*, if the new origin has the coordinates

(h, k, l) with respect to the old axes, and a point has coordinates (x', y', z') with respect to the new axes, and coordinates (x, y, z) with respect to the old axes, then $x = x' + h$, $y = y' + k$, $z = z' + l$.

translation of rectangular axes. Changing the coordinates of points to coordinates referred to new axes parallel to the old. Used to change the form of equations so as to aid in the study of their loci; e.g. one may desire to translate the axes so that the new origin is on the curve, which rids the equation of the constant term, or to translate the axes until they are coincident with the axes of symmetry, as in the case of conics, thus getting rid of the first degree terms.

translation and rotation. A transformation which both translates and rotates the axes. Used, for instance, in the study of the general quadratic in x and y to remove the xy and x and y terms. The transformation formulas are:

$$x = x' \cos \theta - y' \sin \theta + h$$
$$y = x' \sin \theta + y' \cos \theta + k,$$

where h and k are the coordinates of the new origin relative to the old and θ is the angle through which the x-axis is rotated to be parallel to the x'-axis.

TRANS-POSE', *v.* or *n.* (*Algebra*). To move a term from one side of an equation to the other and change its sign. This is equivalent to subtracting the term from both sides. The equation $x + 2 = 0$ becomes $x = -2$ after *transposing* the 2.

transpose of a matrix. The matrix resulting from interchanging the rows and columns in the given matrix.

TRANS'PO-SI'TION, *n.* The act of transposing terms from one side of an equation to the other. See TRANSPOSE.

TRANS-VER'SAL, *adj.* A line intersecting a system of lines. See ANGLE—angles made by a transversal.

TRANS-VERSE', *adj.* **transverse axis of a hyperbola.** See HYPERBOLA.

TRA-PE'ZI-UM, *n.* A quadrilateral, none of whose sides are parallel.

TRAP'E-ZOID, *n.* A quadrilateral which has two parallel sides and two non-parallel sides.

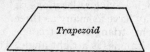

Trapezoid

altitude of a trapezoid. The perpendicular distance between the bases.

area of a trapezoid. The product of its altitude and one half the sum of the bases, written

$$A = h \frac{(b_1 + b_2)}{2}.$$

bases of a trapezoid. The parallel sides.

isosceles trapezoid. A trapezoid in which the non-parallel sides are equal.

TRAPEZOID RULE. A rule for approximating the area between an arc of a curve, a straight line segment, and perpendiculars from the extremities of the curve to the line segment. The rule is as follows: Divide the line segment into equal segments and draw perpendiculars at each division point to intersect the curve, then connect all intersections of the curve with the perpendiculars (including the bounding perpendiculars), in successive pairs, by straight lines. The given area is then approximated by the sum of the areas of the successive trapezoids. The total area of the trapezoids is one half the sum of the bounding perpendiculars (first and last) plus the sum of all the intermediate perpendiculars, multiplied by the common width of the trapezoids. *Syn.* TRAPEZOID FORMULA.

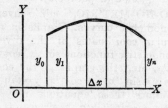

$$\text{area} = \tfrac{1}{2}\Delta x(y_0 + y_n) + \Delta x \sum_{i=1}^{n-1} y_i.$$

TRE'FOIL, *n.* See MULTIFOIL.

TREND, *n.* (*Statistics*). The general drift, tendency, or bent of a set of data; such, for instance, as the price of steel over a long period of time. Particular data will generally fluctuate from the *trend*. See RESIDUAL, and LINE—line of best fit.

trend line. See LINE.

secular trend. (*Statistics.*) A tendency of data to increase (or decrease) over a long period. During any particular year data may actually decrease, but the secular trend throughout many years still be upward. *Syn.* Secular movement.

TRI'AL, *n.* **repeated trial.** See REPEATED—probability of the occurrence of an event in a number of repeated trials.

successive trials. See SUCCESSIVE—successive trials.

TRI'AN'GLE, *n.* (1) The figure formed by connecting three points not in a straight line. (2) A part (region) of a plane bounded by straight line segments joining three points. Six kinds of triangles are illustrated.

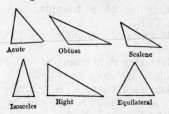

acute triangle. A triangle whose interior angles are all acute. See figure under TRIANGLE.

altitude of a triangle. See ALTITUDE—altitude of a triangle.

ambiguous case in the solution of a plane triangle, or of a spherical triangle. See AMBIGUOUS.

area of a triangle. The product of one half the length of any side and the length of the perpendicular upon that side from the opposite vertex; one half of the base times the altitude. In *analytic geometry*, the area can be expressed as one half of the determinant whose first column consists of the abscissas of the vertices, the second of the ordinates (in the same order) and the third entirely of ones (this is positive if the points are taken around the triangle in counter-clockwise order).

astronomical triangle. The spherical triangle on the celestial sphere which has for its vertices the nearer celestial pole, the zenith, and the celestial body under consideration. See HOUR— hour angle and hour circle.

birectangular triangle. See BIREC-TANGULAR.

circumcenter of a triangle. See CIRCUMCENTER.

congruent triangles. See CONGRU-ENT—congruent figures in geometry.

equal triangles. Triangles whose areas are equal. Such triangles are not necessarily congruent. Sometimes used in the same sense as congruent triangles. See EQUAL.

equiangular triangle. A triangle with all three interior angles equal. It must then also be equilateral.

equilateral triangle. A triangle with all three sides equal. It must then also be equiangular. See figure under TRI-ANGLE.

excenter of a triangle. See EX-CENTER.

incenter of a triangle. See INCEN-TER.

isosceles right triangle. A right triangle which has equal legs.

isosceles triangle. A triangle with two equal sides. See figure under TRI-ANGLE.

oblique triangle. A triangle which contains no right angles.

obtuse triangle. A triangle that contains an obtuse interior angle. See figure under TRIANGLE.

orthocenter of a triangle. The point of intersection of its three altitudes.

Pascal's triangle. See PASCAL—Pascal's triangle.

pedal triangle. See PEDAL.

perimeter of a triangle. The sum of the lengths of its sides.

polar triangle. See POLAR—polar triangle.

quadrantal spherical triangle. A spherical triangle having one side equal to 90° (a quadrant).

reciprocal polar triangles. See RE-

CIPROCAL—reciprocal polar triangles.

right spherical triangle. A spherical triangle having at least one right angle. It may have as many as three.

right triangle. A triangle one of whose angles is a right angle. The side opposite the right angle is called the **hypotenuse** and the other two sides the **legs** of the right triangle. See figure under TRIANGLE.

scalene triangle. A triangle with no two sides equal. See figure under TRI-ANGLE.

spherical isosceles triangle. A spherical triangle having two equal sides.

spherical triangle. See SPHERICAL —spherical triangle.

terrestrial triangle. See TERRES-TRIAL.

triangle of plane sailing. The right spherical triangle (treated as a plane triangle) which has for legs the difference in latitude and the departure of two places, and for its hypotenuse the rhumb line between the two places.

TRI-AN′GU-LAR, *adj.* Like a triangle; having three sides.

triangular number. See NUMBER —triangular numbers.

triangular prism. A prism with triangular bases.

triangular pyramid. A pyramid whose base is a triangle. *Syn.* Tetrahedron.

TRIDENT OF NEWTON. The cubic curve defined by the equation $xy = ax^3 + bx^2 + cx + d$, $(a \neq 0)$. It cuts the x-axis in 1 or 3 points and is asymptotic to the y-axis if $d \neq 0$. If $d = 0$, the equation factors into $x = 0$ (the y-axis) and $y = ax^2 + bx + c$ (a parabola).

TRIG′O-NO-MET′RIC, *adj.* **inverse trigonometric curves.** Graphs in rectangular coordinates of the inverse trigonometric functions $\sin^{-1}x$, $\cos^{-1}x$, $\tan^{-1}x$, etc.; the graphs of the equations $y = \sin^{-1}x$, $y = \cos^{-1}x$, $y = \tan^{-1}x$, etc. Since these equations may be written $x = \sin y$, etc., their graphs are simply graphs of the trigonometric functions with the positive x-axis and y-axis interchanged, or, what is the same, the graphs of the trigonometric functions reflected in the line $y = x$.

inverse trigonometric functions. See INVERSE—inverse trigonometric function.

relations between the trigonometric functions. The relations

$$\sin x = \frac{1}{\csc x}, \qquad \cos x = \frac{1}{\sec x},$$

$$\tan x = \frac{1}{\cot x}, \qquad \tan x = \frac{\sin x}{\cos x},$$

$$\sin^2 x + \cos^2 x = 1, \qquad \tan^2 x + 1 = \sec^2 x,$$

$$\cot^2 x + 1 = \csc^2 x.$$

These can all be derived directly from the definitions of the functions and the *Pythagorean theorem*, and are called the fundamental identities, or relations, of trigonometry. The latter three are called Pythagorean identities.

trigonometric analysis. See ANALYSIS—trigonometric analysis.

trigonometric co-functions. Same as COMPLEMENTARY FUNCTIONS. See COMPLEMENTARY—complementary trigonometric functions.

trigonometric curves. Graphs of the trigonometric functions in rectangular coordinates. See SINE—sine curve, COSINE—cosine curve, COTANGENT—cotangent curve, TANGENT—tangent curve, SECANT—secant curve, and COSECANT—cosecant curve. The term *trigonometric curve* is also applied to the graphs of any function involving only trigonometric functions, such as $\sin 2x + \sin x$ or $\sin x + \tan x$.

trigonometric equation. See EQUATION—trigonometric equation.

trigonometric form (representation) of a complex number. Same as POLAR FORM. See COMPLEX—polar form of a complex number.

trigonometric functions of an acute angle. The ratios of the sides of a right triangle containing the angle. If A is an angle in a right triangle with hypotenuse denoted by c, side opposite A by a and side adjacent by b, the trigonometric functions of A are

$$\frac{a}{c}, \quad \frac{b}{c}, \quad \frac{a}{b}, \quad \frac{b}{a}, \quad \frac{c}{b}, \quad \text{and} \quad \frac{c}{a}.$$

They are named, respectively, sine A,

cosine A, tangent A, cotangent A, secant A, and cosecant A, and written $\sin A$, $\cos A$, $\tan A$, $\text{ctn } A$ (or $\cot A$), $\sec A$, $\csc A$. Other trigonometric functions not so commonly used are versed sine of $A = 1 - \cos A = \text{versine}$ of A, written vers A; coversed sine of $A = 1 - \sin A = \text{versed}$ cosine of A, written covers A; exsecant of $A = (\sec A) - 1$, written exsec A; haversine of $A = \frac{1}{2}$ vers A, written hav A. See below, trigonometric functions of any angle.

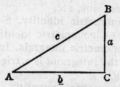

trigonometric functions of any angle. Let A be any angle (less than or greater than a right angle) described about the origin of a system of rectangular coordinates by a line OP with one end at the origin and the other, P, in its final position, having the coordinates (b, a), where b is negative if P is in the second or third quadrants and a is negative if P is in the third or fourth quadrants. If $OP = r$, then

$$\sin A = \frac{a}{r}, \qquad \cos A = \frac{b}{r}, \qquad \tan A = \frac{a}{b},$$

$$\text{ctn } A = \frac{b}{a}, \qquad \sec A = \frac{r}{b}, \qquad \csc A = \frac{r}{a},$$

or

$$\sin A = (\text{ordinate})/r,$$
$$\cos A = (\text{abscissa})/r,$$
$$\tan A = (\text{ordinate})/(\text{abscissa}),$$
$$\text{ctn } A = (\text{abscissa})/(\text{ordinate}),$$
$$\sec A = r/(\text{abscissa}),$$
$$\csc A = r/(\text{ordinate})$$

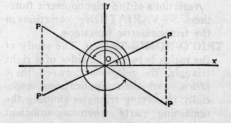

and the other functions are defined in terms of these as in the case of an acute angle (see above, trigonometric functions of an acute angle). Although each function thus defined has the same algebraic sign in two quadrants, if two functions which are not reciprocals are given, the quadrant in which the angle lies is uniquely determined; e.g. if the sine of an angle is positive and the cosine negative, the angle lies in the second quadrant. See GENERAL—general formula for all angles having the same sine, etc.

trigonometric identity. See IDENTITY—trigonometric identity.

trigonometric integrals. Integrals in which the integrand is a trigonometric function.

trigonometric quantity, equation, etc. (1) A quantity, equation, etc., containing only trigonometric terms. (2) A quantity, equation, etc., containing trigonometric and possibly algebraic terms.

trigonometric series. A series of the form

$$a_0 + (a_1 \cos x + b_1 \sin x)$$
$$+ (a_2 \cos 2x + b_2 \sin 2x) + \cdots$$
$$= a_0 + \sum (a_n \cos nx + b_n \sin nx),$$

where the a's and b's are constants. See FOURIER SERIES.

trigonometric substitutions. Substitutions used to rationalize binomial quadratic surds of the forms:

$$\sqrt{a^2 - x^2}, \quad \sqrt{x^2 + a^2}, \quad \sqrt{x^2 - a^2}.$$

The substitutions $x = a \sin u$, $x = a \tan u$, and $x = a \sec u$ reduce these surds to $a \cos u$, $a \sec u$, $a \tan u$, respectively. The quadratic surd $\sqrt{x^2 + px + q}$ can always be put into one of the above forms by completing the square.

variations of the trigonometric functions. See VARIATION—variations of the trigonometric functions.

TRIG'O-NOM'E-TRY, *n.* The study of the ratios between the sides of a right triangle, the relations between these ratios, and their applications, especially in solving triangles (finding the remaining parts when a sufficient

number are known) in surveying, range-finding, navigation, construction work, etc. See SOLUTION—solution of an oblique plane triangle.

spherical trigonometry. See SPHERICAL.

TRI-HE'DRAL, *adj.* **symmetric trihedral angles.** Trihedral angles which have their face angles equal in pairs but arranged in opposite order. Such trihedral angles are not superposable.

trihedral angle. See ANGLE—trihedral angle.

TRI-HE'DRAL, *n.* A figure formed by three non-coplanar lines which intersect in a point.

condition that a directed trihedral be tri-rectangular. If the lines forming the trihedral are L_1, L_2, L_3, the necessary condition is that the value of the determinant whose rows are l_1, m_1, n_1; l_2, m_2, n_2; and l_3, m_3, n_3 (in these orders) be equal to ± 1; where l_1, m_1, n_1; l_2, m_2, n_2; and l_3, m_3, n_3 are, respectively, the direction cosines of the lines L_1, L_2, and L_3, the subscripts denoting the order in which the lines are taken. The positive sign occurs when the trihedral has the same orientation as (is superposable with) the coordinate trihedral.

coordinate trihedral. The trihedral formed by the three axes of a system of Cartesian coordinates in space.

directed trihedral. A trihedral formed by three directed lines. The *coordinate trihedral* is a *directed trihedral*.

right and left-handed trihedrals. See RIGHT, and LEFT.

tri-rectangular trihedral. A trihedral formed by three mutually perpendicular lines.

TRIL'LION, *n.* (1) In the U. S. and France, the number represented by one followed by 12 zeros. (2) In England, the number represented by one followed by 18 zeros.

TRI-NO'MI-AL, *n.* A polynomial of three terms, such as $x^2 - 3x + 2$.

perfect trinomial square. See SQUARE—perfect trinomial square.

TRI'PLE, *adj.* Three fold; consisting of three.

triple integral. An integral requiring three successive integrations for its evaluation. The integral

$$\iiint dxdydz = \int \left\{ \int \left\{ \int dx \right\} dy \right\} dz$$

is the simplest triple integral. See IN-TEGRAL—iterated integral.

triple root of an equation. A root which occurs three times. See MUL-TIPLE—multiple root.

TRI′PLY, *adv.* Containing a property three times; repeating an operation three times.

triply orthogonal system of surfaces. See ORTHOGONAL.

TRI-RECTANGULAR SPHERICAL TRIANGLE. A spherical triangle having three right angles.

TRI-SEC′TION, *n.* The process of dividing into three equal parts.

trisection of an angle. The problem of trisecting any angle with ruler and compasses, alone. It was proved impossible by P. L. Wantzel in 1847. Any angle can be trisected, however, in several ways, for instance, by the use of the *limaçon* of Pascal, the *conchoid* of Nicodemes, or the *trisectrix* of Maclaurin. See TRISECTRIX.

TRI-SEC′TRIX, *n.* The locus of the equation $x^3 + xy^2 + ay^2 - 3ax^2 = 0$. The curve is symmetric with respect to the x-axis, passes through the origin, and has the line $x = -a$ as an asymptote. It is of interest in connection with the problem of trisecting a given angle, for if a line having an angle of inclination $3A$ is drawn through the point $(2a, 0)$, then the line passing through the origin and the point of intersection of this line with the trisectrix has an angle of inclination A. Also called the trisectrix of Maclaurin.

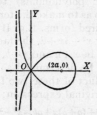

TRIV′I-AL, *adj.* **trivial solutions of a set of homogeneous algebraic equations.** Zero values for all the variables,

trivial because they are a solution of any system of homogeneous equations. Solutions in which at least one of the variables has a value different from zero are called **non-trivial solutions.**

TRO′CHOID, *n.* The plane locus of a point on the radius of a circle, or on the radius produced, as the circle rolls (in a plane) on a fixed straight line. If a is the radius of the rolling circle, b the distance from the center of this circle to the point describing the curve, and θ the angle (in radians) subtended by the arc which has contacted the fixed line in getting to the point under consideration, then the parametric equations of the *trochoid* are $x = a\theta - b \sin \theta$ and $y = a - b \cos \theta$. When b is greater than a, the curve has a loop between every two arches, nodes at $\theta = \theta_1 + \theta n\pi$, where $0 < \theta_1 < \pi$ and $a\theta_1 - b \sin \theta_1 = 0$; it is then called a **prolate cycloid.** If b is less than a, the curve never touches the base line; it is then called a **curtate cycloid.** As b approaches zero, the curve tends to smooth out nearer to the straight line described by the center of the circle. When $b = a$ the curve is a **cycloid.**

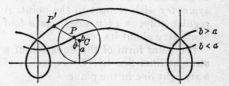

TROY WEIGHT. A system of weights having a pound of 12 ounces as its basic unit. It is used mostly for weighing fine metals. See DENOMINATE NUMBERS in the appendix.

TRUE, *adj.* **true curve surface.** A surface such that a straight edge can touch it in one point only.

true premium policy. An insurance policy in which the policy periods (premium paying periods) are fractional parts of a year. (Compare with *installment premiums.*)

TRUN′CAT-ED, *adj.* **right truncated prism.** A truncated prism in which one of the cutting planes is perpendicular to a lateral edge.

truncated cone. See CONE.

truncated prism. A portion of a prism lying between two non-parallel planes which cut the prism and have their line of intersection outside the prism.

truncated pyramid. See PYRAMID.

TURNING POINT. A point on a curve at which the ordinates of the curve cease increasing and begin decreasing, or vice versa; maximum or minimum points.

TWO, *adj.* **two dimensional geometry.** The study of figures in a plane. See GEOMETRY—plane geometry.

two-fold, three-fold, *n*-fold symmetry. A plane figure has *two-fold symmetry* with respect to a point if after being revolved, in its plane, about the point through 180° it forms the same figure as before. If the angle through which it is revolved is 120°, it is said to have *three-fold symmetry;* if the angle is 180°/*n*, it is said to have *n-fold symmetry* with respect to the point. A regular polygon of *n* sides has *n*-fold symmetry about its center.

two point form of the equation of a straight line. See LINE—equation of a straight line in the plane.

U

UL′TI-MATE, *adj.* **ultimate life table.** (1) A mortality table based on the years after the select period, the latter not entering into consideration in the table. (2) A mortality table using as a basis all the lives of a given age that are available. Compare with *select life table*.

UM-BIL′I-CAL, *adj.* **umbilical point on a surface.** A point in whose neighborhood the surface acts like a sphere (or plane); a point at which the normal curvature is unique (see CURVATURE—normal curvature of a surface). All points on a sphere or plane are umbilical points. The points where an ellipsoid of revo-

lution cuts the axis of revolution are umbilical points.

UM′BRA, *n.* [*pl.* **umbrae.**] The part of the shadow of an object from which all direct light is excluded. In the case of the sun and the earth, as shown in the figure, the region between *B* and *C* is in full shadow, and is known as the *umbra*, while the outer region shades from full illumination at *A* (and *D*) to complete shadow at *B* (and *C*), and is known as the *penumbra*.

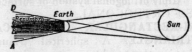

UNBOUNDED FUNCTION. A function which is not bounded; a function whose numerical value can become greater than any chosen constant; a function which can become infinite for some sequence of values of the variable or variables. The function tan x, $0 \leqq x < \frac{1}{2}\pi$, is unbounded.

UNCONDITIONAL INEQUALITY. An inequality that is always true; an inequality that either contains no variables or is true for all values of the variables involved; $3 > 2$ and $x^2 + 1 > x^2$ are unconditional inequalities. See CONDITIONAL—conditional inequality.

UNDEFINED TERM. A term used without specific mathematical definition, whatever meaning it has being purely psychological; terms which satisfy certain axioms, but are not otherwise defined.

UN-DE-TER′MINED, *adj.* **undetermined coefficients.** Parameters (unknowns) inserted in terms (usually in algebraic polynomials) to be determined so as to make the terms take certain desired forms. E.g. If it is desired to factor $x^2 - 3x + 2$, the factors may be taken to be $x + a$ and $x + b$, where a and b are to be determined so as to make the product of these two factors equal to the original expression; i.e.

$$x^2 + (a+b)x + ab \equiv x^2 - 3x + 2,$$

whence $a + b = -3$ and $ab = 2$, from which $a = -1$, $b = -2$. See PARTIAL—partial fractions.

U′NI-FORM, *adj.* **uniform acceleration.** See ACCELERATION.

uniform circular motion. Motion around a circle with constant speed.

uniform continuity of a function on a given interval. Continuity such that it is possible to divide the interval into sub-intervals such that the greatest numerical difference between the largest and the smallest values of the function (oscillation of the function) in every interval is as small as desired. The *sine curve* is uniformly continuous in any interval, while the *tangent curve* is not uniformly continuous in the interval $0 \leq x < \frac{1}{2}\pi$, although it is continuous in this interval. *Tech.* a function $f(x)$ is uniformly continuous in a given interval if for any assigned positive number ϵ there exists a number δ such that $|f(x_1) - f(x_2)| < \epsilon$ whenever $|x_1 - x_2| < \delta$, where x_1 and x_2 are any two numbers in the interval. If the interval is closed (if the end-points are included), then any function which is continuous in the interval is also *uniformly continuous*.

uniform convergence of a series. See CONVERGENCE—uniform convergence.

uniform convergence of a set of functions. Convergence such that the difference between each function and its limit can be made less than the same arbitrary positive number for a common interval of values of the argument. *Tech.* if the set of functions consists of $f_1(x)$, $f_2(x)$, $\cdots$, $f_n(x)$, $\cdots$, they *converge uniformly* to the limits L_1, L_2, $\cdots$, L_n, $\cdots$, as x approaches x_0, if for any $\epsilon > 0$ there can be found a δ such that

$$|f_i(x) - L_i| < \epsilon$$

for all i, when $|x - x_0| < \delta$.

uniform rectilinear velocity. The velocity of a particle when it passes over equal distances in equal intervals of time in a fixed direction. See VELOCITY.

uniform reversionary bonus. See BONUS—uniform reversionary bonus.

uniform scale. See LOGARITHMIC —logarithmic coordinate paper.

U-NIQUE′, *adj.* Leading to one and only one result; consisting of one, and only one. The product of two integers is unique; the square root of an integer is not.

unique inverse. An inverse operation which gives one and only one result. The antilog of 2 is unique, having the *unique* value 100; but arc sin $\frac{1}{2}$ is not *unique*, because it has infinitely many values, namely 30°, 150°, 390°, $\cdots$.

U-NIQUE′LY, *adv.* **uniquely defined.** A concept so defined that it is the only concept that fits that definition.

U′NIT, *n.* A standard of measurement such as an inch, a foot, a centimeter, a pound, or a dollar; a single one of a number, used as the basis of counting or calculating.

complex unit. See COMPLEX— complex unit.

unit circle. A circle whose radius is one unit (one inch, one foot, etc., depending upon what system of measurement is being used).

unit density. See DENSITY—unit density.

unit of force. See FORCE—unit of force.

unit fraction. See FRACTION— unit fraction.

unit of imaginaries. i; i.e. $\sqrt{-1}$.

unit square. A square with its sides equal to unity (one inch, one foot, etc., depending upon what system of measurement is being used).

unit volume, or unit cube. A cube whose edges are all of unit length.

U′NI-TAR′Y, *adj.* Undivided; relating to a unit or units.

unitary analysis. See ANALYSIS — unitary analysis.

UNITED STATES RULE. (*Mathematics of finance.*) A rule for evaluating a debt upon which partial payments have been made. The rule is: Apply each payment first to the interest, any surplus being deducted from the principal. If a payment is less than all interest due, the balance of the interest must not be added to the principal, and cannot draw interest. This is the legal rule.

U′NI-TY, *n.* Same as ONE or 1.

UN-KNOWN', *adj.* **unknown quantity.** A letter or literal expression whose numerical value is implicit in certain given conditions by means of which this value is to be found. It is used chiefly in connection with equations. In the equation $x+2=4x+5$, x is the *unknown*. In word problems, the quantity to be found is called the *unknown*. The *unknown* is also called the *variable*.

UP'PER, *adj.* **least upper bound.** See BOUND.

upper bound of a set of numbers. A number which is greater than or equal to any number in the set.

upper limit of integration. See INTEGRAL—definite integral.

V

VAL'U-A'TION, *n.* Act of finding or determining the value of.

valuation of bonds. See BOND.

VAL'UE, *n.* **absolute value of a complex number.** The square root of the sum of the squares of a and b, where the number is $a+bi$; e.g. the absolute value of $3+4i$ is $\sqrt{9+16}$ or 5.

absolute value of a real negative number. The number taken with a positive sign. It is written with the number between bars, as $|-3|=3$.

absolute value of a vector. The numerical length of the vector (without regard to direction); the square root of the sum of the squares of its components along the axes. The absolute value of $2i+3i+4k$ is $\sqrt{29}$; in general, the absolute value of $ai+bj+ck$ is $\sqrt{a^2+b^2+c^2}$. *Syn.* Numerical value.

accumulated value of an annuity. See ACCUMULATED.

assessed value. See ASSESSED.

book value of a bond. The flat purchase price minus the amount accumulated for amortization of the premium, or plus the amount accumulated to raise the purchase price to the face value, according as the bond has been bought at a premium or discount. (When the dividend rate is higher than the investor's rate, the bond sells at a premium. The income on par value plus premium will be less than the dividend. This difference is deducted from the purchase price and the balance called the *book value*. Continuing thus, the *book value* at maturity equals the par value. When the yield rate is greater than the dividend rate the bond sells at a discount. The income is then greater than the dividend for any period, so the difference is added to the purchase price of the bond to bring it back to par value at maturity. These increasing values are the *book values* of the bond.)

book value of a bond between dividend dates. The purchase price minus the accrued dividend for the fractional part of the dividend period.

book value of a debt on any date. (1) The difference, at the date, between a sinking fund set up to pay the debt and the face value of the debt. (2) The amount which, with interest, would equal the amount of the debt at the time it is due.

book value of depreciating assets, equipment. The difference between the cost price and the accumulated depreciation charges at the date under consideration.

discounted value of an annuity. Same as PRESENT VALUE of an annuity.

future value of a sum of money. See AMOUNT.

general value of an inverse trigonometric function. An expression, involving an arbitrary parameter, which is equal to a value of the inverse function for all integral values of the parameter. The general value of the inverse sine of $\frac{1}{2}$ is $n\times180°+(-1)^n30°$ or $n\pi+(-1)^n\frac{1}{6}\pi$ radians. See GENERAL—general formula for all angles having the same sine, cosine, etc.

line value of a trigonometric function. A single side of a triangle, in a unit circle, which is equal to the value of the function of the angle of the triangle at the center of the circle.

loan value of an insurance policy. See LOAN.

local value. See PLACE—place value.

market value. See MARKET.

numerical value. Same as ABSO-LUTE VALUE.

par value. See PAR.

permissible value. See PERMIS-SIBLE.

place value. See PLACE.

present value. A sum of money which, with accrued interest, will equal a specified sum at some specified future time, or equal several sums at different times, as in the case of the present value (cost) of an annuity (see below).

present value of an annuity due.

$$A = R\frac{(1+i)^n - 1}{i(1+i)^{n-1}} = \frac{R}{i}\,[1 + i - (1+i)^{-n+1}],$$

where A is the present value, R the periodic payment, n the numbers of payments, and i the rate of interest per period.

present value of an ordinary annuity.

$$A = R\frac{(1+i)^n - 1}{i(1+i)^n} = \frac{R}{i}\,[1 - (1+i)^{-n}],$$

where A is the present value, R the periodic payment, n the number of periods, and i the rate of interest per period. See TABLE VI in the appendix.

present value, P, of a sum of money, A_n, due in n years at interest rate i. At simple interest:

$$P = A_n/(1+ni).$$

At compound interest:

$$P = A_n/(1+i)^n = A_n(1+i)^{-n}.$$

principal value of an inverse trigo-nometric function. The numerically smallest value, the positive angle being taken when there are values numeri-cally equal but opposite in sign. The *principal values* of the inverse func-tions of all positive numbers for which the particular function has real values then lie in the first quadrant. In the case of negative numbers, the principal value of the arc-sine is between $-\frac{1}{2}\pi$ and 0; the arc-cosine between $\frac{1}{2}\pi$ and π; and the arc-tangent between $-\frac{1}{2}\pi$ and 0. E.g. the principal values of $\sin^{-1}\frac{1}{2}$, $\sin^{-1}(-\frac{1}{2})$, $\cos^{-1}(-\frac{1}{2})$ and

$\tan^{-1}(-1)$ are, respectively, 30°, $-30°$, 120° and $-45°$. The principal value for a negative number is sometimes defined as the least positive value of the inverse function. See above, gen-eral value of an inverse trigonometric function.

scrap or salvage value. See SCRAP.

surrender value of an insurance policy. See SURRENDER—surrender value of an insurance policy.

value of an algebraic expression. The number obtained by replacing each letter by a number. The *value* of $x + y + 2$ when $x = 3$ and $y = 5$ is 10.

value of an expression containing operational symbols. The result that would be obtained if these indicated operations were carried out. The value of $\sqrt{9}$ is 3; the value of

$$\int_a^b 2x\,dx \text{ is } b^2 - a^2.$$

See EVALUATE.

value of an insurance policy. The difference between the expectation of the future benefit and the expectation of the future net premiums; the differ-ence between the accumulated pre-miums and the accumulated losses. *Syn.* Terminal reserve.

wearing value. Same as REPLACE-MENT COST.

VAN'ISH, *v.* To become zero; to take on the value zero.

VAN'ISH-ING, *adj.* Approaching zero as a limit; taking on the value zero.

VAR'I-A-BIL'I-TY, *n.* (*Statistics*). Same as DISPERSION.

measures of variability. The *range, quartile deviation, average deviation* and *standard deviation.*

VAR'I-A-BLE, *n.* A quantity which can take on any of the numbers of some set, such as the set of real numbers, the rational numbers, all numbers between two given numbers, or all numbers. The set of values which a variable may assume is sometimes stated explicitly and sometimes only implied.

change of variable in differentiation. See DERIVATIVE—derivative of a function of a function.

change of variable in integration. See INTEGRATION—integration by substitution.

cyclic change of variables. Same as CYCLIC PERMUTATION.

dependent variable. See FUNCTION—function of one variable, and function of several variables.

determinant of the coefficients of the variables. See DETERMINANT.

differential of a variable. See DIFFERENTIAL.

function of one or several variables. See FUNCTION.

independent variable. See FUNCTION.

separation of variables. See DIFFERENTIAL—differential equation with variables separable.

VAR'I-ANCE, *n.* The square of the standard deviation, denoted by σ^2. See DEVIATION—standard deviation.

VAR'I-A'TION *n.* **combined variation.** One quantity varying as some combination of other quantities, such as z varying directly as y and inversely as x.

direct variation. When two variables are so related that their ratio remains constant, one of them is said to *vary directly* as the other, or they are said to *vary proportionately*, i.e. when $y/x = c$, or $y = cx$, where c is a constant, y is said to *vary directly* as x. This is sometimes written: $y \propto x$.

inverse variation. When the ratio of one variable to the reciprocal of the other is constant (i.e. when the product of the two variables is constant) one of them is said to *vary inversely* as the other, i.e. if $y = c/x$, or $xy = c$, y is said to *vary inversely* as x, or x to *vary inversely* as y.

joint variation. When one variable *varies directly* as the product of two variables, the one variable is said to *vary jointly* as the other two, i.e. when $x = kyz$, x varies jointly as y and z. When $x = kyz/w$, x is said to vary jointly as y and z and inversely as w.

variation of a function in an interval (a, b). The least upper bound of the sum of the oscillations in the closed sub-intervals $(a, x_1), (x_1, x_2), \cdots, (x_n, b), (a < x_1 < x_2 < \cdots < b)$ of (a, b),

for all possible such subdivisions. A function with finite variation in (a, b) is said to be of *bounded variation* or *limited variation* in (a, b).

variation of parameters. See DIFFERENTIAL—linear differential equations.

variation of sign in an algebraic equation. A change of sign between two successive terms. The equation $x - 2 = 0$ has one *variation of sign*, while $x^3 - x^2 + 2x - 1 = 0$ has three.

variation of sign in an ordered set of numbers. A change of sign between two successive numbers; e.g. the sequence $1, 2, -3, 4, -5$, has three variations of sign.

variation of the trigonometric functions. The range of values they run through as the angle varies from $0°$ to $360°$. The values are usually stated for the angles $0°, 90°, 180°,$ and $270°$, since each function has its greatest or least values (or becomes infinite) at certain of these points. For the sine they are $0, 1, 0, (-1)$; for the cosine $1, 0, (-1), 0$; for the tangent, $0, \infty, 0, \infty$; for the cotangent, $-\infty, 0, (-\infty), 0$; for the secant, $1, \infty, (-1), (-\infty)$; for the cosecant, $-\infty, 1, \infty, (-1)$. The signs ∞ and $-\infty$ here mean that the function increases or decreases, respectively, without limit as the angle approaches the given angle in a counterclockwise direction. The opposite signs (on ∞) would result if the direction were clockwise.

VEC'TOR, *n.* A line which has both magnitude and direction. Its direction is defined relative to some fixed directed line when it is in a given plane, and relative to three fixed directed lines when in space (see below, vector components). *Tech.* A tensor of order one. See TENSOR.

composition of vectors. See COMPOSITION—composition of vectors.

contravariant vector. See CONTRAVARIANT—contravariant vector.

covariant vector. See COVARIANT —covariant vector.

derivative of a vector. See DERIVATIVE—derivative of a vector.

differentiation of a vector. The

process of finding the derivative of the vector.

force vector. See FORCE—force vector.

multiplication of vectors. See MULTIPLICATION—multiplication of two vectors.

position vector. A vector from the origin to a point under consideration. If the point has Cartesian coordinates x, y, and z, the *position vector* is $R = xi + yj + zk$ (see the illustration under **vector components**).

radius vector. See POLAR—polar coordinates, SPHERICAL—spherical coordinates.

scalar product of vectors. See MULTIPLICATION—multiplication of two vectors.

vector acceleration. See ACCELERATION—total acceleration.

vector analysis. The study of vectors, relations between vectors, and their applications. See ADDITION—addition of two vectors, and MULTIPLICATION—multiplication of two vectors.

vector components (components of a vector). (1) The directed lines parallel to the axes of some system of coordinates, usually rectangular, whose vector sum is equal to the given vector. (2) In the plane, directed sides of a triangle of which the given vector is the third side; in space, the directed edges of a parallelepiped of which the given vector is a principal diagonal. If the unit vectors in the direction of the axes are denoted by i, j, and k, then the components parallel to the axes (in space) are of the form xi, yj, and zk, and the vector can be written $xi + yj + zk$, which is the form customarily used. The vector $R = xi + yj + zk$ is shown in the figure.

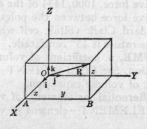

vector product of vectors. See MULTIPLICATION—multiplication of two vectors.

velocity vector. A vector whose magnitude and direction are the same as the magnitude and direction of a given velocity, the magnitude being measured in terms of some linear unit in case of the vector and in terms of some linear unit per unit of time for the magnitude of the velocity. See VELOCITY—vector velocity.

VEC-TO'RI-AL, *adj.* **vectorial angle.** See POLAR—polar coordinates in the plane.

VE-LOC'I-TY, *n.* Directed speed. See below, velocity of a particle.

absolute velocity. Velocity of a body (particle) relative to some point considered stationary, rather than relative to a moving point.

angular velocity. (1) If a particle is moving in a plane, its *angular velocity* about a point in the plane is the rate of change of the angle between a fixed line and the line joining the moving particle to the fixed point. (As far as angular velocity is concerned the particle may as well be considered as moving on a circle.) (2) If a rigid body is rotating about an axis, its *angular velocity* is (is represented by) a vector directed along the axis in the direction a right-hand screw would advance if subject to the given rotation and having a magnitude equal to the angular speed of rotation about the axis (i.e., the number of degrees or radians through which the body rotates per unit of time).

average velocity. The difference between the position vectors of a body at the ends of a given time interval, divided by the length of the interval. If $R = x(t)i + y(t)j + z(t)k$ is the *position vector* of a particle at time t, the average velocity over the time interval Δt is

$$\frac{x(t+\Delta t)-x(t)}{\Delta t} i + \frac{y(t+\Delta t)-y(t)}{\Delta t} j$$

$$+\frac{z(t+\Delta t)-z(t)}{\Delta t} k, \text{ or } \frac{R(t+\Delta t)-R(t)}{\Delta t},$$

which is the resultant of the average

velocities along the x, y and z axes. See VECTOR—vector components.

constant velocity. Uniform velocity in a straight line; the velocity of a particle which passes over equal distances in the same direction in equal time intervals.

curvilinear velocity. The velocity of a particle that is moving along a curve. Its direction is that of the curve, its magnitude the speed of the particle.

instantaneous velocity. See INSTANTANEOUS.

linear velocity. Same as RECTILINEAR VELOCITY.

rectilinear velocity. Velocity of a particle moving along a straight line.

relative velocity. Velocity computed with reference to some moving point.

uniform velocity. (1) The velocity of a particle when it passes over equal distances in equal intervals of time in a fixed direction. In this sense the same as constant velocity. (2) The velocity of a particle when it passes over equal distances in equal intervals of time, as "uniform velocity around a circle."

vector velocity. Velocity expressed as (represented by) a vector; the limit of the *average velocity* as the time interval approaches zero (see above, average velocity). If the coordinates of the moving point are x, y, and z, its *position vector* is $R = xi + yj + zk$, and its *vector velocity* is $dR/dt = (dx/dt)i + (dy/dt)j + (dz/dt)k$.

velocity of a particle. The distance through which it would pass in a given direction in a unit of time if it continued the state of motion it had at the given instant; directed speed; a vector whose magnitude is the speed and whose direction is that of the motion. See SPEED.

VERSED, *adj.* **versed sine and versed cosine.** See TRIGONOMETRIC—trigonometric functions of an acute angle.

VER-SI-E′RA, *n.* See WITCH.

VER′TEX, *n.* [*pl.* vertices] **vertex of an angle.** The point of intersection of the sides of the angle.

opposite vertex to a side (or vertex)

in a triangle or polygon. The vertex separated from the side (or vertex) by the same number of sides no matter which way one counts around the triangle or polygon.

vertex of a cone. See CONICAL SURFACE.

vertex of a parabola, hyperbola, or ellipse. See PARABOLA, HYPERBOLA, and ELLIPSE.

vertex of a pencil of lines. The point through which all of the lines pass.

vertex of a polygon. The point of intersection of two adjacent sides of the polygon.

vertex of a polyhedral angle. See ANGLE—polyhedral angle.

vertex of a polyhedron. The intersection of three or more edges of the polyhedron.

vertex of a pyramid. See PYRAMID.

vertex of a triangle. One of the three points where the sides intersect.

VER′TI-CAL, *adj.* **vertical angles.** Two angles such that each side of one is a prolongation through the vertex of a side of the other.

vertical line. (1) A line perpendicular to a horizontal line. The horizontal line is usually thought of as being directed from left to right. (2) A line perpendicular to the plane of the horizon. (3) A line from the observer to his zenith, i.e. the plumb line.

VI-BRA′TION, *n.* A periodic motion; a motion which is approximately periodic.

forced vibrations. See FORCED.

VIN′CU-LUM, *n.* See AGGREGATION.

VITAL STATISTICS. Statistics relating to the length of life and the number of persons dying during certain years, the kind of statistics from which mortality tables are constructed.

VOLT, *n.* A unit of measure of electromotive force, 1000/1434 of the electromotive force between the poles of the standard Clark voltaic cell when the temperature is 15° centigrade.

VOL′UME, *n.* **coefficient of volume expansion.** See COEFFICIENT—coefficient of volume expansion.

differential or element of volume. See ELEMENT—element of volume.

volume expansion. Increase in volume.

volume of a solid. The number of times it will contain a *unit cube*. See the specific solids for formulas.

volumes of similar solids. See SOLID —similar solids.

VUL′GAR, *adj.* **vulgar fraction.** Same as COMMON FRACTION.

W

WALLIS′ FORMULAS. Formulas giving the values of the definite integrals from 0 to $\frac{1}{2}\pi$ of each of the functions $\sin^m x$, $\cos^m x$, and $\sin^m x \cos^n x$, for m and n any positive integers.

WASTING ASSETS. Same as DEPRECIATING ASSETS.

WATT, *n.* A unit of measure of electric power; the power required to keep a current of one ampere flowing under a potential drop of one volt; 1/736 of one horse-power (English and American): 10^7 ergs per second.

watt hour. A unit of measure of electric energy; the work done by one watt acting for one hour. It equals $36 \cdot 10^9$ ergs.

WAVE, *n.* **wave length** of motion as represented by trigonometric functions. The period of the trigonometric function. See PERIOD—period of a function.

WEARING VALUE of equipment. The difference between the purchase price and the scrap value. Also called **original wearing value.**

remaining wearing value. The difference between the book value and scrap value.

WEDGE, *n.* **elliptic wedge.** The surface generated by a straight line intersecting a given line, remaining parallel to a plane, and intersecting an ellipse with its plane parallel to the given line but not containing it.

spherical wedge. See SPHERICAL —spherical wedge.

WEIGHT, *n.* The gravitational pull on a body. See POUND.

apothecaries weight. The system of weights used by druggists. The pound and the ounce are the same as in troy weight, but the subdivisions of the ounce are different. See DENOMINATE NUMBERS in the appendix.

avoirdupois weight. The system of weights which uses a pound of 16 ounces as its basic unit. See the appendix.

pound of weight. See POUND.

troy weight. The system of weights using a pound consisting of 12 ounces. Used mostly for weighing metals. See DENOMINATE NUMBERS in the appendix.

WEIGHTED MEAN. The kind of mean obtained between quantities by summing the products of each of them by a constant (not all the constants being zero) and dividing by the sum of the constants. E.g. if one desired to give more and more preference to the grades a student makes as the semester advances, he could do so by using a weighted mean. Suppose the grades were 60%, 70%, 80%, 90%. The average would be 75%, but if 1, 2, 3, 4 were used as multipliers in the order they occur, the weighted mean would be $(60+140+240+360)/10$, or 80%. The constants are called the **weights.** The *weighted mean* reduces to the ordinary *mean* or *average* when the weights are all equal.

WEIGHTS, *n.* See WEIGHTED MEAN.

WHOLE, *adj.* **deferred whole life insurance.** See DEFERRED—deferred whole life insurance.

whole life insurance. See LIFE— life insurance.

WIDTH, *n.* Same as BREADTH.

WILSON′S THEOREM: The number $[(n-1)!+1]$ is divisible by n if, and only if, n is a prime. E.g. $4!+1=25$ is divisible by 5, but $5!+1=121$ is not divisible by 6.

WITCH, *n.* A plane cubic curve defined by drawing a circle of radius a, tangent to the x-axis at the origin, then drawing a line through the origin and forming a right triangle with its hypotenuse on this line and one leg parallel to the x-axis, the other parallel to the y-axis, and passing, respectively, through the points of intersection of this line with the circle and the line $y=2a$. The witch is then the locus of the intersection of the legs of all such triangles. Its equation in rectangular coordinates is $x^2y = 4a^2(2a - y)$. The *witch* is usually called the **witch of Agnesi,** after Donna Maria Gaetana Agnesi, who discussed the curve. It is also called the **versiera.**

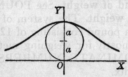

WORK, *n.* The force times the distance passed over when the force is in the direction of the path of motion, as when one drags a weight by a horizontal rope; the component of a force in the direction of motion times the distance passed over by the point of application of this force (the component perpendicular to the direction of motion does no work). If the force is variable and a function of the distance passed over, the total work done by the force in passing from *a* to *b* is the integral from *a* to *b* of the force function with respect to the distance, written

$$W = \int_a^b F(s)ds$$

where $F(s)$ is the component of the force in the direction of the tangent to the path along which it acts.

differential, or element, of work. See ELEMENT—element of work.

WORTH, *n.* **present worth.** Same as PRESENT VALUE.

X

X. (1) The letter most commonly used to denote an **unknown number** or **variable.** (2) Used to denote one of the axes in a system of Cartesian coordinates. See CARTESIAN.

X-AXIS. See CARTESIAN.

Y

Y-AXIS. See CARTESIAN.

YARD, *n.* A unit of English linear measure equal to three feet; the distance between two lines on a specially prepared and carefully preserved bar, at a temperature of 62°F. See DENOMINATE NUMBERS in the appendix.

YEAR, *n.* **civil year.** See CIVIL YEAR.

commercial year. See COMMERCIAL.

sidereal year. See SIDEREAL.

tropical year. The period between successive passages of the same equinox; the period between successive passages (in the same direction) of the sun's center through the plane of the equator. Its mean value is 365 days, 5 hrs., 48 min., 45.7 sec. Because of the precession of the equinoxes this is 20 min., 23.8 sec. shorter than the sidereal year. *Syn. equinoctial year.*

YIELD, *n.* (*Finance*). The rate percent which gives a certain profit. *Syn.* Rate percent yield, yield rate, investor's (investment) rate.

approximate yield rate of a bond. See APPROXIMATE—approximate yield of a bond.

yield of a bond. The rate of interest which a person realizes on an investment in this type of bonds. *Syn.* Effective bond rate, etc. See above, YIELD.

Z

Z-AXIS. See COORDINATE—coordinate planes.

ZE'NITH, *n.* **zenith distance of a star.** The angular distance from the zenith to the star, measured along the great circle through the zenith, the nadir and the star. It is the complement of the altitude. See HOUR—hour angle and hour circle.

zenith of an observer. The point on the celestial sphere directly above the observer; the point where a plumb line, extended upwards, would pierce the celestial sphere.

ZENO'S PARADOX of Achilles and the tortoise: A tortoise has a head start on Achilles equal to the distance from *a* to *b* and both start running, Achilles after the tortoise. Although Achilles runs faster than the tortoise, he would never catch up with the tortoise, since while Achilles goes from *a* to *b*, the tortoise goes from *b* to *c*, and while Achilles goes from *b* to *c*, the tortoise goes from *c* to *d*, etc., this process never ending. The explanation of the fallacy is that motion is measured by space intervals per unit of time, not by numbers of points. If the tortoise travels 10 ft. per second and Achilles 20 ft. and the tortoise starts 10 ft. in advance, Achilles will catch him at the end of the first second.

ZE'RO, *n.* (1) The cardinal number denoting the absence of any of the units that have been under consideration. (2) The ordinal number denoting the initial point, or origin. *Tech.* the quantity which when added to another quantity does not alter the former; if $a+b=a$, b is called *zero.*

division by zero. See DIVISION—division by zero.

division of zero. The quotient of zero and any other number is zero; $0/k=0$ for all k, since $0=k\times0$. See DIVISION—division of one quantity by a second quantity.

factorial zero. Defined as equal to unity. See FACTORIAL.

multiplication by zero. The product of zero and any other number is zero, i.e. $0\times k=k\times0=0$ for all k. See MULTIPLICATION—multiplication of two integers.

real zero of a polynomial. See REAL.

zero angle. (1) The angle between two coincident lines having the same direction. (2) The angle between two parallel lines having the same direction.

zero exponent. See EXPONENT—zero exponent.

zero of a function. A value of the argument for which the function is zero. If the function is $f(x)$, a *zero* is a value of x for which the curve $y=f(x)$ crosses the x-axis. A zero of x^3-4x is 2, since $2^3-4\times2=0$.

zero meridian. See MERIDIAN—principal meridian.

zero of a polynomial. A value of the variable which makes the polynomial zero. See REAL—real zero of a polynomial.

zero of a quadratic. A value of the variable which satisfies the equation formed by equating the quadratic function to zero. See REAL—real zero of a polynomial.

ZONE, *n.* A portion of a sphere bounded by the two intersections of two parallel planes with the sphere. One of the planes may be a tangent plane, in which case one of the circular intersections is a point and the zone is said to be a **zone of one base.**

altitude of a zone. The perpendicular distance between the planes cutting the zone out of the sphere. See ZONE.

area of a zone. The area of a zone is equal to the product of its altitude and the perimeter of a great circle of the sphere, i.e. $2\pi rh$, where r is the radius of the sphere and h the altitude of the zone.

bases of a zone. The intersections with the sphere of the planes forming the zone. When one plane is tangent to the sphere, the zone is said to have only one base, or to be a *zone of one base.*

zone meridian. See MERIDIAN—principal meridian.

zone of one base. See above, ZONE

APPENDIX

Contents:

TABLE I, Common Logarithms...................... 1–18

TABLE II, Trigonometric Functions and Their Logarithms.. 19–23

TABLE III, Amount of One Dollar at Compound Interest for
n Years... 24

TABLE IV, Present Value of One Dollar Due at End of n Years 25

TABLE V, Amount of an Annuity of One Dollar Per Year for
n Years... 26

TABLE VI, Present Value of an Annuity of One Dollar Per
Year for n Years................................. 27

TABLE VII, American Experience Table of Mortality....... 28

TABLE VIII, Squares, Cubes, Square Roots, and Cube Roots
of Integers...................................... 29

DENOMINATE NUMBERS: Length, square and cubic measure, weights, and American and English money systems. 30–32

DIFFERENTIATION FORMULAS.................... 32

INTEGRAL TABLES................................ 33–42

THE GREEK ALPHABET............................ 42

MATHEMATICAL SYMBOLS........................ 43–46

TABLE I

COMMON LOGARITHMS*

To get a natural logarithm, multiply the common logarithm by 2.302585 (=log$_e$ 10).
(See Logarithm, Anti-logarithm, Characteristic, Mantissa, and Proportional Parts.)

N	0	1	2	3	4	5	6	7	8	9
100	00 000	00 043	00 087	00 130	00 173	00 217	00 260	00 303	00 346	00 389
101	432	475	518	561	604	647	689	732	775	817
102	860	903	945	988	01 030	01 072	01 115	01 157	01 199	01 242
103	01 284	01 326	01 368	01 410	452	494	536	578	620	662
104	703	745	787	828	870	912	953	995	02 036	02 078
105	02 119	02 160	02 202	02 243	02 284	02 325	02 366	02 407	02 449	02 490
106	531	572	612	653	694	735	776	816	857	898
107	938	979	03 019	03 060	03 100	03 141	03 181	03 222	03 262	03 302
108	03 342	03 383	423	463	503	543	583	623	663	703
109	743	782	822	862	902	941	981	04 021	04 060	04 100
110	04 139	04 179	04 218	04 258	04 297	04 336	04 376	04 415	04 454	04 493
111	532	571	610	650	689	727	766	805	844	883
112	922	961	999	05 038	05 077	05 115	05 154	05 192	05 231	05 269
113	05 308	05 346	05 385	423	461	500	538	5?6	614	652
114	690	729	767	805	843	881	918	9?6	994	06 032
115	06 070	06 108	06 145	06 183	06 221	06 258	06 296	06 333	06 371	06 408
116	446	483	521	558	595	633	670	707	744	781
117	819	856	893	930	967	07 004	07 041	07 078	07 115	07 151
118	07 188	07 225	07 262	07 298	07 335	372	408	445	482	518
119	555	591	628	664	700	737	773	809	846	882
120	07 918	07 954	07 990	08 027	08 063	08 099	08 135	08 171	08 207	08 243
121	08 279	08 314	08 350	386	422	458	493	529	565	600
122	636	672	707	743	778	814	849	884	920	955
123	991	09 026	09 061	09 096	09 132	09 167	09 202	09 237	09 272	09 307
124	09 342	377	412	447	482	517	552	587	621	656
125	09 691	09 726	09 760	09 795	09 830	09 864	09 899	09 934	09 968	10 003
126	10 037	10 072	10 106	10 140	10 175	10 209	10 243	10 278	10 312	346
127	380	415	449	483	517	551	585	619	653	687
128	721	755	789	823	857	890	924	958	992	11 025
129	11 059	11 093	11 126	11 160	11 193	11 227	11 261	11 294	11 327	361
130	11 394	11 428	11 461	11 494	11 528	11 561	11 594	11 628	11 661	11 694
131	727	760	793	826	860	893	926	959	992	12 024
132	12 057	12 090	12 123	12 156	12 189	12 222	12 254	12 287	12 320	352
133	385	418	450	483	516	548	581	613	646	678
134	710	743	775	808	840	872	905	937	969	13 001
135	13 033	13 066	13 098	13 130	13 162	13 194	13 226	13 258	13 290	13 322
136	354	386	418	450	481	513	545	577	609	640
137	672	704	735	767	799	830	862	893	925	956
138	988	14 019	14 051	14 082	14 114	14 145	14 176	14 208	14 239	14 270
139	14 301	333	364	395	426	457	489	520	551	582
140	14 613	14 644	14 675	14 706	14 737	14 768	14 799	14 829	14 860	14 891
141	922	953	983	15 014	15 045	15 076	15 106	15 137	15 168	15 198
142	15 229	15 259	15 290	320	351	381	412	442	473	503
143	534	564	594	625	655	685	715	746	776	806
144	836	866	897	927	957	987	16 017	16 047	16 077	16 107
145	16 137	16 167	16 197	16 227	16 256	16 286	16 316	16 346	16 376	16 406
146	435	465	495	524	554	584	613	643	673	702
147	732	761	791	820	850	879	909	938	967	997
148	17 026	17 056	17 085	17 114	17 143	17 173	17 202	17 231	17 260	17 289
149	319	348	377	406	435	464	493	522	551	580
150	17 609	17 638	17 667	17 696	17 725	17 754	17 782	17 811	17 840	17 869

Prop. Pts.

	41	42	43
1	4.1	4.2	4.3
2	8.2	8.4	8.6
3	12.3	12.6	12.9
4	16.4	16.8	17.2
5	20.5	21.0	21.5
6	24.6	25.2	25.8
7	28.7	29.4	30.1
8	32.8	33.6	34.4
9	36.9	37.8	38.7

	38	39	40
1	3.8	3.9	4.0
2	7.6	7.8	8.0
3	11.4	11.7	12.0
4	15.2	15.6	16.0
5	19.0	19.5	20.0
6	22.8	23.4	24.0
7	26.6	27.3	28.0
8	30.4	31.2	32.0
9	34.2	35.1	36.0

	35	36	37
1	3.5	3.6	3.7
2	7.0	7.2	7.4
3	10.5	10.8	11.1
4	14.0	14.4	14.8
5	17.5	18.0	18.5
6	21.0	21.6	22.2
7	24.5	25.2	25.9
8	28.0	28.8	29.6
9	31.5	32.4	33.3

	32	33	34
1	3.2	3.3	3.4
2	6.4	6.6	6.8
3	9.6	9.9	10.2
4	12.8	13.2	13.6
5	16.0	16.5	17.0
6	19.2	19.8	20.4
7	22.4	23.1	23.8
8	25.6	26.4	27.2
9	28.8	29.7	30.6

	29	30	31
1	2.9	3.0	3.1
2	5.8	6.0	6.2
3	8.7	9.0	9.3
4	11.6	12.0	12.4
5	14.5	15.0	15.5
6	17.4	18.0	18.6
7	20.3	21.0	21.7
8	23.2	24.0	24.8
9	26.1	27.0	27.9

*Adapted from Mackie and Hoyle's Elementary College Mathematics, by permission of the publishers, Ginn and Company.

TABLE I
COMMON LOGARITHMS

N	0	1	2	3	4	5	6	7	8	9
150	17 609	17 638	17 667	17 696	17 725	17 754	17 782	17 811	17 840	17 869
151	898	926	955	984	18 013	18 041	18 070	18 099	18 127	18 156
152	18 184	18 213	18 241	18 270	298	327	355	384	412	441
153	469	498	526	554	583	611	639	667	696	724
154	752	780	808	837	865	893	921	949	977	19 005
155	19 033	19 061	19 089	19 117	19 145	19 173	19 201	19 229	19 257	19 285
156	312	340	368	396	424	451	479	507	535	562
157	590	618	645	673	700	728	756	783	811	838
158	866	893	921	948	976	20 003	20 030	20 058	20 085	20 112
159	20 140	20 167	20 194	20 222	20 249	276	303	330	358	385
160	20 412	20 439	20 466	20 493	20 520	20 548	20 575	20 602	20 629	20 656
161	683	710	737	763	790	817	844	871	898	925
162	952	978	21 005	21 032	21 059	21 085	21 112	21 139	21 165	21 192
163	21 219	21 245	272	299	325	352	378	405	431	458
164	484	511	537	564	590	617	643	669	696	722
165	21 748	21 775	21 801	21 827	21 854	21 880	21 906	21 932	21 958	21 985
166	22 011	22 037	22 063	22 089	22 115	22 141	22 167	22 194	22 220	22 246
167	272	298	324	350	376	401	427	453	479	505
168	531	557	583	608	634	660	686	712	737	763
169	789	814	840	866	891	917	943	968	994	23 019
170	23 045	23 070	23 096	23 121	23 147	23 172	23 198	23 223	23 249	23 274
171	300	325	350	376	401	426	452	477	502	528
172	553	578	603	629	654	679	704	729	754	779
173	805	830	855	880	905	930	955	980	24 005	24 030
174	24 055	24 080	24 105	24 130	24 155	24 180	24 204	24 229	254	279
175	24 304	24 329	24 353	24 378	24 403	24 428	24 452	24 477	24 502	24 527
176	551	576	601	625	650	674	699	724	748	773
177	797	822	846	871	895	920	944	969	993	25 018
178	25 042	25 066	25 091	25 115	25 139	25 164	25 188	25 212	25 237	261
179	285	310	334	358	382	406	431	455	479	503
180	25 527	25 551	25 575	25 600	25 624	25 648	25 672	25 696	25 720	25 744
181	768	792	816	840	864	888	912	935	959	983
182	26 007	26 031	26 055	26 079	26 102	26 126	26 150	26 174	26 198	26 221
183	245	269	293	316	340	364	387	411	435	458
184	482	505	529	553	576	600	623	647	670	694
185	26 717	26 741	26 764	26 788	26 811	26 834	26 858	26 881	26 905	26 928
186	951	975	998	27 021	27 045	27 068	27 091	27 114	27 138	27 161
187	27 184	27 207	27 231	254	277	300	323	346	370	393
188	416	439	462	485	508	531	554	577	600	623
189	646	669	692	715	738	761	784	807	830	852
190	27 875	27 898	27 921	27 944	27 967	27 989	28 012	28 035	28 058	28 081
191	28 103	28 126	28 149	28 171	28 194	28 217	240	262	285	307
192	330	353	375	398	421	443	466	488	511	533
193	556	578	601	623	646	668	691	713	735	758
194	780	803	825	847	870	892	914	937	959	981
195	29 003	29 026	29 048	29 070	29 092	29 115	29 137	29 159	29 181	29 203
196	226	248	270	292	314	336	358	380	403	425
197	447	469	491	513	535	557	579	601	623	645
198	667	688	710	732	754	776	798	820	842	863
199	885	907	929	951	973	994	30 016	30 038	30 060	30 081
200	30 103	30 125	30 146	30 168	30 190	30 211	30 233	30 255	30 276	30 298

Prop. Pts.

	28	29
1	2.8	2.9
2	5.6	5.8
3	8.4	8.7
4	11.2	11.6
5	14.0	14.5
6	16.8	17.4
7	19.6	20.3
8	22.4	23.2
9	25.2	26.1

	26	27
1	2.6	2.7
2	5.2	5.4
3	7.8	8.1
4	10.4	10.8
5	13.0	13.5
6	15.6	16.2
7	18.2	18.9
8	20.8	21.6
9	23.4	24.3

	24	25
1	2.4	2.5
2	4.8	5.0
3	7.2	7.5
4	9.6	10.0
5	12.0	12.5
6	14.4	15.0
7	16.8	17.5
8	19.2	20.0
9	21.6	22.5

	22	23
1	2.2	2.3
2	4.4	4.6
3	6.6	6.9
4	8.8	9.2
5	11.0	11.5
6	13.2	13.8
7	15.4	16.1
8	17.6	18.4
9	19.8	20.7

	21
1	2.1
2	4.2
3	6.3
4	8.4
5	10.5
6	12.6
7	14.7
8	16.8
9	18.9

TABLE I

COMMON LOGARITHMS

N	0	1	2	3	4	5	6	7	8	9
200	30 103	30 125	30 146	30 168	30 190	30 211	30 233	30 255	30 276	30 298
201	320	341	363	384	406	428	449	471	492	514
202	535	557	578	600	621	643	664	685	707	728
203	750	771	792	814	835	856	878	899	920	942
204	963	984	31 006	31 027	31 048	31 069	31 091	31 112	31 133	31 154
205	31 175	31 197	31 218	31 239	31 260	31 281	31 302	31 323	31 345	31 366
206	387	408	429	450	471	492	513	534	555	576
207	597	618	639	660	681	702	723	744	765	785
208	806	827	848	869	890	911	931	952	973	994
209	32 015	32 035	32 056	32 077	32 098	32 118	32 139	32 160	32 181	32 201
210	32 222	32 243	32 263	32 284	32 305	32 325	32 346	32 366	32 387	32 408
211	428	449	469	490	510	531	552	572	593	613
212	634	654	675	695	715	736	756	777	797	818
213	838	858	879	899	919	940	960	980	33 001	33 021
214	33 041	33 062	33 082	33 102	33 122	33 143	33 163	33 183	203	224
215	33 244	33 264	33 284	33 304	33 325	33 345	33 365	33 385	33 405	33 425
216	445	465	486	506	526	546	566	586	606	626
217	646	666	686	706	726	746	766	786	806	826
218	846	866	885	905	925	945	965	985	34 005	34 025
219	34 044	34 064	34 084	34 104	34 124	34 143	34 163	34 183	203	223
220	34 242	34 262	34 282	34 301	34 321	34 341	34 361	34 380	34 400	34 420
221	439	459	479	498	518	537	557	577	596	616
222	635	655	674	694	713	733	753	772	792	811
223	830	850	869	889	908	928	947	967	986	35 005
224	35 025	35 044	35 064	35 083	35 102	35 122	35 141	35 160	35 180	199
225	35 218	35 238	35 257	35 276	35 295	35 315	35 334	35 353	35 372	35 392
226	411	430	449	468	488	507	526	545	564	583
227	603	622	641	660	679	698	717	736	755	774
228	793	813	832	851	870	889	908	927	946	965
229	984	36 003	36 021	36 040	36 059	36 078	36 097	36 116	36 135	36 154
230	36 173	36 192	36 211	36 229	36 248	36 267	36 286	36 305	36 324	36 342
231	361	380	399	418	436	455	474	493	511	530
232	549	568	586	605	624	642	661	680	698	717
233	736	754	773	791	810	829	847	866	884	903
234	922	940	959	977	996	37 014	37 033	37 051	37 070	37 088
235	37 107	37 125	37 144	37 162	37 181	37 199	37 218	37 236	37 254	37 273
236	291	310	328	346	365	383	401	420	438	457
237	475	493	511	530	548	566	585	603	621	639
238	658	676	694	712	731	749	767	785	803	822
239	840	858	876	894	912	931	949	967	985	38 003
240	38 021	38 039	38 057	38 075	38 093	38 112	38 130	38 148	38 166	38 184
241	202	220	238	256	274	292	310	328	346	364
242	382	399	417	435	453	471	489	507	525	543
243	561	578	596	614	632	650	668	686	703	721
244	739	757	775	792	810	828	846	863	881	899
245	38 917	38 934	38 952	38 970	38 987	39 005	39 023	39 041	39 058	39 076
246	39 094	39 111	39 129	39 146	39 164	182	199	217	235	252
247	270	287	305	322	340	358	375	393	410	428
248	445	463	480	498	515	533	550	568	585	602
249	620	637	655	672	690	707	724	742	759	777
250	39 794	39 811	39 829	39 846	39 863	39 881	39 898	39 915	39 933	39 950

Prop. Pts.

	21	22
1	2.1	2.2
2	4.2	4.4
3	6.3	6.6
4	8.4	8.8
5	10.5	11.0
6	12.6	13.2
7	14.7	15.4
8	16.8	17.6
9	18.9	19.8

	20
1	2.0
2	4.0
3	6.0
4	8.0
5	10.0
6	12.0
7	14.0
8	16.0
9	18.0

	19
1	1.9
2	3.8
3	5.7
4	7.6
5	9.5
6	11.4
7	13.3
8	15.2
9	17.1

	18
1	1.8
2	3.6
3	5.4
4	7.2
5	9.0
6	10.8
7	12.6
8	14.4
9	16.2

	17
1	1.7
2	3.4
3	5.1
4	6.8
5	8.5
6	10.2
7	11.9
8	13.6
9	15.3

TABLE I

COMMON LOGARITHMS

N	0	1	2	3	4	5	6	7	8	9
250	39 794	39 811	39 829	39 846	39 863	39 881	39 898	39 915	39 933	39 950
251	967	985	40 002	40 019	40 037	40 054	40 071	40 088	40 106	40 123
252	40 140	40 157	175	192	209	226	243	261	278	295
253	312	329	346	364	381	398	415	432	449	466
254	483	500	518	535	552	569	586	603	620	637
255	40 654	40 671	40 688	40 705	40 722	40 739	40 756	40 773	40 790	40 807
256	824	841	858	875	892	909	926	943	960	976
257	993	41 010	41 027	41 044	41 061	41 078	41 095	41 111	41 128	41 145
258	41 162	179	196	212	229	246	263	280	296	313
259	330	347	363	380	397	414	430	447	464	481
260	41 497	41 514	41 531	41 547	41 564	41 581	41 597	41 614	41 631	41 647
261	664	681	697	714	731	747	764	780	797	814
262	830	847	863	880	896	913	929	946	963	979
263	996	42 012	42 029	42 045	42 062	42 078	42 095	42 111	42 127	42 144
264	42 160	177	193	210	226	243	259	275	292	308
265	42 325	42 341	42 357	42 374	42 390	42 406	42 423	42 439	42 455	42 472
266	488	504	521	537	553	570	586	602	619	635
267	651	667	684	700	716	732	749	765	781	797
268	813	830	846	862	878	894	911	927	943	959
269	975	991	43 008	43 024	43 040	43 056	43 072	43 088	43 104	43 120
270	43 136	43 152	43 169	43 185	43 201	43 217	43 233	43 249	43 265	43 281
271	297	313	329	345	361	377	393	409	425	441
272	457	473	489	505	521	537	553	569	584	600
273	616	632	648	664	680	696	712	727	743	759
274	775	791	807	823	838	854	870	886	902	917
275	43 933	43 949	43 965	43 981	43 996	44 012	44 028	44 044	44 059	44 075
276	44 091	44 107	44 122	44 138	44 154	170	185	201	217	232
277	248	264	279	295	311	326	342	358	373	389
278	404	420	436	451	467	483	498	514	529	545
279	560	576	592	607	623	638	654	669	685	700
280	44 716	44 731	44 747	44 762	44 778	44 793	44 809	44 824	44 840	44 855
281	871	886	902	917	932	948	963	979	994	45 010
282	45 025	45 040	45 056	45 071	45 086	45 102	45 117	45 133	45 148	163
283	179	194	209	225	240	255	271	286	301	317
284	332	347	362	378	393	408	423	439	454	469
285	45 484	45 500	45 515	45 530	45 545	45 561	45 576	45 591	45 606	45 621
286	637	652	667	682	697	712	728	743	758	773
287	788	803	818	834	849	864	879	894	909	924
288	939	954	969	984	46 000	46 015	46 030	46 045	46 060	46 075
289	46 090	46 105	46 120	46 135	150	165	180	195	210	225
290	46 240	46 255	46 270	46 285	46 300	46 315	46 330	46 345	46 359	46 374
291	389	404	419	434	449	464	479	494	509	523
292	538	553	568	583	598	613	627	642	657	672
293	687	702	716	731	746	761	776	790	805	820
294	835	850	864	879	894	909	923	938	953	967
295	46 982	46 997	47 012	47 026	47 041	47 056	47 070	47 085	47 100	47 114
296	47 129	47 144	159	173	188	202	217	232	246	261
297	276	290	305	319	334	349	363	378	392	407
298	422	436	451	465	480	494	509	524	538	553
299	567	582	596	611	625	640	654	669	683	698
300	47 712	47 727	47 741	47 756	47 770	47 784	47 799	47 813	47 828	47 842

Prop. Pts.

	18		17		16		15		14
1	1.8	1	1.7	1	1.6	1	1.5	1	1.4
2	3.6	2	3.4	2	3.2	2	3.0	2	2.8
3	5.4	3	5.1	3	4.8	3	4.5	3	4.2
4	7.2	4	6.8	4	6.4	4	6.0	4	5.6
5	9.0	5	8.5	5	8.0	5	7.5	5	7.0
6	10.8	6	10.2	6	9.6	6	9.0	6	8.4
7	12.6	7	11.9	7	11.2	7	10.5	7	9.8
8	14.4	8	13.6	8	12.8	8	12.0	8	11.2
9	16.2	9	15.3	9	14.4	9	13.5	9	12.6

TABLE I

COMMON LOGARITHMS

N	0	1	2	3	4	5	6	7	8	9	Prop. Pts.
300	47 712	47 727	47 741	47 756	47 770	47 784	47 799	47 813	47 828	47 842	
301	857	871	885	900	914	929	943	958	972	986	
302	48 001	48 015	48 029	48 044	48 058	48 073	48 087	48 101	48 116	48 130	
303	144	159	173	187	202	216	230	244	259	273	
304	287	302	316	330	344	359	373	387	401	416	
305	48 430	48 444	48 458	48 473	48 487	48 501	48 515	48 530	48 544	48 558	
306	572	586	601	615	629	643	657	671	686	700	
307	714	728	742	756	770	785	799	813	827	841	
308	855	869	883	897	911	926	940	954	968	982	
309	996	49 010	49 024	49 038	49 052	49 066	49 080	49 094	49 108	49 122	
310	49 136	49 150	49 164	49 178	49 192	49 206	49 220	49 234	49 248	49 262	
311	276	290	304	318	332	346	360	374	388	402	
312	415	429	443	457	471	485	499	513	527	541	
313	554	568	582	596	610	624	638	651	665	679	
314	693	707	721	734	748	762	776	790	803	817	
315	49 831	49 845	49 859	49 872	49 886	49 900	49 914	49 927	49 941	49 955	
316	969	982	996	50 010	50 024	50 037	50 051	50 065	50 079	50 092	
317	50 106	50 120	50 133	147	161	174	188	202	215	229	
318	243	256	270	284	297	311	325	338	352	365	
319	379	393	406	420	433	447	461	474	488	501	
320	50 515	50 529	50 542	50 556	50 569	50 583	50 596	50 610	50 623	50 637	
321	651	664	678	691	705	718	732	745	759	772	
322	786	799	813	826	840	853	866	880	893	907	
323	920	934	947	961	974	987	51 001	51 014	51 028	51 041	
324	51 055	51 068	51 081	51 095	51 108	51 121	135	148	162	175	
325	51 188	51 202	51 215	51 228	51 242	51 255	51 268	51 282	51 295	51 308	
326	322	335	348	362	375	388	402	415	428	441	
327	455	468	481	495	508	521	534	548	561	574	
328	587	601	614	627	640	654	667	680	693	706	
329	720	733	746	759	772	786	799	812	825	838	
330	51 851	51 865	51 878	51 891	51 904	51 917	51 930	51 943	51 957	51 970	
331	983	996	52 009	52 022	52 035	52 048	52 061	52 075	52 088	52 101	
332	52 114	52 127	140	153	166	179	192	205	218	231	
333	244	257	270	284	297	310	323	336	349	362	
334	375	388	401	414	427	440	453	466	479	492	
335	52 504	52 517	52 530	52 543	52 556	52 569	52 582	52 595	52 608	52 621	
336	634	647	660	673	686	699	711	724	737	750	
337	763	776	789	802	815	827	840	853	866	879	
338	892	905	917	930	943	956	969	982	994	53 007	
339	53 020	53 033	53 046	53 058	53 071	53 084	53 097	53 110	53 122	135	
340	53 148	53 161	53 173	53 186	53 199	53 212	53 224	53 237	53 250	53 263	
341	275	288	301	314	326	339	352	364	377	390	
342	403	415	428	441	453	466	479	491	504	517	
343	529	542	555	567	580	593	605	618	631	643	
344	656	668	681	694	706	719	732	744	757	769	
345	53 782	53 794	53 807	53 820	53 832	53 845	53 857	53 870	53 882	53 895	
346	908	920	933	945	958	970	983	995	54 008	54 020	
347	54 033	54 045	54 058	54 070	54 083	54 095	54 108	54 120	133	145	
348	158	170	183	195	208	220	233	245	258	270	
349	283	295	307	320	332	345	357	370	382	394	
350	54 407	54 419	54 432	54 444	54 456	54 469	54 481	54 494	54 506	54 518	

Prop. Pts.

15
1	1.5
2	3.0
3	4.5
4	6.0
5	7.5
6	9.0
7	10.5
8	12.0
9	13.5

14
1	1.4
2	2.8
3	4.2
4	5.6
5	7.0
6	8.4
7	9.8
8	11.2
9	12.6

13
1	1.3
2	2.6
3	3.9
4	5.2
5	6.5
6	7.8
7	9.1
8	10.4
9	11.7

12
1	1.2
2	2.4
3	3.6
4	4.8
5	6.0
6	7.2
7	8.4
8	9.6
9	10.8

TABLE I
COMMON LOGARITHMS

N	0	1	2	3	4	5	6	7	8	9	Prop. Pts.
350	54 407	54 419	54 432	54 444	54 456	54 469	54 481	54 494	54 506	54 518	
351	531	543	555	568	580	593	605	617	630	642	
352	654	667	679	691	704	716	728	741	753	765	
353	777	790	802	814	827	839	851	864	876	888	**13**
354	900	913	925	937	949	962	974	986	998	55 011	1 1.3
											2 2.6
355	55 023	55 035	55 047	55 060	55 072	55 084	55 096	55 108	55 121	55 133	3 3.9
356	145	157	169	182	194	206	218	230	242	255	4 5.2
357	267	279	291	303	315	328	340	352	364	376	5 6.5
358	388	400	413	425	437	449	461	473	485	497	6 7.8
359	509	522	534	546	558	570	582	594	606	618	7 9.1
											8 10.4
360	55 630	55 642	55 654	55 666	55 678	55 691	55 703	55 715	55 727	55 739	9 11.7
361	751	763	775	787	799	811	823	835	847	859	
362	871	883	895	907	919	931	943	955	967	979	**12**
363	991	56 003	56 015	56 027	56 038	56 050	56 062	56 074	56 086	56 098	1 1.2
364	56 110	122	134	146	158	170	182	194	205	217	2 2.4
											3 3.6
365	56 229	56 241	56 253	56 265	56 277	56 289	56 301	56 312	56 324	56 336	4 4.8
366	348	360	372	384	396	407	419	431	443	455	5 6.0
367	467	478	490	502	514	526	538	549	561	573	6 7.2
368	585	597	608	620	632	644	656	667	679	691	7 8.4
369	703	714	726	738	750	761	773	785	797	808	8 9.6
											9 10.8
370	56 820	56 832	56 844	56 855	56 867	56 879	56 891	56 902	56 914	56 926	
371	937	949	961	972	984	996	57 008	57 019	57 031	57 043	
372	57 054	57 066	57 078	57 089	57 101	57 113	124	136	148	159	
373	171	183	194	206	217	229	241	252	264	276	
374	287	299	310	322	334	345	357	368	380	392	
375	57 403	57 415	57 426	57 438	57 449	57 461	57 473	57 484	57 496	57 507	
376	519	530	542	553	565	576	588	600	611	623	
377	634	646	657	669	680	692	703	715	726	738	
378	749	761	772	784	795	807	818	830	841	852	
379	864	875	887	898	910	921	933	944	955	967	
380	57 978	57 990	58 001	58 013	58 024	58 035	58 047	58 058	58 070	58 081	**11**
381	58 092	58 104	115	127	138	149	161	172	184	195	1 1.1
382	206	218	229	240	252	263	274	286	297	309	2 2.2
383	320	331	343	354	365	377	388	399	410	422	3 3.3
384	433	444	456	467	478	490	501	512	524	535	4 4.4
											5 5.5
											6 6.6
385	58 546	58 557	58 569	58 580	58 591	58 602	58 614	58 625	58 636	58 647	7 7.7
386	659	670	681	692	704	715	726	737	749	760	8 8.8
387	771	782	794	805	816	827	838	850	861	872	9 9.9
388	883	894	906	917	928	939	950	961	973	984	
389	995	59 006	59 017	59 028	59 040	59 051	59 062	59 073	59 084	59 095	**10**
											1 1.0
390	59 106	59 118	59 129	59 140	59 151	59 162	59 173	59 184	59 195	59 207	2 2.0
391	218	229	240	251	262	273	284	295	306	318	3 3.0
392	329	340	351	362	373	384	395	406	417	428	4 4.0
393	439	450	461	472	483	494	506	517	528	539	5 5.0
394	550	561	572	583	594	605	616	627	638	649	6 6.0
											7 7.0
395	59 660	59 671	59 682	59 693	59 704	59 715	59 726	59 737	59 748	59 759	8 8.0
396	770	780	791	802	813	824	835	846	857	868	9 9.0
397	879	890	901	912	923	934	945	956	966	977	
398	988	999	60 010	60 021	60 032	60 043	60 054	60 065	60 076	60 086	
399	60 097	60 108	119	130	141	152	163	173	184	195	
400	60 206	60 217	60 228	60 239	60 249	60 260	60 271	60 282	60 293	60 304	

TABLE I

COMMON LOGARITHMS

N	0	1	2	3	4	5	6	7	8	9
400	60 206	60 217	60 228	60 239	60 249	60 260	60 271	60 282	60 293	60 304
401	314	325	336	347	358	369	379	390	401	412
402	423	433	444	455	466	477	487	498	509	520
403	531	541	552	563	574	584	595	606	617	627
404	638	649	660	670	681	692	703	713	724	735
405	60 746	60 756	60 767	60 778	60 788	60 799	60 810	60 821	60 831	60 842
406	853	863	874	885	895	906	917	927	938	949
407	959	970	981	991	61 002	61 013	61 023	61 034	61 045	61 055
408	61 066	61 077	61 087	61 098	109	119	130	140	151	162
409	172	183	194	204	215	225	236	247	257	268
410	61 278	61 289	61 300	61 310	61 321	61 331	61 342	61 352	61 363	61 374
411	384	395	405	416	426	437	448	458	469	479
412	490	500	511	521	532	542	553	563	574	584
413	595	606	616	627	637	648	658	669	679	690
414	700	711	721	731	742	752	763	773	784	794
415	61 805	61 815	61 826	61 836	61 847	61 857	61 868	61 878	61 888	61 899
416	909	920	930	941	951	962	972	982	993	62 003
417	62 014	62 024	62 034	62 045	62 055	62 066	62 076	62 086	62 097	107
418	118	128	138	149	159	170	180	190	201	211
419	221	232	242	252	263	273	284	294	304	315
420	62 325	62 335	62 346	62 356	62 366	62 377	62 387	62 397	62 408	62 418
421	428	439	449	459	469	480	490	500	511	521
422	531	542	552	562	572	583	593	603	613	624
423	634	644	655	665	675	685	696	706	716	726
424	737	747	757	767	778	788	798	808	818	829
425	62 839	62 849	62 859	62 870	62 880	62 890	62 900	62 910	62 921	62 931
426	941	951	961	972	982	992	63 002	63 012	63 022	63 033
427	63 043	63 053	63 063	63 073	63 083	63 094	104	114	124	134
428	144	155	165	175	185	195	205	215	225	236
429	246	256	266	276	286	296	306	317	327	337
430	63 347	63 357	63 367	63 377	63 387	63 397	63 407	63 417	63 428	63 438
431	448	458	468	478	488	498	508	518	528	538
432	548	558	568	579	589	599	609	619	629	639
433	649	659	669	679	689	699	709	719	729	739
434	749	759	769	779	789	799	809	819	829	839
435	63 849	63 859	63 869	63 879	63 889	63 899	63 909	63 919	63 929	63 939
436	949	959	969	979	988	998	64 008	64 018	64 028	64 038
437	64 048	64 058	64 068	64 078	64 088	64 098	108	118	128	137
438	147	157	167	177	187	197	207	217	227	237
439	246	256	266	276	286	296	306	316	326	335
440	64 345	64 355	64 365	64 375	64 385	64 395	64 404	64 414	64 424	64 434
441	444	454	464	473	483	493	503	513	523	532
442	542	552	562	572	582	591	601	611	621	631
443	640	650	660	670	680	689	699	709	719	729
444	738	748	758	768	777	787	797	807	816	826
445	64 836	64 846	64 856	64 865	64 875	64 885	64 895	64 904	64 914	64 924
446	933	943	953	963	972	982	992	65 002	65 011	65 021
447	65 031	65 040	65 050	65 060	65 070	65 079	65 089	099	108	118
448	128	137	147	157	167	176	186	196	205	215
449	225	234	244	254	263	273	283	292	302	312
450	65 321	65 331	65 341	65 350	65 360	65 369	65 379	65 389	65 398	65 408

Prop. Pts.

	11
1	1.1
2	2.2
3	3.3
4	4.4
5	5.5
6	6.6
7	7.7
8	8.8
9	9.9

	10
1	1.0
2	2.0
3	3.0
4	4.0
5	5.0
6	6.0
7	7.0
8	8.0
9	9.0

	9
1	.9
2	1.8
3	2.7
4	3.6
5	4.5
6	5.4
7	6.3
8	7.2
9	8.1

TABLE I

COMMON LOGARITHMS

N	0	1	2	3	4	5	6	7	8	9
450	65 321	65 331	65 341	65 350	65 360	65 369	65 379	65 389	65 398	65 408
451	418	427	437	447	456	466	475	485	495	504
452	514	523	533	543	552	562	571	581	591	600
453	610	619	629	639	648	658	667	677	686	696
454	706	715	725	734	744	753	763	772	782	792
455	65 801	65 811	65 820	65 830	65 839	65 849	65 858	65 868	65 877	65 887
456	896	906	916	925	935	944	954	963	973	982
457	992	66 001	66 011	66 020	66 030	66 039	66 049	66 058	66 068	66 077
458	66 087	096	106	115	124	134	143	153	162	172
459	181	191	200	210	219	229	238	247	257	266
460	66 276	66 285	66 295	66 304	66 314	66 323	66 332	66 342	66 351	66 361
461	370	380	389	398	408	417	427	436	445	455
462	464	474	483	492	502	511	521	530	539	549
463	558	567	577	586	596	605	614	624	633	642
464	652	661	671	680	689	699	708	717	727	736
465	66 745	66 755	66 764	66 773	66 783	66 792	66 801	66 811	66 820	66 829
466	839	848	857	867	876	885	894	904	913	922
467	932	941	950	960	969	978	987	997	67 006	67 015
468	67 025	67 034	67 043	67 052	67 062	67 071	67 080	67 089	099	108
469	117	127	136	145	154	164	173	182	191	201
470	67 210	67 219	67 228	67 237	67 247	67 256	67 265	67 274	67 284	67 293
471	302	311	321	330	339	348	357	367	376	385
472	394	403	413	422	431	440	449	459	468	477
473	486	495	504	514	523	532	541	550	560	569
474	578	587	596	605	614	624	633	642	651	660
475	67 669	67 679	67 688	67 697	67 706	67 715	67 724	67 733	67 742	67 752
476	761	770	779	788	797	806	815	825	834	843
477	852	861	870	879	888	897	906	916	925	934
478	943	952	961	970	979	988	997	68 006	68 015	68 024
479	68 034	68 043	68 052	68 061	68 070	68 079	68 088	097	106	115
480	68 124	68 133	68 142	68 151	68 160	68 169	68 178	68 187	68 196	68 205
481	215	224	233	242	251	260	269	278	287	296
482	305	314	323	332	341	350	359	368	377	386
483	395	404	413	422	431	440	449	458	467	476
484	485	494	502	511	520	529	538	547	556	565
485	68 574	68 583	68 592	68 601	68 610	68 619	68 628	68 637	68 646	68 655
486	664	673	681	690	699	708	717	726	735	744
487	753	762	771	780	789	797	806	815	824	833
488	842	851	860	869	878	886	895	904	913	922
489	931	940	949	958	966	975	984	993	69 002	69 011
490	69 020	69 028	69 037	69 046	69 055	69 064	69 073	69 082	69 090	69 099
491	108	117	126	135	144	152	161	170	179	188
492	197	205	214	223	232	241	249	258	267	276
493	285	294	302	311	320	329	338	346	355	364
494	373	381	390	399	408	417	425	434	443	452
495	69 461	69 469	69 478	69 487	69 496	69 504	69 513	69 522	69 531	69 539
496	548	557	566	574	583	592	601	609	618	627
497	636	644	653	662	671	679	688	697	705	714
498	723	732	740	749	758	767	775	784	793	801
499	810	819	827	836	845	854	862	871	880	888
500	69 897	69 906	69 914	69 923	69 932	69 940	69 949	69 958	69 966	69 975

Prop. Pts.

	10
1	1.0
2	2.0
3	3.0
4	4.0
5	5.0
6	6.0
7	7.0
8	8.0
9	9.0

	9
1	0.9
2	1.8
3	2.7
4	3.6
5	4.5
6	5.4
7	6.3
8	7.2
9	8.1

	8
1	0.8
2	1.6
3	2.4
4	3.2
5	4.0
6	4.8
7	5.6
8	6.4
9	7.2

TABLE I

COMMON LOGARITHMS

N	0	1	2	3	4	5	6	7	8	9
500	69 897	69 906	69 914	69 923	69 932	69 940	69 949	69 958	69 966	69 975
501	984	992	70 001	70 010	70 018	70 027	70 036	70 044	70 053	70 062
502	70 070	70 079	088	096	105	114	122	131	140	148
503	157	165	174	183	191	200	209	217	226	234
504	243	252	260	269	278	286	295	303	312	321
505	70 329	70 338	70 346	70 355	70 364	70 372	70 381	70 389	70 398	70 406
506	415	424	432	441	449	458	467	475	484	492
507	501	509	518	526	535	544	552	561	569	578
508	586	595	603	612	621	629	638	646	655	663
509	672	680	689	697	706	714	723	731	740	749
510	70 757	70 766	70 774	70 783	70 791	70 800	70 808	70 817	70 825	70 834
511	842	851	859	868	876	885	893	902	910	919
512	927	935	944	952	961	969	978	986	995	71 003
513	71 012	71 020	71 029	71 037	71 046	71 054	71 063	71 071	71 079	088
514	096	105	113	122	130	139	147	155	164	172
515	71 181	71 189	71 198	71 206	71 214	71 223	71 231	71 240	71 248	71 257
516	265	273	282	290	299	307	315	324	332	341
517	349	357	366	374	383	391	399	408	416	425
518	433	441	450	458	466	475	483	492	500	508
519	517	525	533	542	550	559	567	575	584	592
520	71 600	71 609	71 617	71 625	71 634	71 642	71 650	71 659	71 667	71 675
521	684	692	700	709	717	725	734	742	750	759
522	767	775	784	792	800	809	817	825	834	842
523	850	858	867	875	883	892	900	908	917	925
524	933	941	950	958	966	975	983	991	999	72 008
525	72 016	72 024	72 032	72 041	72 049	72 057	72 066	72 074	72 082	72 090
526	099	107	115	123	132	140	148	156	165	173
527	181	189	198	206	214	222	230	239	247	255
528	263	272	280	288	296	304	313	321	329	337
529	346	354	362	370	378	387	395	403	411	419
530	72 428	72 436	72 444	72 452	72 460	72 469	72 477	72 485	72 493	72 501
531	509	518	526	534	542	550	558	567	575	583
532	591	599	607	616	624	632	640	648	656	665
533	673	681	689	697	705	713	722	730	738	746
534	754	762	770	779	787	795	803	811	819	827
535	72 835	72 843	72 852	72 860	72 868	72 876	72 884	72 892	72 900	72 908
536	916	925	933	941	949	957	965	973	981	989
537	997	73 006	73 014	73 022	73 030	73 038	73 046	73 054	73 062	73 070
538	73 078	086	094	102	111	119	127	135	143	151
539	159	167	175	183	191	199	207	215	223	231
540	73 239	73 247	73 255	73 263	73 272	73 280	73 288	73 296	73 304	73 312
541	320	328	336	344	352	360	368	376	384	392
542	400	408	416	424	432	440	448	456	464	472
543	480	488	496	504	512	520	528	536	544	552
544	560	568	576	584	592	600	608	616	624	632
545	73 640	73 648	73 656	73 664	73 672	73 679	73 687	73 695	73 703	73 711
546	719	727	735	743	751	759	767	775	783	791
547	799	807	815	823	830	838	846	854	862	870
548	878	886	894	902	910	918	926	933	941	949
549	957	965	973	981	989	997	74 005	74 013	74 020	74 028
550	74 036	74 044	74 052	74 060	74 068	74 076	74 084	74 092	74 099	74 107

Prop. Pts.

	9
1	0.9
2	1.8
3	2.7
4	3.6
5	4.5
6	5.4
7	6.3
8	7.2
9	8.1

	8
1	0.8
2	1.6
3	2.4
4	3.2
5	4.0
6	4.8
7	5.6
8	6.4
9	7.2

	7
1	0.7
2	1.4
3	2.1
4	2.8
5	3.5
6	4.2
7	4.9
8	5.6
9	6.3

TABLE I

COMMON LOGARITHMS

N	0	1	2	3	4	5	6	7	8	9
550	74 036	74 044	74 052	74 060	74 068	74 076	74 084	74 092	74 099	74 107
551	115	123	131	139	147	155	162	170	178	186
552	194	202	210	218	225	233	241	249	257	265
553	273	280	288	296	304	312	320	327	335	343
554	351	359	367	374	382	390	398	406	414	421
555	74 429	74 437	74 445	74 453	74 461	74 468	74 476	74 484	74 492	74 500
556	507	515	523	531	539	547	554	562	570	578
557	586	593	601	609	617	624	632	640	648	656
558	663	671	679	687	695	702	710	718	726	733
559	741	749	757	764	772	780	788	796	803	811
560	74 819	74 827	74 834	74 842	74 850	74 858	74 865	74 873	74 881	74 889
561	896	904	912	920	927	935	943	950	958	966
562	974	981	989	997	75 005	75 012	75 020	75 028	75 035	75 043
563	75 051	75 059	75 066	75 074	082	089	097	105	113	120
564	128	136	143	151	159	166	174	182	189	197
565	75 205	75 213	75 220	75 228	75 236	75 243	75 251	75 259	75 266	75 274
566	282	289	297	305	312	320	328	335	343	351
567	358	366	374	381	389	397	404	412	420	427
568	435	442	450	458	465	473	481	488	496	504
569	511	519	526	534	542	549	557	565	572	580
570	75 587	75 595	75 603	75 610	75 618	75 626	75 633	75 641	75 648	75 656
571	664	671	679	686	694	702	709	717	724	732
572	740	747	755	762	770	778	785	793	800	808
573	815	823	831	838	846	853	861	868	876	884
574	891	899	906	914	921	929	937	944	952	959
575	75 967	75 974	75 982	75 989	75 997	76 005	76 012	76 020	76 027	76 035
576	76 042	76 050	76 057	76 065	76 072	080	087	095	103	110
577	118	125	133	140	148	155	163	170	178	185
578	193	200	208	215	223	230	238	245	253	260
579	268	275	283	290	298	305	313	320	328	335
580	76 343	76 350	76 358	76 365	76 373	76 380	76 388	76 395	76 403	76 410
581	418	425	433	440	448	455	462	470	477	485
582	492	500	507	515	522	530	537	545	552	559
583	567	574	582	589	597	604	612	619	626	634
584	641	649	656	664	671	678	686	693	701	708
585	76 716	76 723	76 730	76 738	76 745	76 753	76 760	76 768	76 775	76 782
586	790	797	805	812	819	827	834	842	849	856
587	864	871	879	886	893	901	908	916	923	930
588	938	945	953	960	967	975	982	989	997	77 004
589	77 012	77 019	77 026	77 034	77 041	77 048	77 056	77 063	77 070	078
590	77 085	77 093	77 100	77 107	77 115	77 122	77 129	77 137	77 144	77 151
591	159	166	173	181	188	195	203	210	217	225
592	232	240	247	254	262	269	276	283	291	298
593	305	313	320	327	335	342	349	357	364	371
594	379	386	393	401	408	415	422	430	437	444
595	77 452	77 459	77 466	77 474	77 481	77 488	77 495	77 503	77 510	77 517
596	525	532	539	546	554	561	568	576	583	590
597	597	605	612	619	627	634	641	648	656	663
598	670	677	685	692	699	706	714	721	728	735
599	743	750	757	764	772	779	786	793	801	808
600	77 815	77 822	77 830	77 837	77 844	77 851	77 859	77 866	77 873	77 880

Prop. Pts.

8
1	0.8
2	1.6
3	2.4
4	3.2
5	4.0
6	4.8
7	5.6
8	6.4
9	7.2

7
1	0.7
2	1.4
3	2.1
4	2.8
5	3.5
6	4.2
7	4.9
8	5.6
9	6.3

TABLE I
COMMON LOGARITHMS

N	0	1	2	3	4	5	6	7	8	9
600	77 815	77 822	77 830	77 837	77 844	77 851	77 859	77 866	77 873	77 880
601	887	895	902	909	916	924	931	938	945	952
602	960	967	974	981	988	996	78 003	78 010	78 017	78 025
603	78 032	78 039	78 046	78 053	78 061	78 068	075	082	089	097
604	104	111	118	125	132	140	147	154	161	168
605	78 176	78 183	78 190	78 197	78 204	78 211	78 219	78 226	78 233	78 240
606	247	254	262	269	276	283	290	297	305	312
607	319	326	333	340	347	355	362	369	376	383
608	390	398	405	412	419	426	433	440	447	455
609	462	469	476	483	490	497	504	512	519	526
610	78 533	78 540	78 547	78 554	78 561	78 569	78 576	78 583	78 590	78 597
611	604	611	618	625	633	640	647	654	661	668
612	675	682	689	696	704	711	718	725	732	739
613	746	753	760	767	774	781	789	796	803	810
614	817	824	831	838	845	852	859	866	873	880
615	78 888	78 895	78 902	78 909	78 916	78 923	78 930	78 937	78 944	78 951
616	958	965	972	979	986	993	79 000	79 007	79 014	79 021
617	79 029	79 036	79 043	79 050	79 057	79 064	071	078	085	092
618	099	106	113	120	127	134	141	148	155	162
619	169	176	183	190	197	204	211	218	225	232
620	79 239	79 246	79 253	79 260	79 267	79 274	79 281	79 288	79 295	79 302
621	309	316	323	330	337	344	351	358	365	372
622	379	386	393	400	407	414	421	428	435	442
623	449	456	463	470	477	484	491	498	505	511
624	518	525	532	539	546	553	560	567	574	581
625	79 588	79 595	79 602	79 609	79 616	79 623	79 630	79 637	79 644	79 650
626	657	664	671	678	685	692	699	706	713	720
627	727	734	741	748	754	761	768	775	782	789
628	796	803	810	817	824	831	837	844	851	858
629	865	872	879	886	893	900	906	913	920	927
630	79 934	79 941	79 948	79 955	79 962	79 969	79 975	79 982	79 989	79 996
631	80 003	80 010	80 017	80 024	80 030	80 037	80 044	80 051	80 058	80 065
632	072	079	085	092	099	106	113	120	127	134
633	140	147	154	161	168	175	182	188	195	202
634	209	216	223	229	236	243	250	257	264	271
635	80 277	80 284	80 291	80 298	80 305	80 312	80 318	80 325	80 332	80 339
636	346	353	359	366	373	380	387	393	400	407
637	414	421	428	434	441	448	455	462	468	475
638	482	489	496	502	509	516	523	530	536	543
639	550	557	564	570	577	584	591	598	604	611
640	80 618	80 625	80 632	80 638	80 645	80 652	80 659	80 665	80 672	80 679
641	686	693	699	706	713	720	726	733	740	747
642	754	760	767	774	781	787	794	801	808	814
643	821	828	835	841	848	855	862	868	875	882
644	889	895	902	909	916	922	929	936	943	949
645	80 956	80 963	80 969	80 976	80 983	80 990	80 996	81 003	81 010	81 017
646	81 023	81 030	81 037	81 043	81 050	81 057	81 064	070	077	084
647	090	097	104	111	117	124	131	137	144	151
648	158	164	171	178	184	191	198	204	211	218
649	224	231	238	245	251	258	265	271	278	285
650	81 291	81 298	81 305	81 311	81 318	81 325	81 331	81 338	81 345	81 351

Prop. Pts.

	8
1	0.8
2	1.6
3	2.4
4	3.2
5	4.0
6	4.8
7	5.6
8	6.4
9	7.2

	7
1	0.7
2	1.4
3	2.1
4	2.8
5	3.5
6	4.2
7	4.9
8	5.6
9	6.3

	6
1	0.6
2	1.2
3	1.8
4	2.4
5	3.0
6	3.6
7	4.2
8	4.8
9	5.4

TABLE I

COMMON LOGARITHMS

N	0	1	2	3	4	5	6	7	8	9	Prop. Pts.	
650	81 291	81 298	81 305	81 311	81 318	81 325	81 331	81 338	81 345	81 351		
651	358	365	371	378	385	391	398	405	411	418		
652	425	431	438	445	451	458	465	471	478	485		
653	491	498	505	511	518	525	531	538	544	551		**7**
654	558	564	571	578	584	591	598	604	611	617	1	0.7
655	81 624	81 631	81 637	81 644	81 651	81 657	81 664	81 671	81 677	81 684	2	1.4
656	690	697	704	710	717	723	730	737	743	750	3	2.1
657	757	763	770	776	783	790	796	803	809	816	4	2.8
658	823	829	836	842	849	856	862	869	875	882	5	3.5
659	889	895	902	908	915	921	928	935	941	948	6	4.2
											7	4.9
660	81 954	81 961	81 968	81 974	81 981	81 987	81 994	82 000	82 007	82 014	8	5.6
661	82 020	82 027	82 033	82 040	82 046	82 053	82 060	066	073	079	9	6.3
662	086	092	099	105	112	119	125	132	138	145		
663	151	158	164	171	178	184	191	197	204	210		
664	217	223	230	236	243	249	256	263	269	276		
665	82 282	82 289	82 295	82 302	82 308	82 315	82 321	82 328	82 334	82 341		
666	347	354	360	367	373	380	387	393	400	406		
667	413	419	426	432	439	445	452	458	465	471		
668	478	484	491	497	504	510	517	523	530	536		
669	543	549	556	562	569	575	582	588	595	601		
670	82 607	82 614	82 620	82 627	82 633	82 640	82 646	82 653	82 659	82 666		**6**
671	672	679	685	692	698	705	711	718	724	730	1	0.6
672	737	743	750	756	763	769	776	782	789	795	2	1.2
673	802	808	814	821	827	834	840	847	853	860	3	1.8
674	866	872	879	885	892	898	905	911	918	924	4	2.4
675	82 930	82 937	82 943	82 950	82 956	82 963	82 969	82 975	82 982	82 988	5	3.0
676	995	83 001	83 008	83 014	83 020	83 027	83 033	83 040	83 046	83 052	6	3.6
677	83 059	065	072	078	085	091	097	104	110	117	7	4.2
678	123	129	136	142	149	155	161	168	174	181	8	4.8
679	187	193	200	206	213	219	225	232	238	245	9	5.4
680	83 251	83 257	83 264	83 270	83 276	83 283	83 289	83 296	83 302	83 308		
681	315	321	327	334	340	347	353	359	366	372		
682	378	385	391	398	404	410	417	423	429	436		
683	442	448	455	461	467	474	480	487	493	499		
684	506	512	518	525	531	537	544	550	556	563		
685	83 569	83 575	83 582	83 588	83 594	83 601	83 607	83 613	83 620	83 626		
686	632	639	645	651	658	664	670	677	683	689		
687	696	702	708	715	721	727	734	740	746	753		
688	759	765	771	778	784	790	797	803	809	816		
689	822	828	835	841	847	853	860	866	872	879		
690	83 885	83 891	83 897	83 904	83 910	83 916	83 923	83 929	83 935	83 942		
691	948	954	960	967	973	979	985	992	998	84 004		
692	84 011	84 017	84 023	84 029	84 036	84 042	84 048	84 055	84 061	067		
693	073	080	086	092	098	105	111	117	123	130		
694	136	142	148	155	161	167	173	180	186	192		
695	84 198	84 205	84 211	84 217	84 223	84 230	84 236	84 242	84 248	84 255		
696	261	267	273	280	286	292	298	305	311	317		
697	323	330	336	342	348	354	361	367	373	379		
698	386	392	398	404	410	417	423	429	435	442		
699	448	454	460	466	473	479	485	491	497	504		
700	84 510	84 516	84 522	84 528	84 535	84 541	84 547	84 553	84 559	84 566		

12

TABLE I

COMMON LOGARITHMS

N	0	1	2	3	4	5	6	7	8	9
700	84 510	84 516	84 522	84 528	84 535	84 541	84 547	84 553	84 559	84 566
701	572	578	584	590	597	603	609	615	621	628
702	634	640	646	652	658	665	671	677	683	689
703	696	702	708	714	720	726	733	739	745	751
704	757	763	770	776	782	788	794	800	807	813
705	84 819	84 825	84 831	84 837	84 844	84 850	84 856	84 862	84 868	84 874
706	880	887	893	899	905	911	917	924	930	936
707	942	948	954	960	967	973	979	985	991	997
708	85 003	85 009	85 016	85 022	85 028	85 034	85 040	85 046	85 052	85 058
709	065	071	077	083	089	095	101	107	114	120
710	85 126	85 132	85 138	85 144	85 150	85 156	85 163	85 169	85 175	85 181
711	187	193	199	205	211	217	224	230	236	242
712	248	254	260	266	272	278	285	291	297	303
713	309	315	321	327	333	339	345	352	358	364
714	370	376	382	388	394	400	406	412	418	425
715	85 431	85 437	85 443	85 449	85 455	85 461	85 467	85 473	85 479	85 485
716	491	497	503	509	516	522	528	534	540	546
717	552	558	564	570	576	582	588	594	600	606
718	612	618	625	631	637	643	649	655	661	667
719	673	679	685	691	697	703	709	715	721	727
720	85 733	85 739	85 745	85 751	85 757	85 763	85 769	85 775	85 781	85 788
721	794	800	806	812	818	824	830	836	842	848
722	854	860	866	872	878	884	890	896	902	908
723	914	920	926	932	938	944	950	956	962	968
724	974	980	986	992	998	86 004	86 010	86 016	86 022	86 028
725	86 034	86 040	86 046	86 052	86 058	86 064	86 070	86 076	86 082	86 088
726	094	100	106	112	118	124	130	136	141	147
727	153	159	165	171	177	183	189	195	201	207
728	213	219	225	231	237	243	249	255	261	267
729	273	279	285	291	297	303	308	314	320	326
730	86 332	86 338	86 344	86 350	86 356	86 362	86 368	86 374	86 380	86 386
731	392	398	404	410	415	421	427	433	439	445
732	451	457	463	469	475	481	487	493	499	504
733	510	516	522	528	534	540	546	552	558	564
734	570	576	581	587	593	599	605	611	617	623
735	86 629	86 635	86 641	86 646	86 652	86 658	86 664	86 670	86 676	86 682
736	688	694	700	705	711	717	723	729	735	741
737	747	753	759	764	770	776	782	788	794	800
738	806	812	817	823	829	835	841	847	853	859
739	864	870	876	882	888	894	900	906	911	917
740	86 923	86 929	86 935	86 941	86 947	86 953	86 958	86 964	86 970	86 976
741	982	988	994	999	87 005	87 011	87 017	87 023	87 029	87 035
742	87 040	87 046	87 052	87 058	064	070	075	081	087	093
743	099	105	111	116	122	128	134	140	146	151
744	157	163	169	175	181	186	192	198	204	210
745	87 216	87 221	87 227	87 233	87 239	87 245	87 251	87 256	87 262	87 268
746	274	280	286	291	297	303	309	315	320	326
747	332	338	344	349	355	361	367	373	379	384
748	390	396	402	408	413	419	425	431	437	442
749	448	454	460	466	471	477	483	489	495	500
750	87 506	87 512	87 518	87 523	87 529	87 535	87 541	87 547	87 552	87 558

Prop. Pts.

	7
1	0.7
2	1.4
3	2.1
4	2.8
5	3.5
6	4.2
7	4.9
8	5.6
9	6.3

	6
1	0.6
2	1.2
3	1.8
4	2.4
5	3.0
6	3.6
7	4.2
8	4.8
9	5.4

	5
1	.5
2	1.0
3	1.5
4	2.0
5	2.5
6	3.0
7	3.5
8	4.0
9	4.5

TABLE I
COMMON LOGARITHMS

N	0	1	2	3	4	5	6	7	8	9	Prop. Pts.
750	87 506	87 512	87 518	87 523	87 529	87 535	87 541	87 547	87 552	87 558	
751	564	570	576	581	587	593	599	604	610	616	
752	622	628	633	639	645	651	656	662	668	674	
753	679	685	691	697	703	708	714	720	726	731	**6**
754	737	743	749	754	760	766	772	777	783	789	1 0.6
											2 1.2
755	87 795	87 800	87 806	87 812	87 818	87 823	87 829	87 835	87 841	87 846	3 1.8
756	852	858	864	869	875	881	887	892	898	904	4 2.4
757	910	915	921	927	933	938	944	950	955	961	5 3.0
758	967	973	978	984	990	996	88 001	88 007	88 013	88 018	6 3.6
759	88 024	88 030	88 036	88 041	88 047	88 053	058	064	070	076	7 4.2
											8 4.8
760	88 081	88 087	88 093	88 098	88 104	88 110	88 116	88 121	88 127	88 133	9 5.4
761	138	144	150	156	161	167	173	178	184	190	
762	195	201	207	213	218	224	230	235	241	247	
763	252	258	264	270	275	281	287	292	298	304	
764	309	315	321	326	332	338	343	349	355	360	
765	88 366	88 372	88 377	88 383	88 389	88 395	88 400	88 406	88 412	88 417	
766	423	429	434	440	446	451	457	463	468	474	
767	480	485	491	497	502	508	513	519	525	530	
768	536	542	547	553	559	564	570	576	581	587	
769	593	598	604	610	615	621	627	632	638	643	
770	88 649	88 655	88 660	88 666	88 672	88 677	88 683	88 689	88 694	88 700	
771	705	711	717	722	728	734	739	745	750	756	**5**
772	762	767	773	779	784	790	795	801	807	812	1 0.5
773	818	824	829	835	840	846	852	857	863	868	2 1.0
774	874	880	885	891	897	902	908	913	919	925	3 1.5
											4 2.0
775	88 930	88 936	88 941	88 947	88 953	88 958	88 964	88 969	88 975	88 981	5 2.5
776	986	992	997	89 003	89 009	89 014	89 020	89 025	89 031	89 037	6 3.0
777	89 042	89 048	89 053	059	064	070	076	081	087	092	7 3.5
778	098	104	109	115	120	126	131	137	143	148	8 4.0
779	154	159	165	170	176	182	187	193	198	204	9 4.5
780	89 209	89 215	89 221	89 226	89 232	89 237	89 243	89 248	89 254	89 260	
781	265	271	276	282	287	293	298	304	310	315	
782	321	326	332	337	343	348	354	360	365	371	
783	376	382	387	393	398	404	409	415	421	426	
784	432	437	443	448	454	459	465	470	476	481	
785	89 487	89 492	89 498	89 504	89 509	89 515	89 520	89 526	89 531	89 537	
786	542	548	553	559	564	570	575	581	586	592	
787	597	603	609	614	620	625	631	636	642	647	
788	653	658	664	669	675	680	686	691	697	702	
789	708	713	719	724	730	735	741	746	752	757	
790	89 763	89 768	89 774	89 779	89 785	89 790	89 796	89 801	89 807	89 812	
791	818	823	829	834	840	845	851	856	862	867	
792	873	878	883	889	894	900	905	911	916	922	
793	927	933	938	944	949	955	960	966	971	977	
794	982	988	993	998	90 004	90 009	90 015	90 020	90 026	90 031	
795	90 037	90 042	90 048	90 053	90 059	90 064	90 069	90 075	90 080	90 086	
796	091	097	102	108	113	119	124	129	135	140	
797	146	151	157	162	168	173	179	184	189	195	
798	200	206	211	217	222	227	233	238	244	249	
799	255	260	266	271	276	282	287	293	298	304	
800	90 309	90 314	90 320	90 325	90 331	90 336	90 342	90 347	90 352	90 358	

TABLE I

COMMON LOGARITHMS

N	0	1	2	3	4	5	6	7	8	9	Prop. Pts.
800	90 309	90 314	90 320	90 325	90 331	90 336	90 342	90 347	90 352	90 358	
801	363	369	374	380	385	390	396	401	407	412	
802	417	423	428	434	439	445	450	455	461	466	
803	472	477	482	488	493	499	504	509	515	520	
804	526	531	536	542	547	553	558	563	569	574	
805	90 580	90 585	90 590	90 596	90 601	90 607	90 612	90 617	90 623	90 628	
806	634	639	644	650	655	660	666	671	677	682	
807	687	693	698	703	709	714	720	725	730	736	
808	741	747	752	757	763	768	773	779	784	789	
809	795	800	806	811	816	822	827	832	838	843	
810	90 849	90 854	90 859	90 865	90 870	90 875	90 881	90 886	90 891	90 897	
811	902	907	913	918	924	929	934	940	945	950	
812	956	961	966	972	977	982	988	993	998	91 004	
813	91 009	91 014	91 020	91 025	91 030	91 036	91 041	91 046	91 052	057	
814	062	068	073	078	084	089	094	100	105	110	
815	91 116	91 121	91 126	91 132	91 137	91 142	91 148	91 153	91 158	91 164	
816	169	174	180	185	190	196	201	206	212	217	
817	222	228	233	238	243	249	254	259	265	270	
818	275	281	286	291	297	302	307	312	318	323	
819	328	334	339	344	350	355	360	365	371	376	
820	91 381	91 387	91 392	91 397	91 403	91 408	91 413	91 418	91 424	91 429	
821	434	440	445	450	455	461	466	471	477	482	
822	487	492	498	503	508	514	519	524	529	535	
823	540	545	551	556	561	566	572	577	582	587	
824	593	598	603	609	614	619	624	630	635	640	
825	91 645	91 651	91 656	91 661	91 666	91 672	91 677	91 682	91 687	91 693	
826	698	703	709	714	719	724	730	735	740	745	
827	751	756	761	766	772	777	782	787	793	798	
828	803	808	814	819	824	829	834	840	845	850	
829	855	861	866	871	876	882	887	892	897	903	
830	91 908	91 913	91 918	91 924	91 929	91 934	91 939	91 944	91 950	91 955	
831	960	965	971	976	981	986	991	997	92 002	92 007	
832	92 012	92 018	92 023	92 028	92 033	92 038	92 044	92 049	054	059	
833	065	070	075	080	085	091	096	101	106	111	
834	117	122	127	132	137	143	148	153	158	163	
835	92 169	92 174	92 179	92 184	92 189	92 195	92 200	92 205	92 210	92 215	
836	221	226	231	236	241	247	252	257	262	267	
837	273	278	283	288	293	298	304	309	314	319	
838	324	330	335	340	345	350	355	361	366	371	
839	376	381	387	392	397	402	407	412	418	423	
840	92 428	92 433	92 438	92 443	92 449	92 454	92 459	92 464	92 469	92 474	
841	480	485	490	495	500	505	511	516	521	526	
842	531	536	542	547	552	557	562	567	572	578	
843	583	588	593	598	603	609	614	619	624	629	
844	634	639	645	650	655	660	665	670	675	681	
845	92 686	92 691	92 696	92 701	92 706	92 711	92 716	92 722	92 727	92 732	
846	737	742	747	752	758	763	768	773	778	783	
847	788	793	799	804	809	814	819	824	829	834	
848	840	845	850	855	860	865	870	875	881	886	
849	891	896	901	906	911	916	921	927	932	937	
850	92 942	92 947	92 952	92 957	92 962	92 967	92 973	92 978	92 983	92 988	

Prop. Pts.

	6
1	0.6
2	1.2
3	1.8
4	2.4
5	3.0
6	3.6
7	4.2
8	4.8
9	5.4

	5
1	0.5
2	1.0
3	1.5
4	2.0
5	2.5
6	3.0
7	3.5
8	4.0
9	4.5

TABLE I
COMMON LOGARITHMS

N	0	1	2	3	4	5	6	7	8	9
850	92 942	92 947	92 952	92 957	92 962	92 967	92 973	92 978	92 983	92 988
851	993	998	93 003	93 008	93 013	93 018	93 024	93 029	93 034	93 039
852	93 044	93 049	054	059	064	069	075	080	085	090
853	095	100	105	110	115	120	125	131	136	141
854	146	151	156	161	166	171	176	181	186	192
855	93 197	93 202	93 207	93 212	93 217	93 222	93 227	93 232	93 237	93 242
856	247	252	258	263	268	273	278	283	288	293
857	298	303	308	313	318	323	328	334	339	344
858	349	354	359	364	369	374	379	384	389	394
859	399	404	409	414	420	425	430	435	440	445
860	93 450	93 455	93 460	93 465	93 470	93 475	93 480	93 485	93 490	93 495
861	500	505	510	515	520	526	531	536	541	546
862	551	556	561	566	571	576	581	586	591	596
863	601	606	611	616	621	626	631	636	641	646
864	651	656	661	666	671	676	682	687	692	697
865	93 702	93 707	93 712	93 717	93 722	93 727	93 732	93 737	93 742	93 747
866	752	757	762	767	772	777	782	787	792	797
867	802	807	812	817	822	827	832	837	842	847
868	852	857	862	867	872	877	882	887	892	897
869	902	907	912	917	922	927	932	937	942	947
870	93 952	93 957	93 962	93 967	93 972	93 977	93 982	93 987	93 992	93 997
871	94 002	94 007	94 012	94 017	94 022	94 027	94 032	94 037	94 042	94 047
872	052	057	062	067	072	077	082	086	091	096
873	101	106	111	116	121	126	131	136	141	146
874	151	156	161	166	171	176	181	186	191	196
875	94 201	94 206	94 211	94 216	94 221	94 226	94 231	94 236	94 240	94 245
876	250	255	260	265	270	275	280	285	290	295
877	300	305	310	315	320	325	330	335	340	345
878	349	354	359	364	369	374	379	384	389	394
879	399	404	409	414	419	424	429	433	438	443
880	94 448	94 453	94 458	94 463	94 468	94 473	94 478	94 483	94 488	94 493
881	498	503	507	512	517	522	527	532	537	542
882	547	552	557	562	567	571	576	581	586	591
883	596	601	606	611	616	621	626	630	635	640
884	645	650	655	660	665	670	675	680	685	689
885	94 694	94 699	94 704	94 709	94 714	94 719	94 724	94 729	94 734	94 738
886	743	748	753	758	763	768	773	778	783	787
887	792	797	802	807	812	817	822	827	832	836
888	841	846	851	856	861	866	871	876	880	885
889	890	895	900	905	910	915	919	924	929	934
890	94 939	94 944	94 949	94 954	94 959	94 963	94 968	94 973	94 978	94 983
891	988	993	998	95 002	95 007	95 012	95 017	95 022	95 027	95 032
892	95 036	95 041	95 046	051	056	061	066	071	075	080
893	085	090	095	100	105	109	114	119	124	129
894	134	139	143	148	153	158	163	168	173	177
895	95 182	95 187	95 192	95 197	95 202	95 207	95 211	95 216	95 221	95 226
896	231	236	240	245	250	255	260	265	270	274
897	279	284	289	294	299	303	308	313	318	323
898	328	332	337	342	347	352	357	361	366	371
899	376	381	386	390	395	400	405	410	415	419
900	95 424	95 429	95 434	95 439	95 444	95 448	95 453	95 458	95 463	95 468

Prop. Pts.

	6		5		4
1	0.6	1	0.5	1	0.4
2	1.2	2	1.0	2	0.8
3	1.8	3	1.5	3	1.2
4	2.4	4	2.0	4	1.6
5	3.0	5	2.5	5	2.0
6	3.6	6	3.0	6	2.4
7	4.2	7	3.5	7	2.8
8	4.8	8	4.0	8	3.2
9	5.4	9	4.5	9	3.6

TABLE I

COMMON LOGARITHMS

N	0	1	2	3	4	5	6	7	8	9
900	95 424	95 429	95 434	95 439	95 444	95 448	95 453	95 458	95 463	95 468
901	472	477	482	487	492	497	501	506	511	516
902	521	525	530	535	540	545	550	554	559	564
903	569	574	578	583	588	593	598	602	607	612
904	617	622	626	631	636	641	646	650	655	660
905	95 665	95 670	95 674	95 679	95 684	95 689	95 694	95 698	95 703	95 708
906	713	718	722	727	732	737	742	746	751	756
907	761	766	770	775	780	785	789	794	799	804
908	809	813	818	823	828	832	837	842	847	852
909	856	861	866	871	875	880	885	890	895	899
910	95 904	95 909	95 914	95 918	95 923	95 928	95 933	95 938	95 942	95 947
911	952	957	961	966	971	976	980	985	990	995
912	999	96 004	96 009	96 014	96 019	96 023	96 028	96 033	96 038	96 042
913	96 047	052	057	061	066	071	076	080	085	090
914	095	099	104	109	114	118	123	128	133	137
915	96 142	96 147	96 152	96 156	96 161	96 166	96 171	96 175	96 180	96 185
916	190	194	199	204	209	213	218	223	227	232
917	237	242	246	251	256	261	265	270	275	280
918	284	289	294	298	303	308	313	317	322	327
919	332	336	341	346	350	355	360	365	369	374
920	96 379	96 384	96 388	96 393	96 398	96 402	96 407	96 412	96 417	96 421
921	426	431	435	440	445	450	454	459	464	468
922	473	478	483	487	492	497	501	506	511	515
923	520	525	530	534	539	544	548	553	558	562
924	567	572	577	581	586	591	595	600	605	609
925	96 614	96 619	96 624	96 628	96 633	96 638	96 642	96 647	96 652	96 656
926	661	666	670	675	680	685	689	694	699	703
927	708	713	717	722	727	731	736	741	745	750
928	755	759	764	769	774	778	783	788	792	797
929	802	806	811	816	820	825	830	834	839	844
930	96 848	96 853	96 858	96 862	96 867	96 872	96 876	96 881	96 886	96 890
931	895	900	904	909	914	918	923	928	932	937
932	942	946	951	956	960	965	970	974	979	984
933	988	993	997	97 002	97 007	97 011	97 016	97 021	97 025	97 030
934	97 035	97 039	97 044	049	053	058	063	067	072	077
935	97 081	97 086	97 090	97 095	97 100	97 104	97 109	97 114	97 118	97 123
936	128	132	137	142	146	151	155	160	165	169
937	174	179	183	188	192	197	202	206	211	216
938	220	225	230	234	239	243	248	253	257	262
939	267	271	276	280	285	290	294	299	304	308
940	97 313	97 317	97 322	97 327	97 331	97 336	97 340	97 345	97 350	97 354
941	359	364	368	373	377	382	387	391	396	400
942	405	410	414	419	424	428	433	437	442	447
943	451	456	460	465	470	474	479	483	488	493
944	497	502	506	511	516	520	525	529	534	539
945	97 543	97 548	97 552	97 557	97 562	97 566	97 571	97 575	97 580	97 585
946	589	594	598	603	607	612	617	621	626	630
947	635	640	644	649	653	658	663	667	672	676
948	681	685	690	695	699	704	708	713	717	722
949	727	731	736	740	745	749	754	759	763	768
950	97 772	97 777	97 782	97 786	97 791	97 795	97 800	97 804	97 809	97 813

Prop. Pts.

	5
1	0.5
2	1.0
3	1.5
4	2.0
5	2.5
6	3.0
7	3.5
8	4.0
9	4.5

	4
1	0.4
2	0.8
3	1.2
4	1.6
5	2.0
6	2.4
7	2.8
8	3.2
9	3.6

TABLE I

COMMON LOGARITHMS

N	0	1	2	3	4	5	6	7	8	9
950	97 772	97 777	97 782	97 786	97 791	97 795	97 800	97 804	97 809	97 813
951	818	823	827	832	836	841	845	850	855	859
952	864	868	873	877	882	886	891	896	900	905
953	909	914	918	923	928	932	937	941	946	950
954	955	959	964	968	973	978	982	987	991	996
955	98 000	98 005	98 009	98 014	98 019	98 023	98 028	98 032	98 037	98 041
956	046	050	055	059	064	068	073	078	082	087
957	091	096	100	105	109	114	118	123	127	132
958	137	141	146	150	155	159	164	168	173	177
959	182	186	191	195	200	204	209	214	218	223
960	98 227	98 232	98 236	98 241	98 245	98 250	98 254	98 259	98 263	98 268
961	272	277	281	286	290	295	299	304	308	313
962	318	322	327	331	336	340	345	349	354	358
963	363	367	372	376	381	385	390	394	399	403
964	408	412	417	421	426	430	435	439	444	448
965	98 453	98 457	98 462	98 466	98 471	98 475	98 480	98 484	98 489	98 493
966	498	502	507	511	516	520	525	529	534	538
967	543	547	552	556	561	565	570	574	579	583
968	588	592	597	601	605	610	614	619	623	628
969	632	637	641	646	650	655	659	664	668	673
970	98 677	98 682	98 686	98 691	98 695	98 700	98 704	98 709	98 713	98 717
971	722	726	731	735	740	744	749	753	758	762
972	767	771	776	780	784	789	793	798	802	807
973	811	816	820	825	829	834	838	843	847	851
974	856	860	865	869	874	878	883	887	892	896
975	98 900	98 905	98 909	98 914	98 918	98 923	98 927	98 932	98 936	98 941
976	945	949	954	958	963	967	972	976	981	985
977	989	994	998	99 003	99 007	99 012	99 016	99 021	99 025	99 029
978	99 034	99 038	99 043	047	052	056	061	065	069	074
979	078	083	087	092	096	100	105	109	114	118
980	99 123	99 127	99 131	99 136	99 140	99 145	99 149	99 154	99 158	99 162
981	167	171	176	180	185	189	193	198	202	207
982	211	216	220	224	229	233	238	242	247	251
983	255	260	264	269	273	277	282	286	291	295
984	300	304	308	313	317	322	326	330	335	339
985	99 344	99 348	99 352	99 357	99 361	99 366	99 370	99 374	99 379	99 383
986	388	392	396	401	405	410	414	419	423	427
987	432	436	441	445	449	454	458	463	467	471
988	476	480	484	489	493	498	502	506	511	515
989	520	524	528	533	537	542	546	550	555	559
990	99 564	99 568	99 572	99 577	99 581	99 585	99 590	99 594	99 599	99 603
991	607	612	616	621	625	629	634	638	642	647
992	651	656	660	664	669	673	677	682	686	691
993	695	699	704	708	712	717	721	726	730	734
994	739	743	747	752	756	760	765	769	774	778
995	99 782	99 787	99 791	99 795	99 800	99 804	99 808	99 813	99 817	99 822
996	826	830	835	839	843	848	852	856	861	865
997	870	874	878	883	887	891	896	900	904	909
998	913	917	922	926	930	935	939	944	948	952
999	957	961	965	970	974	978	983	987	991	996
1000	00 000	00 004	00 009	00 013	00 017	00 022	00 026	00 030	00 035	00 039

Prop. Pts

	5
1	0.5
2	1.0
3	1.5
4	2.0
5	2.5
6	3.0
7	3.5
8	4.0
9	4.5

	4
1	0.4
2	0.8
3	1.2
4	1.6
5	2.0
6	2.4
7	2.8
8	3.2
9	3.6

18

TABLE II
TRIGONOMETRIC FUNCTIONS AND THEIR LOGARITHMS
(See: Characteristic, and Mantissa.)

ANGLE Radians	Degrees	Sine Value	Log	Tangent Value	Log	Cotangent Value	Log	Cosine Value	Log		
.0000	0°00′	.0000	—	.0000	—	—	—	1.0000	.0000	90°00′	1.5708
.0029	10	.0029	.4637	.0029	.4637	343.77	.5363	1.0000	.0000	50	1.5679
.0058	20	.0058	.7648	.0058	.7648	171.89	.2352	1.0000	.0000	40	1.5650
.0087	30	.0087	.9408	.0087	.9409	114.59	.0591	1.0000	.0000	30	1.5621
.0116	40	.0116	.0658	.0116	.0658	85.940	.9342	.9999	.0000	20	1.5592
.0145	50	.0145	.1627	.0145	.1627	68.750	.8373	.9999	.0000	10	1.5563
.0175	1°00′	.0175	.2419	.0175	.2419	57.290	.7581	.9998	.9999	89°00′	1.5533
.0204	10	.0204	.3088	.0204	.3089	49.104	.6911	.9998	.9999	50	1.5504
.0233	20	.0233	.3668	.0233	.3669	42.964	.6331	.9997	.9999	40	1.5475
.0262	30	.0262	.4179	.0262	.4181	38.188	.5819	.9997	.9999	30	1.5446
.0291	40	.0291	.4637	.0291	.4638	34.368	.5362	.9996	.9998	20	1.5417
.0320	50	.0320	.5050	.0320	.5053	31.242	.4947	.9995	.9998	10	1.5388
.0349	2°00′	.0349	.5428	.0349	.5431	28.636	.4569	.9994	.9997	88°00′	1.5359
.0378	10	.0378	.5776	.0378	.5779	26.432	.4221	.9993	.9997	50	1.5330
.0407	20	.0407	.6097	.0407	.6101	24.542	.3899	.9992	.9996	40	1.5301
.0436	30	.0436	.6397	.0437	.6401	22.904	.3599	.9990	.9996	30	1.5272
.0465	40	.0465	.6677	.0466	.6682	21.470	.3318	.9989	.9995	20	1.5243
.0495	50	.0494	.6940	.0495	.6945	20.206	.3055	.9988	.9995	10	1.5213
.0524	3°00′	.0523	.7188	.0524	.7194	19.081	.2806	.9986	.9994	87°00′	1.5184
.0553	10	.0552	.7423	.0553	.7429	18.075	.2571	.9985	.9993	50	1.5155
.0582	20	.0581	.7645	.0582	.7652	17.169	.2348	.9983	.9993	40	1.5126
.0611	30	.0610	.7857	.0612	.7865	16.350	.2135	.9981	.9992	30	1.5097
.0640	40	.0640	.8059	.0641	.8067	15.605	.1933	.9980	.9991	20	1.5068
.0669	50	.0669	.8251	.0670	.8261	14.924	.1739	.9978	.9990	10	1.5039
.0698	4°00′	.0698	.8436	.0699	.8446	14.301	.1554	.9976	.9989	86°00′	1.5010
.0727	10	.0727	.8613	.0729	.8624	13.727	.1376	.9974	.9989	50	1.4981
.0756	20	.0756	.8783	.0758	.8795	13.197	.1205	.9971	.9988	40	1.4952
.0785	30	.0785	.8946	.0787	.8960	12.706	.1040	.9969	.9987	30	1.4923
.0814	40	.0814	.9104	.0816	.9118	12.251	.0882	.9967	.9986	20	1.4893
.0844	50	.0843	.9256	.0846	.9272	11.826	.0728	.9964	.9985	10	1.4864
.0873	5°00′	.0872	.9403	.0875	.9420	11.430	.0580	.9962	.9983	85°00′	1.4835
.0902	10	.0901	.9545	.0904	.9563	11.059	.0437	.9959	.9982	50	1.4806
.0931	20	.0929	.9682	.0934	.9701	10.712	.0299	.9957	.9981	40	1.4777
.0960	30	.0958	.9816	.0963	.9836	10.385	.0164	.9954	.9980	30	1.4748
.0989	40	.0987	.9945	.0992	.9966	10.078	.0034	.9951	.9979	20	1.4719
.1018	50	.1016	.0070	.1022	.0093	9.7882	.9907	.9948	.9977	10	1.4690
.1047	6°00′	.1045	.0192	.1051	.0216	9.5144	.9784	.9945	.9976	84°00′	1.4661
.1076	10	.1074	.0311	.1080	.0336	9.2553	.9664	.9942	.9975	50	1.4632
.1105	20	.1103	.0426	.1110	.0453	9.0098	.9547	.9939	.9973	40	1.4603
.1134	30	.1132	.0539	.1139	.0567	8.7769	.9433	.9936	.9972	30	1.4573
.1164	40	.1161	.0648	.1169	.0678	8.5555	.9322	.9932	.9971	20	1.4544
.1193	50	.1190	.0755	.1198	.0786	8.3450	.9214	.9929	.9969	10	1.4515
.1222	7°00′	.1219	.0859	.1228	.0891	8.1443	.9109	.9925	.9968	83°00′	1.4486
.1251	10	.1248	.0961	.1257	.0995	7.9530	.9005	.9922	.9966	50	1.4457
.1280	20	.1276	.1060	.1287	.1096	7.7704	.8904	.9918	.9964	40	1.4428
.1309	30	.1305	.1157	.1317	.1194	7.5958	.8806	.9914	.9963	30	1.4399
.1338	40	.1334	.1252	.1346	.1291	7.4287	.8709	.9911	.9961	20	1.4370
.1367	50	.1363	.1345	.1376	.1385	7.2687	.8615	.9907	.9959	10	1.4341
.1396	8°00′	.1392	.1436	.1405	.1478	7.1154	.8522	.9903	.9958	82°00′	1.4312
.1425	10	.1421	.1525	.1435	.1569	6.9682	.8431	.9899	.9956	50	1.4283
.1454	20	.1449	.1612	.1465	.1658	6.8269	.8342	.9894	.9954	40	1.4254
.1484	30	.1478	.1697	.1495	.1745	6.6912	.8255	.9890	.9952	30	1.4224
.1513	40	.1507	.1781	.1524	.1831	6.5606	.8169	.9886	.9950	20	1.4195
.1542	50	.1536	.1863	.1554	.1915	6.4348	.8085	.9881	.9948	10	1.4166
.1571	9°00′	.1564	.1943	.1584	.1997	6.3138	.8003	.9877	.9946	81°00′	1.4137

Value	Log Cosine	Value	Log Cotangent	Value	Log Tangent	Value	Log Sine	Degrees	Radians

19

TABLE II
TRIGONOMETRIC FUNCTIONS AND THEIR LOGARITHMS

ANGLE Radians	Degrees	Sine Value	Log	Tangent Value	Log	Cotangent Value	Log	Cosine Value	Log		
.1571	9°00′	.1564	.1943	.1584	.1997	6.3138	.8003	.9877	.9946	81°00′	1.4137
.1600	10	.1593	.2022	.1614	.2078	6.1970	.7922	.9872	.9944	50	1.4108
.1629	20	.1622	.2100	.1644	.2158	6.0844	.7842	.9868	.9942	40	1.4079
.1658	30	.1650	.2176	.1673	.2236	5.9758	.7764	.9863	.9940	30	1.4050
.1687	40	.1679	.2251	.1703	.2313	5.8708	.7687	.9858	.9938	20	1.4021
.1716	50	.1708	.2324	.1733	.2389	5.7694	.7611	.9853	.9936	10	1.3992
.1745	10°00′	.1736	.2397	.1763	.2463	5.6713	.7537	.9848	.9934	80°00′	1.3963
.1774	10	.1765	.2468	.1793	.2536	5.5764	.7464	.9843	.9931	50	1.3934
.1804	20	.1794	.2538	.1823	.2609	5.4845	.7391	.9838	.9929	40	1.3904
.1833	30	.1822	.2606	.1853	.2680	5.3955	.7320	.9833	.9927	30	1.3875
.1862	40	.1851	.2674	.1883	.2750	5.3093	.7250	.9827	.9924	20	1.3846
.1891	50	.1880	.2740	.1914	.2819	5.2257	.7181	.9822	.9922	10	1.3817
.1920	11°00′	.1908	.2806	.1944	.2887	5.1446	.7113	.9816	.9919	79°00′	1.3788
.1949	10	.1937	.2870	.1974	.2953	5.0658	.7047	.9811	.9917	50	1.3759
.1978	20	.1965	.2934	.2004	.3020	4.9894	.6980	.9805	.9914	40	1.3730
.2007	30	.1994	.2997	.2035	.3085	4.9152	.6915	.9799	.9912	30	1.3701
.2036	40	.2022	.3058	.2065	.3149	4.8430	.6851	.9793	.9909	20	1.3672
.2065	50	.2051	.3119	.2095	.3212	4.7729	.6788	.9787	.9907	10	1.3643
.2094	12°00′	.2079	.3179	.2126	.3275	4.7046	.6725	.9781	.9904	78°00′	1.3614
.2123	10	.2108	.3238	.2156	.3336	4.6382	.6664	.9775	.9901	50	1.3584
.2153	20	.2136	.3296	.2186	.3397	4.5736	.6603	.9769	.9899	40	1.3555
.2182	30	.2164	.3353	.2217	.3458	4.5107	.6542	.9763	.9896	30	1.3526
.2211	40	.2193	.3410	.2247	.3517	4.4494	.6483	.9757	.9893	20	1.3497
.2240	50	.2221	.3466	.2278	.3576	4.3897	.6424	.9750	.9890	10	1.3468
.2269	13°00′	.2250	.3521	.2309	.3634	4.3315	.6366	.9744	.9887	77°00′	1.3439
.2298	10	.2278	.3575	.2339	.3691	4.2747	.6309	.9737	.9884	50	1.3410
.2327	20	.2306	.3629	.2370	.3748	4.2193	.6252	.9730	.9881	40	1.3381
.2356	30	.2334	.3682	.2401	.3804	4.1653	.6196	.9724	.9878	30	1.3352
.2385	40	.2363	.3734	.2432	.3859	4.1126	.6141	.9717	.9875	20	1.3323
.2414	50	.2391	.3786	.2462	.3914	4.0611	.6086	.9710	.9872	10	1.3294
.2443	14°00′	.2419	.3837	.2493	.3968	4.0108	.6032	.9703	.9869	76°00′	1.3265
.2473	10	.2447	.3887	.2524	.4021	3.9617	.5979	.9696	.9866	50	1.3235
.2502	20	.2476	.3937	.2555	.4074	3.9136	.5926	.9689	.9863	40	1.3206
.2531	30	.2504	.3986	.2586	.4127	3.8667	.5873	.9681	.9859	30	1.3177
.2560	40	.2532	.4035	.2617	.4178	3.8208	.5822	.9674	.9856	20	1.3148
.2589	50	.2560	.4083	.2648	.4230	3.7760	.5770	.9667	.9853	10	1.3119
.2618	15°00′	.2588	.4130	.2679	.4281	3.7321	.5719	.9659	.9849	75°00′	1.3090
.2647	10	.2616	.4177	.2711	.4331	3.6891	.5669	.9652	.9846	50	1.3061
.2676	20	.2644	.4223	.2742	.4381	3.6470	.5619	.9644	.9843	40	1.3032
.2705	30	.2672	.4269	.2773	.4430	3.6059	.5570	.9636	.9839	30	1.3003
.2734	40	.2700	.4314	.2805	.4479	3.5656	.5521	.9628	.9836	20	1.2974
.2763	50	.2728	.4359	.2836	.4527	3.5261	.5473	.9621	.9832	10	1.2945
.2793	16°00′	.2756	.4403	.2867	.4575	3.4874	.5425	.9613	.9828	74°00′	1.2915
.2822	10	.2784	.4447	.2899	.4622	3.4495	.5378	.9605	.9825	50	1.2886
.2851	20	.2812	.4491	.2931	.4669	3.4124	.5331	.9596	.9821	40	1.2857
.2880	30	.2840	.4533	.2962	.4716	3.3759	.5284	.9588	.9817	30	1.2828
.2909	40	.2868	.4576	.2994	.4762	3.3402	.5238	.9580	.9814	20	1.2799
.2938	50	.2896	.4618	.3026	.4808	3.3052	.5192	.9572	.9810	10	1.2770
.2967	17°00′	.2924	.4659	.3057	.4853	3.2709	.5147	.9563	.9806	73°00′	1.2741
.2996	10	.2952	.4700	.3089	.4898	3.2371	.5102	.9555	.9802	50	1.2712
.3025	20	.2979	.4741	.3121	.4943	3.2041	.5057	.9546	.9798	40	1.2683
.3054	30	.3007	.4781	.3153	.4987	3.1716	.5013	.9537	.9794	30	1.2654
.3083	40	.3035	.4821	.3185	.5031	3.1397	.4969	.9528	.9790	20	1.2625
.3113	50	.3062	.4861	.3217	.5075	3.1084	.4925	.9520	.9786	10	1.2595
.3142	18°00′	.3090	.4900	.3249	.5118	3.0777	.4882	.9511	.9782	72°00′	1.2566

Value	Log Cosine	Value	Log Cotangent	Value	Log Tangent	Value	Log Sine	Degrees	Radians

TABLE II
TRIGONOMETRIC FUNCTIONS AND THEIR LOGARITHMS

ANGLE Radians	Degrees	Sine Value	Log	Tangent Value	Log	Cotangent Value	Log	Cosine Value	Log		
.3142	18°00′	.3090	.4900	.3249	.5118	3.0777	.4882	.9511	.9782	72°00′	1.2566
.3171	10	.3118	.4939	.3281	.5161	3.0475	.4839	.9502	.9778	50	1.2537
.3200	20	.3145	.4977	.3314	.5203	3.0178	.4797	.9492	.9774	40	1.2508
.3229	30	.3173	.5015	.3346	.5245	2.9887	.4755	.9483	.9770	30	1.2479
.3258	40	.3201	.5052	.3378	.5287	2.9600	.4713	.9474	.9765	20	1.2450
.3287	50	.3228	.5090	.3411	.5329	2.9319	.4671	.9465	.9761	10	1.2421
.3316	19°00′	.3256	.5126	.3443	.5370	2.9042	.4630	.9455	.9757	71°00′	1.2392
.3345	10	.3283	.5163	.3476	.5411	2.8770	.4589	.9446	.9752	50	1.2363
.3374	20	.3311	.5199	.3508	.5451	2.8502	.4549	.9436	.9748	40	1.2334
.3403	30	.3338	.5235	.3541	.5491	2.8239	.4509	.9426	.9743	30	1.2305
.3432	40	.3365	.5270	.3574	.5531	2.7980	.4469	.9417	.9739	20	1.2275
.3462	50	.3393	.5306	.3607	.5571	2.7725	.4429	.9407	.9734	10	1.2246
.3491	20°00′	.3420	.5341	.3640	.5611	2.7475	.4389	.9397	.9730	70°00′	1.2217
.3520	10	.3448	.5375	.3673	.5650	2.7228	.4350	.9387	.9725	50	1.2188
.3549	20	.3475	.5409	.3706	.5689	2.6985	.4311	.9377	.9721	40	1.2159
.3578	30	.3502	.5443	.3739	.5727	2.6746	.4273	.9367	.9716	30	1.2130
.3607	40	.3529	.5477	.3772	.5766	2.6511	.4234	.9356	.9711	20	1.2101
.3636	50	.3557	.5510	.3805	.5804	2.6279	.4196	.9346	.9706	10	1.2072
.3665	21°00′	.3584	.5543	.3839	.5842	2.6051	.4158	.9336	.9702	69°00′	1.2043
.3694	10	.3611	.5576	.3872	.5879	2.5826	.4121	.9325	.9697	50	1.2014
.3723	20	.3638	.5609	.3906	.5917	2.5605	.4083	.9315	.9692	40	1.1985
.3752	30	.3665	.5641	.3939	.5954	2.5386	.4046	.9304	.9687	30	1.1956
.3782	40	.3692	.5673	.3973	.5991	2.5172	.4009	.9293	.9682	20	1.1926
.3811	50	.3719	.5704	.4006	.6028	2.4960	.3972	.9283	.9677	10	1.1897
.3840	22°00′	.3746	.5736	.4040	.6064	2.4751	.3936	.9272	.9672	68°00′	1.1868
.3869	10	.3773	.5767	.4074	.6100	2.4545	.3900	.9261	.9667	50	1.1839
.3898	20	.3800	.5798	.4108	.6136	2.4342	.3864	.9250	.9661	40	1.1810
.3927	30	.3827	.5828	.4142	.6172	2.4142	.3828	.9239	.9656	30	1.1781
.3956	40	.3854	.5859	.4176	.6208	2.3945	.3792	.9228	.9651	20	1.1752
.3985	50	.3881	.5889	.4210	.6243	2.3750	.3757	.9216	.9646	10	1.1723
.4014	23°00′	.3907	.5919	.4245	.6279	2.3559	.3721	.9205	.9640	67°00′	1.1694
.4043	10	.3934	.5948	.4279	.6314	2.3369	.3686	.9194	.9635	50	1.1665
.4072	20	.3961	.5978	.4314	.6348	2.3183	.3652	.9182	.9629	40	1.1636
.4102	30	.3987	.6007	.4348	.6383	2.2998	.3617	.9171	.9624	30	1.1606
.4131	40	.4014	.6036	.4383	.6417	2.2817	.3583	.9159	.9618	20	1.1577
.4160	50	.4041	.6065	.4417	.6452	2.2637	.3548	.9147	.9613	10	1.1548
.4189	24°00′	.4067	.6093	.4452	.6486	2.2460	.3514	.9135	.9607	66°00′	1.1519
.4218	10	.4094	.6121	.4487	.6520	2.2286	.3480	.9124	.9602	50	1.1490
.4247	20	.4120	.6149	.4522	.6553	2.2113	.3447	.9112	.9596	40	1.1461
.4276	30	.4147	.6177	.4557	.6587	2.1943	.3413	.9100	.9590	30	1.1432
.4305	40	.4173	.6205	.4592	.6620	2.1775	.3380	.9088	.9584	20	1.1403
.4334	50	.4200	.6232	.4628	.6654	2.1609	.3346	.9075	.9579	10	1.1374
.4363	25°00′	.4226	.6259	.4663	.6687	2.1445	.3313	.9063	.9573	65°00′	1.1345
.4392	10	.4253	.6286	.4699	.6720	2.1283	.3280	.9051	.9567	50	1.1316
.4422	20	.4279	.6313	.4734	.6752	2.1123	.3248	.9038	.9561	40	1.1286
.4451	30	.4305	.6340	.4770	.6785	2.0965	.3215	.9026	.9555	30	1.1257
.4480	40	.4331	.6366	.4806	.6817	2.0809	.3183	.9013	.9549	20	1.1228
.4509	50	.4358	.6392	.4841	.6850	2.0655	.3150	.9001	.9543	10	1.1199
.4538	26°00′	.4384	.6418	.4877	.6882	2.0503	.3118	.8988	.9537	64°00′	1.1170
.4567	10	.4410	.6444	.4913	.6914	2.0353	.3086	.8975	.9530	50	1.1141
.4596	20	.4436	.6470	.4950	.6946	2.0204	.3054	.8962	.9524	40	1.1112
.4625	30	.4462	.6495	.4986	.6977	2.0057	.3023	.8949	.9518	30	1.1083
.4654	40	.4488	.6521	.5022	.7009	1.9912	.2991	.8936	.9512	20	1.1054
.4683	50	.4514	.6546	.5059	.7040	1.9768	.2960	.8923	.9505	10	1.1025
.4712	27°00′	.4540	.6570	.5095	.7072	1.9626	.2928	.8910	.9499	63°00′	1.0996

Value	Log	Value	Log	Value	Log	Value	Log	Degrees	Radians
Cosine		Cotangent		Tangent		Sine			

TABLE II
TRIGONOMETRIC FUNCTIONS AND THEIR LOGARITHMS

ANGLE Radians	Degrees	Sine Value	Log	Tangent Value	Log	Cotangent Value	Log	Cosine Value	Log		
.4712	27°00′	.4540	.6570	.5095	.7072	1.9626	.2928	.8910	.9499	63°00′	1.0996
.4741	10	.4566	.6595	.5132	.7103	1.9486	.2897	.8897	.9492	50	1.0966
.4771	20	.4592	.6620	.5169	.7134	1.9347	.2866	.8884	.9486	40	1.0937
.4800	30	.4617	.6644	.5206	.7165	1.9210	.2835	.8870	.9479	30	1.0908
.4829	40	.4643	.6668	.5243	.7196	1.9074	.2804	.8857	.9473	20	1.0879
.4858	50	.4669	.6692	.5280	.7226	1.8940	.2774	.8843	.9466	10	1.0850
.4887	28°00′	.4695	.6716	.5317	.7257	1.8807	.2743	.8829	.9459	62°00′	1.0821
.4916	10	.4720	.6740	.5354	.7287	1.8676	.2713	.8816	.9453	50	1.0792
.4945	20	.4746	.6763	.5392	.7317	1.8546	.2683	.8802	.9446	40	1.0763
.4974	30	.4772	.6787	.5430	.7348	1.8418	.2652	.8788	.9439	30	1.0734
.5003	40	.4797	.6810	.5467	.7378	1.8291	.2622	.8774	.9432	20	1.0705
.5032	50	.4823	.6833	.5505	.7408	1.8165	.2592	.8760	.9425	10	1.0676
.5061	29°00′	.4848	.6856	.5543	.7438	1.8040	.2562	.8746	.9418	61°00′	1.0647
.5091	10	.4874	.6878	.5581	.7467	1.7917	.2533	.8732	.9411	50	1.0617
.5120	20	.4899	.6901	.5619	.7497	1.7796	.2503	.8718	.9404	40	1.0588
.5149	30	.4924	.6923	.5658	.7526	1.7675	.2474	.8704	.9397	30	1.0559
.5178	40	.4950	.6946	.5696	.7556	1.7556	.2444	.8689	.9390	20	1.0530
.5207	50	.4975	.6968	.5735	.7585	1.7437	.2415	.8675	.9383	10	1.0501
.5236	30°00′	.5000	.6990	.5774	.7614	1.7321	.2386	.8660	.9375	60°00′	1.0472
.5265	10	.5025	.7012	.5812	.7644	1.7205	.2356	.8646	.9368	50	1.0443
.5294	20	.5050	.7033	.5851	.7673	1.7090	.2327	.8631	.9361	40	1.0414
.5323	30	.5075	.7055	.5890	.7701	1.6977	.2299	.8616	.9353	30	1.0385
.5352	40	.5100	.7076	.5930	.7730	1.6864	.2270	.8601	.9346	20	1.0356
.5381	50	.5125	.7097	.5969	.7759	1.6753	.2241	.8587	.9338	10	1.0327
.5411	31°00′	.5150	.7118	.6009	.7788	1.6643	.2212	.8572	.9331	59°00′	1.0297
.5440	10	.5175	.7139	.6048	.7816	1.6534	.2184	.8557	.9323	50	1.0268
.5469	20	.5200	.7160	.6088	.7845	1.6426	.2155	.8542	.9315	40	1.0239
.5498	30	.5225	.7181	.6128	.7873	1.6319	.2127	.8526	.9308	30	1.0210
.5527	40	.5250	.7201	.6168	.7902	1.6212	.2098	.8511	.9300	20	1.0181
.5556	50	.5275	.7222	.6208	.7930	1.6107	.2070	.8496	.9292	10	1.0152
.5585	32°00′	.5299	.7242	.6249	.7958	1.6003	.2042	.8480	.9284	58°00′	1.0123
.5614	10	.5324	.7262	.6289	.7986	1.5900	.2014	.8465	.9276	50	1.0094
.5643	20	.5348	.7282	.6330	.8014	1.5798	.1986	.8450	.9268	40	1.0065
.5672	30	.5373	.7302	.6371	.8042	1.5697	.1958	.8434	.9260	30	1.0036
.5701	40	.5398	.7322	.6412	.8070	1.5597	.1930	.8418	.9252	20	1.0007
.5730	50	.5422	.7342	.6453	.8097	1.5497	.1903	.8403	.9244	10	.9977
.5760	33°00′	.5446	.7361	.6494	.8125	1.5399	.1875	.8387	.9236	57°00′	.9948
.5789	10	.5471	.7380	.6536	.8153	1.5301	.1847	.8371	.9228	50	.9919
.5818	20	.5495	.7400	.6577	.8180	1.5204	.1820	.8355	.9219	40	.9890
.5847	30	.5519	.7419	.6619	.8208	1.5108	.1792	.8339	.9211	30	.9861
.5876	40	.5544	.7438	.6661	.8235	1.5013	.1765	.8323	.9203	20	.9832
.5905	50	.5568	.7457	.6703	.8263	1.4919	.1737	.8307	.9194	10	.9803
.5934	34°00′	.5592	.7476	.6745	.8290	1.4826	.1710	.8290	.9186	56°00′	.9774
.5963	10	.5616	.7494	.6787	.8317	1.4733	.1683	.8274	.9177	50	.9745
.5992	20	.5640	.7513	.6830	.8344	1.4641	.1656	.8258	.9169	40	.9716
.6021	30	.5664	.7531	.6873	.8371	1.4550	.1629	.8241	.9160	30	.9687
.6050	40	.5688	.7550	.6916	.8398	1.4460	.1602	.8225	.9151	20	.9657
.6080	50	.5712	.7568	.6959	.8425	1.4370	.1575	.8208	.9142	10	.9628
.6109	35°00′	.5736	.7586	.7002	.8452	1.4281	.1548	.8192	.9134	55°00′	.9599
.6138	10	.5760	.7604	.7046	.8479	1.4193	.1521	.8175	.9125	50	.9570
.6167	20	.5783	.7622	.7089	.8506	1.4106	.1494	.8158	.9116	40	.9541
.6196	30	.5807	.7640	.7133	.8533	1.4019	.1467	.8141	.9107	30	.9512
.6225	40	.5831	.7657	.7177	.8559	1.3934	.1441	.8124	.9098	20	.9483
.6254	50	.5854	.7675	.7221	.8586	1.3848	.1414	.8107	.9089	10	.9454
.6283	36°00′	.5878	.7692	.7265	.8613	1.3764	.1387	.8090	.9080	54°00′	.9425

		Value Log Cosine		Value Log Cotangent		Value Log Tangent		Value Log Sine		Degrees	Radians

TABLE II
TRIGONOMETRIC FUNCTIONS AND THEIR LOGARITHMS

ANGLE Radians	Degrees	Sine Value	Log	Tangent Value	Log	Cotangent Value	Log	Cosine Value	Log		
.6283	36°00′	.5878	.7692	.7265	.8613	1.3764	.1387	.8090	.9080	54°00′	.9425
.6312	10	.5901	.7710	.7310	.8639	1.3680	.1361	.8073	.9070	50	.9396
.6341	20	.5925	.7727	.7355	.8666	1.3597	.1334	.8056	.9061	40	.9367
.6370	30	.5948	.7744	.7400	.8692	1.3514	.1308	.8039	.9052	30	.9338
.6400	40	.5972	.7761	.7445	.8718	1.3432	.1282	.8021	.9042	20	.9308
.6429	50	.5995	.7778	.7490	.8745	1.3351	.1255	.8004	.9033	10	.9279
.6458	37°00′	.6018	.7795	.7536	.8771	1.3270	.1229	.7986	.9023	53°00′	.9250
.6487	10	.6041	.7811	.7581	.8797	1.3190	.1203	.7969	.9014	50	.9221
.6516	20	.6065	.7828	.7627	.8824	1.3111	.1176	.7951	.9004	40	.9192
.6545	30	.6088	.7844	.7673	.8850	1.3032	.1150	.8934	.8995	30	.9163
.6574	40	.6111	.7861	.7720	.8876	1.2954	.1124	.7916	.8985	20	.9134
.6603	50	.6134	.7877	.7766	.8902	1.2876	.1098	.7898	.8975	10	.9105
.6632	38°00′	.6157	.7893	.7813	.8928	1.2799	.1072	.7880	.8965	52°00′	.9076
.6661	10	.6180	.7910	.7860	.8954	1.2723	.1046	.7862	.8955	50	.9047
.6690	20	.6202	.7926	.7907	.8980	1.2647	.1020	.7844	.8945	40	.9018
.6720	30	.6225	.7941	.7954	.9006	1.2572	.0994	.7826	.8935	30	.8988
.6749	40	.6248	.7957	.8002	.9032	1.2497	.0968	.7808	.8925	20	.8959
.6778	50	.6271	.7973	.8050	.9058	1.2423	.0942	.7790	.8915	10	.8930
.6807	39°00′	.6293	.7989	.8098	.9084	1.2349	.0916	.7771	.8905	51°00′	.8901
.6836	10	.6316	.8004	.8146	.9110	1.2276	.0890	.7753	.8895	50	.8872
.6865	20	.6338	.8020	.8195	.9135	1.2203	.0865	.7735	.8884	40	.8843
.6894	30	.6361	.8035	.8243	.9161	1.2131	.0839	.7716	.8874	30	.8814
.6923	40	.6383	.8050	.8292	.9187	1.2059	.0813	.7698	.8864	20	.8785
.6952	50	.6406	.8066	.8342	.9212	1.1988	.0788	.7679	.8853	10	.8756
.6981	40°00′	.6428	.8081	.8391	.9238	1.1918	.0762	.7660	.8843	50°00′	.8727
.7010	10	.6450	.8096	.8441	.9264	1.1847	.0736	.7642	.8832	50	.8698
.7039	20	.6472	.8111	.8491	.9289	1.1778	.0711	.7623	.8821	40	.8668
.7069	30	.6494	.8125	.8541	.9315	1.1708	.0685	.7604	.8810	30	.8639
.7098	40	.6517	.8140	.8591	.9341	1.1640	.0659	.7585	.8800	20	.8610
.7127	50	.6539	.8155	.8642	.9366	1.1571	.0634	.7566	.8789	10	.8581
.7156	41°00′	.6561	.8169	.8693	.9392	1.1504	.0608	.7547	.8778	49°00′	.8552
.7185	10	.6583	.8184	.8744	.9417	1.1436	.0583	.7528	.8767	50	.8523
.7214	20	.6604	.8198	.8796	.9443	1.1369	.0557	.7509	.8756	40	.8494
.7243	30	.6626	.8213	.8847	.9468	1.1303	.0532	.7490	.8745	30	.8465
.7272	40	.6648	.8227	.8899	.9494	1.1237	.0506	.7470	.8733	20	.8436
.7301	50	.6670	.8241	.8952	.9519	1.1171	.0481	.7451	.8722	10	.8407
.7330	42°00′	.6691	.8255	.9004	.9544	1.1106	.0456	.7431	.8711	48°00′	.8378
.7359	10	.6713	.8269	.9057	.9570	1.1041	.0430	.7412	.8699	50	.8348
.7389	20	.6734	.8283	.9110	.9595	1.0977	.0405	.7392	.8688	40	.8319
.7418	30	.6756	.8297	.9163	.9621	1.0913	.0379	.7373	.8676	30	.8290
.7447	40	.6777	.8311	.9217	.9646	1.0850	.0354	.7353	.8665	20	.8261
.7476	50	.6799	.8324	.9271	.9671	1.0786	.0329	.7333	.8653	10	.8232
.7505	43°00′	.6820	.8338	.9325	.9697	1.0724	.0303	.7314	.8641	47°00′	.8203
.7534	10	.6841	.8351	.9380	.9722	1.0661	.0278	.7294	.8629	50	.8174
.7563	20	.6862	.8365	.9435	.9747	1.0599	.0253	.7274	.8618	40	.8145
.7592	30	.6884	.8378	.9490	.9772	1.0538	.0228	.7254	.8606	30	.8116
.7621	40	.6905	.8391	.9545	.9798	1.0477	.0202	.7234	.8594	20	.8087
.7650	50	.6926	.8405	.9601	.9823	1.0416	.0177	.7214	.8582	10	.8058
.7679	44°00′	.6947	.8418	.9657	.9848	1.0355	.0152	.7193	.8569	46°00′	.8029
.7709	10	.6967	.8431	.9713	.9874	1.0295	.0126	.7173	.8557	50	.7999
.7738	20	.6988	.8444	.9770	.9899	1.0235	.0101	.7153	.8545	40	.7970
.7767	30	.7009	.8457	.9827	.9924	1.0176	.0076	.7133	.8532	30	.7941
.7796	40	.7030	.8469	.9884	.9949	1.0117	.0051	.7112	.8520	20	.7912
.7825	50	.7050	.8482	.9942	.9975	1.0058	.0025	.7092	.8507	10	.7883
.7854	45°00′	.7071	.8495	1.0000	.0000	1.0000	.0000	.7071	.8495	45°00′	.7854

Value	Log Cosine	Value	Log Cotangent	Value	Log Tangent	Value	Log Sine	Degrees	Radians

TABLE III

Amount of One Dollar at Compound Interest for n Years

$$s = (1+r)^n$$

n	2%	2½%	3%	3½%	4%	4½%	5%	6%	7%
1	1.0200	1.0250	1.0300	1.0350	1.0400	1.0450	1.0500	1.0600	1.0700
2	1.0404	1.0506	1.0609	1.0712	1.0816	1.0920	1.1025	1.1236	1.1449
3	1.0612	1.0769	1.0927	1.1087	1.1249	1.1412	1.1576	1.1910	1.2250
4	1.0824	1.1038	1.1255	1.1475	1.1699	1.1925	1.2155	1.2625	1.3108
5	1.1041	1.1314	1.1593	1.1877	1.2167	1.2462	1.2763	1.3382	1.4026
6	1.12 2	1.1597	1.1941	1.2293	1.2653	1.3023	1.3401	1.4185	1.5007
7	1.1487	1.1887	1.2299	1.2723	1.3159	1.3609	1.4071	1.5036	1.6058
8	1.1717	1.2184	1.2668	1.3168	1.3686	1.4221	1.4775	1.5938	1.7182
9	1.1951	1.2489	1.3048	1.3629	1.4233	1.4861	1.5513	1.6895	1.8385
10	1.2190	1.2801	1.3439	1.4106	1.4802	1.5530	1.6289	1.7908	1.9672
11	1.2434	1.3121	1.3842	1.4600	1.5395	1.6229	1.7103	1.8983	2.1049
12	1.2682	1.3449	1.4258	1.5111	1.6010	1.6959	1.7959	2.0122	2.2522
13	1.2936	1.3785	1.4685	1.5640	1.6651	1.7722	1.8856	2.1329	2.4098
14	1.3195	1.4130	1.5126	1.6187	1.7317	1.8519	1.9799	2.2609	2.5785
15	1.3459	1.4483	1.5580	1.6753	1.8009	1.9353	2.0789	2.3966	2.7590
16	1.3728	1.4845	1.6047	1.7340	1.8730	2.0224	2.1829	2.5404	2.9522
17	1.4002	1.5216	1.6528	1.7947	1.9479	2.1134	2.2920	2.6928	3.1588
18	1.4282	1.5597	1.7024	1.8575	2.0258	2.2085	2.4066	2.8543	3.3799
19	1.4568	1.5987	1.7535	1.9225	2.1068	2.3079	2.5270	3.0256	3.6165
20	1.4859	1.6386	1.8061	1.9898	2.1911	2.4117	2.6533	3.2071	3.8697
21	1.5157	1.6796	1.8603	2.0594	2.2788	2.5202	2.7860	3.3996	4.1406
22	1.5460	1.7216	1.9161	2.1315	2.3699	2.6337	2.9253	3.6035	4.4304
23	1.5769	1.7646	1.9736	2.2061	2.4647	2.7522	3.0715	3.8197	4.7405
24	1.6084	1.8087	2.0328	2.2833	2.5633	2.8760	3.2251	4.0489	5.0724
25	1.6406	1.8539	2.0938	2.3632	2.6658	3.0054	3.3864	4.2919	5.4274
26	1.6734	1.9003	2.1566	2.4460	2.7725	3.1407	3.5557	4.5494	5.8074
27	1.7069	1.9478	2.2213	2.5316	2.8834	3.2820	3.7335	4.8223	6.2139
28	1.7410	1.9965	2.2879	2.6202	2.9987	3.4297	3.9201	5.1117	6.6488
29	1.7758	2.0464	2.3566	2.7119	3.1187	3.5840	4.1161	5.4184	7.1143
30	1.8114	2.0976	2.4273	2.8068	3.2434	3.7453	4.3219	5.7435	7.6123
31	1.8476	2.1500	2.5001	2.9050	3.3731	3.9139	4.5380	6.0881	8.1451
32	1.8845	2.2038	2.5751	3.0067	3.5081	4.0900	4.7649	6.4534	8.7153
33	1.9222	2.2589	2.6523	3.1119	3.6484	4.2740	5.0032	6.8406	9.3253
34	1.9607	2.3153	2.7319	3.2209	3.7943	4.4664	5.2533	7.2510	9.9781
35	1.9999	2.3732	2.8139	3.3336	3.9461	4.6673	5.5160	7.6861	10.6766
36	2.0399	2.4325	2.8983	3.4503	4.1039	4.8774	5.7918	8.1473	11.4239
37	2.0807	2.4933	2.9852	3.5710	4.2681	5.0969	6.0814	8.6361	12.2236
38	2.1223	2.5557	3.0748	3.6960	4.4388	5.3262	6.3855	9.1543	13.0793
39	2.1647	2.6196	3.1670	3.8254	4.6164	5.5659	6.7048	9.7035	13.9948
40	2.2080	2.6851	3.2620	3.9593	4.8010	5.8164	7.0400	10.2857	14.9745
41	2.2522	2.7522	3.3599	4.0978	4.9931	6.0781	7.3920	10.9029	16.0227
42	2.2972	2.8210	3.4607	4.2413	5.1928	6.3516	7.7616	11.5570	17.1443
43	2.3432	2.8915	3.5645	4.3897	5.4005	6.6374	8.1497	12.2505	18.3444
44	2.3901	2.9638	3.6715	4.5433	5.6165	6.9361	8.5572	12.9855	19.6285
45	2.4379	3.0379	3.7816	4.7024	5.8412	7.2482	8.9850	13.7646	21.0025
46	2.4866	3.1139	3.8950	4.8669	6.0748	7.5744	9.4343	14.5905	22.4726
47	2.5363	3.1917	4.0119	5.0373	6.3178	7.9153	9.9060	15.4659	24.0457
48	2.5871	3.2715	4.1323	5.2136	6.5705	8.2715	10.4013	16.3939	25.7289
49	2.6388	3.3533	4.2562	5.3961	6.8333	8.6437	10.9213	17.3775	27.5299
50	2.6916	3.4371	4.3839	5.5849	7.1067	9.0326	11.4674	18.4202	29.4570

TABLE IV

Present Value of One Dollar Due at End of n Years

$$p = 1/(1+r)^n$$

n	2%	2½%	3%	3½%	4%	4½%	5%	6%	7%
1	.98039	.97561	.97087	.96618	.96154	.95694	.95238	.94340	.93458
2	.96117	.95181	.94260	.93351	.92456	.91573	.90703	.89000	.87344
3	.94232	.92860	.91514	.90194	.88900	.87630	.86384	.83962	.81630
4	.92385	.90595	.88849	.87144	.85480	.83856	.82270	.79209	.76290
5	.90573	.88385	.86261	.84197	.82193	.80245	.78353	.74726	.71299
6	.88797	.86230	.83748	.81350	.79031	.76790	.74622	.70496	.66634
7	.87056	.84127	.81309	.78599	.75992	.73483	.71068	.66506	.62275
8	.85349	.82075	.78941	.75941	.73069	.70319	.67684	.62741	.58201
9	.83676	.80073	.76642	.73373	.70259	.67290	.64461	.59190	.54393
10	.82035	.78120	.74409	.70892	.67556	.64393	.61391	.55839	.50835
11	.80426	.76214	.72242	.68495	.64958	.61620	.58468	.52679	.47509
12	.78849	.74356	.70138	.66178	.62460	.58966	.55684	.49697	.44401
13	.77303	.72542	.68095	.63940	.60057	.56427	.53032	.46884	.41496
14	.75788	.70773	.66112	.61778	.57748	.53997	.50507	.44230	.38782
15	.74301	.69047	.64186	.59689	.55526	.51672	.48102	.41727	.36245
16	.72845	.67362	.62317	.57671	.53391	.49447	.45811	.39365	.33873
17	.71416	.65720	.60502	.55720	.51337	.47318	.43630	.37136	.31657
18	.70016	.64117	.58739	.53836	.49363	.45280	.41552	.35034	.29586
19	.68643	.62553	.57029	.52016	.47464	.43330	.39573	.33051	.27651
20	.67297	.61027	.55368	.50257	.45639	.41464	.37689	.31180	.25842
21	.65978	.59539	.53755	.48557	.43883	.39679	.35894	.29416	.24151
22	.64684	.58086	.52189	.46915	.42196	.37970	.34185	.27751	.22571
23	.63416	.56670	.50669	.45329	.40573	.36335	.32557	.26180	.21095
24	.62172	.55288	.49193	.43796	.39012	.34770	.31007	.24698	.19715
25	.60953	.53939	.47761	.42315	.37512	.33273	.29530	.23300	.18425
26	.59758	.52623	.46369	.40884	.36069	.31840	.28124	.21981	.17220
27	.58586	.51340	.45019	.39501	.34682	.30469	.26785	.20737	.16093
28	.57437	.50088	.43708	.38165	.33348	.29157	.25509	.19563	.15040
29	.56311	.48866	.42435	.36875	.32065	.27902	.24295	.18456	.14056
30	.55207	.47674	.41199	.35628	.30832	.26700	.23138	.17411	.13137
31	.54125	.46511	.39999	.34423	.29646	.25550	.22036	.16425	.12277
32	.53063	.45377	.38834	.33259	.28506	.24450	.20987	.15496	.11474
33	.52023	.44270	.37703	.32134	.27409	.23397	.19987	.14619	.10723
34	.51003	.43191	.36604	.31048	.26355	.22390	.19035	.13791	.10022
35	.50003	.42137	.35538	.29998	.25342	.21425	.18129	.13011	.09366
36	.49022	.41109	.34503	.28983	.24367	.20503	.17266	.12274	.08754
37	.48061	.40107	.33498	.28003	.23430	.19620	.16444	.11580	.08181
38	.47119	.39128	.32523	.27056	.22529	.18775	.15661	.10924	.07646
39	.46195	.38174	.31575	.26141	.21662	.17967	.14915	.10306	.07146
40	.45289	.37243	.30656	.25257	.20829	.17193	.14205	.09722	.06678
41	.44401	.36335	.29763	.24403	.20028	.16453	.13528	.09172	.06241
42	.43530	.35448	.28896	.23578	.19257	.15744	.12884	.08653	.05833
43	.42677	.34584	.28054	.22781	.18517	.15066	.12270	.08163	.05451
44	.41840	.33740	.27237	.22010	.17805	.14417	.11686	.07701	.05095
45	.41020	.32917	.26444	.21266	.17120	.13796	.11130	.07265	.04761
46	.40215	.32115	.25674	.20547	.16461	.13202	.10600	.06854	.04450
47	.39427	.31331	.24926	.19852	.15828	.12634	.10095	.06466	.04159
48	.38654	.30567	.24200	.19181	.15219	.12090	.09614	.06100	.03887
49	.37896	.29822	.23495	.18532	.14634	.11569	.09156	.05755	.03632
50	.37153	.29094	.22811	.17905	.14071	.11071	.08720	.05429	.03395

TABLE V

Amount of an Annuity of One Dollar Per Year for n Years

$$s_{\overline{n}|i} = \frac{(1+i)^n - 1}{i}$$

n	2%	2½%	3%	3½%	4%	4½%	5%	6%	7%
1	1.0000	1.0000	1.0000	1.0000	1.0000	1.0000	1.0000	1.0000	1.0000
2	2.0200	2.0250	2.0300	2.0350	2.0400	2.0450	2.0500	2.0600	2.0700
3	3.0604	3.0756	3.0909	3.1062	3.1216	3.1370	3.1525	3.1836	3.2149
4	4.1216	4.1525	4.1836	4.2149	4.2465	4.2782	4.3101	4.3746	4.4399
5	5.2040	5.2563	5.3091	5.3625	5.4163	5.4707	5.5256	5.6371	5.7507
6	6.3081	6.3877	6.4684	6.5502	6.6330	6.7169	6.8019	6.9753	7.1533
7	7.4343	7.5474	7.6625	7.7794	7.8983	8.0192	8.1420	8.3938	8.6540
8	8.5830	8.7361	8.8923	9.0517	9.2142	9.3800	9.5491	9.8975	10.2598
9	9.7546	9.9545	10.1591	10.3685	10.5828	10.8021	11.0266	11.4913	11.9780
10	10.9497	11.2034	11.4639	11.7314	12.0061	12.2882	12.5779	13.1808	13.8164
11	12.1687	12.4835	12.8708	13.1420	13.4864	13.8412	14.2068	14.9716	15.7836
12	13.4121	13.7956	14.1920	14.6020	15.0258	15.4640	15.9171	16.8699	17.8885
13	14.6803	15.1404	15.6178	16.1130	16.6268	17.1599	17.7130	18.8821	20.1406
14	15.9739	16.5190	17.0863	17.6770	18.2919	18.9321	19.5986	21.0151	22.5505
15	17.2934	17.9319	18.5989	19.2957	20.0236	20.7841	21.5786	23.2760	25.1290
16	18.6393	19.3802	20.1569	20.9710	21.8245	22.7193	23.6575	25.6725	27.8881
17	20.0121	20.8647	21.7616	22.7050	23.6975	24.7417	25.8404	28.2129	30.8402
18	21.4123	22.3863	23.4144	24.4997	25.6454	26.8551	28.1324	30.9057	33.9990
19	22.8406	23.9460	25.1169	26.3572	27.6712	29.0636	30.5390	33.7600	37.3790
20	24.2974	25.5447	26.8704	28.2797	29.7781	31.3714	33.0660	36.7856	40.9955
21	25.7833	27.1833	28.6765	30.2695	31.9692	33.7831	35.7193	39.9927	44.8652
22	27.2990	28.8629	30.5368	32.3289	34.2480	36.3034	38.5052	43.3923	49.0057
23	28.8450	30.5844	32.4529	34.4604	36.6179	38.9370	41.4305	46.9958	53.4361
24	30.4219	32.3490	34.4265	36.6665	39.0826	41.6892	44.5020	50.8156	58.1767
25	32.0303	34.1578	36.4593	38.9499	41.6459	44.5652	47.7271	54.8645	63.2490
26	33.6709	36.0117	38.5530	41.3131	44.3117	47.5706	51.1135	59.1564	68.6765
27	35.3443	37.9120	40.7096	43.7591	47.0842	50.7113	54.6691	63.7058	74.4838
28	37.0512	39.8598	42.9309	46.2906	49.9676	53.9933	58.4026	68.5281	80.6977
29	38.7922	41.8563	45.2189	48.9108	52.9663	57.4230	62.3227	73.6398	87.3465
30	40.5681	43.9027	47.5754	51.6227	56.0849	61.0071	66.4388	79.0582	94.4608
31	42.3794	46.0003	50.0027	54.4295	59.3283	64.7524	70.7608	84.8017	102.0730
32	44.2270	48.1503	52.5028	57.3345	62.7015	68.6662	75.2988	90.8898	110.2182
33	46.1116	50.3540	55.0778	60.3412	66.2095	72.7562	80.0638	97.3432	118.9334
34	48.0338	52.6129	57.7302	63.4532	69.8579	77.0303	85.0670	104.1838	128.2588
35	49.9945	54.9282	60.4621	66.6740	73.6522	81.4966	90.3203	111.4348	138.2369
36	51.9944	57.3014	63.2759	70.0076	77.5983	86.1640	95.8363	119.1209	148.9135
37	54.0343	59.7339	66.1742	73.4579	81.7022	91.0413	101.6281	127.2681	160.3374
38	56.1149	62.2273	69.1594	77.0289	85.9703	96.1382	107.7095	135.9042	172.5610
39	58.2372	64.7830	72.2342	80.7249	90.4091	101.4644	114.0950	145.0585	185.6403
40	60.4020	67.4026	75.4013	84.5503	95.0255	107.0303	120.7998	154.7620	199.6351
41	62.6100	70.0876	78.6633	88.5095	99.8265	112.8467	127.8398	165.0477	214.6096
42	64.8622	72.8398	82.0232	92.6074	104.8196	118.9248	135.2318	175.9505	230.6322
43	67.1595	75.6608	85.4839	96.8486	110.0124	125.2764	142.9933	187.5076	247.7765
44	69.5027	78.5523	89.0484	101.2383	115.4129	131.9138	151.1430	199.7580	266.1209
45	71.8927	81.5161	92.7199	105.7817	121.0294	138.8500	159.7002	212.7435	285.7493
46	74.3306	84.5540	96.5015	110.4840	126.8706	146.0982	168.6852	226.5081	306.7518
47	76.8172	87.6679	100.3965	115.3510	132.9454	153.6726	178.1194	241.0986	329.2244
48	79.3535	90.8596	104.4084	120.3883	139.2632	161.5879	188.0254	256.5645	353.2701
49	81.9406	94.1311	108.5406	125.6018	145.8337	169.8594	198.4267	272.9584	378.9990
50	84.5794	97.4843	112.7969	130.9979	152.6671	178.5030	209.3480	290.3359	406.5289

TABLE VI

Present Value of an Annuity of One Dollar Per Year for n Years

$$a_{\overline{n}|i} = \frac{1-(1+i)^{-n}}{i}$$

n	2%	2½%	3%	3½%	4%	4½%	5%	6%	7%
1	.9804	.9756	.9709	.9662	.9615	.9569	.9524	.9434	.9346
2	1.9416	1.9274	1.9135	1.8997	1.8861	1.8727	1.8594	1.8334	1.8080
3	2.8839	2.8560	2.8286	2.8016	2.7751	2.7490	2.7232	2.6730	2.6243
4	3.8077	3.7620	3.7171	3.6731	3.6299	3.5875	3.5460	3.4651	3.3872
5	4.7135	4.6458	4.5797	4.5151	4.4518	4.3900	4.3295	4.2124	4.1002
6	5.6014	5.5081	5.4172	5.3286	5.2421	5.1579	5.0757	4.9173	4.7665
7	6.4720	6.3494	6.2303	6.1145	6.0021	5.8927	5.7864	5.5824	5.3893
8	7.3255	7.1701	7.0197	6.8740	6.7327	6.5959	6.4632	6.2098	5.9713
9	8.1622	7.9709	7.7861	7.6077	7.4353	7.2688	7.1078	6.8017	6.5152
10	8.9826	8.7521	8.5302	8.3166	8.1109	7.9127	7.7217	7.3601	7.0236
11	9.7868	9.5142	9.2526	9.0016	8.7605	8.5289	8.3064	7.8869	7.4987
12	10.5753	10.2578	9.9540	9.6633	9.3851	9.1186	8.8633	8.3838	7.9427
13	11.3484	10.9832	10.6350	10.3027	9.9856	9.6829	9.3936	8.8527	8.3577
14	12.1062	11.6909	11.2961	10.9205	10.5631	10.2228	9.8986	9.2950	8.7455
15	12.8493	12.3814	11.9379	11.5174	11.1184	10.7395	10.3797	9.7122	9.1079
16	13.5777	13.0550	12.5611	12.0941	11.6523	11.2340	10.8378	10.1059	9.4466
17	14.2919	13.7122	13.1661	12.6513	12.1657	11.7072	11.2741	10.4773	9.7632
18	14.9920	14.3534	13.7535	13.1897	12.6593	12.1600	11.6896	10.8276	10.0591
19	15.6785	14.9789	14.3238	13.7098	13.1339	12.5933	12.0853	11.1581	10.3356
20	16.3514	15.5892	14.8775	14.2124	13.5903	13.0079	12.4622	11.4699	10.5940
21	17.0112	16.1845	15.4150	14.6980	14.0292	13.4047	12.8212	11.7641	10.8355
22	17.6580	16.7654	15.9369	15.1671	14.4511	13.7844	13.1630	12.0416	11.0612
23	18.2922	17.3321	16.4436	15.6204	14.8568	14.1478	13.4886	12.3034	11.2722
24	18.9139	17.8850	16.9355	16.0584	15.2470	14.4955	13.7986	12.5504	11.4693
25	19.5235	18.4244	17.4131	16.4815	15.6221	14.8282	14.0939	12.7834	11.6536
26	20.1210	18.9506	17.8768	16.8904	15.9828	15.1466	14.3752	13.0032	11.8258
27	20.7069	19.4640	18.3270	17.2854	16.3296	15.4513	14.6430	13.2105	11.9867
28	21.2813	19.9649	18.7641	17.6670	16.6631	15.7429	14.8981	13.4062	12.1371
29	21.8444	20.4535	19.1885	18.0358	16.9837	16.0219	15.1411	13.5907	12.2777
30	22.3965	20.9303	19.6004	18.3920	17.2920	16.2889	15.3725	13.7648	12.4090
31	22.9377	21.3954	20.0004	18.7363	17.5885	16.5444	15.5928	13.9291	12.5318
32	23.4683	21.8392	20.3888	19.0689	17.8736	16.7889	15.8027	14.0840	12.6466
33	23.9886	22.2919	20.7658	19.3902	18.1476	17.0229	16.0025	14.2302	12.7538
34	24.4986	22.7238	21.1318	19.7007	18.4112	17.2468	16.1929	14.3681	12.8540
35	24.9986	23.1452	21.4872	20.0007	18.6646	17.4610	16.3742	14.4982	12.9477
36	25.4888	23.5563	21.8323	20.2905	18.9083	17.6660	16.5469	14.6210	13.0352
37	25.9695	23.9673	22.1672	20.5705	19.1426	17.8622	16.7113	14.7368	13.1170
38	26.4406	24.3486	22.4925	20.8411	19.3679	18.0500	16.8679	14.8460	13.1935
39	26.9026	24.7303	22.8082	21.1025	19.5845	18.2297	17.0170	14.9491	13.2649
40	27.3555	25.1028	23.1148	21.3551	19.7928	18.4016	17.1591	15.0463	13.3317
41	27.7995	25.4661	23.4124	21.5991	19.9931	18.5661	17.2944	15.1380	13.3941
42	28.2348	25.8206	23.7014	21.8349	20.1856	18.7236	17.4232	15.2245	13.4524
43	28.6616	26.1664	23.9819	22.0627	20.3708	18.8742	17.5459	15.3062	13.5070
44	29.0800	26.5038	24.2543	22.2828	20.5488	19.0184	17.6628	15.3832	13.5579
45	29.4902	26.8330	24.5187	22.4955	20.7200	19.1563	17.7741	15.4558	13.6055
46	29.8923	27.1542	24.7754	22.7009	20.8847	19.2884	17.8801	15.5244	13.6500
47	30.2866	27.4675	25.0247	22.8994	21.0429	19.4147	17.9810	15.5890	13.6910
48	30.6731	27.7732	25.2667	23.0912	21.1951	19.5356	18.0772	15.6500	13.7305
49	31.0521	28.0714	25.5017	23.2766	21.3415	19.6513	18.1687	15.7076	13.7668
50	31.4236	28.3623	25.7298	23.4556	21.4822	19.7620	18.2559	15.7619	13.8007

TABLE VII
AMERICAN EXPERIENCE TABLE OF MORTALITY

Age x	Number living l_x	Number of deaths d_x	Yearly probability of dying q_x	Yearly probability of living p_x	Age x	Number living l_x	Number of deaths d_x	Yearly probability of dying q_x	Yearly probability of living p_x
10	100,000	749	0.007 490	0.992 510	53	66,797	1,091	0.016 333	0.983 667
11	99,251	746	0.007 516	0.992 484	54	65,706	1,143	0.017 396	0.982 604
12	98,505	743	0.007 543	0.992 457	55	64,563	1,199	0.018 571	0.981 429
13	97,762	740	0.007 569	0.992 431	56	63,364	1,260	0.019 885	0.980 115
14	97,022	737	0.007 596	0.992 404	57	62,104	1,325	0.021 335	0.978 665
15	96,285	735	0.007 634	0.992 366	58	60.779	1,394	0.022 936	0.977 064
16	95,550	732	0.007 661	0.992 339	59	59,385	1,468	0.024 720	0.975 280
17	94,818	729	0.007 688	0.992 312	60	57,917	1,546	0.026 693	0.973 307
18	94,089	727	0.007 727	0.992 273	61	56,371	1,628	0.028 880	0.971 120
19	93,362	725	0.007 765	0.992 235	62	54,743	1,713	0.031 292	0.968 708
20	92,637	723	0.007 805	0.992 195	63	53,030	1,800	0.033 943	0.966 057
21	91,914	722	0.007 855	0.992 145	64	51,230	1,889	0.036 873	0.963 127
22	91,192	721	0.007 906	0.992 094	65	49,341	1,980	0.040 129	0.959 871
23	90,471	720	0.007 958	0.992 042	66	47,361	2,070	0.043 707	0.956 293
24	89,751	719	0.008 011	0.991 989	67	45,291	2,158	0.047 647	0.952 353
25	89,032	718	0.008 065	0.991 935	68	43,133	2,243	0.052 002	0.947 998
26	88,314	718	0.008 130	0.991 870	69	40,890	2,321	0.056 762	0.943 238
27	87,596	718	0.008 197	0.991 803	70	38,569	2,391	0.061 993	0.938 007
28	86,878	718	0.008 264	0.991 736	71	36,178	2,448	0.067 665	0.932 335
29	86,160	719	0.008 345	0.991 655	72	33,730	2,487	0.073 733	0.926 267
30	85,441	720	0.008 427	0.991 573	73	31,243	2,505	0.080 178	0.919 822
31	84,721	721	0.008 510	0.991 490	74	28,738	2,501	0.087 028	0.912 972
32	84,000	723	0.008 607	0.991 393	75	26,237	2,476	0.094 371	0.905 629
33	83,277	726	0.008 718	0.991 282	76	23,761	2,431	0.102 311	0.897 689
34	82,551	729	0.008 831	0.991 169	77	21,330	2,369	0.111 064	0.888 936
35	81,822	732	0.008 946	0.991 054	78	18,961	2,291	0.120 827	0.879 173
36	81,090	737	0.009 089	0.990 911	79	16,670	2,196	0.131 734	0.868 266
37	80,353	742	0.009 234	0.990 766	80	14,474	2,091	0.144 466	0.855 534
38	79,611	749	0.009 408	0.990 592	81	12,383	1,964	0.158 605	0.841 395
39	78,862	756	0.009 586	0.990 414	82	10,419	1,816	0.174 297	0.825 703
40	78,106	765	0.009 794	0.990 206	83	8,603	1,648	0.191 561	0.808 439
41	77,341	774	0.010 008	0.989 992	84	6,955	1,470	0.211 359	0.788 641
42	76,567	785	0.010 252	0.989 748	85	5,485	1,292	0.235 552	0.764 448
43	75,782	797	0.010 517	0.989 483	86	4,193	1,114	0.265 681	0.734 319
44	74,985	812	0.010 829	0.989 171	87	3,079	933	0.303 020	0.696 980
45	74,173	828	0.011 163	0.988 837	88	2,146	744	0.346 692	0.653 308
46	73,345	848	0.011 562	0.988 438	89	1,402	555	0.395 863	0.604 137
47	72,497	870	0.012 000	0.988 000	90	847	385	0.454 545	0.545 455
48	71,627	896	0.012 509	0.987 491	91	462	246	0.532 468	0.467 532
49	70,731	927	0.013 106	0.986 894	92	216	137	0.634 259	0.365 741
50	69,804	962	0.013 781	0.986 219	93	79	58	0.734 177	0.265 823
51	68,842	1,001	0.014 541	0.985 459	94	21	18	0.857 143	0.142 857
52	67,841	1,044	0.015 389	0.984 611	95	3	3	1.000 000	0.000 000

TABLE VIII

Squares, Cubes, Square Roots, and Cube Roots of Integers

No.	Square	Cube	Square root	Cube root	No.	Square	Cube	Square root	Cube root
1	1	1	1.0000	1.00000	51	2 601	132 651	7.1414	3.70843
2	4	8	1.4142	1.25992	52	2 704	140 608	7.2111	3.73251
3	9	27	1.7321	1.44225	53	2 809	148 877	7.2801	3.75629
4	16	64	2.0000	1.58740	54	2 916	157 464	7.3485	3.77976
5	25	125	2.2361	1.70998	55	3 025	166 375	7.4162	3.80295
6	36	216	2.4495	1.81712	56	3 136	175 616	7.4833	3.82586
7	49	343	2.6458	1.91293	57	3 249	185 193	7.5498	3.84850
8	64	512	2.8284	2.00000	58	3 364	195 112	7.6158	3.87088
9	81	729	3.0000	2.08008	59	3 481	205 379	7.6811	3.89300
10	100	1 000	3.1623	2.15443	60	3 600	216 000	7.7460	3.91487
11	121	1 331	3.3166	2.22398	61	3 721	226 981	7.8102	3.93650
12	144	1 728	3.4641	2.28943	62	3 844	238 328	7.8740	3.95789
13	169	2 197	3.6056	2.35133	63	3 969	250 047	7.9373	3.97906
14	196	2 744	3.7417	2.41014	64	4 096	262 144	8.0000	4.00000
15	225	3 375	3.8730	2.46621	65	4 225	274 625	8.0623	4.02073
16	256	4 096	4.0000	2.51984	66	4 356	287 496	8.1240	4.04124
17	289	4 913	4.1231	2.57128	67	4 489	300 763	8.1854	4.06155
18	324	5 832	4.2426	2.62074	68	4 624	314 432	8.2462	4.08166
19	361	6 859	4.3589	2.66840	69	4 761	328 509	8.3066	4.10157
20	400	8 000	4.4721	2.71442	70	4 900	343 000	8.3666	4.12129
21	441	9 261	4.5826	2.75892	71	5 041	357 911	8.4261	4.14082
22	484	10 648	4.6904	2.80204	72	5 184	373 248	8.4853	4.16017
23	529	12 167	4.7958	2.84387	73	5 329	389 017	8.5440	4.17934
24	576	13 824	4.8990	2.88450	74	5 476	405 224	8.6023	4.19834
25	625	15 625	5.0000	2.92402	75	5 625	421 875	8.6603	4.21716
26	676	17 576	5.0990	2.96250	76	5 776	438 976	8.7178	4.23582
27	729	19 683	5.1962	3.00000	77	5 929	456 533	8.7750	4.25432
28	784	21 952	5.2915	3.03659	78	6 084	474 552	8.8318	4.27266
29	841	24 389	5.3852	3.07232	79	6 241	493 039	8.8882	4.29084
30	900	27 000	5.4772	3.10723	80	6 400	512 000	8.9443	4.30887
31	961	29 791	5.5678	3.14138	81	6 561	531 441	9.0000	4.32675
32	1 024	32 768	5.6569	3.17480	82	6 724	551 368	9.0554	4.34448
33	1 089	35 937	5.7446	3.20753	83	6 889	571 787	9.1104	4.36207
34	1 156	39 304	5.8310	3.23961	84	7 056	592 704	9.1652	4.37952
35	1 225	42 875	5.9161	3.27107	85	7 225	614 125	9.2195	4.39683
36	1 296	46 656	6.0000	3.30193	86	7 396	636 056	9.2736	4.41400
37	1 369	50 653	6.0828	3.33222	87	7 569	658 503	9.3274	4.43105
38	1 444	54 872	6.1644	3.36198	88	7 744	681 472	9.3808	4.44796
39	1 521	59 319	6.2450	3.39121	89	7 921	704 969	9.4340	4.46475
40	1 600	64 000	6.3246	3.41995	90	8 100	729 000	9.4868	4.48140
41	1 681	68 921	6.4031	3.44822	91	8 281	753 571	9.5394	4.49794
42	1 764	74 088	6.4807	3.47603	92	8 464	778 688	9.5917	4.51436
43	1 849	79 507	6.5574	3.50340	93	8 649	804 357	9.6437	4.53065
44	1 936	85 184	6.6332	3.53035	94	8 836	830 584	9.6954	4.54684
45	2 025	91 125	6.7082	3.55689	95	9 025	857 375	9.7468	4.56290
46	2 116	97 336	6.7823	3.58305	96	9 216	884 736	9.7980	4.57886
47	2 209	103 823	6.8557	3.60883	97	9 409	912 673	9.8489	4.59470
48	2 304	110 592	6.9282	3.63424	98	9 604	941 192	9.8995	4.61044
49	2 401	117 649	7.0000	3.65931	99	9 801	970 299	9.9499	4.62607
50	2 500	125 000	7.0711	3.68403					

DENOMINATE NUMBERS

LENGTH

```
    1  hand = 4 inches
    1  palm = 3 inches (sometimes 4 in.)
    1  span = 9 inches
   12  inches (in.) = 1 foot (ft.)
    1  (military) pace = 2½ feet
    3  feet = 1 yard (yd.)
  16½  feet = 5½ yards = 1 rod (rd.)
   40  rods = 1 furlong
 5280  feet = 320 rods = 1 mile (mi.)
```

METRIC LINEAR MEASURE

```
myr'i-a-me'ter = 10,000 m. = 6.214 miles
kil'o-meter = 1,000 m. = 0.6214 mile
hec'to-me'ter = 100 m. = 328 feet, 1 inch
dec'a-me'ter = 10 m. = 393.7 inches
me'ter = 1 m. = 39.37 inches
dec'i-me'ter = 1/10 m. = 3.937 inches
cen'ti-me'ter = 1/100 m. = 0.3937 inch
mil'li-me'ter = 1/1000 m. = 0.03937 inch
mi'cron = 1/1,000,000 m. = .00003937 inch
```

SURVEYORS' MEASURE

```
 7.92  inches = 1 link (li.)
   25  links = 1 rod (rd.)
    4  rods = 1 (Gunter's) chain
  100  links = 1 (Gunter's) chain
   66  feet = 1 (Gunter's) chain
   80  chains = 1 mile
       (An engineers' chain, or measuring
          tape, is usually 100 feet long).
  625  square links = 1 square rod
   16  square rods = 1 square chain
   10  square chains = 1 acre
   36  square miles = 1 township
```

MARINER'S MEASURE

```
    6  feet = 1 fathom
  120  fathoms = 1 cable lgth. (or cable)
  7½  cable lgths. = 1 mile
5,280  feet = 1 statute mile
6,080.27 feet = 1 nautical mile (U. S. Coast
                    Survey)
3 nautical miles = 1 marine league.
```

AREA

```
  144  square inches = 1 square foot
    9  square feet = 1 square yard
 30¼  square yards = 1 square rod
   40  sq. rods = 1 rood
43,560 square ft. = 160 square rds. = 1 acre
  640  acres = 1 square mile
```

CUBIC MEASURE

```
 1728  cubic inches = 1 cubic foot
   27  cubic feet = 1 cubic yard
 24¾  cubic feet = 1 perch
```

METRIC VOLUME MEASURE

```
kil'o-li'ter (stere) = 1,000 liters
hec'to-li'ter = 100 liters
dec'a-li'ter = 10 liters
li'ter = 1 cu. dm.
dec'i-li'ter = 1/10 liter
cen'ti-li'ter = 1/100 liter
mil'li-li'ter = 1/1000 liter
```
(One *liter* equals .908 qt. *dry measure* and
   1.0567 qt. *liquid measure*.)

DRY MEASURE

```
2 pints = 1 quart
8 quarts = 1 peck
4 pecks = 1 bushel
```
In the United States one *bushel* contains
   2150.42 cubic inches; in Great Britain,
   2218.2.
One bushel of:
   corn, shelled = 56 lbs.
   corn on cob = 70 lbs.
   wheat, beans, peas, Irish potatoes = 60 lbs.
   barley = 48 lbs.
   oats = 32 lbs.
   sweet potatoes = 55 lbs.

LIQUID MEASURE

```
 4 gills = 1 pint
 2 pints = 1 quart
 4 quarts = 1 gallon
 1 gallon = 231 cubic inches
31½ gallons = 1 barrel
63 gallons = 1 hogshead
```

APOTHECARIES' FLUID MEASURE

```
60 minims = 1 fluid dram
 8 fluid drams = 1 fluid ounce
16 fluid ounces = 1 pint
 8 pints = 1 gallon
```

WOOD MEASURE

```
16 cubic feet = 1 cord foot
 8 cord feet or 128 cubic feet = 1 cord
```
A cord of wood is 8 ft. long, 4 ft. wide, and
   4 ft. high.

BOARD MEASURE

1 ft. B. M. = 1 piece 1 ft. square and 1 inch,
   or less, thick. For pieces more than 1 inch
   thick, the B. M. is the product of the area
   in feet by the thickness in inches.

AVOIRDUPOIS WEIGHT

(used in weighing all articles except drugs,
   gold, silver, and precious stones).
   27 11/32 grains (gr.) = 1 dram (dr.)

16   drams = 1 ounce (oz.) = 28.571 grams
16   ounces = 1 pound (℔)
14   pounds = 1 stone (English)
25   pounds = 1 quarter
4   quarters = 1 hundredweight (cwt.)
20   hundredweight = 1 ton (T.)
2000   pounds = 1 ton
2240   pounds = 1 long ton, or gross ton.
2352   pounds = 1 Cornish mining ton.
2204.6   pounds = 1000 kilograms = 1 metric
    ton

TROY WEIGHT

24 grains = 1 pennyweight
20 pennyweight = 1 ounce
12 ounces = 1 pound
1 pound = 5760 grains
1 carat = 3.168 grains

APOTHECARIES' WEIGHT

20 grains = 1 scruple
3 scruples = 1 dram
8 drams = 1 ounce
12 ounces = 1 pound
The pound, ounce and grain have the same
    weight as those of Troy Weight.

METRIC WEIGHT

mil'lier' = 1,000,000 gr. = 2,204.6 ℔s.
quin'tal = 100,000 gr. = 220.46 ℔s.
myr'i-a-gram = 10,000 gr. = 22.046 ℔s.
kil'o-gram = 1,000 gr. = 2.205 ℔s.
hec'to-gram = 100 gr. = 3.527 ozs.
dec'a-gram = 10 gr. = 0.353 oz.
gram = 1 gr. = 15.432 grains = 0.035 oz.
dec'i-gram = 1/10 gr. = 1.543 grs.
cen'ti-gram = 1/100 gr. = 0.154 gr.
mil'li-gram = 1/1000 gr. = 0.015 gr.

PAPER MEASURE

24   sheets = 1 quire
20   sheets = 1 quire of outsides
25   sheets = 1 printers' quire
20   quires = 1 ream
$21\frac{1}{2}$ quires = 1 printers' ream
2   reams = 1 bundle
4   reams = 1 printers' bundle
10   reams = 1 bale
60   skins = 1 roll of parchment
480   sheets = 1 short ream
500   sheets = 1 long ream

TIME

60 seconds = 1 minute
60 minutes = 1 hour
24 hours = 1 day
7 days = 1 week
365 days = 1 common year
366 days = 1 leap year

12 months = 1 year
360 days = 1 commercial year
    1 sidereal year = 365 days, 6 hrs., 9 min., 9.5
    sec.
    1 tropical (equinoctial) year = 365 days, 5
    hrs., 48 min., 45.7 sec.
100 years = 1 century
10 years = 1 decade

UNITED STATES MONEY

10 mills (m.) = 1 cent (ct. or ¢)
10 cents = 1 dime (di.)
10 dimes = 1 dollar ($)
10 dollars = 1 eagle
5 cents = 1 nickel
5 nickels = 1 quarter
2 quarters = 1 half-dollar

ENGLISH MONEY

(the left column consists of the coins in actual
use).
1 farthing (copper) = $\frac{1}{4}$ penny
1 halfpenny (copper) = $\frac{1}{2}$ penny
1 penny (copper) = $\frac{1}{12}$ shilling
6 pence (silver) = $\frac{1}{2}$ shilling
1 shilling (silver) = 12 pence
1 florin (silver) = 2 shillings
$\frac{1}{2}$ crown (silver) = $2\frac{1}{2}$ shillings
1 crown (silver) = 5 shillings
1 pound sterling (gold) = 20 shillings
The *pound* (£) is normally about $5, the
shilling 25¢.

CIRCULAR MEASURE

60 seconds (″) = 1 minute (′)
60 minutes = 1 degree (°)
360 degrees = 1 circumference
    1 radian = 57° 17′ 44″.806
    1 degree = .01745329 radians
    1 mil = 1/6400 of a circumference
69 miles = 1 degree of latitude, approxi-
    mately.

MISCELLANEOUS

12 units = 1 dozen
12 dozen = 1 gross
12 gross = 1 great gross
20 units = 1 score
1 teaspoonful = $\frac{1}{4}$ tablespoonful (medical)
          = $\frac{1}{3}$ tablespoonful (cooking)
1 tablespoonfull = $\frac{1}{2}$ fluid ounce
1 bushel = 2150.42 cu. in. or $\frac{4}{5}$ cu. ft.
1 U. S. gallon = 231 cu. in.
1 gallon = 231 cu. in.
1 cu. ft. = 7.48 gal.
1 cu. ft. water = 62.425 ℔s. (max. density)
1 gallon water = 8.337 ℔s.
1 cu. ft. air = 0.0807 ℔. (at 32° F.)
1 liter = .264178 gallon (U. S.)

1 inch = 2.54 centimeters
g (acceleration of gravity) = 32.16 feet per sec. per sec.
g (legal) = 980.665 cm./sec.²
1 horse power = 550 ft. ℔ per sec. (legal) = 745. 70 watts (legal)
e = Naperian Base = 2.71828 18284
w = 3.14159 26535 89793 23846
M = log₁₀e = 0.43429 44819 03251

$1/M = 2.30258$ 50929 94045 68402
1 astronomical unit = 93,000,000 miles (approx.) = the mean distance between the sun and the earth.
1 light year = 59×10^{11} miles = the distance traveled by light in 1 year.
1 parsec = the distance of a star at which the angle subtended by the radius of the earth's orbit is 1″ (about 3.3 light years).

DIFFERENTIATION FORMULAS
(See Derivative of a Function of one Variable)

In the following formulas, u, v and y are functions of x which possess derivatives with respect to x, the other letters are constants and log $u = \log_e u$.

$$\frac{dc}{dx} = 0,$$

$$\frac{d}{dx} x = 1.$$

$$\frac{d}{dx}(cv) = c\frac{dv}{dx}.$$

$$\frac{d}{dx} x^n = nx^{n-1}$$

$$\frac{dy}{dx} = \frac{dy}{du}\frac{du}{dx}.$$

$$\frac{d}{dx}(u + v) = \frac{du}{dx} + \frac{dv}{dx},$$

$$\frac{d}{dx}(uv) = u\frac{dv}{dx} + v\frac{du}{dx},$$

$$\frac{d}{dx}\left(\frac{u}{v}\right) = \frac{v\dfrac{du}{dx} - u\dfrac{dv}{dx}}{v^2},$$

$$\frac{du^n}{dx} = nu^{n-1}\frac{du}{dx}.$$

n any number (*positive or negative, integral or fractional*),

$$\frac{d}{dx}(\sin u) = \cos u \cdot \frac{du}{dx}.$$

$$\frac{d}{dx}(\cos u) = -\sin u\frac{du}{dx}.$$

$$\frac{d}{dx}(\tan u) = \sec^2 u\frac{du}{dx}.$$

$$\frac{d}{dx}(\cot u) = -\csc^2 u\frac{du}{dx}.$$

$$\frac{d}{dx}(\sec u) = \sec u \tan u\frac{du}{dx},$$

$$\frac{d}{dx}(\csc u) = -\csc u \cot u\frac{du}{dx}.$$

$$\frac{d}{dx}(\log u) = \frac{\dfrac{du}{dx}}{u},$$

$$\frac{d}{dx}(\log_a u) = \log_a e \cdot \frac{\dfrac{du}{dx}}{u},$$

$$\frac{d}{dx}(e^u) = e^u \cdot \frac{du}{dx}.$$

$$\frac{d}{dx}(a^u) = \log a \cdot a^u \cdot \frac{du}{dx},$$

$$\frac{d}{dx}(\text{arc } \sin u) = \frac{\dfrac{du}{dx}}{\sqrt{1 - u^2}}.$$

$$\frac{d}{dx}(\text{arc } \cos u) = -\frac{\dfrac{du}{dx}}{\sqrt{1 - u^2}}.$$

$$\frac{d}{dx}(\text{arc } \tan u) = \frac{\dfrac{du}{dx}}{1 + u^2}.$$

$$\frac{d}{dx}(\text{arc } \cot u) = -\frac{\dfrac{du}{dx}}{1 + u^2}.$$

$$\frac{d}{dx}(\text{arc } \sec u) = \frac{\dfrac{du}{dx}}{u\sqrt{u^2 - 1}},$$

$$-\pi < \sec^{-1} u < -\frac{\pi}{2}, \quad 0 < \sec^{-1} u < \frac{\pi}{2}.$$

$$\frac{d}{dx}(\text{arc } \csc u) = -\frac{\dfrac{du}{dx}}{u\sqrt{u^2 - 1}}.$$

$$-\pi < \csc^{-1} u < -\frac{\pi}{2}, \quad 0 < \csc^{-1} u < \frac{\pi}{2}.$$

INTEGRAL TABLES*

In the following tables, the constant of integration, **C**, is omitted but should be added to the result of every integration. The letter **x** represents any variable; **u** represents any function of **x**; the remaining letters represent arbitrary constants, unless otherwise indicated; all angles are in radians. **Unless otherwise mentioned** $\log_e u \equiv \log u$.

Short Table of Integrals.

1. $\int df(x) = f(x)$.

2. $d\int f(x)dx = f(x)dx$.

3. $\int 0 \cdot dx = C.$

4. $\int a f(x)\, dx = a \int f(x)\, dx$.

5. $\int (u \pm v)dx = \int udx \pm \int vdx$.

6. $\int u\, dv = uv - \int v\, du$.

7. $\int \frac{u\, dv}{dx}\, dx = uv - \int v \frac{du}{dx}\, dx$.

8. $\int f(y)dx = \int \frac{f(y)dy}{\frac{dy}{dx}}$.

9. $\int u^n\, du = \frac{u^{n+1}}{n+1}, \; n \neq -1.$

10. $\int \frac{du}{u} = \log u$.

11. $\int e^u\, du = e^u$.

12. $\int b^u\, du = \frac{b^u}{\log b}$.

13. $\int \sin u\, du = -\cos u$.

14. $\int \cos u\, du = \sin u$.

15. $\int \tan u\, du = \log \sec u = -\log \cos u$.

16. $\int \operatorname{ctn} u\, du = \log \sin u = -\log \csc u$.

17. $\int \sec u\, du = \log (\sec u + \tan u) = \log \tan \left(\frac{u}{2} + \frac{\pi}{4}\right)$.

18. $\int \csc u\, du = \log (\csc u - \operatorname{ctn} u) = \log \tan \frac{u}{2}$.

19. $\int \sin^2 u\, du = \frac{1}{2} u - \frac{1}{2} \sin u \cos u$.

20. $\int \cos^2 u\, du = \frac{1}{2} u + \frac{1}{2} \sin u \cos u$.

21. $\int \sec^2 u\, du = \tan u$.

22. $\int \csc^2 u\, du = -\operatorname{ctn} u$.

23. $\int \tan^2 u\, du = \tan u - u$.

24. $\int \operatorname{ctn}^2 u\, du = -\operatorname{ctn} u - u$.

25. $\int \frac{du}{u^2 + a^2} = \frac{1}{a} \tan^{-1} \frac{u}{a}$.

26. $\int \frac{du}{u^2 - a^2} = \frac{1}{2a} \log \left(\frac{u-a}{u+a}\right) = -\frac{1}{a} \operatorname{ctnh}^{-1}\left(\frac{u}{a}\right)$, if $u^2 > a^2$,

$\qquad = \frac{1}{2a} \log \left(\frac{a-u}{a+u}\right) = -\frac{1}{a} \tanh^{-1}\left(\frac{u}{a}\right)$, if $u^2 < a^2$.

27. $\int \frac{du}{\sqrt{a^2 - u^2}} = \sin^{-1}\left(\frac{u}{a}\right)$.

28. $\int \frac{du}{\sqrt{u^2 \pm a^2}} = \log \left(u + \sqrt{u^2 \pm a^2}\right)$.

29. $\int \frac{du}{\sqrt{2 au - u^2}} = \cos^{-1}\left(\frac{a-u}{a}\right)$.

30. $\int \frac{du}{u\sqrt{u^2 - a^2}} = \frac{1}{a} \sec^{-1}\left(\frac{u}{a}\right)$.

31. $\int \frac{du}{u\sqrt{a^2 \pm u^2}} = -\frac{1}{a} \log \left(\frac{a + \sqrt{a^2 \pm u^2}}{u}\right)$.*

32. $\int \sqrt{a^2 - u^2} \cdot du = \frac{1}{2} \left(u\sqrt{a^2 - u^2} + a^2 \sin^{-1} \frac{u}{a}\right)$.

33. $\int \sqrt{u^2 \pm a^2}\, du = \frac{1}{2}\left[u\sqrt{u^2 \pm a^2} \pm a^2 \log \left(u + \sqrt{u^2 \pm a^2}\right)\right]$.*

34. $\int \sinh u\, du = \cosh u$.

35. $\int \cosh u\, du = \sinh u$.

36. $\int \tanh u\, du = \log (\cosh u)$.

37. $\int \operatorname{ctnh} u\, du = \log (\sinh u)$.

38. $\int \operatorname{sech} u\, du = \sin^{-1} (\tanh u)$.

39. $\int \operatorname{csch} u\, du = \log \left(\tanh \frac{u}{2}\right)$.

40. $\int \operatorname{sech} u \cdot \tanh u \cdot du = -\operatorname{sech} u$.

41. $\int \operatorname{csch} u \cdot \operatorname{ctnh} u \cdot du = -\operatorname{csch} u$.

Expressions Containing $(ax + b)$.

42. $\int (ax+b)^n dx = \frac{1}{a(n+1)} (ax+b)^{n+1}, \; n \neq -1$.

43. $\int \frac{dx}{ax+b} = \frac{1}{a} \log_e (ax+b)$.

44. $\int \frac{dx}{(ax+b)^2} = -\frac{1}{a(ax+b)}$.

45. $\int \frac{dx}{(ax+b)^3} = -\frac{1}{2a(ax+b)^2}$.

46. $\int x(ax+b)^n\, dx = \frac{1}{a^2(n+2)} (ax+b)^{n+2}$

$\qquad - \frac{b}{a^2(n+1)} (ax+b)^{n+1}, \; n \neq -1, -2$

---

* $\log \left(\frac{u + \sqrt{u^2 + a^2}}{a}\right) = \sinh^{-1}\left(\frac{u}{a}\right)$; $\log \left(\frac{a + \sqrt{a^2 - u^2}}{u}\right) = \operatorname{sech}^{-1}\left(\frac{u}{a}\right)$;

$\log \left(\frac{u + \sqrt{u^2 - a^2}}{a}\right) = \cosh^{-1}\left(\frac{u}{a}\right)$; $\log \left(\frac{a + \sqrt{a^2 + u^2}}{u}\right) = \operatorname{csch}^{-1}\left(\frac{u}{a}\right)$.

* These tables were taken, with permission, from "Handbook of Mathematical Tables and Formulas," Handbook Publishers, Inc., Sandusky, Ohio, edited by Richard S. Burington, Associate Professor of Mathematics, Case School of Applied Science.

47. $\int \frac{xdx}{ax+b} = \frac{x}{a} - \frac{b}{a^2} \log{(ax+b)}.$

48. $\int \frac{xdx}{(ax+b)^2} = \frac{b}{a^2(ax+b)} + \frac{1}{a^2} \log{(ax+b)}.$

49. $\int \frac{xdx}{(ax+b)^3} = \frac{b}{2a^2(ax+b)^2} - \frac{1}{a^2(ax+b)}$

50. $\int x^2(ax+b)^n dx = \frac{1}{a^3}\Big[\frac{(ax+b)^{n+3}}{n+3}$
$- 2b \frac{(ax+b)^{n+2}}{n+2} + b^2\frac{(ax+b)^{n+1}}{n+1} \Big], n \neq -1, -2, -3.$

51. $\int \frac{x^2 dx}{ax+b} = \frac{1}{a^3}\Big[\frac{1}{2}(ax+b)^2 - 2b(ax+b) + b^2\log{(ax+b)} \Big].$

52. $\int \frac{x^2 dx}{(ax+b)^2} = \frac{1}{a^3}\Big[(ax+b) - 2b\log{(ax+b)} - \frac{b^2}{ax+b} \Big].$

53. $\int \frac{x^2\,dx}{(ax+b)^3} = \frac{1}{a^3}\Big[\log{(ax+b)} + \frac{2b}{ax+b} - \frac{b^2}{2(ax+b)^2} \Big].$

54. $\int x^m(ax+b)^n\,dx$
$= \frac{1}{a(m+n+1)}\Big[x^m(ax+b)^{n+1} - mb\int x^{m-1}(ax+b)^n dx \Big],$
$= \frac{1}{m+n+1}\Big[x^{m+1}(ax+b)^n + nb\int x^m(ax+b)^{n-1}dx \Big],$
$$m > 0,\ m+n+1 \neq 0.$$

55. $\int \frac{dx}{x(ax+b)} = \frac{1}{b}\log{\frac{x}{ax+b}}.$

56. $\int \frac{dx}{x^2(ax+b)} = -\frac{1}{bx} + \frac{a}{b^2}\log{\frac{ax+b}{x}}.$

57. $\int \frac{dx}{x^3(ax+b)} = \frac{2ax-b}{2b^2x^2} + \frac{a^2}{b^3}\log{\frac{x}{ax+b}}.$

58. $\int \frac{dx}{x(ax+b)^2} = \frac{1}{b(ax+b)} - \frac{1}{b^2}\log{\frac{ax+b}{x}}.$

59. $\int \frac{dx}{x(ax+b)^3} = \frac{1}{b^3}\Big[\frac{1}{2}\Big(\frac{ax+2b}{ax+b}\Big)^2 + \log{\frac{x}{ax+b}} \Big].$

60. $\int \frac{dx}{x^2(ax+b)^2} = -\frac{b+2ax}{b^2x(ax+b)} + \frac{2a}{b^3}\log{\frac{ax+b}{x}}.$

61. $\int \sqrt{ax+b}\,dx = \frac{2}{3a}\sqrt{(ax+b)^3}$

62. $\int x\sqrt{ax+b}\,dx = \frac{2(3ax-2b)}{15a^2}\sqrt{(ax+b)^3}$

63. $\int x^2\sqrt{ax+b}\,dx = \frac{2(15a^2x^2 - 12abx + 8b^2)\sqrt{(ax+b)^3}}{105a^3}$

64. $\int x^3\sqrt{ax+b}\,dx$
$= \frac{2(35a^3x^3 - 30a^2bx^2 + 24ab^2x - 16b^3)\sqrt{(ax+b)^3}}{315a^4}.$

65. $\int x^n\sqrt{ax+b}\,dx = \frac{2}{a^{n+1}}\int u^2(u^2-b)^n du,\ u = \sqrt{ax+b}.$

66. $\int \frac{\sqrt{ax+b}}{x}\,dx = 2\sqrt{ax+b} + b\int \frac{dx}{x\sqrt{ax+b}}.$

67. $\int \frac{dx}{\sqrt{ax+b}} = \frac{2\sqrt{ax+b}}{a}.$

68. $\int \frac{xdx}{\sqrt{ax+b}} = \frac{2(ax-2b)}{3a^2}\sqrt{ax+b}.$

69. $\int \frac{x^2dx}{\sqrt{ax+b}} = \frac{2(3a^2x^2 - 4abx + 8b^2)}{15a^3}\sqrt{ax+b}.$

70. $\int \frac{x^3dx}{\sqrt{ax+b}} = \frac{2(5a^3x^3 - 6a^2bx^2 + 8ab^2x - 16b^3)}{35a^4}\sqrt{ax+b}.$

71. $\int \frac{x^n dx}{\sqrt{ax+b}} = \frac{2}{a^{n+1}}\int (u^2-b)^n du,\ u = \sqrt{ax+b}.$

72. $\int \frac{dx}{x\sqrt{ax+b}} = \frac{1}{\sqrt{b}}\log{\frac{\sqrt{ax+b}-\sqrt{b}}{\sqrt{ax+b}+\sqrt{b}}},$ for $b > 0.$

73. $\int \frac{dx}{x\sqrt{ax+b}} = \frac{2}{\sqrt{-b}}\tan^{-1}\sqrt{\frac{ax+b}{-b}},$ or $\frac{-2}{\sqrt{b}}\tanh^{-1}\sqrt{\frac{ax+b}{b}},\ b < 0.$

74. $\int \frac{dx}{x^2\sqrt{ax+b}} = -\frac{\sqrt{ax+b}}{bx} - \frac{a}{2b}\int \frac{dx}{x\sqrt{ax+b}}.$

75. $\int \frac{dx}{x^3\sqrt{ax+b}} = -\frac{\sqrt{ax+b}}{2bx^2} + \frac{3a\sqrt{ax+b}}{4b^2x} + \frac{3a^2}{8b^2}\int \frac{dx}{x\sqrt{ax+b}}.$

76. $\int \frac{dx}{x^n(ax+b)^m} = -\frac{1}{b^{m+n-1}}\int \frac{(u-a)^{m+n-2}du}{u^m},\ u = \frac{ax+b}{x}.$

77. $\int (ax+b)^{\pm\frac{n}{2}}\,dx = \frac{2(ax+b)^{\frac{2\pm n}{2}}}{a(2 \pm n)}$

78. $\int x(ax+b)^{\pm\frac{n}{2}}\,dx = \frac{2}{a^2}\Big[\frac{(ax+b)^{\frac{4\pm n}{2}}}{4 \pm n} - \frac{b(ax+b)^{\frac{2\pm n}{2}}}{2 \pm n} \Big].$

79. $\int \frac{dx}{x(ax+b)^{\frac{n}{2}}} = \frac{1}{b}\int \frac{dx}{x(ax+b)^{\frac{n-2}{2}}} - \frac{a}{b}\int \frac{dx}{(ax+b)^{\frac{n}{2}}}.$

80. $\int \frac{x^m dx}{\sqrt{ax+b}} = \frac{2x^m\sqrt{ax+b}}{(2m+1)a} - \frac{2mb}{(2m+1)a}\int \frac{x^{m-1}dx}{\sqrt{ax+b}}.$

81. $\int \frac{dx}{x^n\sqrt{ax+b}} = \frac{-\sqrt{ax+b}}{(n-1)bx^{n-1}} - \frac{(2n-3)a}{(2n-2)b}\int \frac{dx}{x^{n-1}\sqrt{ax+b}}.$

82. $\int \frac{(ax+b)^{\frac{n}{2}}}{x}\,dx = a\int (ax+b)^{\frac{n-2}{2}}\,dx + b\int \frac{(ax+b)^{\frac{n-2}{2}}}{x}\,dx.$

83. $\int \frac{dx}{(ax+b)(cx+d)} = \frac{1}{bc-ad}\log{\frac{cx+d}{ax+b}},\ bc - ad \neq 0.$

84. $\int \frac{dx}{(ax+b)^2(cx+d)}$
$= \frac{1}{bc-ad}\Big[\frac{1}{ax+b} + \frac{c}{bc-ad}\log{\Big(\frac{cx+d}{ax+b}\Big)} \Big],\ bc - ad \neq 0.$

85. $\int (ax+b)^n(cx+d)^m\,dx = \frac{1}{(m+n+1)a}\Big[(ax+b)^{n+1}(cx+d)^m$
$- m(bc-ad)\int (ax+b)^n(cx+d)^{m-1}\,dx \Big].$

86. $\int \frac{dx}{(ax+b)^n(cx+d)^m} = \frac{1}{(m-1)(bc-ad)}\Big[\frac{1}{(ax+b)^{n-1}(cx+d)^{m-1}}$
$- a(m+n-2)\int \frac{dx}{(ax+b)^n(cx+d)^{m-1}} \Big],\ m > 1,\ n > 0,\ bc - ad \neq 0.$

87. $\int \frac{(ax+b)^n}{(cx+d)^m}\,dx$
$= -\frac{1}{(m-1)(bc-ad)}\Big[\frac{(ax+b)^{n+1}}{(cx+d)^{m-1}} + (m-n-2)a\int \frac{(ax+b)^n dx}{(cx+d)^{m-1}} \Big]$
$= \frac{-1}{(m-n-1)c}\Big[\frac{(ax+b)^n}{(cx+d)^{m-1}} + n(bc-ad)\int \frac{(ax+b)^{n-1}}{(cx+d)^m}\,dx \Big].$

88. $\int \frac{xdx}{(ax+b)(cx+d)} = \frac{1}{bc-ad}\Big[\frac{b}{a}\log{(ax+b)}$
$- \frac{d}{c}\log{(cx+d)} \Big],\ bc - ad \neq 0.$

89. $\int \frac{xdx}{(ax+b)^2(cx+d)} = \frac{1}{bc-ad}\Big[-\frac{b}{a(ax+b)}$
$- \frac{d}{bc-ad}\log{\frac{cx+d}{ax+b}} \Big],\ bc - ad \neq 0.$

90. $\int \frac{cx+d}{\sqrt{ax+b}}\,dx = \frac{2}{3a^2}(3ad - 2bc + acx)\sqrt{ax+b}.$

91. $\int \frac{\sqrt{ax+b}}{cx+d}\,dx = \frac{2\sqrt{ax+b}}{c}$

$\quad - \frac{2}{c}\sqrt{\frac{ad-bc}{c}}\,\tan^{-1}\sqrt{\frac{c(ax+b)}{ad-bc}},\, c>0,\, ad>bc.$

92. $\int \frac{\sqrt{ax+b}}{cx+d}\,dx = \frac{2\sqrt{ax+b}}{c}$

$\quad + \frac{1}{c}\sqrt{\frac{bc-ad}{c}}\,\log\frac{\sqrt{c(ax+b)}-\sqrt{bc-ad}}{\sqrt{c(ax+b)}+\sqrt{bc-ad}},\, c>0,\, bc>ad.$

93. $\int \frac{dx}{(cx+d)\sqrt{ax+b}} = \frac{2}{\sqrt{c}\sqrt{ad-bc}}\,\tan^{-1}\sqrt{\frac{c(ax+b)}{ad-bc}},$
$\quad c>0,\, ad>bc.$

94. $\int \frac{dx}{(cx+d)\sqrt{ax+b}}$

$\quad = \frac{1}{\sqrt{c}\sqrt{bc-ad}}\log\frac{\sqrt{c(ax+b)}-\sqrt{bc-ad}}{\sqrt{c(ax+b)}+\sqrt{bc-ad}}\, c>0,\, bc>ad.$

Expressions Containing ax^2+c, ax^n+c, $x^2\pm p^2$, and p^2-x^2.

95. $\int \frac{dx}{p^2+x^2} = \frac{1}{p}\tan^{-1}\frac{x}{p}, \text{ or } -\frac{1}{p}\operatorname{ctn}^{-1}\!\left(\frac{x}{p}\right).$

96. $\int \frac{dx}{p^2-x^2} = \frac{1}{2p}\log\frac{p+x}{p-x}, \text{ or } \frac{1}{p}\tanh^{-1}\!\left(\frac{x}{p}\right).$

97. $\int \frac{dx}{ax^2+c} = \frac{1}{\sqrt{ac}}\tan^{-1}\left(x\sqrt{\frac{a}{c}}\right),\, a \text{ and } c>0.$

98. $\int \frac{dx}{ax^2+c} = \frac{1}{2\sqrt{-ac}}\log\frac{x\sqrt{a}-\sqrt{-c}}{x\sqrt{a}+\sqrt{-c}}\, a>0,\, c<0.$

$\quad = \frac{1}{2\sqrt{-ac}}\log\frac{\sqrt{c}+x\sqrt{-a}}{\sqrt{c}-x\sqrt{-a}},\, a<0,\, c>0.$

99. $\int \frac{dx}{(ax^2+c)^n} = \frac{1}{2(n-1)c}\cdot\frac{x}{(ax^2+c)^{n-1}}$

$\quad + \frac{2n-3}{2(n-1)c}\int\frac{dx}{(ax^2+c)^{n-1}},\, n \text{ a positive integer.}$

100. $\int x(ax^2+c)^n\,dx = \frac{1}{2a}\frac{(ax^2+c)^{n+1}}{n+1},\, n\neq-1.$

101. $\int \frac{x}{ax^2+c}\,dx = \frac{1}{2a}\log(ax^2+c).$

102. $\int \frac{dx}{x(ax^2+c)} = \frac{1}{2c}\log\frac{ax^2}{ax^2+c}.$

103. $\int \frac{dx}{x^2(ax^2+c)} = -\frac{1}{cx}-\frac{a}{c}\int\frac{dx}{ax^2+c}.$

104. $\int \frac{x^2\,dx}{ax^2+c} = \frac{x}{a}-\frac{c}{a}\int\frac{dx}{ax^2+c}.$

105. $\int \frac{x^n\,dx}{ax^2+c} = \frac{x^{n-1}}{a(n-1)}-\frac{c}{a}\int\frac{x^{n-2}\,dx}{ax^2+c},\, n\neq1.$

106. $\int \frac{x^2\,dx}{(ax^2+c)^n} = -\frac{1}{2(n-1)a}\cdot\frac{x}{(ax^2+c)^{n-1}}$

$\quad + \frac{1}{2(n-1)a}\int\frac{dx}{(ax^2+c)^{n-1}}$

107. $\int \frac{dx}{x^2(ax^2+c)^n} = \frac{1}{c}\int\frac{dx}{x^2(ax^2+c)^{n-1}}-\frac{a}{c}\int\frac{dx}{(ax^2+c)^n}.$

108. $\int \sqrt{x^2\pm p^2}\,dx = \frac{1}{2}\left[x\sqrt{x^2\pm p^2}\pm p^2\log(x+\sqrt{x^2\pm p^2})\right].$

109. $\int \sqrt{p^2-x^2}\,dx = \frac{1}{2}\left[x\sqrt{p^2-x^2}+p^2\sin^{-1}\left(\frac{x}{p}\right)\right]$

110. $\int \frac{dx}{\sqrt{x^2\pm p^2}} = \log(x+\sqrt{x^2\pm p^2}).$

111. $\int \frac{dx}{\sqrt{p^2-x^2}} = \sin^{-1}\left(\frac{x}{p}\right) \text{ or } -\cos^{-1}\left(\frac{x}{p}\right).$

112. $\int \sqrt{ax^2+c}\,dx = \frac{x}{2}\sqrt{ax^2+c}$

$\quad + \frac{c}{2\sqrt{a}}\log\left(x\sqrt{a}+\sqrt{ax^2+c}\right),\, a>0.$

113. $\int \sqrt{ax^2+c}\,dx = \frac{x}{2}\sqrt{ax^2+c}+\frac{c}{2\sqrt{-a}}\sin^{-1}\left(x\sqrt{\frac{-a}{c}}\right),\, a<0.$

114. $\int \frac{dx}{\sqrt{ax^2+c}} = \frac{1}{\sqrt{a}}\log(x\sqrt{a}+\sqrt{ax^2+c}),\, a>0.$

115. $\int \frac{dx}{\sqrt{ax^2+c}} = \frac{1}{\sqrt{-a}}\sin^{-1}\left(x\sqrt{\frac{-a}{c}}\right),\, a<0.$

116. $\int x\sqrt{ax^2+c}\cdot dx = \frac{1}{3a}(ax^2+c)^{\frac{3}{2}}.$

117. $\int x^2\sqrt{ax^2+c}\,dx = \frac{x}{4a}\sqrt{(ax^2+c)^3}-\frac{cx}{8a}\sqrt{ax^2+c}$

$\quad - \frac{c^2}{8\sqrt{a^3}}\log\left(x\sqrt{a}+\sqrt{ax^2+c}\right),\, a>0.$

118. $\int x^2\sqrt{ax^2+c}\,dx = \frac{x}{4a}\sqrt{(ax^2+c)^3}-\frac{cx}{8a}\sqrt{ax^2+c}$

$\quad - \frac{c^2}{8a\sqrt{-a}}\sin^{-1}\left(x\sqrt{\frac{-a}{c}}\right),\, a<0.$

119. $\int \frac{x\,dx}{\sqrt{ax^2+c}} = \frac{1}{a}\sqrt{ax^2+c}.$

120. $\int \frac{x^2\,dx}{\sqrt{ax^2+c}} = \frac{x}{a}\sqrt{ax^2+c}-\frac{1}{a}\int\sqrt{ax^2+c}\,dx.$

121. $\int \frac{\sqrt{ax^2+c}}{x}\,dx = \sqrt{ax^2+c}+\sqrt{c}\log\frac{\sqrt{ax^2+c}-\sqrt{c}}{x},\, c>0.$

122. $\int \frac{\sqrt{ax^2+c}}{x}\,dx = \sqrt{ax^2+c}-\sqrt{-c}\tan^{-1}\frac{\sqrt{ax^2+c}}{\sqrt{-c}},\, c<0.$

123. $\int \frac{dx}{x\sqrt{p^2\pm x^2}} = -\frac{1}{p}\log\left(\frac{p+\sqrt{p^2\pm x^2}}{x}\right).$

124. $\int \frac{dx}{x\sqrt{x^2-p^2}} = \frac{1}{p}\cos^{-1}\left(\frac{p}{x}\right), \text{ or } -\frac{1}{p}\sin^{-1}\left(\frac{p}{x}\right).$

125. $\int \frac{dx}{x\sqrt{ax^2+c}} = \frac{1}{\sqrt{c}}\log\frac{\sqrt{ax^2+c}-\sqrt{c}}{x},\, c>0.$

126. $\int \frac{dx}{x\sqrt{ax^2+c}} = \frac{1}{\sqrt{-c}}\sec^{-1}\left(x\sqrt{\frac{-a}{c}}\right),\, c<0.$

127. $\int \frac{dx}{x^2\sqrt{ax^2+c}} = -\frac{\sqrt{ax^2+c}}{cx}.$

128. $\int \frac{x^n\,dx}{\sqrt{ax^2+c}} = \frac{x^{n-1}\sqrt{ax^2+c}}{na}-\frac{(n-1)c}{na}\int\frac{x^{n-2}\,dx}{\sqrt{ax^2+c}},\, n>0.$

129. $\int x^n\sqrt{ax^2+c}\,dx = \frac{x^{n-1}(ax^2+c)^{\frac{3}{2}}}{(n+2)a}$

$\quad - \frac{(n-1)c}{(n+2)a}\int x^{n-2}\sqrt{ax^2+c}\cdot dx,\, n>0.$

130. $\int \frac{\sqrt{ax^2+c}}{x^n}\,dx = -\frac{(ax^2+c)^{\frac{3}{2}}}{c(n-1)x^{n-1}}$

$\quad - \frac{(n-4)a}{(n-1)c}\int\frac{\sqrt{ax^2+c}}{x^{n-2}}\,dx,\, n>1.$

131. $\displaystyle\int \frac{dx}{x^n\sqrt{ax^2+c}} = -\frac{\sqrt{ax^2+c}}{c(n-1)x^{n-1}}$
$\displaystyle\qquad -\frac{(n-2)\,a}{(n-1)\,c}\int \frac{dx}{x^{n-2}\sqrt{ax^2+c}},\ n>1.$

132. $\displaystyle\int (ax^2+c)^{\frac{3}{2}}\,dx = \frac{x}{8}\,(2ax^2+5c)\sqrt{ax^2+c}$
$\displaystyle\qquad +\frac{3c^2}{8\sqrt{a}}\log\,(x\sqrt{a}+\sqrt{ax^2+c}),\ a>0.$

133. $\displaystyle\int (ax^2+c)^{\frac{3}{2}}\,dx = \frac{x}{8}\,(2ax^2+5c)\sqrt{ax^2+c}$
$\displaystyle\qquad +\frac{3c^2}{8\sqrt{-a}}\,\sin^{-1}\left(x\sqrt{\frac{-a}{c}}\right),\ a<0.$

134. $\displaystyle\int \frac{dx}{(ax^2+c)^{\frac{3}{2}}} = \frac{x}{c\sqrt{ax^2+c}}$

135. $\displaystyle\int x(ax^2+c)^{\frac{3}{2}}\,dx = \frac{1}{5a}(ax^2+c)^{\frac{5}{2}}.$

136. $\displaystyle\int x^2(ax^2+c)^{\frac{3}{2}}\,dx = \frac{x^3}{6}(ax^2+c)^{\frac{3}{2}}+\frac{c}{2}\int x^2\sqrt{ax^2+c}\,dx.$

137. $\displaystyle\int x^n(ax^2+c)^{\frac{3}{2}}\,dx = \frac{x^{n+1}(ax^2+c)^{\frac{3}{2}}}{n+4}+\frac{3c}{n+4}\int x^n\sqrt{ax^2+c}\,dx.$

138. $\displaystyle\int \frac{xdx}{(ax^2+c)^{\frac{3}{2}}} = -\frac{1}{a\sqrt{ax^2+c}}.$

139. $\displaystyle\int \frac{x^2dx}{(ax^2+c)^{\frac{3}{2}}} = -\frac{x}{a\sqrt{ax^2+c}}$
$\displaystyle\qquad +\frac{1}{a\sqrt{a}}\log\,(x\sqrt{a}+\sqrt{ax^2+c}),\ a>0.$

140. $\displaystyle\int \frac{x^2dx}{(ax^2+c)^{\frac{3}{2}}} = -\frac{x}{a\sqrt{ax^2+c}}$
$\displaystyle\qquad +\frac{1}{a\sqrt{-a}}\,\sin^{-1}\left(x\sqrt{\frac{-a}{c}}\right),\quad a<0.$

141. $\displaystyle\int \frac{x^3dx}{(ax^2+c)^{\frac{3}{2}}} = -\frac{x^2}{a\sqrt{ax^2+c}}+\frac{2}{a^2}\sqrt{ax^2+c}.$

142. $\displaystyle\int \frac{dx}{x(ax^n+c)} = \frac{1}{cn}\log\frac{x^n}{ax^n+c}.$

143. $\displaystyle\int \frac{dx}{(ax^n+c)^m} = \frac{1}{c}\int \frac{dx}{(ax^n+c)^{m-1}}-\frac{a}{c}\int \frac{x^ndx}{(ax^n+c)^m}.$

144. $\displaystyle\int \frac{dx}{x\sqrt{ax^n+c}} = \frac{1}{n\sqrt{c}}\log\frac{\sqrt{ax^n+c}-\sqrt{c}}{\sqrt{ax^n+c}+\sqrt{c}},\ c>0.$

145. $\displaystyle\int \frac{dx}{x\sqrt{ax^n+c}} = \frac{2}{n\sqrt{-c}}\,\sec^{-1}\sqrt{\frac{-ax^n}{c}},\ c<0.$

146. $\displaystyle\int x^{m-1}(ax^n+c)^p dx$

$\displaystyle\qquad = \frac{1}{m+np}\left[x^m(ax^n+c)^p+npc\int x^{m-1}(ax^n+c)^{p-1}dx\right]$

$\displaystyle= \frac{1}{cn(p+1)}\left[-x^m(ax^n+c)^{p+1}+(m+np+n)\int x^{m-1}(ax^n+c)^{p+1}dx\right].$

$\displaystyle= \frac{1}{a(m+np)}\left[x^{m-n}(ax^n+c)^{p+1}-(m-n)c\int x^{m-n-1}(ax^n+c)^p dx\right]$

$\displaystyle= \frac{1}{mc}\left[x^m(ax^n+c)^{p+1}-(m+np+n)\int x^{m+n-1}(ax^n+c)^p dx\right]$

147. $\displaystyle\int \frac{x^m dx}{(ax^n+c)^p} = \frac{1}{a}\int \frac{x^{m-n}dx}{(ax^n+c)^{p-1}}-\frac{c}{a}\int \frac{x^{m-n}dx}{(ax^n+c)^p}.$

148. $\displaystyle\int \frac{dx}{x^m(ax^n+c)^p} = \frac{1}{c}\int \frac{dx}{x^m(ax^n+c)^{p-1}}-\frac{a}{c}\int \frac{dx}{x^{m-n}(ax^n+c)^p}.$

Expressions Containing (ax^2+bx+c).

149. $\displaystyle\int \frac{dx}{ax^2+bx+c} = \frac{1}{\sqrt{b^2-4ac}}\log\frac{2ax+b-\sqrt{b^2-4ac}}{2ax+b+\sqrt{b^2-4ac}},\ b^2>4ac.$

150. $\displaystyle\int \frac{dx}{ax^2+bx+c} = \frac{2}{\sqrt{4ac-b^2}}\,\tan^{-1}\frac{2ax+b}{\sqrt{4ac-b^2}},\quad b^2<4ac.$

151. $\displaystyle\int \frac{dx}{ax^2+bx+c} = -\frac{2}{2ax+b},\ b^2=4ac.$

152. $\displaystyle\int \frac{dx}{(ax^2+bx+c)^{n+1}} = \frac{2ax+b}{n(4ac-b^2)(ax^2+bx+c)^n}$
$\displaystyle\qquad +\frac{2(2n-1)a}{n(4ac-b^2)}\int \frac{dx}{(ax^2+bx+c)^n}.$

153. $\displaystyle\int \frac{xdx}{ax^2+bx+c} = \frac{1}{2a}\log\,(ax^2+bx+c)-\frac{b}{2a}\int \frac{dx}{ax^2+bx+c}.$

154. $\displaystyle\int \frac{x^2dx}{ax^2+bx+c} = \frac{x}{a}-\frac{b}{2a^2}\log\,(ax^2+bx+c)$
$\displaystyle\qquad +\frac{b^2-2ac}{2a^2}\int \frac{dx}{ax^2+bx+c}.$

155. $\displaystyle\int \frac{x^ndx}{ax^2+bx+c} = \frac{x^{n-1}}{(n-1)a}-\frac{c}{a}\int \frac{x^{n-2}dx}{ax^2+bx+c}$
$\displaystyle\qquad -\frac{b}{a}\int \frac{x^{n-1}dx}{ax^2+bx+c}$

156. $\displaystyle\int \frac{xdx}{(ax^2+bx+c)^{n+1}} = \frac{-(2c+bx)}{n(4ac-b^2)(ax^2+bx+c)^n}$
$\displaystyle\qquad -\frac{b(2n-1)}{n(4ac-b^2)}\int \frac{dx}{(ax^2+bx+c)^n}$

157. $\displaystyle\int \frac{x^m dx}{(ax^2+bx+c)^{n+1}} = -\frac{x^{m-1}}{a(2n-m+1)(ax^2+bx+c)^n}$
$\displaystyle\qquad -\frac{n-m+1}{2n-m+1}\cdot\frac{b}{a}\int \frac{x^{m-1}dx}{(ax^2+bx+c)^{n+1}}$
$\displaystyle\qquad +\frac{m-1}{2n-m+1}\cdot\frac{c}{a}\int \frac{x^{m-2}dx}{(ax^2+bx+c)^{n+1}}$

158. $\displaystyle\int \frac{dx}{x(ax^2+bx+c)} = \frac{1}{2c}\log\frac{x^2}{ax^2+bx+c}-\frac{b}{2c}\int \frac{dx}{(ax^2+bx+c)}.$

159. $\displaystyle\int \frac{dx}{x^2(ax^2+bx+c)} = \frac{b}{2c^2}\log\left(\frac{ax^2+bx+c}{x^2}\right)-\frac{1}{cx}$
$\displaystyle\qquad +\left(\frac{b^2}{2c^2}-\frac{a}{c}\right)\int \frac{dx}{(ax^2+bx+c)}$

160. $\displaystyle\int \frac{dx}{x^m(ax^2+bx+c)^{n+1}} = -\frac{1}{(m-1)cx^{m-1}(ax^2+bx+c)^n}$
$\displaystyle\qquad -\frac{(n+m-1)}{m-1}\cdot\frac{b}{c}\int \frac{dx}{x^{m-1}(ax^2+bx+c)^{n+1}}$
$\displaystyle\qquad -\frac{(2n+m-1)}{m-1}\cdot\frac{a}{c}\int \frac{dx}{x^{m-2}(ax^2+bx+c)^{n+1}}$

161. $\displaystyle\int \frac{dx}{x(ax^2+bx+c)^n} = \frac{1}{2c(n-1)(ax^2+bx+c)^{n-1}}$
$\displaystyle\qquad -\frac{b}{2c}\int \frac{dx}{(ax^2+bx+c)^n}+\frac{1}{c}\int \frac{dx}{x(ax^2+bx+c)^{n-1}}$

162. $\displaystyle\int \frac{dx}{\sqrt{ax^2+bx+c}} = \frac{1}{\sqrt{a}}\log\,(2ax+b+2\sqrt{a}\sqrt{ax^2+bx+c}),\ a>0.$

163. $\displaystyle\int \frac{dx}{\sqrt{ax^2+bx+c}} = \frac{1}{\sqrt{-a}}\sin^{-1}\frac{-2ax-b}{\sqrt{b^2-4ac}},\ a<0.$

164. $\displaystyle\int \frac{xdx}{\sqrt{ax^2+bx+c}} = \frac{\sqrt{ax^2+bx+c}}{a}-\frac{b}{2a}\int \frac{dx}{\sqrt{ax^2+bx+c}}.$

165. $\displaystyle\int \frac{x^n dx}{\sqrt{ax^2+bx+c}} = \frac{x^{n-1}}{an}\sqrt{ax^2+bx+c}$
$\displaystyle\qquad -\frac{b(2n-1)}{2an}\int \frac{x^{n-1}dx}{\sqrt{ax^2+bx+c}}-\frac{c(n-1)}{an}\int \frac{x^{n-2}dx}{\sqrt{ax^2+bx+c}}.$

166. $\displaystyle\int \sqrt{ax^2+bx+c}\,dx = \frac{2ax+b}{4a}\sqrt{ax^2+bx+c}$
$\displaystyle\qquad +\frac{4ac-b^2}{8a}\int \frac{dx}{\sqrt{ax^2+bx+c}}$

167. $\displaystyle\int x\sqrt{ax^2+bx+c}\,dx = \frac{(ax^2+bx+c)^{\frac{3}{2}}}{3a}-\frac{b}{2a}\int \sqrt{ax^2+bx+c}\,dx.$

168. $\displaystyle\int x^2\sqrt{ax^2+bx+c}\cdot dx = \left(x-\frac{5b}{6a}\right)\frac{(ax^2+bx+c)^{\frac{3}{2}}}{4a}$
$\displaystyle\qquad +\frac{(5b^2-4ac)}{16a^2}\int \sqrt{ax^2+bx+c}\,dx.$

169. $\int \dfrac{dx}{x\sqrt{ax^2+bx+c}} = -\dfrac{1}{\sqrt{c}}\log\left(\dfrac{\sqrt{ax^2+bx+c}+\sqrt{c}}{x} + \dfrac{b}{2\sqrt{c}}\right), c>0.$

170. $\int \dfrac{dx}{x\sqrt{ax^2+bx+c}} = \dfrac{1}{\sqrt{-c}}\sin^{-1}\dfrac{bx+2c}{x\sqrt{b^2-4ac}}, c<0.$

171. $\int \dfrac{dx}{x\sqrt{ax^2+bx}} = -\dfrac{2}{bx}\sqrt{ax^2+bx}, c=0.$

172. $\int \dfrac{dx}{x^n\sqrt{ax^2+bx+c}} = -\dfrac{\sqrt{ax^2+bx+c}}{c(n-1)x^{n-1}}$
$+\dfrac{b(3-2n)}{2c(n-1)}\int\dfrac{dx}{x^{n-1}\sqrt{ax^2+bx+c}} + \dfrac{a(2-n)}{c(n-1)}\int\dfrac{dx}{x^{n-2}\sqrt{ax^2+bx+c}}.$

173. $\int \dfrac{dx}{(ax^2+bx+c)^{\frac{3}{2}}} = \dfrac{2(2ax+b)}{(b^2-4ac)\sqrt{ax^2+bx+c}}, b^2\neq 4ac.$

174. $\int \dfrac{dx}{(ax^2+bx+c)^{\frac{3}{2}}} = -\dfrac{1}{2\sqrt{a^3}(x+b/2a)^2}, b^2=4ac.$

Miscellaneous Algebraic Expressions.

175. $\int \sqrt{2px-x^2}\,dx = \dfrac{1}{2}\Big[(x-p)\sqrt{2px-x^2}+p^2\sin^{-1}[(x-p)/p]\Big].$

176. $\int \dfrac{dx}{\sqrt{2px-x^2}} = \cos^{-1}\left(\dfrac{p-x}{p}\right).$

177. $\int \dfrac{dx}{\sqrt{ax+b}\cdot\sqrt{cx+d}} = \dfrac{2}{\sqrt{-ac}}\tan^{-1}\sqrt{\dfrac{-c(ax+b)}{a(cx+d)}}$
$\quad\text{or } \dfrac{2}{\sqrt{ac}}\tanh^{-1}\sqrt{\dfrac{c(ax+b)}{a(cx+d)}}.$

178. $\int \sqrt{ax+b}\cdot\sqrt{cx+d}\,dx =$
$\quad \dfrac{(2acx+bc+ad)\sqrt{ax+b}\cdot\sqrt{cx+d}}{4ac}$
$\quad + \dfrac{(ad-bc)^2}{8ac}\int\dfrac{dx}{\sqrt{ax+b}\cdot\sqrt{cx+d}}.$

179. $\int \sqrt{\dfrac{cx+d}{ax+b}}\,dx = \dfrac{\sqrt{ax+b}\cdot\sqrt{cx+d}}{a}$
$\quad + \dfrac{(ad-bc)}{2a}\int\dfrac{dx}{\sqrt{ax+b}\cdot\sqrt{cx+d}}.$

180. $\int \sqrt{\dfrac{x+b}{x+d}}\,dx = \sqrt{x+d}\cdot\sqrt{x+b}$
$\quad + (b-d)\log[\sqrt{x+d}+\sqrt{x+b}].$

181. $\int \sqrt{\dfrac{1+x}{1-x}}\,dx = \sin^{-1}x - \sqrt{1-x^2}.$

182. $\int \sqrt{\dfrac{p-x}{q+x}}\,dx = \sqrt{p-x}\cdot\sqrt{q+x} + (p+q)\sin^{-1}\sqrt{\dfrac{x+q}{p+q}}.$

183. $\int \sqrt{\dfrac{p+x}{q-x}}\,dx = -\sqrt{p+x}\cdot\sqrt{q-x} + (p+q)\sin^{-1}\sqrt{\dfrac{q-x}{p+q}}.$

184. $\int \dfrac{dx}{\sqrt{x-p}\cdot\sqrt{q-x}} = 2\sin^{-1}\sqrt{\dfrac{x-p}{q-p}}.$

Expressions Containing sin ax.

185. $\int \sin ax\,dx = -\dfrac{1}{a}\cos ax.$

186. $\int \sin^2 ax\,dx = \dfrac{x}{2} - \dfrac{\sin 2ax}{4a}.$

187. $\int \sin^3 ax\,dx = -\dfrac{1}{a}\cos ax + \dfrac{1}{3a}\cos^3 ax.$

188. $\int \sin^4 ax\,dx = \dfrac{3x}{8} - \dfrac{3\sin 2ax}{16a} - \dfrac{\sin^3 ax\cos ax}{4a}.$

189. $\int \sin^n ax\,dx = -\dfrac{\sin^{n-1}ax\cos ax}{na} + \dfrac{n-1}{n}\int \sin^{n-2}ax\,dx,$
$\quad (n \text{ pos. integer}).$

190. $\int \dfrac{dx}{\sin ax} = \dfrac{1}{a}\log\tan\dfrac{ax}{2} = \dfrac{1}{a}\log(\csc ax - \operatorname{ctn} ax).$

191. $\int \dfrac{dx}{\sin^2 ax} = \int \csc^2 ax\,dx = -\dfrac{1}{a}\operatorname{ctn} ax.$

192. $\int \dfrac{dx}{\sin^n ax} = -\dfrac{1}{a(n-1)}\dfrac{\cos ax}{\sin^{n-1}ax} + \dfrac{n-2}{n-1}\int\dfrac{dx}{\sin^{n-2}ax},$
$\quad n \text{ integer} > 1.$

193. $\int \dfrac{dx}{1\pm\sin ax} = \mp\dfrac{1}{a}\tan\left(\dfrac{\pi}{4}\mp\dfrac{ax}{2}\right).$

194. $\int \dfrac{dx}{b+c\sin ax} = \dfrac{-2}{a\sqrt{b^2-c^2}}\tan^{-1}\left[\sqrt{\dfrac{b-c}{b+c}}\tan\left(\dfrac{\pi}{4}-\dfrac{ax}{2}\right)\right], b^2>c^2.$

195. $\int \dfrac{dx}{b+c\sin ax} = \dfrac{-1}{a\sqrt{c^2-b^2}}\log\dfrac{c+b\sin ax+\sqrt{c^2-b^2}\cdot\cos ax}{b+c\sin ax}, c^2>b^2.$

196. $\int \sin ax\sin bx\,dx = \dfrac{\sin(a-b)x}{2(a-b)} - \dfrac{\sin(a+b)x}{2(a+b)}, a^2\neq b^2.$

197. $\int \sqrt{1+\sin x}\,dx = \pm 2\left(\sin\dfrac{x}{2}-\cos\dfrac{x}{2}\right);$ use + sign
when $(8k-1)\dfrac{\pi}{2} < x \leq (8k+3)\dfrac{\pi}{2}$, otherwise −, k an integer.

198. $\int \sqrt{1-\sin x}\,dx = \pm 2\left(\sin\dfrac{x}{2}+\cos\dfrac{x}{2}\right);$ use +.sign
when $(8k-3)\dfrac{\pi}{2} < x \leq (8k+1)\dfrac{\pi}{2}$, otherwise −, k an integer.

Expressions Involving cos ax.

199. $\int \cos ax\,dx = \dfrac{1}{a}\sin ax.$

200. $\int \cos^2 ax\,dx = \dfrac{x}{2} + \dfrac{\sin 2ax}{4a}.$

201. $\int \cos^3 ax\,dx = \dfrac{1}{a}\sin ax - \dfrac{1}{3a}\sin^3 ax.$

202. $\int \cos^4 ax\,dx = \dfrac{3x}{8} + \dfrac{3\sin 2ax}{16a} + \dfrac{\cos^3 ax\sin ax}{4a}.$

203. $\int \cos^n ax\,dx = \dfrac{\cos^{n-1}ax\sin ax}{na} + \dfrac{n-1}{n}\int \cos^{n-2}ax\,dx,$
$\quad (n \text{ pos. integer}).$

204. $\int \dfrac{dx}{\cos ax} = \dfrac{1}{a}\log\tan\left(\dfrac{ax}{2}+\dfrac{\pi}{4}\right) = \dfrac{1}{a}\log(\tan ax + \sec ax).$

205. $\int \dfrac{dx}{\cos^2 ax} = \dfrac{1}{a}\tan ax.$

206. $\int \dfrac{dx}{\cos^n ax} = \dfrac{1}{a(n-1)}\dfrac{\sin ax}{\cos^{n-1}ax} + \dfrac{n-2}{n-1}\int\dfrac{dx}{\cos^{n-2}ax},$
$\quad n \text{ integer} > 1.$

207. $\int \dfrac{dx}{1+\cos ax} = \dfrac{1}{a}\tan\dfrac{ax}{2}.$

210. $\int \dfrac{dx}{1-\cos ax} = -\dfrac{1}{a}\operatorname{ctn}\dfrac{ax}{2}.$

208. $\int \sqrt{1+\cos x}\cdot dx = \pm\sqrt{2}\int\cos\dfrac{x}{2}\,dx = \pm 2\sqrt{2}\sin\dfrac{x}{2}.$
Use + when $(4k-1)\pi < x \leq (4k+1)\pi$, otherwise −, k an integer.

209. $\int \sqrt{1-\cos x}\cdot dx = \pm\sqrt{2}\int\sin\dfrac{x}{2}\,dx = \mp 2\sqrt{2}\cos\dfrac{x}{2}.$
Use top signs when $4k\pi < x \leq (4k+2)\pi$, otherwise bottom signs.

210. $\int \dfrac{dx}{b+c\cos ax} = \dfrac{1}{a\sqrt{b^2-c^2}}\tan^{-1}\left(\dfrac{\sqrt{b^2-c^2}\cdot\sin ax}{c+b\cos ax}\right), b^2>c^2.$

211. $\int \dfrac{dx}{b+c\cos ax} = \dfrac{1}{a\sqrt{c^2-b^2}}\tanh^{-1}\left[\dfrac{\sqrt{c^2-b^2}\cdot\sin ax}{c+b\cos ax}\right], c^2>b^2.$

212. $\int \cos ax\cdot\cos bx\,dx = \dfrac{\sin(a-b)x}{2(a-b)} + \dfrac{\sin(a+b)x}{2(a+b)}, a^2\neq b^2.$

Expressions Containing sin ax and cos ax.

213. $\int \sin ax\cos bx\,dx = -\dfrac{1}{2}\left[\dfrac{\cos(a-b)x}{a-b} + \dfrac{\cos(a+b)x}{a+b}\right], a^2\neq b^2.$

214. $\int \sin^n ax\cos ax\,dx = \dfrac{1}{a(n+1)}\sin^{n+1}ax, n\neq -1.$

215. $\int \cos^n ax\sin ax\,dx = -\dfrac{1}{a(n+1)}\cos^{n+1}ax, n\neq -1.$

216. $\int \dfrac{\sin ax}{\cos ax} dx = -\dfrac{1}{a} \log \cos ax.$

217. $\int \dfrac{\cos ax}{\sin ax} dx = \dfrac{1}{a} \log \sin ax.$

218. $\int (b + c \sin ax)^n \cos ax\, dx = \dfrac{1}{ac(n+1)}(b + c \sin ax)^{n+1}, n \neq -1.$

219. $\int (b + c \cos ax)^n \sin ax\, dx = -\dfrac{1}{ac(n+1)}(b + c \cos ax)^{n+1}, n \neq -1.$

220. $\int \dfrac{\cos ax\, dx}{b + c \sin ax} = \dfrac{1}{ac} \log(b + c \sin ax).$

221. $\int \dfrac{\sin ax}{b + c \cos ax} dx = -\dfrac{1}{ac} \log(b + c \cos ax).$

222. $\int \dfrac{dx}{b \sin ax + c \cos ax} = \dfrac{1}{a\sqrt{b^2+c^2}}\left[\log \tan \tfrac{1}{2}\left(ax + \tan^{-1}\dfrac{c}{b}\right)\right].$

223. $\int \dfrac{dx}{b + c \cos ax + d \sin ax} = \dfrac{-1}{a\sqrt{b^2-c^2-d^2}} \sin^{-1} U,$

$U \equiv \left[\dfrac{c^2 + d^2 + b(c \cos ax + a \sin ax)}{\sqrt{c^2 + d^2}\,(b + c \cos ax + d \sin ax)}\right]$; or $= \dfrac{1}{a\sqrt{c^2 + d^2 - b^2}} \log V,$

$V \equiv \left[\dfrac{c^2 + d^2 + b(c \cos ax + d \sin ax) + \sqrt{c^2 + d^2 - b^2}\,(c \sin ax - d \cos ax)}{\sqrt{c^2 + d^2}\,(b + c \cos ax + d \sin ax)}\right],$

$b^2 \neq c^2 + d^2, -\pi < ax < \pi.$

224. $\int \dfrac{dx}{b + c \cos ax + d \sin ax}$

$= \dfrac{1}{ab}\left[\dfrac{b - (c + d) \cos ax + (c - d) \sin ax}{b + (c - d) \cos ax + (c + d) \sin ax}\right], b^2 = c^2 + d^2.$

225. $\int \dfrac{\sin^2 ax\, dx}{b + c \cos^2 ax} = \dfrac{1}{ac}\sqrt{\dfrac{b+c}{b}} \tan^{-1}\left(\sqrt{\dfrac{b}{b+c}} \cdot \tan ax\right) - \dfrac{x}{c}.$

226. $\int \dfrac{\sin ax \cos ax\, dx}{b \cos^2 ax + c \sin^2 ax} = \dfrac{1}{2a(c-b)} \log(b \cos^2 ax + c \sin^2 ax).$

227. $\int \dfrac{dx}{b^2 \cos^2 ax - c^2 \sin^2 ax} = \dfrac{1}{2abc} \log \dfrac{b \cos ax + c \sin ax}{b \cos ax - c \sin ax}.$

228. $\int \dfrac{dx}{b^2 \cos^2 ax + c^2 \sin^2 ax} = \dfrac{1}{abc} \tan^{-1}\left(\dfrac{c \tan ax}{b}\right).$

229. $\int \sin^2 ax \cos^2 ax\, dx = \dfrac{x}{8} - \dfrac{\sin 4 ax}{32\, a}.$

230. $\int \dfrac{dx}{\sin ax \cos ax} = \dfrac{1}{a} \log \tan ax.$

231. $\int \dfrac{dx}{\sin^2 ax \cos^2 ax} = \dfrac{1}{a}(\tan ax - \operatorname{ctn} ax).$

232. $\int \dfrac{\sin^2 ax}{\cos ax} dx = \dfrac{1}{a}\left[-\sin ax + \log \tan\left(\dfrac{ax}{2} + \dfrac{\pi}{4}\right)\right].$

233. $\int \dfrac{\cos^2 ax}{\sin ax} dx = \dfrac{1}{a}\left[\cos ax + \log \tan \dfrac{ax}{2}\right].$

234. $\int \sin^m ax \cos^n ax\, dx = -\dfrac{\sin^{m-1} ax \cos^{n+1} ax}{a(m+n)}$
$+ \dfrac{m-1}{m+n} \int \sin^{m-2} ax \cos^n ax\, dx, \; m, n > 0.$

235. $\int \sin^m ax \cos^n ax\, dx = \dfrac{\sin^{m+1} ax \cos^{n-1} ax}{a(m+n)}$
$+ \dfrac{n-1}{m+n} \int \sin^m ax \cos^{n-2} ax\, dx, \; m, n > 0.$

236. $\int \dfrac{\sin^m ax}{\cos^n ax} dx = \dfrac{\sin^{m+1} ax}{a(n-1)\cos^{n-1} ax}$
$- \dfrac{m-n+2}{n-1} \int \dfrac{\sin^m ax}{\cos^{n-2} ax} dx, \; m, n > 0, n \neq 1.$

237. $\int \dfrac{\cos^n ax}{\sin^m ax} dx = \dfrac{-\cos^{n+1} ax}{a(m-1)\sin^{m-1} ax}$
$+ \dfrac{m-n-2}{(m-1)} \int \dfrac{\cos^n ax}{\sin^{m-2} ax} dx, \; m, n, > 0, m \neq 1.$

238. $\int \dfrac{dx}{\sin^m ax \cos^n ax} = \dfrac{1}{a(n-1)} \dfrac{1}{\sin^{m-1} ax \cos^{n-1} ax}$
$+ \dfrac{m+n-2}{(n-1)} \int \dfrac{dx}{\sin^m ax \cos^{n-2} ax}.$

239. $\int \dfrac{dx}{\sin^m ax \cos^n ax} = -\dfrac{1}{a(m-1)} \dfrac{1}{\sin^{m-1} ax \cos^{n-1} ax}$
$+ \dfrac{m+n-2}{(m-1)} \int \dfrac{dx}{\sin^{m-2} ax \cos^n ax}.$

240. $\int \dfrac{\sin^{2n} ax}{\cos ax} dx = \int \dfrac{(1 - \cos^2 ax)^n}{\cos ax} dx.$ (Expand, divide, and use 203).

241. $\int \dfrac{\cos^{2n} ax}{\sin ax} dx = \int \dfrac{(1 - \sin^2 ax)^n}{\sin ax} dx.$ (Expand, divide, and use 189).

242. $\int \dfrac{\sin^{2n+1} ax}{\cos ax} dx = \int \dfrac{(1 - \cos^2 ax)^n}{\cos ax} \sin ax\, dx.$ (Expand, divide, and use 215).

243. $\int \dfrac{\cos^{2n+1} ax}{\sin ax} dx = \int \dfrac{(1 - \sin^2 ax)^n}{\sin ax} \cos ax\, dx.$ (Expand, divide, and use 214).

Expressions Containing tan ax or ctn ax (tan $ax = 1/\operatorname{ctn} ax$).

244. $\int \tan ax\, dx = -\dfrac{1}{a} \log \cos ax.$

245. $\int \tan^2 ax\, dx = \dfrac{1}{a} \tan ax - x.$

246. $\int \tan^3 ax\, dx = \dfrac{1}{2a} \tan^2 ax + \dfrac{1}{a} \log \cos ax.$

247. $\int \tan^n ax\, dx = \dfrac{1}{a(n-1)} \tan^{n-1} ax - \int \tan^{n-2} ax\, dx,$
$n \text{ integer} > 1.$

248. $\int \operatorname{ctn} u\, du = \log \sin u, \text{ or } -\log \csc u, \text{ where } u \text{ is any function of } x.$

249. $\int \operatorname{ctn}^2 ax\, dx = \int \dfrac{dx}{\tan^2 ax} = -\dfrac{1}{a} \operatorname{ctn} ax - x.$

250. $\int \operatorname{ctn}^3 ax\, dx = -\dfrac{1}{2a} \operatorname{ctn}^2 ax - \dfrac{1}{a} \log \sin ax.$

251. $\int \operatorname{ctn}^n ax\, dx = \int \dfrac{dx}{\tan^n ax} = -\dfrac{1}{a(n-1)} \operatorname{ctn}^{n-1} ax$
$- \int \operatorname{ctn}^{n-2} ax\, dx, n \text{ integer} > 1.$

252. $\int \dfrac{dx}{b + c \tan ax} = \int \dfrac{\operatorname{ctn} ax\, dx}{b \operatorname{ctn} ax + c}$
$= \dfrac{1}{b^2 + c^2}\left[bx + \dfrac{c}{a} \log(b \cos ax + c \sin ax)\right].$

253. $\int \dfrac{dx}{b + c \operatorname{ctn} ax} = \int \dfrac{\tan ax\, dx}{b \tan ax + c}$
$= \dfrac{1}{b^2 + c^2}\left[bx - \dfrac{c}{a} \log(c \cos ax + b \sin ax)\right].$

254. $\int \dfrac{dx}{\sqrt{b + c \tan^2 ax}} = \dfrac{1}{a\sqrt{b-c}} \sin^{-1}\left(\sqrt{\dfrac{b-c}{b}} \sin ax\right), b \text{ pos.}, b^2 > c^2.$

38

Expressions Containing sec *ax*=1/cos *ax* or csc *ax* = 1/sin *ax.*

255. $\int \sec ax \, dx = \frac{1}{a} \log \tan \left(\frac{ax}{2} + \frac{\pi}{4} \right).$

256. $\int \sec^2 ax \, dx = \frac{1}{a} \tan ax.$

257. $\int \sec^3 ax \, dx = \frac{1}{2a}\left[\tan ax \sec ax + \log \tan\left(\frac{ax}{2} + \frac{\pi}{4}\right)\right].$

258. $\int \sec^n ax \, dx = \frac{1}{a(n-1)} \frac{\sin ax}{\cos^{n-1} ax}$
$+ \frac{n-2}{n-1} \int \sec^{n-2} ax \, dx, \, n \text{ integer} > 1.$

259. $\int \csc ax \, dx = \frac{1}{a} \log \tan \frac{ax}{2}.$

260. $\int \csc^2 ax \, dx = -\frac{1}{a} \operatorname{ctn} ax.$

261. $\int \csc^3 ax \, dx = \frac{1}{2a}\left[- \operatorname{ctn} ax \csc ax + \log \tan \frac{ax}{2}\right].$

262. $\int \csc^n ax \, dx = -\frac{1}{a(n-1)} \frac{\cos ax}{\sin^{n-1} ax}$
$+ \frac{n-2}{n-1} \int \csc^{n-2} ax \, dx, \, n \text{ integer} > 1.$

Expressions Containing tan *ax* and sec *ax* or ctn *ax* and csc *ax.*

263. $\int \tan ax \sec ax \, dx = \frac{1}{a} \sec ax.$

264. $\int \tan^n ax \sec^2 ax \, dx = \frac{1}{a(n+1)} \tan^{n+1} ax, \, n \neq -1.$

265. $\int \tan ax \sec^n ax \, dx = \frac{1}{an} \sec^n ax, \, n \neq 0.$

266. $\int \operatorname{ctn} ax \csc ax \, dx = -\frac{1}{a} \csc ax.$

267. $\int \operatorname{ctn}^n ax \csc^2 ax \, dx = -\frac{1}{a(n+1)} \operatorname{ctn}^{n+1} ax, \, n \neq -1.$

268. $\int \operatorname{ctn} ax \csc^n ax \, dx = -\frac{1}{an} \csc^n ax, \, n \neq 0.$

269. $\int \frac{\csc^2 ax \, dx}{\operatorname{ctn} ax} = -\frac{1}{a} \log \operatorname{ctn} ax.$

Expressions Containing Algebraic and Trigonometric Functions.

270. $\int x \sin ax \, dx = \frac{1}{a^2} \sin ax - \frac{1}{a} x \cos ax.$

271. $\int x^2 \sin ax \, dx = \frac{2x}{a^2} \sin ax + \frac{2}{a^3} \cos ax - \frac{x^2}{a} \cos ax.$

272. $\int x^3 \sin ax \, dx = \frac{3x^2}{a^2} \sin ax - \frac{6}{a^4} \sin ax - \frac{x^3}{a} \cos ax + \frac{6x}{a^3} \cos ax.$

273. $\int x \sin^2 ax \, dx = \frac{x^2}{4} - \frac{x \sin 2ax}{4a} - \frac{\cos 2ax}{8a^2}.$

274. $\int x^2 \sin^2 ax \, dx = \frac{x^3}{6} - \left(\frac{x^2}{4a} - \frac{1}{8a^3} \right) \sin 2ax - \frac{x \cos 2ax}{4a^2}.$

275. $\int x^3 \sin^2 ax \, dx = \frac{x^4}{8} - \left(\frac{x^3}{4a} - \frac{3x}{8a^3} \right) \sin 2ax$
$- \left(\frac{3x^2}{8a^2} - \frac{3}{16a^4} \right) \cos 2ax.$

276. $\int x \sin^3 ax \, dx = \frac{x \cos 3ax}{12a} - \frac{\sin 3ax}{36a^2} - \frac{3x \cos ax}{4a} + \frac{3 \sin ax}{4a^2}.$

277. $\int x^n \sin ax \, dx = -\frac{1}{a} x^n \cos ax + \frac{n}{a} \int x^{n-1} \cos ax \, dx, \, n > 0.$

278. $\int \frac{\sin ax \, dx}{x} = ax - \frac{(ax)^3}{3 \cdot 3!} + \frac{(ax)^5}{5 \cdot 5!} - \cdots.$

279. $\int \frac{\sin ax \, dx}{x^m} = \frac{-1}{(m-1)} \frac{\sin ax}{x^{m-1}} + \frac{a}{(m-1)} \int \frac{\cos ax \, dx}{x^{m-1}}.$

280. $\int x \cos ax \, dx = \frac{1}{a^2} \cos ax + \frac{1}{a} x \sin ax.$

281. $\int x^2 \cos ax \, dx = \frac{2x}{a^2} \cos ax - \frac{2}{a^3} \sin ax + \frac{x^2}{a} \sin ax.$

282. $\int x^3 \cos ax \, dx = \frac{(3a^2x^2 - 6) \cos ax}{a^4} + \frac{(a^2x^3 - 6x) \sin ax}{a^3}.$

283. $\int x \cos^2 ax \, dx = \frac{x^2}{4} + \frac{x \sin 2ax}{4a} + \frac{\cos 2ax}{8a^2}.$

284. $\int x^2 \cos^2 ax \, dx = \frac{x^3}{6} + \left(\frac{x^2}{4a} - \frac{1}{8a^3} \right) \sin 2ax + \frac{x \cos 2ax}{4a^2}.$

285. $\int x^3 \cos^2 ax \, dx = \frac{x^4}{8} + \left(\frac{x^3}{4a} - \frac{3x}{8a^3} \right) \sin 2ax$
$+ \left(\frac{3x^2}{8a^2} - \frac{3}{16a^4} \right) \cos 2ax.$

286. $\int x \cos^3 ax \, dx = \frac{x \sin 3ax}{12a} + \frac{\cos 3ax}{36a^2} + \frac{3x \sin ax}{4a} + \frac{3 \cos ax}{4a^2}.$

287. $\int x^n \cos ax \, dx = \frac{1}{a} x^n \sin ax - \frac{n}{a} \int x^{n-1} \sin ax \, dx, \, n \text{ pos.}$

288. $\int \frac{\cos ax \, dx}{x} = \log ax - \frac{(ax)^2}{2 \cdot 2!} + \frac{(ax)^4}{4 \cdot 4!} - \cdots.$

289. $\int \frac{\cos ax}{x^m} dx = -\frac{1}{(m-1)} \cdot \frac{\cos ax}{x^{m-1}} - \frac{a}{(m-1)} \int \frac{\sin ax \, dx}{x^{m-1}}.$

Expressions Containing Exponential and Logarithmic Functions.

290. $\int e^{ax} \, dx = \frac{1}{a} e^{ax}, \quad \int b^{ax} \, dx = \frac{b^{ax}}{a \log b}.$

291. $\int x e^{ax} \, dx = \frac{e^{ax}}{a^2} (ax - 1), \int x b^{ax} \, dx = \frac{x b^{ax}}{a \log b} - \frac{b^{ax}}{a^2 (\log b)^2}.$

292. $\int x^2 e^{ax} dx = \frac{e^{ax}}{a^3}(a^2 x^2 - 2ax + 2).$

293. $\int x^n e^{ax} \, dx = \frac{1}{a} x^n e^{ax} - \frac{n}{a} \int x^{n-1} e^{ax} \, dx, \quad n \text{ pos.}$

294. $\int x^n e^{ax} dx = \frac{e^{ax}}{a^{n+1}} \left[(ax)^n - n(ax)^{n-1} + n(n-1)(ax)^{n-2} \right.$
$\left. - \cdots + (-1)^n n! \right], \, n \text{ pos. integ.}$

295. $\int x^n e^{-ax} dx = -\frac{e^{-ax}}{a^{n+1}} \left[(ax)^n + n(ax)^{n-1} + n(n-1)(ax)^{n-2} \right.$
$\left. + \cdots + n! \right], \, n \text{ pos. integ.}$

296. $\int x^n b^{ax} \, dx = \frac{x^n b^{ax}}{a \log b} - \frac{n}{a \log b} \int x^{n-1} b^{ax} \, dx, \quad n \text{ pos.}$

297. $\int \frac{e^{ax}}{x} dx = \log x + ax + \frac{(ax)^2}{2 \cdot 2!} + \frac{(ax)^3}{3 \cdot 3!} + \cdots.$

298. $\int \frac{e^{ax}}{x^n} dx = \frac{1}{n-1} \left[-\frac{e^{ax}}{x^{n-1}} + a \int \frac{e^{ax}}{x^{n-1}} dx \right], \, n \text{ integ.} > 1.$

299. $\int \frac{dx}{b + c e^{ax}} = \frac{1}{ab} [ax - \log (b + c e^{ax})].$

300. $\int \frac{e^{ax} \, dx}{b + c e^{ax}} = \frac{1}{ac} \log (b + c e^{ax}).$

301. $\int \frac{dx}{b e^{ax} + c e^{-ax}} = \frac{1}{a \sqrt{bc}} \tan^{-1} \left(e^{ax} \sqrt{\frac{b}{c}} \right), \, b \text{ and } c \text{ pos.}$

302. $\int e^{ax} \sin bx \, dx = \frac{e^{ax}}{a^2 + b^2} \, (a \sin bx - b \cos bx).$

39

303. $\int e^{ax} \sin bx \sin cx \, dx = \dfrac{e^{ax}[(b-c) \sin (b-c)x + a \cos (b-c)x]}{2[a^2 + (b-c)^2]}$
$- \dfrac{e^{ax}[(b+c) \sin (b+c)x + a \cos (b+c)x]}{2[a^2 + (b+c)^2]}.$

304. $\int e^{ax} \cos bx \, dx = \dfrac{e^{ax}}{a^2 + b^2} (a \cos bx + b \sin bx).$

305. $\int e^{ax} \cos bx \cos cx \, dx = \dfrac{e^{ax}[(b-c) \sin (b-c)x + a \cos (b-c)x]}{2[a^2 + (b-c)^2]}$
$+ \dfrac{e^{ax}[(b+c) \sin (b+c)x + a \cos (b+c)x]}{2[a^2 + (b+c)^2]}$

306. $\int e^{ax} \sin bx \cos cx \, dx = \dfrac{e^{ax}[a \sin (b-c)x - (b-c) \cos (b-c)x]}{2[a^2 + (b-c)^2]}$
$+ \dfrac{e^{ax}[a \sin (b+c)x - (b+c) \cos (b+c)x]}{2[a^2 + (b+c)^2]}.$

307. $\int e^{ax} \sin bx \sin (bx + c) \, dx =$
$\dfrac{e^{ax} \cos c}{2a} - \dfrac{e^{ax} [a \cos (2bx+c) + 2b \sin (2bx+c)]}{2(a^2 + 4b^2)}$

308. $\int e^{ax} \cos bx \cos (bx + c) \, dx =$
$\dfrac{e^{ax} \cos c}{2a} + \dfrac{e^{ax} [a \cos (2bx+c) + 2b \sin (2bx+c)]}{2(a^2 + 4b^2)}$

309. $\int e^{ax} \cos bx \sin (bx + c) \, dx =$
$\dfrac{e^{ax} \sin c}{2a} + \dfrac{e^{ax} [a \sin (2bx+c) - 2b \cos (2bx+c)]}{2(a^2 + 4b^2)}$

310. $\int e^{ax} \sin bx \cos (bx + c) \, dx =$
$- \dfrac{e^{ax} \sin c}{2a} + \dfrac{e^{ax} [a \sin (2bx+c) - 2b \cos (2bx+c)]}{2(a^2 + 4b^2)}$

311. $\int x e^{ax} \sin bx = \dfrac{xe^{ax}}{a^2 + b^2} (a \sin bx - b \cos bx)$
$- \dfrac{e^{ax}}{(a^2 + b^2)^2} [(a^2 - b^2) \sin bx - 2ab \cos bx].$

312. $\int x e^{ax} \cos bx \, dx = \dfrac{xe^{ax}}{a^2 + b^2} (a \cos bx + b \sin bx)$
$- \dfrac{e^{ax}}{(a^2 + b^2)^2} [(a^2 - b^2) \cos bx + 2ab \sin bx].$

313. $\int e^{ax} \cos^n bx \, dx = \dfrac{e^{ax} \cos^{n-1} bx (a \cos bx + nb \sin bx)}{a^2 + n^2 b^2}$
$+ \dfrac{n(n-1)b^2}{a^2 + n^2 b^2} \int e^{ax} \cos^{n-2} bx \, dx.$

314. $\int e^{ax} \sin^n bx \, dx = \dfrac{e^{ax} \sin^{n-1} bx (a \sin bx - nb \cos bx)}{a^2 + n^2 b^2}$
$+ \dfrac{n(n-1)b^2}{a^2 + n^2 b^2} \int e^{ax} \sin^{n-2} bx \, dx.$

315. $\int \log ax \, dx = x \log ax - x.$

316. $\int x \log ax \, dx = \dfrac{x^2}{2} \log ax - \dfrac{x^2}{4}.$

317. $\int x^2 \log ax \, dx = \dfrac{x^3}{3} \log ax - \dfrac{x^3}{9}.$

318. $\int (\log ax)^2 \, dx = x(\log ax)^2 - 2x \log ax + 2x.$

319. $\int (\log ax)^n \, dx = x (\log ax)^n - n \int (\log ax)^{n-1} \, dx, \quad n \text{ pos.}$

320. $\int x^n \log ax \, dx = x^{n+1} \left[\dfrac{\log ax}{n+1} - \dfrac{1}{(n+1)^2} \right], \quad n \neq -1.$

321. $\int x^n (\log ax)^m \, dx = \dfrac{x^{n+1}}{n+1} (\log ax)^m - \dfrac{m}{n+1} \int x^n (\log ax)^{m-1} dx.$

322. $\int \dfrac{(\log ax)^n}{x} \, dx = \dfrac{(\log ax)^{n+1}}{n+1}, \quad n \neq -1.$

323. $\int \dfrac{dx}{x \log ax} = \log (\log ax).$

324. $\int \dfrac{dx}{x (\log ax)^n} = - \dfrac{1}{(n-1)(\log ax)^{n-1}}$

325. $\int \dfrac{x^n dx}{(\log ax)^m} = \dfrac{-x^{n+1}}{(m-1)(\log ax)^{m-1}} + \dfrac{n+1}{m-1} \int \dfrac{x^n dx}{(\log ax)^{m-1}}, m \neq 1.$

326. $\int \dfrac{x^n dx}{\log ax} = \dfrac{1}{a^{n+1}} \int \dfrac{e^y dy}{y}, \quad y = (n+1) \log ax.$

327. $\int \dfrac{x^n dx}{\log ax} = \dfrac{1}{a^{n+1}} \left[\log | \log ax | + (n+1) \log ax \right.$
$\left. + \dfrac{(n+1)^2 (\log ax)^2}{2 \cdot 2!} + \dfrac{(n+1)^3 (\log ax)^3}{3 \cdot 3!} + \cdots \right].$

328. $\int \dfrac{dx}{\log ax} = \dfrac{1}{a} \left[\log (\log ax) + \log ax + \dfrac{(\log ax)^2}{2 \cdot 2!} \right.$
$\left. + \dfrac{(\log ax)^3}{3 \cdot 3!} + \cdots \right].$

329. $\int \sin (\log ax) \, dx = \dfrac{x}{2} [\sin (\log ax) - \cos (\log ax)].$

330. $\int \cos (\log ax) \, dx = \dfrac{x}{2} [\sin (\log ax) + \cos (\log ax)].$

331. $\int e^{ax} \log bx \, dx = \dfrac{1}{a} e^{ax} \log bx - \dfrac{1}{a} \int \dfrac{e^{ax}}{x} \, dx.$

Expressions Containing Inverse Trigonometric Functions

332. $\int \sin^{-1} ax \, dx = x \sin^{-1} ax + \dfrac{1}{a} \sqrt{1 - a^2 x^2}.$

333. $\int (\sin^{-1} ax)^2 \, dx = x (\sin^{-1} ax)^2 - 2x + \dfrac{2}{a} \sqrt{1 - a^2 x^2} \sin^{-1} ax.$

334. $\int x \sin^{-1} ax \, dx = \dfrac{x^2}{2} \sin^{-1} ax - \dfrac{1}{4a^2} \sin^{-1} ax + \dfrac{x}{4a} \sqrt{1 - a^2 x^2}.$

335. $\int x^n \sin^{-1} ax \, dx = \dfrac{x^{n+1}}{n+1} \sin^{-1} ax$
$- \dfrac{a}{n+1} \int \dfrac{x^{n+1} dx}{\sqrt{1 - a^2 x^2}}, n \neq -1.$

336. $\int \dfrac{\sin^{-1} ax \, dx}{x} = ax + \dfrac{1}{2 \cdot 3 \cdot 3} (ax)^3 + \dfrac{1 \cdot 3}{2 \cdot 4 \cdot 5 \cdot 5} (ax)^5$
$+ \dfrac{1 \cdot 3 \cdot 5}{2 \cdot 4 \cdot 6 \cdot 7 \cdot 7} (ax)^7 + \cdots, a^2 x^2 < 1.$

337. $\int \dfrac{\sin^{-1} ax \, dx}{x^2} = - \dfrac{1}{x} \sin^{-1} ax - a \log \left| \dfrac{1 + \sqrt{1 - a^2 x^2}}{ax} \right|.$

338. $\int \cos^{-1} ax \, dx = x \cos^{-1} ax - \dfrac{1}{a} \sqrt{1 - a^2 x^2}.$

339. $\int (\cos^{-1} ax)^2 \, dx = x(\cos^{-1} ax)^2 - 2x - \dfrac{2}{a} \sqrt{1 - a^2 x^2} \cos^{-1} ax.$

340. $\int x \cos^{-1} ax \, dx = \dfrac{x^2}{2} \cos^{-1} ax - \dfrac{1}{4a^2} \cos^{-1} ax - \dfrac{x}{4a} \sqrt{1 - a^2 x^2}.$

341. $\int x^n \cos^{-1} ax \, dx = \dfrac{x^{n+1}}{n+1} \cos^{-1} ax$
$+ \dfrac{a}{n+1} \int \dfrac{x^{n+1} dx}{\sqrt{1 - a^2 x^2}}, n \neq -1.$

$342. \int \frac{\cos^{-1} ax \, dx}{x} = \frac{\pi}{2} \log |ax| - ax - \frac{1}{2 \cdot 3 \cdot 3} (ax)^3 - \frac{1 \cdot 3}{2 \cdot 4 \cdot 5 \cdot 5} (ax)^5$
$\qquad\qquad\qquad - \frac{1 \cdot 3 \cdot 5}{2 \cdot 4 \cdot 6 \cdot 7 \cdot 7} (ax)^7 - \cdots, \ a^2 x^2 < 1.$

$343. \int \frac{\cos^{-1} ax \, dx}{x^2} = -\frac{1}{x} \cos^{-1} ax + a \log \left| \frac{1 + \sqrt{1 - a^2 x^2}}{ax} \right|.$

$344. \int \tan^{-1} ax \, dx = x \tan^{-1} ax - \frac{1}{2a} \log (1 + a^2 x^2).$

$345. \int x^n \tan^{-1} ax \, dx = \frac{x^{n+1}}{n+1} \tan^{-1} ax - \frac{a}{n+1} \int \frac{x^{n+1} dx}{1 + a^2 x^2}, \ n \neq -1.$

$346. \int \frac{\tan^{-1} ax \, dx}{x^2} = -\frac{1}{x} \tan^{-1} ax - \frac{a}{2} \log \left(\frac{1 + a^2 x^2}{a^2 x^2} \right).$

$347. \int \mathrm{ctn}^{-1} ax \, dx = x \, \mathrm{ctn}^{-1} ax + \frac{1}{2a} \log (1 + a^2 x^2).$

$348. \int x^n \, \mathrm{ctn}^{-1} ax \, dx = \frac{x^{n+1}}{n+1} \mathrm{ctn}^{-1} ax + \frac{a}{n+1} \int \frac{x^{n+1} dx}{1 + a^2 x^2}, \ n \neq -1.$

$349. \int \frac{\mathrm{ctn}^{-1} ax \, dx}{x^2} = -\frac{1}{x} \mathrm{ctn}^{-1} ax + \frac{a}{2} \log \left(\frac{1 + a^2 x^2}{a^2 x^2} \right).$

$350. \int \sec^{-1} ax \, dx = x \sec^{-1} ax - \frac{1}{a} \log (ax + \sqrt{a^2 x^2 - 1}).$

$351. \int x^n \sec^{-1} ax \, dx = \frac{x^{n+1}}{n+1} \sec^{-1} ax \pm \frac{1}{n+1} \int \frac{x^n dx}{\sqrt{a^2 x^2 - 1}}, \ n \neq -1.$
Use $+$ sign when $\frac{\pi}{2} < \sec^{-1} ax < \pi$; $-$ sign when $0 < \sec^{-1} ax < \frac{\pi}{2}$.

$352. \int \csc^{-1} ax \, dx = x \csc^{-1} ax + \frac{1}{a} \log (ax + \sqrt{a^2 x^2 - 1}).$

$353. \int x^n \csc^{-1} ax \, dx = \frac{x^{n+1}}{n+1} \csc^{-1} ax \pm \frac{1}{n+1} \int \frac{x^n dx}{\sqrt{a^2 x^2 - 1}}, \ n \neq -1.$
Use $+$ sign when $0 < \csc^{-1} ax < \frac{\pi}{2}$; $-$ sign when $-\frac{\pi}{2} < \csc^{-1} ax < 0$.

Definite Integrals

$354. \int_0^\infty \frac{a \, dx}{a^2 + x^2} = \frac{\pi}{2}$, if $a > 0$; $\ 0$, if $a = 0$; $\ \frac{-\pi}{2}$, if $a < 0$.

$355. \int_0^\infty x^{n-1} e^{-x} dx = \int_0^1 \left[\log \frac{1}{x} \right]^{n-1} dx = \Gamma(n).$
$\qquad \Gamma(n+1) = n \cdot \Gamma(n)$, if $n > 0$. $\qquad \Gamma(2) = \Gamma(1) = 1.$
$\qquad \Gamma(n+1) = n!$, if n is an integer. $\qquad \Gamma(\frac{1}{2}) = \sqrt{\pi}.$

$356. \int_0^\infty e^{-zx} \cdot z^n \cdot x^{n-1} dx = \Gamma(n), \ z > 0.$

$357. \int_0^1 x^{m-1} (1-x)^{n-1} dx = \int_0^\infty \frac{x^{m-1} dx}{(1+x)^{m+n}} = \frac{\Gamma(m) \Gamma(n)}{\Gamma(m+n)}$

$358. \int_0^\infty \frac{x^{n-1}}{1+x} dx = \frac{\pi}{\sin n\pi}, \ 0 < n < 1.$

$359. \int_0^{\frac{\pi}{2}} \sin^n x \, dx = \int_0^{\frac{\pi}{2}} \cos^n x \, dx$
$\qquad = \frac{1}{2} \sqrt{\pi} \cdot \frac{\Gamma \left(\frac{n}{2} + \frac{1}{2} \right)}{\Gamma \left(\frac{n}{2} + 1 \right)}$, if $n > -1$;
$\qquad = \frac{1 \cdot 3 \cdot 5 \cdots (n-1)}{2 \cdot 4 \cdot 6 \cdots (n)} \cdot \frac{\pi}{2}$, if n is an even integer;
$\qquad = \frac{2 \cdot 4 \cdot 6 \cdots (n-1)}{1 \cdot 3 \cdot 5 \cdot 7 \cdots n}$, if n is an odd integer.

$360. \int_0^\infty \frac{\sin^2 x}{x^2} dx = \frac{\pi}{2}.$
$361. \int_0^\infty \frac{\sin ax}{x} dx = \frac{\pi}{2}$, if $a > 0$.

$362. \int_0^\infty \frac{\sin x \cos ax}{x} dx = 0$, if $a < -1$, or $a > 1$;
$\qquad\qquad\qquad\qquad = \frac{\pi}{4}$, if $a = -1$, or $a = 1$;
$\qquad\qquad\qquad\qquad = \frac{\pi}{2}$, if $-1 < a < 1$.

$363. \int_0^\pi \sin^2 ax \, dx = \int_0^\pi \cos^2 ax \, dx = \frac{\pi}{2}.$

$364. \int_0^{\pi/a} \sin ax \cdot \cos ax \, dx = \int_0^\pi \sin ax \cdot \cos ax \, dx = 0.$

$365. \int_0^\pi \sin ax \sin bx \, dx = \int_0^\pi \cos ax \cos bx \, dx = 0, \ a \neq b.$

$366. \int_0^\pi \sin ax \cos bx \, dx = \frac{2a}{a^2 - b^2}$, if $a - b$ is odd;
$\qquad\qquad\qquad\qquad = 0$, if $a - b$ is even.

$367. \int_0^\infty \frac{\sin ax \sin bx}{x^2} dx = \frac{1}{2} \pi a$, if $a < b.$

$368. \int_0^\infty \cos (x^2) \, dx = \int_0^\infty \sin (x^2) dx = \frac{1}{2} \sqrt{\frac{\pi}{2}}.$

$369. \int_0^\infty e^{-a^2 x^2} dx = \frac{\sqrt{\pi}}{2a} = \frac{1}{2a} \Gamma \left(\frac{1}{2} \right)$, if $a > 0.$

$370. \int_0^\infty x^n \cdot e^{-ax} dx = \frac{\Gamma(n+1)}{a^{n+1}},$
$\qquad\qquad\qquad = \frac{n!}{a^{n+1}}$, if n is a positive integer, $a > 0.$

$371. \int_0^\infty x^{2n} e^{-ax^2} dx = \frac{1 \cdot 3 \cdot 5 \cdots (2n-1)}{2^{n+1} a^n} \sqrt{\frac{\pi}{a}}.$

$372. \int_0^\infty \sqrt{x} \ e^{-ax} dx = \frac{1}{2a} \sqrt{\frac{\pi}{a}}.$
$373. \int_0^\infty \frac{e^{-ax}}{\sqrt{x}} dx = \sqrt{\frac{\pi}{a}}.$

$374. \int_0^\infty e^{(-x^2 - a^2/x^2)} dx = \frac{1}{2} e^{-2a} \sqrt{\pi}$, if $a > 0.$

$375. \int_0^\infty e^{-ax} \cos bx \, dx = \frac{a}{a^2 + b^2}$, if $a > 0.$

$376. \int_0^\infty e^{-ax} \sin bx \, dx = \frac{b}{a^2 + b^2}$, if $a > 0.$

$377. \int_0^\infty \frac{e^{-ax} \sin x}{x} dx = \mathrm{ctn}^{-1} a, \ a > 0.$

$378. \int_0^\infty e^{-a^2 x^2} \cos bx \, dx = \frac{\sqrt{\pi} \cdot e^{-\frac{b^2}{4a^2}}}{2a}$, if $a > 0.$

$379. \int_0^1 (\log x)^n \, dx = (-1)^n \cdot n!, \ n$ pos. integ.

$380. \int_0^1 \frac{\log x}{1-x} dx = -\frac{\pi^2}{6}.$
$381. \int_0^1 \frac{\log x}{1+x} dx = -\frac{\pi^2}{12}.$

$382. \int_0^1 \frac{\log x}{1-x^2} dx = -\frac{\pi^2}{8}.$
$383. \int_0^1 \frac{\log x}{\sqrt{1-x^2}} dx = -\frac{\pi}{2} \log 2.$

$384. \int_0^1 \log \left(\frac{1+x}{1-x} \right) \cdot \frac{dx}{x} = \frac{\pi^2}{4}.$
$385. \int_0^\infty \log \left(\frac{e^x + 1}{e^x - 1} \right) dx = \frac{\pi^2}{4}.$

$386. \int_0^1 \frac{dx}{\sqrt{\log(1/x)}} = \sqrt{\pi}.$

$387. \int_0^{\frac{\pi}{2}} \log \sin x \, dx = \int_0^{\frac{\pi}{2}} \log \cos x \, dx = -\frac{\pi}{2} \log_e 2.$

$388. \int_0^\pi x \log \sin x \, dx = -\frac{\pi^2}{2} \cdot \log_e 2.$

41

$$389. \int_0^1 \log(\log x)\, dx = \int_0^\infty e^{-x} \log x\, dx = \gamma = 0.5772157 \cdots .$$

$$390. \int_0^1 \left(\log \frac{1}{x}\right)^{\frac{1}{2}} dx = \frac{\sqrt{\pi}}{2}.$$

$$391. \int_0^1 \left(\log \frac{1}{x}\right)^{-\frac{1}{2}} dx = \sqrt{\pi}.$$

$$392. \int_0^1 x^m \log\left(\frac{1}{x}\right)^n dx = \frac{\Gamma(n+1)}{(m+1)^{n+1}}, \text{ if } m+1>0, \ n+1>0.$$

$$393. \int_0^\pi \log(a \pm b \cos x)\, dx = \pi \log\left(\frac{a + \sqrt{a^2 - b^2}}{2}\right), a \geq b.$$

$$394. \int_0^{\frac{\pi}{2}} \frac{\log(1+\sin a \cos x)}{\cos x} dx = \pi a.$$

$$395. \int_0^1 \frac{x^b - x^a}{\log x} dx = \log \frac{1+b}{1+a}.$$

$$396. \int_0^\pi \frac{dx}{a + b \cos x} = \frac{\pi}{\sqrt{a^2 - b^2}}, \text{ if } a > b > 0.$$

$$397. \int_0^{\frac{\pi}{2}} \frac{dx}{a + b \cos x} = \frac{\cos^{-1}\left(\frac{b}{a}\right)}{\sqrt{a^2 - b^2}}, a > b.$$

$$398. \int_0^\infty \frac{\cos ax\, dx}{1 + x^2} = \frac{\pi}{2} \cdot e^{-a}, \text{ if } a > 0; = \frac{\pi}{2} e^a, \text{ if } a < 0.$$

$$399. \int_0^\infty \frac{\cos x\, dx}{\sqrt{x}} = \int_0^\infty \frac{\sin x\, dx}{\sqrt{x}} = \sqrt{\frac{\pi}{2}}.$$

$$400. \int_0^\infty \frac{e^{-ax} - e^{-bx}}{x} dx = \log \frac{b}{a}.$$

$$401. \int_0^\infty \frac{\tan^{-1} ax - \tan^{-1} bx}{x} dx = \frac{\pi}{2} \log \frac{a}{b}.$$

$$402. \int_0^\infty \frac{\cos ax - \cos bx}{x} dx = \log \frac{b}{a}.$$

$$403. \int_0^{\frac{\pi}{2}} \frac{dx}{a^2 \cos^2 x + b^2 \sin^2 x} = \frac{\pi}{2ab}.$$

$$404. \int_0^{\frac{\pi}{2}} \frac{dx}{(a^2 \cos^2 x + b^2 \sin^2 x)^2} = \frac{\pi(a^2 + b^2)}{4a^3 b^3}.$$

$$405. \int_0^\pi \frac{(a - b \cos x)dx}{a^2 - 2ab \cos x + b^2} = 0, \text{ if } a^2 < b^2;$$
$$= \frac{\pi}{a}, \text{ if } a^2 > b^2;$$
$$= \frac{\pi}{2a}, \text{ if } a = b.$$

$$406. \int_0^\infty \frac{1+x^2}{1+x^4} dx = \frac{\pi}{4} \sqrt{2}.$$

$$407. \int_0^1 \frac{\log(1+x)}{x} dx = \frac{1}{1^2} - \frac{1}{2^2} + \frac{1}{3^2} - \frac{1}{4^2} + \cdots = \frac{\pi^2}{12}.$$

$$408. \int_{-\infty}^x \frac{e^{-xu}}{u} du = \gamma + \log x - x + \frac{x^2}{2 \cdot 2!} - \frac{x^3}{3 \cdot 3!} + \frac{x^4}{4 \cdot 4!} - \cdots,$$
$$\text{where } \gamma = \lim_{t \to \infty}\left(1 + \frac{1}{2} + \frac{1}{3} + \cdots + \frac{1}{t} - \log t\right) = 0.5772157 \cdots .$$

$$409. \int_{-\infty}^x \frac{\cos xu}{u} du = \gamma + \log x - \frac{x^2}{2 \cdot 2!} + \frac{x^4}{4 \cdot 4!} - \frac{x^6}{6 \cdot 6!} + \cdots,$$
$$\text{where } \gamma = 0.5772157 \cdots .$$

$$410. \int_{-\infty}^x \frac{e^{xu} - e^{-xu}}{u} du = 2\left(x + \frac{x^3}{3 \cdot 3!} + \frac{x^5}{5 \cdot 5!} + \cdots\right).$$

$$411. \int_0^1 \frac{1 - e^{-xu}}{u} du = x - \frac{x^2}{2 \cdot 2!} + \frac{x^3}{3 \cdot 3!} - \frac{x^4}{4 \cdot 4!} + \cdots .$$

$$412. \int_0^{\frac{\pi}{2}} \frac{dx}{\sqrt{1 - K^2 \sin^2 x}} = \frac{\pi}{2}\left[1 + \left(\frac{1}{2}\right)^2 K^2 + \left(\frac{1 \cdot 3}{2 \cdot 4}\right)^2 K^4 + \left(\frac{1 \cdot 3 \cdot 5}{2 \cdot 4 \cdot 6}\right)^2 K^6 + \cdots \right],$$
$$\text{if } K^2 < 1.$$

$$413. \int_0^{\frac{\pi}{2}} \sqrt{1 - K^2 \sin^2 x}\, dx = \frac{\pi}{2}\left[1 - \left(\frac{1}{2}\right)^2 K^2 \right.$$
$$\left. - \left(\frac{1 \cdot 3}{2 \cdot 4}\right)^2 \frac{K^4}{3} - \left(\frac{1 \cdot 3 \cdot 5}{2 \cdot 4 \cdot 6}\right)^2 \frac{K^6}{5} - \cdots \right], \text{if } K^2 < 1.$$

$$414. \int_0^\infty e^{-ax} \cosh bx\, dx = \frac{a}{a^2 - b^2}, a > 0, a^2 \neq b^2.$$

$$415. \int_0^\infty e^{-ax} \sinh bx\, dx = \frac{b}{a^2 - b^2}, a > 0, a^2 \neq b^2.$$

$$416. \int_0^\infty x e^{-ax} \sin bx\, dx = \frac{2ab}{(a^2 + b^2)^2}, a > 0.$$

$$417. \int_0^\infty x e^{-ax} \cos bx\, dx = \frac{a^2 - b^2}{(a^2 + b^2)^2}, a > 0.$$

$$418. \int_0^\infty x^2 e^{-ax} \sin bx\, dx = \frac{2b(3a^2 - b^2)}{(a^2 + b^2)^3}, a > 0.$$

$$419. \int_0^\infty x^2 e^{-ax} \cos bx\, dx = \frac{2a(a^2 - 3b^2)}{(a^2 + b^2)^3}, a > 0.$$

$$420. \int_0^\infty x^3 e^{-ax} \sin bx\, dx = \frac{24ab(a^2 - b^2)}{(a^2 + b^2)^4}, a > 0.$$

$$421. \int_0^\infty x^3 e^{-ax} \cos bx\, dx = \frac{6(a^4 - 6a^2 b^2 + b^4)}{(a^2 + b^2)^4}, a > 0.$$

$$422. \int_0^\infty x^n e^{-ax} \sin bx\, dx = \frac{i \cdot n! \, [(a - ib)^{n+1} - (a + ib)^{n+1}]}{2(a^2 + b^2)^{n+1}}, a > 0.$$

$$423. \int_0^\infty x^n e^{-ax} \cos bx\, dx = \frac{n! \, [(a - ib)^{n+1} + (a + ib)^{n+1}]}{2(a^2 + b^2)^{n+1}}, a > 0.$$

GREEK ALPHABET

Letters	Names	Letters	Names	Letters	Names
A α	Alpha	I ι	Iota	P ρ	Rho
B β	Beta	K κ	Kappa	Σ σ s	Sigma
Γ γ	Gamma	Λ λ	Lambda	T τ	Tau
Δ δ	Delta	M μ	Mu	Υ υ	Upsilon
E ε	Epsilon	N ν	Nu	Φ φ	Phi
Z ζ	Zeta	Ξ ξ	Xi	X χ	Chi
H η	Eta	O o	Omicron	Ψ ψ	Psi
Θ θ	Theta	Π π	Pi	Ω ω	Omega

MATHEMATICAL SYMBOLS
Arithmetic and Algebra

$+$ Plus; positive.

$-$ Minus; negative.

$\pm$ Plus or minus; positive or negative.

$\mp$ Minus or plus; negative or positive.

ab, $a \cdot b$, $a \times b$ a times b; a multiplied by b.

a/b, $a \div b$, $a:b$ a divided by b; the ratio of a to b.

$=$, $::$ Equals (the symbol $::$ is practically obsolete).

$a/b = c/d$ or $a:b::c:d$ A proportion; a is to b as c is to d (the second form is seldom used).

$\equiv$ Identical; identically equal to.

$\neq$ Does not equal.

$\cong$ or $\simeq$ Congruent; approximately equal (not common).

$\sim$ or $\frown$ Equivalent; similar.

$>$ Greater than.

$<$ Less than.

$\geqq$, or $\geq$ Greater than or equal to.

$\leqq$, or $\leq$ Less than or equal to.

a^n $a\,a\,a\,\cdots$ to n factors.

$\sqrt{a}$, $a^{1/2}$ The positive square root of a.

$\sqrt[n]{a}$, $a^{1/n}$ nth root of a, usually means the *principle* nth root.

a^{-n} The reciprocal of a^n; $1/a^n$.

$(\;)$ Parentheses.

$[\;]$ Brackets.

$\{\;\}$ Brace.

———   Vinculum (used as a symbol of aggregation).

G.C.D. or g.c.d.   Greatest common divisor.

L.C.D. or l.c.d.   Least common denominator.

L.C.M. or l.c.m.   Least common multiple.

(a,b) The G.C.D. of a and b; the interval from a to b.

$[a,b]$ The L.C.M. of a and b.

$a\,|\,b$ a divides b.

e The base of the system of natural logarithms;
$$\lim_{n \to \infty} (1+1/n)^n = 2.7182818285\cdot$$

$\log a$, $\log_{10} a$ Common (Briggsian) logarithm of a, $\log a$ is used for $\log_{10} a$ when the context shows that the base is 10.

$\ln a$, $\log a$, $\log_e a$ Natural (Naperian) logarithm of a.

antilog   Antilogarithm.

colog   Cologarithm.

exp x e^x, where e is the base of the natural system of logarithms (2.718 $\cdots$).

$a \propto b$ a varies directly as b; a is directly proportional to b (seldom used).

i (or j)   square root of -1; $\sqrt{-1}$. j is used in physics where i denotes current, but i is almost universally used in mathematics.

ω_1, ω_2, ω_3 or 1, ω, ω^2 The three cube roots of unity.

$n!$ (or $\lfloor n$)   Factorial n; n factorial; $1 \cdot 2 \cdot 3 \cdots n$.

a' a prime.

a'' a double prime; a second.

$a^{[n]}$ a n prime.

a_n a sub n, a subscript n.

$f(x)$, $F(x)$, $\phi(x)$, etc.   Function of x.

$|z|$ absolute value of z; numerical value of z. Modulus z.

$\bar{z}$ or **conj** z Conjugate of z.

arg z Argument, amplitude, or phase of z.

$R(z)$ Real part of z; $R(z) = x$, if $z = x+iy$ and x and y are real.

$I(z)$ Imaginary part of z; $I(z) = y$, if $z = x+iy$ and x and y are real.

$x \equiv a \pmod{p}$ $x-a$ is divisible by p, read: x is congruent to a modulus p.

σ Standard deviation.

r Correlation coefficient.

i, j, k Unit vectors along the coordinate axes.

$a \cdot b$, $S ab$, (ab) Scalar product, or dot product, of the vectors a and b.

$a \times b$, $V ab$, $[ab]$ Vector product, or cross product, of the vectors a and b.

[abc] The *scalar triple product* of the vectors **a**, **b** and **c**: $(a \times b) \cdot c$, $a \cdot (b \times c)$, or $b \cdot (c \times a)$.

$P(n,r)$, $_nP_r$ The number of permutations of n things taken r at a time; $n!/(n-r)! = n(n-1)(n-2) \cdots (n-r+1)$.

$_nC_r$, $\{^n_r\}$, C_r^n, or $C(n, r)$ The number of combinations of n things taken r at a time: $n!/[r!(n-r)!]$; the $(r+1)$th binomial coefficient.

$|a_{ij}|$ The determinant whose element in the ith row and jth column is a_{ij}.

$\|a_{ij}\|$ or (a_{ij}) The matrix whose element

in the ith row and the jth column is a_{ij}.

The determinant $| abc \cdots | \quad \begin{vmatrix} a_1 & a_2 & \cdots \\ b_1 & b_2 & \cdots \\ & \cdots \cdots & \end{vmatrix}$

$\|abc \cdots \|$ or $(abc \cdots)$ The matrix $\begin{Vmatrix} a_1 & a_2 & \cdots \\ b_1 & b_2 & \cdots \\ & \cdots \cdots & \end{Vmatrix}$ or $\begin{pmatrix} a_1 & a_2 & \cdots \\ b_1 & b_2 & \cdots \\ & \cdots \cdots & \end{pmatrix}$

$\begin{pmatrix} a & b & c & \cdots \\ b & c & d & \cdots \end{pmatrix}$ or $(abcd \cdots)$. The permutation which replaces a by b, b by c, c by d, etc.

Trigonometry and Hyperbolic Functions

$a°$ a degrees (angle).

a' a minutes (angle).

a'' a seconds (angle).

$a^{(r)}$ a radians, unusual.

s One-half the sum of the lengths of the sides of a triangle (plane or spherical).

S, σ One-half the sum of the angles of a spherical triangle.

E Spherical excess.

sin Sine.

cos Cosine.

tan Tangent.

ctn (or **cot**) Cotangent.

sec Secant.

csc Cosecant.

covers Coversed sine or coversine.

exsec Exsecant.

gd (or **amh**) Gudermannian (or hyperbolic amplitude).

hav Haversine.

vers Versed sine or versine.

$\sin^{-1} x$ (or **arc sin** x) The principal value of the angle whose sine is x (when x is real); anti-sine x; inverse sine x.

$\sin^2 x$, $\cos^2 x$, etc. $(\sin x)^2$, $(\cos x)^2$, etc.

sinh Hyperbolic sine.

cosh Hyperbolic cosine.

tanh Hyperbolic tangent.

ctnh (or **coth**) Hyperbolic cotangent.

sech Hyperbolic secant.

csch Hyperbolic cosecant.

$\sinh^{-1} x$ (or **arc-sinh** x) The number whose hyperbolic sine is x; anti-hyperbolic sine of x; inverse hyperbolic sine of x.

Elementary and Analytic Geometry

$\angle$ Angle.

$\angle$s Angles.

$\perp$ Perpendicular; is perpendicular to.

$\perp$s Perpendiculars.

$\|$ Parallel; is parallel to.

$\|$s Parallels.

$\cong$, $\equiv$ Congruent; is congruent to.

$\therefore$ Therefore; hence

$\triangle$ Triangle.

⧍ Triangles.

▱ Parallelogram

□ Square.

○ Circle.

Ⓢ Circles.

π The ratio of the circumference of a circle to the diameter, the Greek letter pi, equal to 3.1415926536-.

(x, y) Rectangular coordinates of a point in a plane.

(x, y, z) Rectangular coordinates of a point in space.

r, θ Polar coordinates.

χ The angle from the radius vector to the tangent to a curve.

ρ (or r), θ, ϕ Spherical coordinates:

ϕ = co-latitude (or longitude),
θ = longitude (or co-latitude).

r, θ, z Cylindrical coordinates.

$\cos \alpha$, $\cos \beta$, $\cos \gamma$ Direction cosines.

l, m, n Direction numbers.

e Eccentricity of conics.

p Semi-latus rectum (usage general in U. S.).

m Slope.

$P(x, y)$ or $P:(x, y)$ Point P with co-ordinates x and y in the plane.

$P(x, y, z)$ or $P:(x, y, z)$ Point P with coordinates x, y, z in space.

(AB,CD) or $(AB|CD)$ The cross ratio of the elements (points, lines, etc.) A, B, C, and D, the quotient of the ratio in which C divides AB by the ratio in which D divides AB.

Calculus

$\dfrac{dy}{dx}$, $\dfrac{df(x)}{dx}$, y', $f'(x)$, $D_x y$ The derivative of y with respect to x, where $y = f(x)$.

$\dfrac{d^n y}{dx^n}$, $y^{(n)}$, $f^{(n)}(x)$, $D_x^n y$ The nth derivative of $y = f(x)$ with respect to x.

$\dfrac{\partial u}{\partial x}$, u_x, $f_x(x, y)$, $D_x u$ The partial derivative of $u = f(x, y)$ with respect to x.

$\dfrac{\partial^2 u}{\partial y \partial x}$, u_{xy}, $f_{xy}(x, y)$, $D_y(D_x u)$ The second partial derivative of $u = f(x, y)$, taken first with respect to x, and then with respect to y.

Δy An increment of y.

∂y A variation in y; an increment of y.

dy Differential y.

$\dot{s}$, ds/dt, v The derivative of s with respect to t; speed.

$\ddot{s}$, dv/dt, d^2s/dt^2, a The second derivative of s with respect to the time t; acceleration.

ω, α Angular speed and angular acceleration, respectively.

$\sum\limits_1^n$ or $\sum\limits_{i=1}^n$ Sum to n terms.

$\sum$ Sum of infinitely many terms.

$\prod\limits_1^n$ or $\prod\limits_{i=1}^n$ Product of n terms.

$\prod$ Product of infinitely many terms.

$\lim\limits_{x \to a}(y) = b$, or $\lim\limits_{x = a}(y) = b$ The limit of y as x approaches a is b.

$F(x) \rvert_a^b$ $F(b) - F(a)$.

$\int f(x)\, dx$ Integral of $f(x)$ with respect to x, the primitive of $f(x)$.

$\int_a^b f(x)\, dx$ The definite integral of $f(x)$, between the limits a and b.

I Moment of inertia.

k Radius of gyration.

$\bar{x}$, $\bar{y}$, $\bar{z}$ Coordinates of the center of mass.

s (or σ) Length of arc.

ρ Radius of curvature.

κ Curvature of a curve.

τ Torsion of a curve.

$\overline{\lim\limits_{n \to \infty}}\, t_n$ The greatest of the limits of the sequence (t_n); the largest number which is a limit point of the set of numbers (t_n).

$\underline{\lim\limits_{n \to \infty}}\, t_n$ The least of the limits of the sequence (t_n); the smallest number which is a limit-point of the set of points (t_n).

$\overline{\int_a^b}$ The upper Darboux integral.

$\underline{\int_a^b}$ The lower Darboux integral.

$f(x) \sim \sum\limits_0^\infty A_n$ The series is an asymptotic expansion of the function $f(x)$.

$x_n \sim y_n$ Limit $x_n/y_n = 1$; x_n and y_n are *asymptotically equal*.

$[a_n]$, (a_n) The sequence a_1, a_2, $\cdots$ $a_n \cdots$.

B_1, B_2, B_3, $\cdots$ The Bernoullian numbers. The Bernoullian numbers are also sometimes taken as B_1, B_3. B_5, $\cdots$.

$\Gamma(z)$ The Gamma function.

∇ Del: the operator

$$\left(i\,\frac{\partial}{\partial x} + j\,\frac{\partial}{\partial y} + k\,\frac{\partial}{\partial z}\right).$$

45

∇u or grad u Gradient of u:
$$\left(i\,\frac{\partial u}{\partial x}+j\,\frac{\partial u}{\partial y}+k\,\frac{\partial u}{\partial z}\right).$$

$\nabla \cdot \mathbf{v}$ or div $\mathbf{v}$ Divergence of $\mathbf{v}$.

$\nabla \times \mathbf{F}$ Curl of $\mathbf{F}$.

∇^2 or $\triangle$ The Laplacian operator:
$$\frac{\partial^2}{\partial x^2}+\frac{\partial^2}{\partial y^2}+\frac{\partial^2}{\partial z^2}.$$

Mathematics of Finance

%   Percent.

$ Dollar, dollars.

¢   Cent; cents.

@   At.

P Principal; present value.

$j_{(p)}$ Nominal rate (p conversion periods per year).

i, j, r Rate of interest.

s Compound amount of $1 for n periods; $s=(1+i)^n$.

n Number of periods or years, usually years.

v^n Present value of $1 ($n$ periods); $v^n = 1/(1+i)^n$.

l_x Number of persons living at age x (mortality table).

d_x Number of deaths per year of persons of age x (mortality table).

p_x Probability of a person of age x living one year.

q_x Probability of a person of age x dying within one year.

D_x $v^x l_x$.

C_x $v^{x+1}d_x$.

N_x $D_x + D_{x+1} + D_{x+2} + \cdots$ to table limit.

M_x $C_x + C_{x+1} + C_{x+2} + \cdots$ to table limit.

a_x Present value of a life annuity of $1 at age x; N_{x+1}/D_x.

$\mathbf{a}_x$ Present value of a (life) annuity due of $1 at age x; $1 + a_x$.

U_x D_x/D_{x+1}.

k_x C_x/D_{x+1}.

A_x Net single premium for $1 of whole life insurance taken out at age x.

P_x Net annual premium for an insurance of $1 at age x on the ordinary life plan.

$_nA_x$ Net single premium for $1 of term insurance for n years for a person aged x.

$_nP_x$ Premium for a limited payment life policy of $1 with a term of n years at age x.

$_nV_x$ Terminal reserve, at the end of n years after the policy was issued, on an ordinary life policy of $1 for a life aged x.

$_nE_x$ The present value of a pure endowment to be paid in n years to a person of age x.

R Annual rent.

$s_{\overline{n}|}$ or $s_{\overline{n}|i}$ Compound amount of $1 per annum for n years at interest rate i; $[(1+i)^n - 1]/i$.

$s_{\overline{n}|}^{(p)}$ or $s_{\overline{n}|i}^{(p)}$ Amount of $1 per annum for n years at interest rate i when payable in p equal installments at intervals of $(1/p)$th part of a year.

$a_{\overline{n}|}$ or $a_{\overline{n}|i}$ Present value of $1 per annum for n years at interest rate i; $[1 - (1+i)^{-n}]/i$.

$a_{\overline{n}|}^{(p)}$ or $a_{\overline{n}|i}^{(p)}$ Present value of $1 per annum for n years at interest rate i if payable in p installments at intervals of $(1/p)$th part of a year.

$A_{\overline{xn}|}$ Net single premium for an endowment insurance for $1 for n years at age x.

$P_{\overline{xn}|}$ Net annual premium for an n-year endowment policy for $1 taken out at age x.

$A_{\overline{xn}|}^1$ or $|_nA_x$ Net single premium for an endowment policy of $1 for n years taken out at age x.

$P_{\overline{xn}|}^1$ or $|_nP_x$ Net annual premium for a term insurance of $1 for n years at age x.